Calculus

Math 1C for Foothill College

James Stewart

CENGAGE
Learning™

Australia • Brazil • Japan • Korea • Mexico • Singapore • Spain • United Kingdom • United States

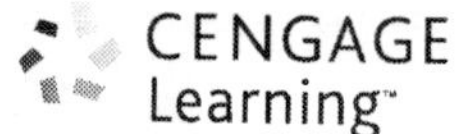

Calculus: Math 1C for Foothill College

James Stewart

Executive Editors:
Maureen Staudt
Michael Stranz

Senior Project Development Manager:
Linda DeStefano

Marketing Specialist:
Sara Mercurio
Lindsay Shapiro

Senior Production / Manufacturing Manager:
Donna M. Brown

PreMedia Supervisor:
Joel Brennecke

Rights & Permissions Specialist:
Kalina Hintz
Todd Osborne

Cover Image:
Getty Images*

* Unless otherwise noted, all cover images used by Custom Solutions, a part of Cengage Learning, have been supplied courtesy of Getty Images with the exception of the Earthview cover image, which has been supplied by the National Aeronautics and Space Administration (NASA).

ISBN-13: 978-1-111-03075-9

ISBN-10: 1-111-03075-8

Cengage Learning
5191 Natorp Boulevard
Mason, Ohio 45040
USA

Cengage Learning is a leading provider of customized learning solutions with office locations around the globe, including Singapore, the United Kingdom, Australia, Mexico, Brazil, and Japan. Locate your local office at: **international.cengage.com/region**

Cengage Learning products are represented in Canada by Nelson Education, Ltd.

For your lifelong learning solutions, visit **www.cengage.com/custom**

Visit our corporate website at **www.cengage.com**

Printed in the United States of America

Custom Table of Contents

8	Infinite Sequences and Series	553
9	Vectors and the Geometry of Space	633
11	Partial Derivatives	737
	Appendix B- Coordinate Geometry	A7
	Appendix D- Precise Definitions of Limits	A26
	Appendix E- A Few Proofs	A36
	Appendix F- Sigma Notation	A41
	Appendix H-Polar Coordinates	A55
	Answers to Odd Numbered Questions-	A111
	Index	A135

thomasmayerarchive.com

8 Infinite Sequences and Series

Infinite sequences and series were introduced briefly in *A Preview of Calculus* in connection with Zeno's paradoxes and the decimal representation of numbers. Their importance in calculus stems from Newton's idea of representing functions as sums of infinite series. For instance, in finding areas he often integrated a function by first expressing it as a series and then integrating each term of the series. We will pursue his idea in Section 8.7 in order to integrate such functions as e^{-x^2}. (Recall that we have previously been unable to do this.) Many of the functions that arise in mathematical physics and chemistry, such as Bessel functions, are defined as sums of series, so it is important to be familiar with the basic concepts of convergence of infinite sequences and series.

Physicists also use series in another way, as we will see in Section 8.8. In studying fields as diverse as optics, special relativity, and electromagnetism, they analyze phenomena by replacing a function with the first few terms in the series that represents it.

8.1 Sequences

A **sequence** can be thought of as a list of numbers written in a definite order:

$$a_1, a_2, a_3, a_4, \ldots, a_n, \ldots$$

The number a_1 is called the *first term*, a_2 is the *second term*, and in general a_n is the *nth term*. We will deal exclusively with infinite sequences and so each term a_n will have a successor a_{n+1}.

Notice that for every positive integer n there is a corresponding number a_n and so a sequence can be defined as a function whose domain is the set of positive integers. But we usually write a_n instead of the function notation $f(n)$ for the value of the function at the number n.

Notation: The sequence $\{a_1, a_2, a_3, \ldots\}$ is also denoted by

$$\{a_n\} \qquad \text{or} \qquad \{a_n\}_{n=1}^{\infty}$$

EXAMPLE 1 Describing sequences Some sequences can be defined by giving a formula for the nth term. In the following examples we give three descriptions of the sequence: one by using the preceding notation, another by using the defining formula, and a third by writing out the terms of the sequence. Notice that n doesn't have to start at 1.

(a) $\left\{\dfrac{n}{n+1}\right\}_{n=1}^{\infty}$ $\qquad a_n = \dfrac{n}{n+1}$ $\qquad \left\{\dfrac{1}{2}, \dfrac{2}{3}, \dfrac{3}{4}, \dfrac{4}{5}, \ldots, \dfrac{n}{n+1}, \ldots\right\}$

(b) $\left\{\dfrac{(-1)^n(n+1)}{3^n}\right\}$ $\qquad a_n = \dfrac{(-1)^n(n+1)}{3^n}$ $\qquad \left\{-\dfrac{2}{3}, \dfrac{3}{9}, -\dfrac{4}{27}, \dfrac{5}{81}, \ldots, \dfrac{(-1)^n(n+1)}{3^n}, \ldots\right\}$

(c) $\left\{\sqrt{n-3}\right\}_{n=3}^{\infty}$ $\qquad a_n = \sqrt{n-3},\ n \geqslant 3$ $\qquad \{0, 1, \sqrt{2}, \sqrt{3}, \ldots, \sqrt{n-3}, \ldots\}$

(d) $\left\{\cos\dfrac{n\pi}{6}\right\}_{n=0}^{\infty}$ $\qquad a_n = \cos\dfrac{n\pi}{6},\ n \geqslant 0$ $\qquad \left\{1, \dfrac{\sqrt{3}}{2}, \dfrac{1}{2}, 0, \ldots, \cos\dfrac{n\pi}{6}, \ldots\right\}$

V EXAMPLE 2 Find a formula for the general term a_n of the sequence

$$\left\{\frac{3}{5}, -\frac{4}{25}, \frac{5}{125}, -\frac{6}{625}, \frac{7}{3125}, \ldots\right\}$$

assuming that the pattern of the first few terms continues.

SOLUTION We are given that

$$a_1 = \frac{3}{5} \qquad a_2 = -\frac{4}{25} \qquad a_3 = \frac{5}{125} \qquad a_4 = -\frac{6}{625} \qquad a_5 = \frac{7}{3125}$$

Notice that the numerators of these fractions start with 3 and increase by 1 whenever we go to the next term. The second term has numerator 4, the third term has numerator 5; in general, the nth term will have numerator $n + 2$. The denominators are the powers of 5, so a_n has denominator 5^n. The signs of the terms are alternately positive and negative, so we need to multiply by a power of -1. In Example 1(b) the factor $(-1)^n$ meant we started with a negative term. Here we want to start with a positive term and so we use $(-1)^{n-1}$ or $(-1)^{n+1}$. Therefore

$$a_n = (-1)^{n-1}\frac{n+2}{5^n}$$

EXAMPLE 3 Here are some sequences that don't have simple defining equations.

(a) The sequence $\{p_n\}$, where p_n is the population of the world as of January 1 in the year n.

(b) If we let a_n be the digit in the nth decimal place of the number e, then $\{a_n\}$ is a well-defined sequence whose first few terms are

$$\{7, 1, 8, 2, 8, 1, 8, 2, 8, 4, 5, \dots\}$$

(c) The **Fibonacci sequence** $\{f_n\}$ is defined recursively by the conditions

$$f_1 = 1 \qquad f_2 = 1 \qquad f_n = f_{n-1} + f_{n-2} \qquad n \geqslant 3$$

Each term is the sum of the two preceding terms. The first few terms are

$$\{1, 1, 2, 3, 5, 8, 13, 21, \dots\}$$

This sequence arose when the 13th-century Italian mathematician known as Fibonacci solved a problem concerning the breeding of rabbits (see Exercise 47).

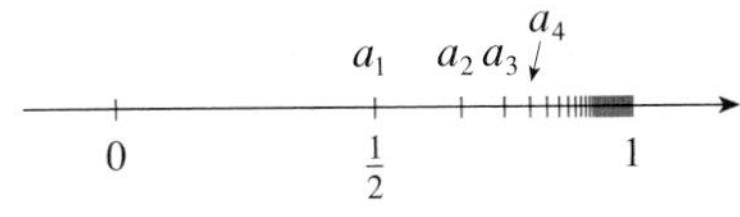

FIGURE 1

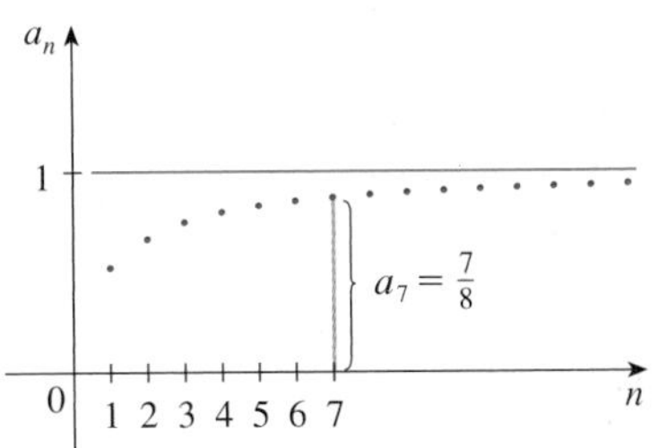

FIGURE 2

A sequence such as the one in Example 1(a), $a_n = n/(n+1)$, can be pictured either by plotting its terms on a number line, as in Figure 1, or by plotting its graph, as in Figure 2. Note that, since a sequence is a function whose domain is the set of positive integers, its graph consists of isolated points with coordinates

$$(1, a_1) \qquad (2, a_2) \qquad (3, a_3) \qquad \dots \qquad (n, a_n) \qquad \dots$$

From Figure 1 or Figure 2 it appears that the terms of the sequence $a_n = n/(n+1)$ are approaching 1 as n becomes large. In fact, the difference

$$1 - \frac{n}{n+1} = \frac{1}{n+1}$$

can be made as small as we like by taking n sufficiently large. We indicate this by writing

$$\lim_{n\to\infty} a_n = \lim_{n\to\infty} \frac{n}{n+1} = 1$$

In general, the notation

$$\lim_{n\to\infty} a_n = L$$

means that the terms of the sequence $\{a_n\}$ approach L as n becomes large. Notice that the following definition of the limit of a sequence is very similar to the definition of a limit of a function at infinity given in Section 2.5.

1 Definition A sequence $\{a_n\}$ has the **limit** L and we write

$$\lim_{n \to \infty} a_n = L \qquad \text{or} \qquad a_n \to L \text{ as } n \to \infty$$

if we can make the terms a_n as close to L as we like by taking n sufficiently large. If $\lim_{n \to \infty} a_n$ exists, we say the sequence **converges** (or is **convergent**). Otherwise, we say the sequence **diverges** (or is **divergent**).

A more precise definition of the limit of a sequence is given in Appendix D.

Figure 3 illustrates Definition 1 by showing the graphs of two sequences that have the limit L.

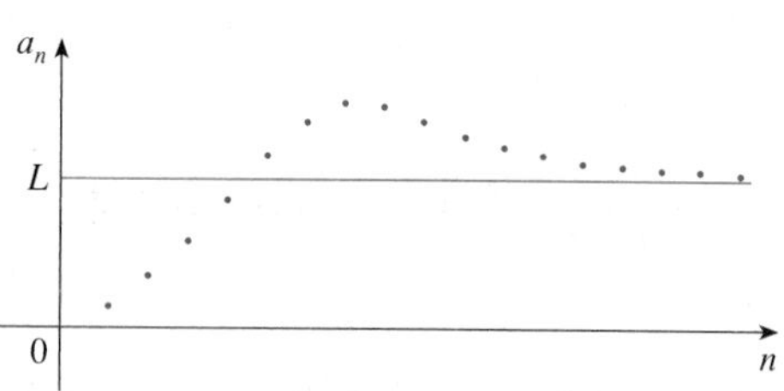

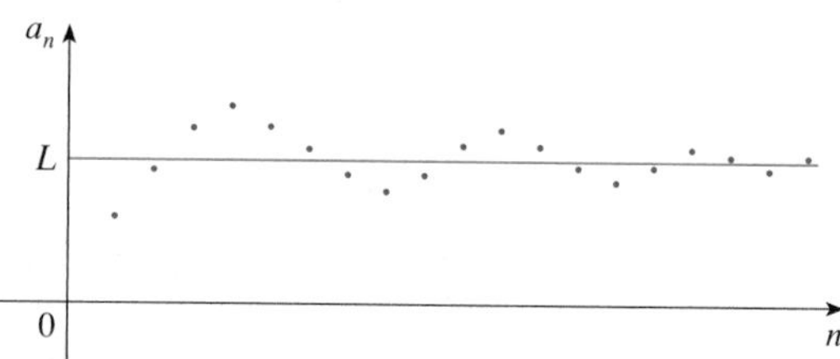

FIGURE 3
Graphs of two sequences with $\lim_{n \to \infty} a_n = L$

If you compare Definition 1 with Definition 2.5.4 you will see that the only difference between $\lim_{n \to \infty} a_n = L$ and $\lim_{x \to \infty} f(x) = L$ is that n is required to be an integer. Thus we have the following theorem, which is illustrated by Figure 4.

2 Theorem If $\lim_{x \to \infty} f(x) = L$ and $f(n) = a_n$ when n is an integer, then $\lim_{n \to \infty} a_n = L$.

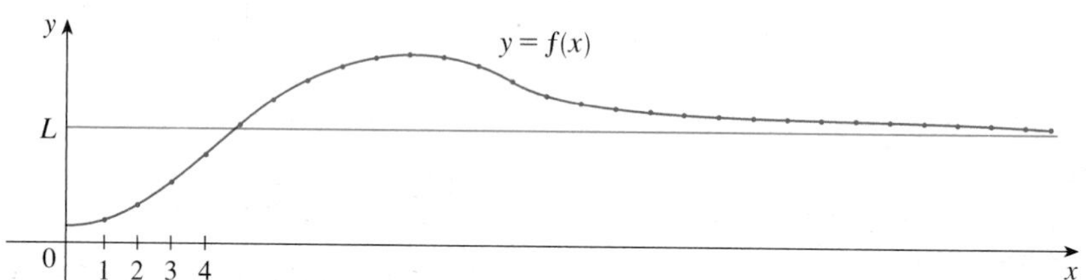

FIGURE 4

In particular, since we know from Section 2.5 that $\lim_{x \to \infty} (1/x^r) = 0$ when $r > 0$, we have

3
$$\lim_{n \to \infty} \frac{1}{n^r} = 0 \qquad \text{if } r > 0$$

If a_n becomes large as n becomes large, we use the notation

$$\lim_{n \to \infty} a_n = \infty$$

In this case the sequence $\{a_n\}$ is divergent, but in a special way. We say that $\{a_n\}$ diverges to ∞.

The Limit Laws given in Section 2.3 also hold for the limits of sequences and their proofs are similar.

Limit Laws for Sequences

If $\{a_n\}$ and $\{b_n\}$ are convergent sequences and c is a constant, then

$$\lim_{n\to\infty} (a_n + b_n) = \lim_{n\to\infty} a_n + \lim_{n\to\infty} b_n$$

$$\lim_{n\to\infty} (a_n - b_n) = \lim_{n\to\infty} a_n - \lim_{n\to\infty} b_n$$

$$\lim_{n\to\infty} ca_n = c \lim_{n\to\infty} a_n \qquad \lim_{n\to\infty} c = c$$

$$\lim_{n\to\infty} (a_n b_n) = \lim_{n\to\infty} a_n \cdot \lim_{n\to\infty} b_n$$

$$\lim_{n\to\infty} \frac{a_n}{b_n} = \frac{\lim_{n\to\infty} a_n}{\lim_{n\to\infty} b_n} \quad \text{if } \lim_{n\to\infty} b_n \neq 0$$

$$\lim_{n\to\infty} a_n^p = \left[\lim_{n\to\infty} a_n\right]^p \text{ if } p > 0 \text{ and } a_n > 0$$

The Squeeze Theorem can also be adapted for sequences as follows (see Figure 5).

Squeeze Theorem for Sequences

If $a_n \leqslant b_n \leqslant c_n$ for $n \geqslant n_0$ and $\lim_{n\to\infty} a_n = \lim_{n\to\infty} c_n = L$, then $\lim_{n\to\infty} b_n = L$.

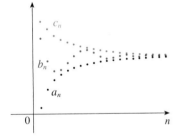

FIGURE 5
The sequence $\{b_n\}$ is squeezed between the sequences $\{a_n\}$ and $\{c_n\}$.

Another useful fact about limits of sequences is given by the following theorem, which follows from the Squeeze Theorem because $-|a_n| \leqslant a_n \leqslant |a_n|$.

4 Theorem If $\lim_{n\to\infty} |a_n| = 0$, then $\lim_{n\to\infty} a_n = 0$.

EXAMPLE 4 Find $\lim_{n\to\infty} \dfrac{n}{n+1}$.

SOLUTION The method is similar to the one we used in Section 2.5: Divide numerator and denominator by the highest power of n that occurs in the denominator and then use the Limit Laws.

$$\lim_{n\to\infty} \frac{n}{n+1} = \lim_{n\to\infty} \frac{1}{1+\dfrac{1}{n}} = \frac{\lim_{n\to\infty} 1}{\lim_{n\to\infty} 1 + \lim_{n\to\infty} \dfrac{1}{n}}$$

$$= \frac{1}{1+0} = 1$$

This shows that the guess we made earlier from Figures 1 and 2 was correct.

Here we used Equation 3 with $r = 1$.

EXAMPLE 5 Applying l'Hospital's Rule to a related function Calculate $\lim_{n\to\infty} \dfrac{\ln n}{n}$.

SOLUTION Notice that both numerator and denominator approach infinity as $n \to \infty$. We can't apply l'Hospital's Rule directly because it applies not to sequences but to functions of a real variable. However, we can apply l'Hospital's Rule to the related function $f(x) = (\ln x)/x$ and obtain

$$\lim_{x \to \infty} \frac{\ln x}{x} = \lim_{x \to \infty} \frac{1/x}{1} = 0$$

Therefore, by Theorem 2, we have

$$\lim_{n \to \infty} \frac{\ln n}{n} = 0$$

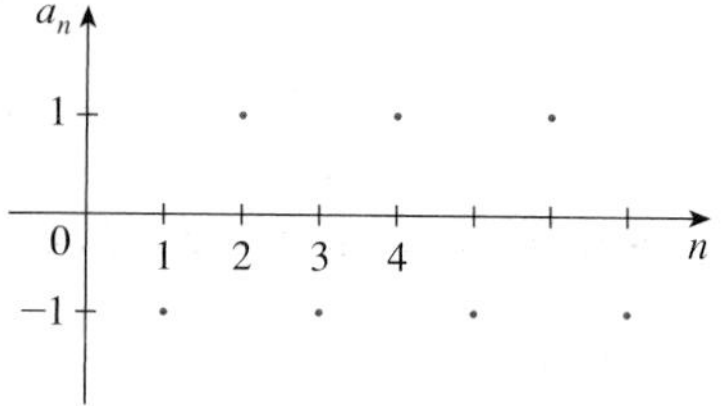

FIGURE 6

EXAMPLE 6 Determine whether the sequence $a_n = (-1)^n$ is convergent or divergent.

SOLUTION If we write out the terms of the sequence, we obtain

$$\{-1, 1, -1, 1, -1, 1, -1, \ldots\}$$

The graph of this sequence is shown in Figure 6. Since the terms oscillate between 1 and -1 infinitely often, a_n does not approach any number. Thus $\lim_{n \to \infty} (-1)^n$ does not exist; that is, the sequence $\{(-1)^n\}$ is divergent.

The graph of the sequence in Example 7 is shown in Figure 7 and supports the answer.

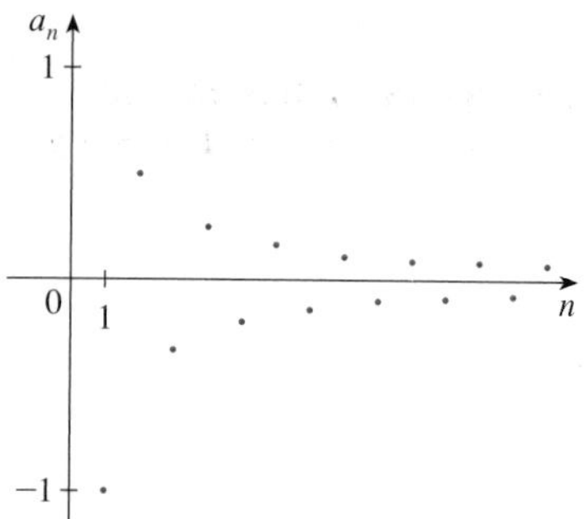

FIGURE 7

EXAMPLE 7 Evaluate $\lim_{n \to \infty} \frac{(-1)^n}{n}$ if it exists.

SOLUTION We first calculate the limit of the absolute value:

$$\lim_{n \to \infty} \left| \frac{(-1)^n}{n} \right| = \lim_{n \to \infty} \frac{1}{n} = 0$$

Therefore, by Theorem 4,

$$\lim_{n \to \infty} \frac{(-1)^n}{n} = 0$$

The following theorem says that if we apply a continuous function to the terms of a convergent sequence, the result is also convergent. The proof is given in Appendix E.

5 Theorem If $\lim_{n \to \infty} a_n = L$ and the function f is continuous at L, then

$$\lim_{n \to \infty} f(a_n) = f(L)$$

EXAMPLE 8 Find $\lim_{n \to \infty} \sin(\pi/n)$.

SOLUTION Because the sine function is continuous at 0, Theorem 5 enables us to write

$$\lim_{n \to \infty} \sin(\pi/n) = \sin\left(\lim_{n \to \infty} (\pi/n)\right) = \sin 0 = 0$$

V EXAMPLE 9 Using the Squeeze Theorem Discuss the convergence of the sequence $a_n = n!/n^n$, where $n! = 1 \cdot 2 \cdot 3 \cdot \cdots \cdot n$.

SOLUTION Both numerator and denominator approach infinity as $n \to \infty$ but here we have no corresponding function for use with l'Hospital's Rule ($x!$ is not defined when x is not an integer). Let's write out a few terms to get a feeling for what happens to a_n

Creating Graphs of Sequences

Some computer algebra systems have special commands that enable us to create sequences and graph them directly. With most graphing calculators, however, sequences can be graphed by using parametric equations. For instance, the sequence in Example 9 can be graphed by entering the parametric equations

$$x = t \qquad y = t!/t^t$$

and graphing in dot mode, starting with $t = 1$ and setting the t-step equal to 1. The result is shown in Figure 8.

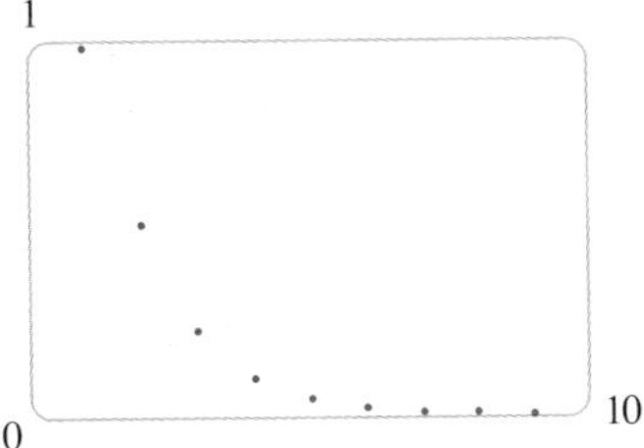

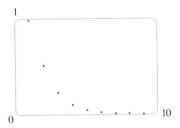

FIGURE 8

as n gets large:

$$a_1 = 1 \qquad a_2 = \frac{1 \cdot 2}{2 \cdot 2} \qquad a_3 = \frac{1 \cdot 2 \cdot 3}{3 \cdot 3 \cdot 3}$$

6 $$a_n = \frac{1 \cdot 2 \cdot 3 \cdot \cdots \cdot n}{n \cdot n \cdot n \cdot \cdots \cdot n}$$

It appears from these expressions and the graph in Figure 8 that the terms are decreasing and perhaps approach 0. To confirm this, observe from Equation 6 that

$$a_n = \frac{1}{n}\left(\frac{2 \cdot 3 \cdot \cdots \cdot n}{n \cdot n \cdot \cdots \cdot n}\right)$$

Notice that the expression in parentheses is at most 1 because the numerator is less than (or equal to) the denominator. So

$$0 < a_n \leqslant \frac{1}{n}$$

We know that $1/n \to 0$ as $n \to \infty$. Therefore $a_n \to 0$ as $n \to \infty$ by the Squeeze Theorem.

V EXAMPLE 10 **Limit of a geometric sequence** For what values of r is the sequence $\{r^n\}$ convergent?

SOLUTION We know from Section 2.5 and the graphs of the exponential functions in Section 1.5 that $\lim_{x\to\infty} a^x = \infty$ for $a > 1$ and $\lim_{x\to\infty} a^x = 0$ for $0 < a < 1$. Therefore, putting $a = r$ and using Theorem 2, we have

$$\lim_{n\to\infty} r^n = \begin{cases} \infty & \text{if } r > 1 \\ 0 & \text{if } 0 < r < 1 \end{cases}$$

For the cases $r = 1$ and $r = 0$ we have

$$\lim_{n\to\infty} 1^n = \lim_{n\to\infty} 1 = 1 \qquad \text{and} \qquad \lim_{n\to\infty} 0^n = \lim_{n\to\infty} 0 = 0$$

If $-1 < r < 0$, then $0 < |r| < 1$, so

$$\lim_{n\to\infty} |r^n| = \lim_{n\to\infty} |r|^n = 0$$

and therefore $\lim_{n\to\infty} r^n = 0$ by Theorem 4. If $r \leqslant -1$, then $\{r^n\}$ diverges as in Example 6. Figure 9 shows the graphs for various values of r. (The case $r = -1$ is shown in Figure 6.)

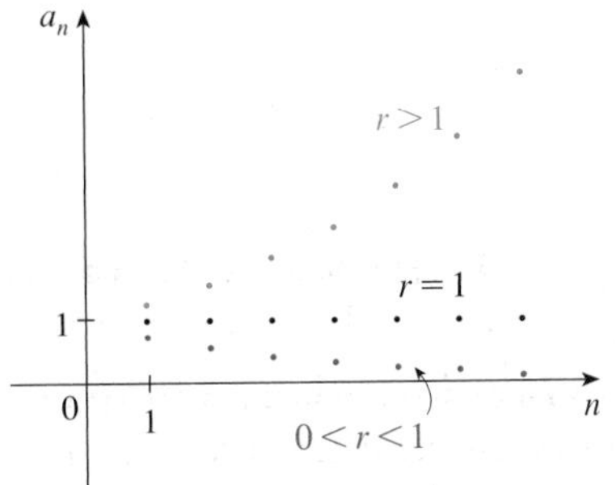

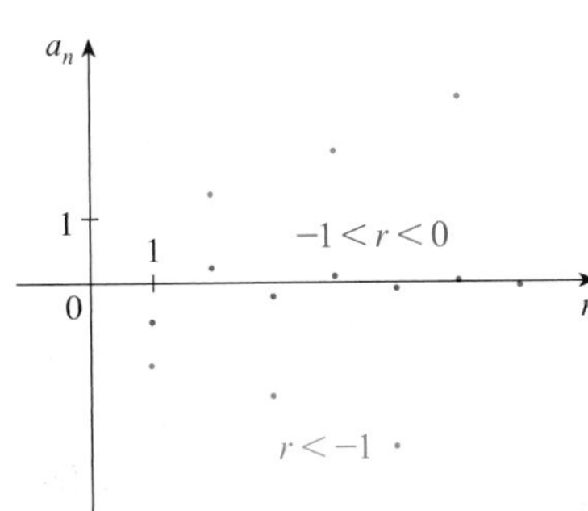

FIGURE 9
The sequence $a_n = r^n$

The results of Example 10 are summarized for future use as follows.

7 The sequence $\{r^n\}$ is convergent if $-1 < r \leqslant 1$ and divergent for all other values of r.

$$\lim_{n\to\infty} r^n = \begin{cases} 0 & \text{if } -1 < r < 1 \\ 1 & \text{if } r = 1 \end{cases}$$

Definition A sequence $\{a_n\}$ is called **increasing** if $a_n < a_{n+1}$ for all $n \geqslant 1$, that is, $a_1 < a_2 < a_3 < \cdots$. It is called **decreasing** if $a_n > a_{n+1}$ for all $n \geqslant 1$. A sequence is **monotonic** if it is either increasing or decreasing.

EXAMPLE 11 The sequence $\left\{\dfrac{3}{n+5}\right\}$ is decreasing because

The right side is smaller because it has a larger denominator.

$$\frac{3}{n+5} > \frac{3}{(n+1)+5} = \frac{3}{n+6}$$

and so $a_n > a_{n+1}$ for all $n \geqslant 1$.

EXAMPLE 12 Show that the sequence $a_n = \dfrac{n}{n^2+1}$ is decreasing.

SOLUTION 1 We must show that $a_{n+1} < a_n$, that is,

$$\frac{n+1}{(n+1)^2+1} < \frac{n}{n^2+1}$$

This inequality is equivalent to the one we get by cross-multiplication:

$$\begin{aligned} \frac{n+1}{(n+1)^2+1} < \frac{n}{n^2+1} \quad &\iff \quad (n+1)(n^2+1) < n[(n+1)^2+1] \\ &\iff \quad n^3+n^2+n+1 < n^3+2n^2+2n \\ &\iff \quad 1 < n^2+n \end{aligned}$$

Since $n \geqslant 1$, we know that the inequality $n^2+n > 1$ is true. Therefore $a_{n+1} < a_n$ and so $\{a_n\}$ is decreasing.

SOLUTION 2 Consider the function $f(x) = \dfrac{x}{x^2+1}$.

$$f'(x) = \frac{x^2+1-2x^2}{(x^2+1)^2} = \frac{1-x^2}{(x^2+1)^2} < 0 \qquad \text{whenever } x^2 > 1$$

Thus f is decreasing on $(1, \infty)$ and so $f(n) > f(n+1)$. Therefore $\{a_n\}$ is decreasing.

Definition A sequence $\{a_n\}$ is **bounded above** if there is a number M such that

$$a_n \leqslant M \qquad \text{for all } n \geqslant 1$$

It is **bounded below** if there is a number m such that

$$m \leqslant a_n \qquad \text{for all } n \geqslant 1$$

If it is bounded above and below, then $\{a_n\}$ is a **bounded sequence**.

For instance, the sequence $a_n = n$ is bounded below $(a_n > 0)$ but not above. The sequence $a_n = n/(n + 1)$ is bounded because $0 < a_n < 1$ for all n.

We know that not every bounded sequence is convergent [for instance, the sequence $a_n = (-1)^n$ satisfies $-1 \leqslant a_n \leqslant 1$ but is divergent, from Example 6] and not every monotonic sequence is convergent $(a_n = n \to \infty)$. But if a sequence is both bounded *and* monotonic, then it must be convergent. This fact is stated without proof as Theorem 8, but intuitively you can understand why it is true by looking at Figure 10. If $\{a_n\}$ is increasing and $a_n \leqslant M$ for all n, then the terms are forced to crowd together and approach some number L.

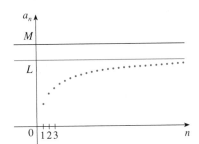

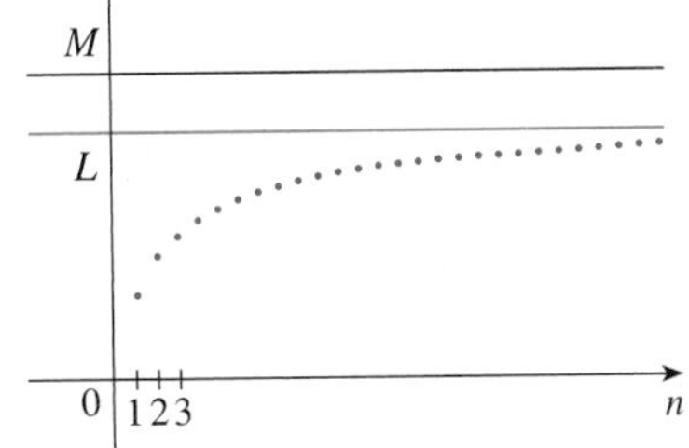

FIGURE 10

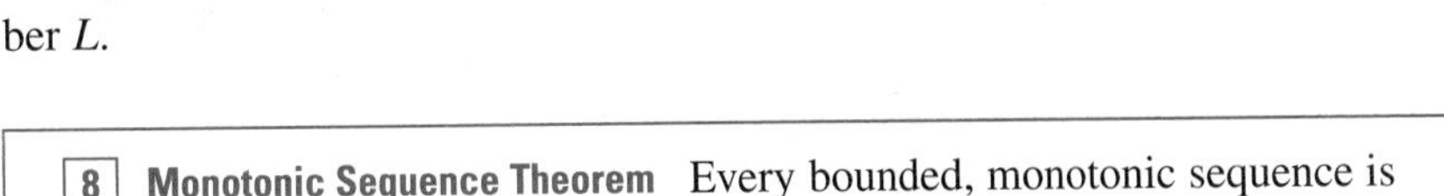

8 **Monotonic Sequence Theorem** Every bounded, monotonic sequence is convergent.

EXAMPLE 13 **The limit of a recursively defined sequence** Investigate the sequence $\{a_n\}$ defined by the *recurrence relation*

$$a_1 = 2 \qquad a_{n+1} = \tfrac{1}{2}(a_n + 6) \qquad \text{for } n = 1, 2, 3, \ldots$$

SOLUTION We begin by computing the first several terms:

$$a_1 = 2 \qquad a_2 = \tfrac{1}{2}(2 + 6) = 4 \qquad a_3 = \tfrac{1}{2}(4 + 6) = 5$$

$$a_4 = \tfrac{1}{2}(5 + 6) = 5.5 \qquad a_5 = 5.75 \qquad a_6 = 5.875$$

$$a_7 = 5.9375 \qquad a_8 = 5.96875 \qquad a_9 = 5.984375$$

Mathematical induction is often used in dealing with recursive sequences. See page 84 for a discussion of the Principle of Mathematical Induction.

These initial terms suggest that the sequence is increasing and the terms are approaching 6. To confirm that the sequence is increasing, we use mathematical induction to show that $a_{n+1} > a_n$ for all $n \geqslant 1$. This is true for $n = 1$ because $a_2 = 4 > a_1$. If we assume that it is true for $n = k$, then we have

$$a_{k+1} > a_k$$

so

$$a_{k+1} + 6 > a_k + 6$$

and

$$\tfrac{1}{2}(a_{k+1} + 6) > \tfrac{1}{2}(a_k + 6)$$

Thus

$$a_{k+2} > a_{k+1}$$

We have deduced that $a_{n+1} > a_n$ is true for $n = k + 1$. Therefore the inequality is true for all n by induction.

Next we verify that $\{a_n\}$ is bounded by showing that $a_n < 6$ for all n. (Since the sequence is increasing, we already know that it has a lower bound: $a_n \geqslant a_1 = 2$ for all n.) We know that $a_1 < 6$, so the assertion is true for $n = 1$. Suppose it is true for $n = k$. Then

$$a_k < 6$$

so

$$a_k + 6 < 12$$

and

$$\tfrac{1}{2}(a_k + 6) < \tfrac{1}{2}(12) = 6$$

Thus

$$a_{k+1} < 6$$

This shows, by mathematical induction, that $a_n < 6$ for all n.

Since the sequence $\{a_n\}$ is increasing and bounded, the Monotonic Sequence Theorem guarantees that it has a limit. The theorem doesn't tell us what the value of the limit is. But now that we know $L = \lim_{n\to\infty} a_n$ exists, we can use the given recurrence relation to write

$$\lim_{n\to\infty} a_{n+1} = \lim_{n\to\infty} \tfrac{1}{2}(a_n + 6) = \tfrac{1}{2}\left(\lim_{n\to\infty} a_n + 6\right) = \tfrac{1}{2}(L + 6)$$

Since $a_n \to L$, it follows that $a_{n+1} \to L$ too (as $n \to \infty$, $n + 1 \to \infty$ also). So we have

$$L = \tfrac{1}{2}(L + 6)$$

Solving this equation for L, we get $L = 6$, as we predicted.

8.1 Exercises

1. (a) What is a sequence?
   (b) What does it mean to say that $\lim_{n\to\infty} a_n = 8$?
   (c) What does it mean to say that $\lim_{n\to\infty} a_n = \infty$?

2. (a) What is a convergent sequence? Give two examples.
   (b) What is a divergent sequence? Give two examples.

3. List the first six terms of the sequence defined by

$$a_n = \frac{n}{2n + 1}$$

Does the sequence appear to have a limit? If so, find it.

4. List the first nine terms of the sequence $\{\cos(n\pi/3)\}$. Does this sequence appear to have a limit? If so, find it. If not, explain why.

5–10 Find a formula for the general term a_n of the sequence, assuming that the pattern of the first few terms continues.

5. $\left\{1, \frac{1}{3}, \frac{1}{5}, \frac{1}{7}, \frac{1}{9}, \ldots\right\}$

6. $\left\{1, \frac{1}{3}, \frac{1}{9}, \frac{1}{27}, \frac{1}{81}, \ldots\right\}$

7. $\{2, 7, 12, 17, \ldots\}$

8. $\left\{-\frac{1}{4}, \frac{2}{9}, -\frac{3}{16}, \frac{4}{25}, \ldots\right\}$

9. $\left\{1, -\frac{2}{3}, \frac{4}{9}, -\frac{8}{27}, \ldots\right\}$

10. $\{5, 1, 5, 1, 5, 1, \ldots\}$

11–34 Determine whether the sequence converges or diverges. If it converges, find the limit.

11. $a_n = \dfrac{3 + 5n^2}{n + n^2}$

12. $a_n = \dfrac{n^3}{n^3 + 1}$

13. $a_n = 1 - (0.2)^n$

14. $a_n = \dfrac{n^3}{n + 1}$

15. $a_n = e^{1/n}$

16. $a_n = \dfrac{3^{n+2}}{5^n}$

17. $a_n = \tan\left(\dfrac{2n\pi}{1 + 8n}\right)$

18. $a_n = \sqrt{\dfrac{n + 1}{9n + 1}}$

19. $a_n = \dfrac{(-1)^{n-1}n}{n^2 + 1}$

20. $a_n = \dfrac{(-1)^n n^3}{n^3 + 2n^2 + 1}$

21. $\left\{\dfrac{e^n + e^{-n}}{e^{2n} - 1}\right\}$

22. $a_n = \cos(2/n)$

Graphing calculator or computer with graphing software required 1. Homework Hints available in TEC

23. $\{n^2e^{-n}\}$

24. $\{\arctan 2n\}$

25. $a_n = \dfrac{\cos^2 n}{2^n}$

26. $\{n \cos n\pi\}$

27. $a_n = \left(1 + \dfrac{2}{n}\right)^n$

28. $a_n = \sqrt[n]{2^{1+3n}}$

29. $\left\{\dfrac{(2n-1)!}{(2n+1)!}\right\}$

30. $a_n = \dfrac{\sin 2n}{1 + \sqrt{n}}$

31. $\{0, 1, 0, 0, 1, 0, 0, 0, 1, \dots\}$

32. $a_n = \dfrac{(\ln n)^2}{n}$

33. $a_n = \ln(2n^2 + 1) - \ln(n^2 + 1)$

34. $a_n = \dfrac{(-3)^n}{n!}$

35–40 Use a graph of the sequence to decide whether the sequence is convergent or divergent. If the sequence is convergent, guess the value of the limit from the graph and then prove your guess. (See the margin note on page 559 for advice on graphing sequences.)

35. $a_n = 1 + (-2/e)^n$

36. $a_n = \sqrt{n}\,\sin(\pi/\sqrt{n})$

37. $a_n = \sqrt{\dfrac{3 + 2n^2}{8n^2 + n}}$

38. $a_n = \sqrt[n]{3^n + 5^n}$

39. $a_n = \dfrac{n^2 \cos n}{1 + n^2}$

40. $a_n = \dfrac{1 \cdot 3 \cdot 5 \cdot \cdots \cdot (2n-1)}{(2n)^n}$

---

41. If \$1000 is invested at 6% interest, compounded annually, then after n years the investment is worth $a_n = 1000(1.06)^n$ dollars.
(a) Find the first five terms of the sequence $\{a_n\}$.
(b) Is the sequence convergent or divergent? Explain.

42. If you deposit \$100 at the end of every month into an account that pays 3% interest per year compounded monthly, the amount of interest accumulated after n months is given by the sequence

$$I_n = 100\left(\frac{1.0025^n - 1}{0.0025} - n\right)$$

(a) Find the first six terms of the sequence.
(b) How much interest will you have earned after two years?

43. A fish farmer has 5000 catfish in his pond. The number of catfish increases by 8% per month and the farmer harvests 300 catfish per month.
(a) Show that the catfish population P_n after n months is given recursively by

$$P_n = 1.08P_{n-1} - 300 \qquad P_0 = 5000$$

(b) How many catfish are in the pond after six months?

44. Find the first 40 terms of the sequence defined by

$$a_{n+1} = \begin{cases} \frac{1}{2}a_n & \text{if } a_n \text{ is an even number} \\ 3a_n + 1 & \text{if } a_n \text{ is an odd number} \end{cases}$$

and $a_1 = 11$. Do the same if $a_1 = 25$. Make a conjecture about this type of sequence.

45. (a) Determine whether the sequence defined as follows is convergent or divergent:

$$a_1 = 1 \qquad a_{n+1} = 4 - a_n \qquad \text{for } n \geqslant 1$$

(b) What happens if the first term is $a_1 = 2$?

46. (a) If $\lim_{n\to\infty} a_n = L$, what is the value of $\lim_{n\to\infty} a_{n+1}$?
(b) A sequence $\{a_n\}$ is defined by

$$a_1 = 1 \qquad a_{n+1} = 1/(1 + a_n) \quad \text{for } n \geqslant 1$$

Find the first ten terms of the sequence correct to five decimal places. Does it appear that the sequence is convergent? If so, estimate the value of the limit to three decimal places.
(c) Assuming that the sequence in part (b) has a limit, use part (a) to find its exact value. Compare with your estimate from part (b).

47. (a) Fibonacci posed the following problem: Suppose that rabbits live forever and that every month each pair produces a new pair which becomes productive at age 2 months. If we start with one newborn pair, how many pairs of rabbits will we have in the nth month? Show that the answer is f_n, where $\{f_n\}$ is the Fibonacci sequence defined in Example 3(c).
(b) Let $a_n = f_{n+1}/f_n$ and show that $a_{n-1} = 1 + 1/a_{n-2}$. Assuming that $\{a_n\}$ is convergent, find its limit.

48. Find the limit of the sequence

$$\left\{\sqrt{2},\ \sqrt{2\sqrt{2}},\ \sqrt{2\sqrt{2\sqrt{2}}},\ \dots\right\}$$

49–52 Determine whether the sequence is increasing, decreasing, or not monotonic. Is the sequence bounded?

49. $a_n = \dfrac{1}{2n + 3}$

50. $a_n = \dfrac{2n - 3}{3n + 4}$

51. $a_n = n(-1)^n$

52. $a_n = n + \dfrac{1}{n}$

---

53. Suppose you know that $\{a_n\}$ is a decreasing sequence and all its terms lie between the numbers 5 and 8. Explain why the sequence has a limit. What can you say about the value of the limit?

54. A sequence $\{a_n\}$ is given by $a_1 = \sqrt{2}$, $a_{n+1} = \sqrt{2 + a_n}$.
(a) By induction or otherwise, show that $\{a_n\}$ is increasing and bounded above by 3. Apply the Monotonic Sequence Theorem to show that $\lim_{n\to\infty} a_n$ exists.
(b) Find $\lim_{n\to\infty} a_n$.

55. Show that the sequence defined by

$$a_1 = 1 \qquad a_{n+1} = 3 - \frac{1}{a_n}$$

is increasing and $a_n < 3$ for all n. Deduce that $\{a_n\}$ is convergent and find its limit.

56. Show that the sequence defined by

$$a_1 = 2 \qquad a_{n+1} = \frac{1}{3 - a_n}$$

satisfies $0 < a_n \leqslant 2$ and is decreasing. Deduce that the sequence is convergent and find its limit.

57. We know that $\lim_{n\to\infty} (0.8)^n = 0$ [from (7) with $r = 0.8$]. Use logarithms to determine how large n has to be so that $(0.8)^n < 0.000001$.

58. (a) Let $a_1 = a$, $a_2 = f(a)$, $a_3 = f(a_2) = f(f(a))$, . . . , $a_{n+1} = f(a_n)$, where f is a continuous function. If $\lim_{n\to\infty} a_n = L$, show that $f(L) = L$.
(b) Illustrate part (a) by taking $f(x) = \cos x$, $a = 1$, and estimating the value of L to five decimal places.

59. The size of an undisturbed fish population has been modeled by the formula

$$p_{n+1} = \frac{bp_n}{a + p_n}$$

where p_n is the fish population after n years and a and b are positive constants that depend on the species and its environment. Suppose that the population in year 0 is $p_0 > 0$.
(a) Show that if $\{p_n\}$ is convergent, then the only possible values for its limit are 0 and $b - a$.
(b) Show that $p_{n+1} < (b/a)p_n$.
(c) Use part (b) to show that if $a > b$, then $\lim_{n\to\infty} p_n = 0$; in other words, the population dies out.
(d) Now assume that $a < b$. Show that if $p_0 < b - a$, then $\{p_n\}$ is increasing and $0 < p_n < b - a$. Show also that if $p_0 > b - a$, then $\{p_n\}$ is decreasing and $p_n > b - a$. Deduce that if $a < b$, then $\lim_{n\to\infty} p_n = b - a$.

60. A sequence is defined recursively by

$$a_1 = 1 \qquad a_{n+1} = 1 + \frac{1}{1 + a_n}$$

Find the first eight terms of the sequence $\{a_n\}$. What do you notice about the odd terms and the even terms? By considering the odd and even terms separately, show that $\{a_n\}$ is convergent and deduce that

$$\lim_{n\to\infty} a_n = \sqrt{2}$$

This gives the **continued fraction expansion**

$$\sqrt{2} = 1 + \cfrac{1}{2 + \cfrac{1}{2 + \cdots}}$$

LABORATORY PROJECT CAS Logistic Sequences

A sequence that arises in ecology as a model for population growth is defined by the **logistic difference equation**

$$p_{n+1} = kp_n(1 - p_n)$$

where p_n measures the size of the population of the nth generation of a single species. To keep the numbers manageable, p_n is a fraction of the maximal size of the population, so $0 \leqslant p_n \leqslant 1$. Notice that the form of this equation is similar to the logistic differential equation in Section 7.5. The discrete model—with sequences instead of continuous functions—is preferable for modeling insect populations, where mating and death occur in a periodic fashion.

An ecologist is interested in predicting the size of the population as time goes on, and asks these questions: Will it stabilize at a limiting value? Will it change in a cyclical fashion? Or will it exhibit random behavior?

Write a program to compute the first n terms of this sequence starting with an initial population p_0, where $0 < p_0 < 1$. Use this program to do the following.

1. Calculate 20 or 30 terms of the sequence for $p_0 = \frac{1}{2}$ and for two values of k such that $1 < k < 3$. Graph each sequence. Do the sequences appear to converge? Repeat for a different value of p_0 between 0 and 1. Does the limit depend on the choice of p_0? Does it depend on the choice of k?

2. Calculate terms of the sequence for a value of k between 3 and 3.4 and plot them. What do you notice about the behavior of the terms?

CAS Computer algebra system required

3. Experiment with values of k between 3.4 and 3.5. What happens to the terms?

4. For values of k between 3.6 and 4, compute and plot at least 100 terms and comment on the behavior of the sequence. What happens if you change p_0 by 0.001? This type of behavior is called *chaotic* and is exhibited by insect populations under certain conditions.

8.2 Series

What do we mean when we express a number as an infinite decimal? For instance, what does it mean to write

$$\pi = 3.14159\ 26535\ 89793\ 23846\ 26433\ 83279\ 50288\ldots$$

The current record is that π has been computed to 1,241,100,000,000 (more than a trillion) decimal places by Shigeru Kondo and his collaborators.

The convention behind our decimal notation is that any number can be written as an infinite sum. Here it means that

$$\pi = 3 + \frac{1}{10} + \frac{4}{10^2} + \frac{1}{10^3} + \frac{5}{10^4} + \frac{9}{10^5} + \frac{2}{10^6} + \frac{6}{10^7} + \frac{5}{10^8} + \cdots$$

where the three dots ($\cdots$) indicate that the sum continues forever, and the more terms we add, the closer we get to the actual value of π.

In general, if we try to add the terms of an infinite sequence $\{a_n\}_{n=1}^{\infty}$ we get an expression of the form

$$\boxed{1} \qquad a_1 + a_2 + a_3 + \cdots + a_n + \cdots$$

which is called an **infinite series** (or just a **series**) and is denoted, for short, by the symbol

$$\sum_{n=1}^{\infty} a_n \qquad \text{or} \qquad \sum a_n$$

Does it make sense to talk about the sum of infinitely many terms?

It would be impossible to find a finite sum for the series

$$1 + 2 + 3 + 4 + 5 + \cdots + n + \cdots$$

because if we start adding the terms we get the cumulative sums 1, 3, 6, 10, 15, 21, . . . and, after the nth term, we get $n(n + 1)/2$, which becomes very large as n increases.

However, if we start to add the terms of the series

$$\frac{1}{2} + \frac{1}{4} + \frac{1}{8} + \frac{1}{16} + \frac{1}{32} + \frac{1}{64} + \cdots + \frac{1}{2^n} + \cdots$$

n	Sum of first n terms
1	0.50000000
2	0.75000000
3	0.87500000
4	0.93750000
5	0.96875000
6	0.98437500
7	0.99218750
10	0.99902344
15	0.99996948
20	0.99999905
25	0.99999997

we get $\frac{1}{2}, \frac{3}{4}, \frac{7}{8}, \frac{15}{16}, \frac{31}{32}, \frac{63}{64}, \ldots, 1 - 1/2^n, \ldots$. The table shows that as we add more and more terms, these *partial sums* become closer and closer to 1. (See also Figure 11 in *A Preview of Calculus,* page 8.) In fact, by adding sufficiently many terms of the series we can make the partial sums as close as we like to 1. So it seems reasonable to say that the sum of this infinite series is 1 and to write

$$\sum_{n=1}^{\infty} \frac{1}{2^n} = \frac{1}{2} + \frac{1}{4} + \frac{1}{8} + \frac{1}{16} + \cdots + \frac{1}{2^n} + \cdots = 1$$

We use a similar idea to determine whether or not a general series (1) has a sum. We consider the **partial sums**

$$s_1 = a_1$$

$$s_2 = a_1 + a_2$$

$$s_3 = a_1 + a_2 + a_3$$

$$s_4 = a_1 + a_2 + a_3 + a_4$$

and, in general,

$$s_n = a_1 + a_2 + a_3 + \cdots + a_n = \sum_{i=1}^{n} a_i$$

These partial sums form a new sequence $\{s_n\}$, which may or may not have a limit. If $\lim_{n\to\infty} s_n = s$ exists (as a finite number), then, as in the preceding example, we call it the sum of the infinite series $\Sigma\, a_n$.

2 Definition Given a series $\sum_{n=1}^{\infty} a_n = a_1 + a_2 + a_3 + \cdots$, let s_n denote its nth partial sum:

$$s_n = \sum_{i=1}^{n} a_i = a_1 + a_2 + \cdots + a_n$$

If the sequence $\{s_n\}$ is convergent and $\lim_{n\to\infty} s_n = s$ exists as a real number, then the series $\Sigma\, a_n$ is called **convergent** and we write

$$a_1 + a_2 + \cdots + a_n + \cdots = s \qquad \text{or} \qquad \sum_{n=1}^{\infty} a_n = s$$

The number s is called the **sum** of the series. If the sequence $\{s_n\}$ is divergent, then the series is called **divergent**.

Thus the sum of a series is the limit of the sequence of partial sums. So when we write $\sum_{n=1}^{\infty} a_n = s$ we mean that by adding sufficiently many terms of the series we can get as close as we like to the number s. Notice that

$$\sum_{n=1}^{\infty} a_n = \lim_{n\to\infty} \sum_{i=1}^{n} a_i$$

Compare with the improper integral

$$\int_1^{\infty} f(x)\,dx = \lim_{t\to\infty} \int_1^t f(x)\,dx$$

To find this integral we integrate from 1 to t and then let $t \to \infty$. For a series, we sum from 1 to n and then let $n \to \infty$.

EXAMPLE 1 An important example of an infinite series is the **geometric series**

$$a + ar + ar^2 + ar^3 + \cdots + ar^{n-1} + \cdots = \sum_{n=1}^{\infty} ar^{n-1} \qquad a \neq 0$$

Each term is obtained from the preceding one by multiplying it by the **common ratio** r. (We have already considered the special case where $a = \frac{1}{2}$ and $r = \frac{1}{2}$ on page 565.)

If $r = 1$, then $s_n = a + a + \cdots + a = na \to \pm\infty$. Since $\lim_{n\to\infty} s_n$ doesn't exist, the geometric series diverges in this case.

If $r \neq 1$, we have

$$s_n = a + ar + ar^2 + \cdots + ar^{n-1}$$

and

$$rs_n = \qquad ar + ar^2 + \cdots + ar^{n-1} + ar^n$$

Figure 1 provides a geometric demonstration of the result in Example 1. If the triangles are constructed as shown and s is the sum of the series, then, by similar triangles,

$$\frac{s}{a} = \frac{a}{a - ar} \quad \text{so} \quad s = \frac{a}{1 - r}$$

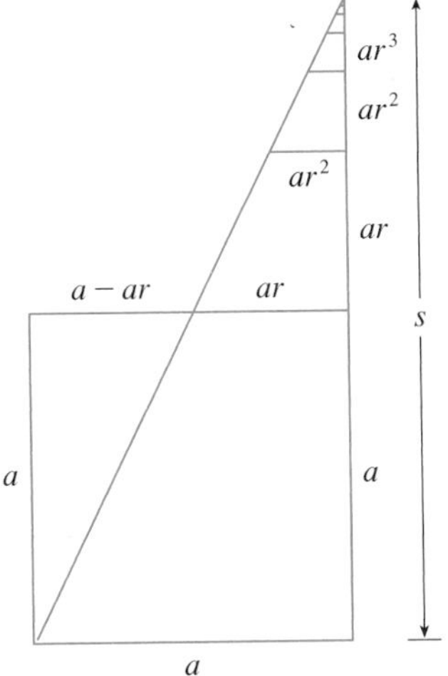

FIGURE 1

Subtracting these equations, we get

$$s_n - rs_n = a - ar^n$$

$$\boxed{3} \qquad s_n = \frac{a(1 - r^n)}{1 - r}$$

If $-1 < r < 1$, we know from (8.1.7) that $r^n \to 0$ as $n \to \infty$, so

$$\lim_{n\to\infty} s_n = \lim_{n\to\infty} \frac{a(1 - r^n)}{1 - r} = \frac{a}{1 - r} - \frac{a}{1 - r} \lim_{n\to\infty} r^n = \frac{a}{1 - r}$$

Thus when $|r| < 1$ the geometric series is convergent and its sum is $a/(1 - r)$.

If $r \leqslant -1$ or $r > 1$, the sequence $\{r^n\}$ is divergent by (8.1.7) and so, by Equation 3, $\lim_{n\to\infty} s_n$ does not exist. Therefore the geometric series diverges in those cases.

We summarize the results of Example 1 as follows.

> **4** The geometric series
>
> $$\sum_{n=1}^{\infty} ar^{n-1} = a + ar + ar^2 + \cdots$$
>
> is convergent if $|r| < 1$ and its sum is
>
> $$\sum_{n=1}^{\infty} ar^{n-1} = \frac{a}{1 - r} \qquad |r| < 1$$
>
> If $|r| \geqslant 1$, the geometric series is divergent.

In words: The sum of a convergent geometric series is

$$\frac{\text{first term}}{1 - \text{common ratio}}$$

V EXAMPLE 2 Find the sum of the geometric series

$$5 - \tfrac{10}{3} + \tfrac{20}{9} - \tfrac{40}{27} + \cdots$$

SOLUTION The first term is $a = 5$ and the common ratio is $r = -\frac{2}{3}$. Since $|r| = \frac{2}{3} < 1$, the series is convergent by (4) and its sum is

$$5 - \frac{10}{3} + \frac{20}{9} - \frac{40}{27} + \cdots = \frac{5}{1 - \left(-\frac{2}{3}\right)} = \frac{5}{\frac{5}{3}} = 3$$

What do we really mean when we say that the sum of the series in Example 2 is 3? Of course, we can't literally add an infinite number of terms, one by one. But, according to Definition 2, the total sum is the limit of the sequence of partial sums. So, by taking the sum of sufficiently many terms, we can get as close as we like to the number 3. The table shows the first ten partial sums s_n and the graph in Figure 2 shows how the sequence of partial sums approaches 3.

n	s_n
1	5.000000
2	1.666667
3	3.888889
4	2.407407
5	3.395062
6	2.736626
7	3.175583
8	2.882945
9	3.078037
10	2.947975

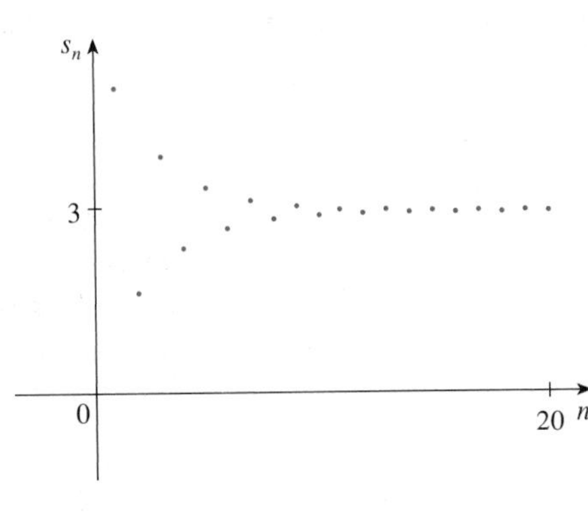

FIGURE 2

EXAMPLE 3 Is the series $\sum_{n=1}^{\infty} 2^{2n}3^{1-n}$ convergent or divergent?

SOLUTION Let's rewrite the nth term of the series in the form ar^{n-1}:

Another way to identify a and r is to write out the first few terms:

$$4 + \tfrac{16}{3} + \tfrac{64}{9} + \cdots$$

$$\sum_{n=1}^{\infty} 2^{2n}3^{1-n} = \sum_{n=1}^{\infty} (2^2)^n 3^{-(n-1)} = \sum_{n=1}^{\infty} \frac{4^n}{3^{n-1}} = \sum_{n=1}^{\infty} 4\left(\tfrac{4}{3}\right)^{n-1}$$

We recognize this series as a geometric series with $a = 4$ and $r = \frac{4}{3}$. Since $r > 1$, the series diverges by (4).

V EXAMPLE 4 Expressing a repeating decimal as a rational number
Write the number $2.3\overline{17} = 2.3171717\ldots$ as a ratio of integers.

SOLUTION

$$2.3171717\ldots = 2.3 + \frac{17}{10^3} + \frac{17}{10^5} + \frac{17}{10^7} + \cdots$$

After the first term we have a geometric series with $a = 17/10^3$ and $r = 1/10^2$. Therefore

$$2.3\overline{17} = 2.3 + \frac{\dfrac{17}{10^3}}{1 - \dfrac{1}{10^2}} = 2.3 + \frac{\dfrac{17}{1000}}{\dfrac{99}{100}}$$

$$= \frac{23}{10} + \frac{17}{990} = \frac{1147}{495}$$

EXAMPLE 5 A series with variable terms Find the sum of the series $\sum_{n=0}^{\infty} x^n$, where $|x| < 1$.

TEC Module 8.2 explores a series that depends on an angle θ in a triangle and enables you to see how rapidly the series converges when θ varies.

SOLUTION Notice that this series starts with $n = 0$ and so the first term is $x^0 = 1$. (With series, we adopt the convention that $x^0 = 1$ even when $x = 0$.) Thus

$$\sum_{n=0}^{\infty} x^n = 1 + x + x^2 + x^3 + x^4 + \cdots$$

This is a geometric series with $a = 1$ and $r = x$. Since $|r| = |x| < 1$, it converges and (4) gives

$$\boxed{5} \qquad \sum_{n=0}^{\infty} x^n = \frac{1}{1 - x}$$

EXAMPLE 6 A telescoping sum Show that the series $\sum_{n=1}^{\infty} \frac{1}{n(n+1)}$ is convergent, and find its sum.

SOLUTION This is not a geometric series, so we go back to the definition of a convergent series and compute the partial sums.

$$s_n = \sum_{i=1}^{n} \frac{1}{i(i+1)} = \frac{1}{1 \cdot 2} + \frac{1}{2 \cdot 3} + \frac{1}{3 \cdot 4} + \cdots + \frac{1}{n(n+1)}$$

We can simplify this expression if we use the partial fraction decomposition

$$\frac{1}{i(i+1)} = \frac{1}{i} - \frac{1}{i+1}$$

(see Section 5.7). Thus we have

Notice that the terms cancel in pairs. This is an example of a **telescoping sum**: Because of all the cancellations, the sum collapses (like a pirate's collapsing telescope) into just two terms.

$$\begin{aligned} s_n &= \sum_{i=1}^{n} \frac{1}{i(i+1)} = \sum_{i=1}^{n} \left(\frac{1}{i} - \frac{1}{i+1} \right) \\ &= \left(1 - \frac{1}{2}\right) + \left(\frac{1}{2} - \frac{1}{3}\right) + \left(\frac{1}{3} - \frac{1}{4}\right) + \cdots + \left(\frac{1}{n} - \frac{1}{n+1}\right) \\ &= 1 - \frac{1}{n+1} \end{aligned}$$

Figure 3 illustrates Example 6 by showing the graphs of the sequence of terms $a_n = 1/[n(n+1)]$ and the sequence $\{s_n\}$ of partial sums. Notice that $a_n \to 0$ and $s_n \to 1$. See Exercises 56 and 57 for two geometric interpretations of Example 6.

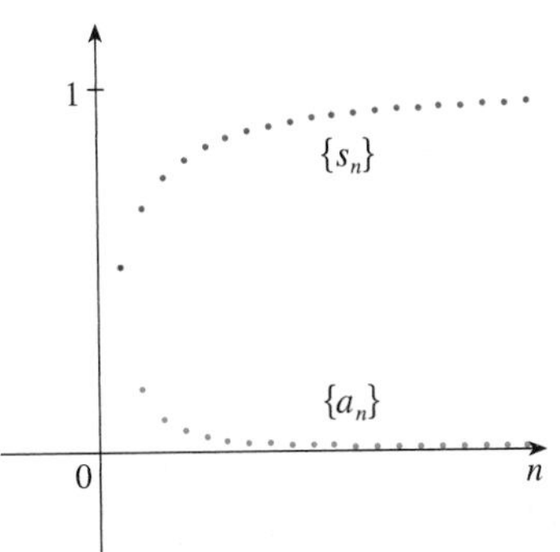

FIGURE 3

and so

$$\lim_{n \to \infty} s_n = \lim_{n \to \infty} \left(1 - \frac{1}{n+1}\right) = 1 - 0 = 1$$

Therefore the given series is convergent and

$$\sum_{n=1}^{\infty} \frac{1}{n(n+1)} = 1$$

V EXAMPLE 7 Show that the **harmonic series**

$$\sum_{n=1}^{\infty} \frac{1}{n} = 1 + \frac{1}{2} + \frac{1}{3} + \frac{1}{4} + \cdots$$

is divergent.

SOLUTION For this particular series it's convenient to consider the partial sums $s_2, s_4, s_8, s_{16}, s_{32}, \ldots$ and show that they become large.

$$s_2 = 1 + \tfrac{1}{2}$$

$$s_4 = 1 + \tfrac{1}{2} + \left(\tfrac{1}{3} + \tfrac{1}{4}\right) > 1 + \tfrac{1}{2} + \left(\tfrac{1}{4} + \tfrac{1}{4}\right) = 1 + \tfrac{2}{2}$$

$$\begin{aligned} s_8 &= 1 + \tfrac{1}{2} + \left(\tfrac{1}{3} + \tfrac{1}{4}\right) + \left(\tfrac{1}{5} + \tfrac{1}{6} + \tfrac{1}{7} + \tfrac{1}{8}\right) \\ &> 1 + \tfrac{1}{2} + \left(\tfrac{1}{4} + \tfrac{1}{4}\right) + \left(\tfrac{1}{8} + \tfrac{1}{8} + \tfrac{1}{8} + \tfrac{1}{8}\right) \\ &= 1 + \tfrac{1}{2} + \tfrac{1}{2} + \tfrac{1}{2} = 1 + \tfrac{3}{2} \end{aligned}$$

$$\begin{aligned} s_{16} &= 1 + \tfrac{1}{2} + \left(\tfrac{1}{3} + \tfrac{1}{4}\right) + \left(\tfrac{1}{5} + \cdots + \tfrac{1}{8}\right) + \left(\tfrac{1}{9} + \cdots + \tfrac{1}{16}\right) \\ &> 1 + \tfrac{1}{2} + \left(\tfrac{1}{4} + \tfrac{1}{4}\right) + \left(\tfrac{1}{8} + \cdots + \tfrac{1}{8}\right) + \left(\tfrac{1}{16} + \cdots + \tfrac{1}{16}\right) \\ &= 1 + \tfrac{1}{2} + \tfrac{1}{2} + \tfrac{1}{2} + \tfrac{1}{2} = 1 + \tfrac{4}{2} \end{aligned}$$

Similarly, $s_{32} > 1 + \tfrac{5}{2}$, $s_{64} > 1 + \tfrac{6}{2}$, and in general

$$s_{2^n} > 1 + \frac{n}{2}$$

The method used in Example 7 for showing that the harmonic series diverges is due to the French scholar Nicole Oresme (1323–1382).

This shows that $s_{2^n} \to \infty$ as $n \to \infty$ and so $\{s_n\}$ is divergent. Therefore the harmonic series diverges.

6 Theorem If the series $\sum_{n=1}^{\infty} a_n$ is convergent, then $\lim_{n\to\infty} a_n = 0$.

PROOF Let $s_n = a_1 + a_2 + \cdots + a_n$. Then $a_n = s_n - s_{n-1}$. Since $\Sigma\, a_n$ is convergent, the sequence $\{s_n\}$ is convergent. Let $\lim_{n\to\infty} s_n = s$. Since $n - 1 \to \infty$ as $n \to \infty$, we also have $\lim_{n\to\infty} s_{n-1} = s$. Therefore

$$\lim_{n\to\infty} a_n = \lim_{n\to\infty} (s_n - s_{n-1}) = \lim_{n\to\infty} s_n - \lim_{n\to\infty} s_{n-1}$$
$$= s - s = 0$$

Note 1: With any *series* $\Sigma\, a_n$ we associate two *sequences:* the sequence $\{s_n\}$ of its partial sums and the sequence $\{a_n\}$ of its terms. If $\Sigma\, a_n$ is convergent, then the limit of the sequence $\{s_n\}$ is s (the sum of the series) and, as Theorem 6 asserts, the limit of the sequence $\{a_n\}$ is 0.

Note 2: The converse of Theorem 6 is not true in general. If $\lim_{n\to\infty} a_n = 0$, we cannot conclude that $\Sigma\, a_n$ is convergent. Observe that for the harmonic series $\Sigma\, 1/n$ we have $a_n = 1/n \to 0$ as $n \to \infty$, but we showed in Example 7 that $\Sigma\, 1/n$ is divergent.

7 The Test for Divergence If $\lim_{n\to\infty} a_n$ does not exist or if $\lim_{n\to\infty} a_n \neq 0$, then the series $\sum_{n=1}^{\infty} a_n$ is divergent.

The Test for Divergence follows from Theorem 6 because, if the series is not divergent, then it is convergent, and so $\lim_{n\to\infty} a_n = 0$.

EXAMPLE 8 Using the Test for Divergence Show that the series $\sum_{n=1}^{\infty} \frac{n^2}{5n^2 + 4}$ diverges.

SOLUTION

$$\lim_{n\to\infty} a_n = \lim_{n\to\infty} \frac{n^2}{5n^2 + 4} = \lim_{n\to\infty} \frac{1}{5 + 4/n^2} = \frac{1}{5} \neq 0$$

So the series diverges by the Test for Divergence.

Note 3: If we find that $\lim_{n\to\infty} a_n \neq 0$, we know that $\Sigma\, a_n$ is divergent. If we find that $\lim_{n\to\infty} a_n = 0$, we know *nothing* about the convergence or divergence of $\Sigma\, a_n$. Remember the warning in Note 2: If $\lim_{n\to\infty} a_n = 0$, the series $\Sigma\, a_n$ might converge or it might diverge.

8 Theorem If $\Sigma\, a_n$ and $\Sigma\, b_n$ are convergent series, then so are the series $\Sigma\, ca_n$ (where c is a constant), $\Sigma\, (a_n + b_n)$, and $\Sigma\, (a_n - b_n)$, and

(i) $\sum_{n=1}^{\infty} ca_n = c \sum_{n=1}^{\infty} a_n$ (ii) $\sum_{n=1}^{\infty} (a_n + b_n) = \sum_{n=1}^{\infty} a_n + \sum_{n=1}^{\infty} b_n$

(iii) $\sum_{n=1}^{\infty} (a_n - b_n) = \sum_{n=1}^{\infty} a_n - \sum_{n=1}^{\infty} b_n$

These properties of convergent series follow from the corresponding Limit Laws for Sequences in Section 8.1. For instance, here is how part (ii) of Theorem 8 is proved:

Let

$$s_n = \sum_{i=1}^{n} a_i \qquad s = \sum_{n=1}^{\infty} a_n \qquad t_n = \sum_{i=1}^{n} b_i \qquad t = \sum_{n=1}^{\infty} b_n$$

The nth partial sum for the series $\Sigma\,(a_n + b_n)$ is

$$u_n = \sum_{i=1}^{n} (a_i + b_i)$$

and, using Equation 5.2.10, we have

$$\begin{aligned}\lim_{n\to\infty} u_n &= \lim_{n\to\infty} \sum_{i=1}^{n} (a_i + b_i) = \lim_{n\to\infty} \left(\sum_{i=1}^{n} a_i + \sum_{i=1}^{n} b_i \right) \\ &= \lim_{n\to\infty} \sum_{i=1}^{n} a_i + \lim_{n\to\infty} \sum_{i=1}^{n} b_i \\ &= \lim_{n\to\infty} s_n + \lim_{n\to\infty} t_n = s + t\end{aligned}$$

Therefore $\Sigma\,(a_n + b_n)$ is convergent and its sum is

$$\sum_{n=1}^{\infty} (a_n + b_n) = s + t = \sum_{n=1}^{\infty} a_n + \sum_{n=1}^{\infty} b_n$$

□

EXAMPLE 9 Find the sum of the series $\displaystyle\sum_{n=1}^{\infty} \left(\frac{3}{n(n+1)} + \frac{1}{2^n} \right)$.

SOLUTION The series $\Sigma\, 1/2^n$ is a geometric series with $a = \frac{1}{2}$ and $r = \frac{1}{2}$, so

$$\sum_{n=1}^{\infty} \frac{1}{2^n} = \frac{\frac{1}{2}}{1 - \frac{1}{2}} = 1$$

In Example 6 we found that

$$\sum_{n=1}^{\infty} \frac{1}{n(n+1)} = 1$$

So, by Theorem 8, the given series is convergent and

$$\begin{aligned}\sum_{n=1}^{\infty} \left(\frac{3}{n(n+1)} + \frac{1}{2^n} \right) &= 3 \sum_{n=1}^{\infty} \frac{1}{n(n+1)} + \sum_{n=1}^{\infty} \frac{1}{2^n} \\ &= 3 \cdot 1 + 1 = 4\end{aligned}$$

Note 4: A finite number of terms doesn't affect the convergence or divergence of a series. For instance, suppose that we were able to show that the series

$$\sum_{n=4}^{\infty} \frac{n}{n^3 + 1}$$

is convergent. Since

$$\sum_{n=1}^{\infty} \frac{n}{n^3 + 1} = \frac{1}{2} + \frac{2}{9} + \frac{3}{28} + \sum_{n=4}^{\infty} \frac{n}{n^3 + 1}$$

it follows that the entire series $\sum_{n=1}^{\infty} n/(n^3 + 1)$ is convergent. Similarly, if it is known that the series $\sum_{n=N+1}^{\infty} a_n$ converges, then the full series

$$\sum_{n=1}^{\infty} a_n = \sum_{n=1}^{N} a_n + \sum_{n=N+1}^{\infty} a_n$$

is also convergent.

8.2 Exercises

1. (a) What is the difference between a sequence and a series?
(b) What is a convergent series? What is a divergent series?

2. Explain what it means to say that $\sum_{n=1}^{\infty} a_n = 5$.

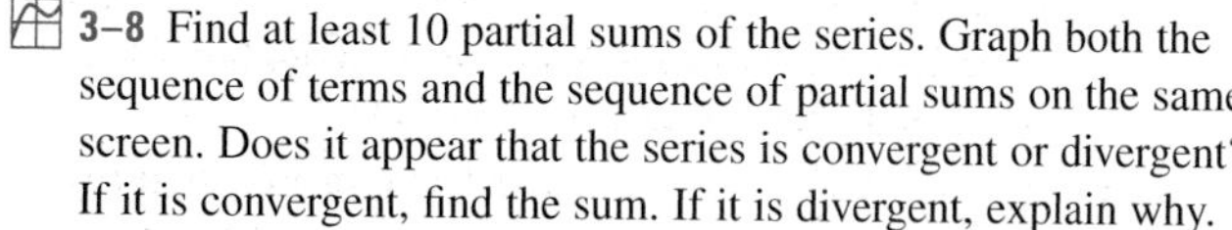

3–8 Find at least 10 partial sums of the series. Graph both the sequence of terms and the sequence of partial sums on the same screen. Does it appear that the series is convergent or divergent? If it is convergent, find the sum. If it is divergent, explain why.

3. $\displaystyle\sum_{n=1}^{\infty} \frac{12}{(-5)^n}$

4. $\displaystyle\sum_{n=1}^{\infty} \cos n$

5. $\displaystyle\sum_{n=1}^{\infty} \frac{n}{\sqrt{n^2+4}}$

6. $\displaystyle\sum_{n=1}^{\infty} \frac{7^{n+1}}{10^n}$

7. $\displaystyle\sum_{n=1}^{\infty} \left(\frac{1}{\sqrt{n}} - \frac{1}{\sqrt{n+1}}\right)$

8. $\displaystyle\sum_{n=2}^{\infty} \frac{1}{n(n+2)}$

9. Let $a_n = \dfrac{2n}{3n+1}$.
(a) Determine whether $\{a_n\}$ is convergent.
(b) Determine whether $\sum_{n=1}^{\infty} a_n$ is convergent.

10. (a) Explain the difference between

$$\sum_{i=1}^{n} a_i \quad \text{and} \quad \sum_{j=1}^{n} a_j$$

(b) Explain the difference between

$$\sum_{i=1}^{n} a_i \quad \text{and} \quad \sum_{i=1}^{n} a_j$$

11–18 Determine whether the geometric series is convergent or divergent. If it is convergent, find its sum.

11. $3 - 4 + \frac{16}{3} - \frac{64}{9} + \cdots$

12. $4 + 3 + \frac{9}{4} + \frac{27}{16} + \cdots$

13. $10 - 2 + 0.4 - 0.08 + \cdots$

14. $1 + 0.4 + 0.16 + 0.064 + \cdots$

15. $\displaystyle\sum_{n=1}^{\infty} 6(0.9)^{n-1}$

16. $\displaystyle\sum_{n=1}^{\infty} \frac{10^n}{(-9)^{n-1}}$

17. $\displaystyle\sum_{n=0}^{\infty} \frac{\pi^n}{3^{n+1}}$

18. $\displaystyle\sum_{n=0}^{\infty} \frac{1}{(\sqrt{2})^n}$

19–30 Determine whether the series is convergent or divergent. If it is convergent, find its sum.

19. $\displaystyle\sum_{n=1}^{\infty} \frac{n-1}{3n-1}$

20. $\displaystyle\sum_{k=1}^{\infty} \frac{k(k+2)}{(k+3)^2}$

21. $\displaystyle\sum_{k=2}^{\infty} \frac{k^2}{k^2-1}$

22. $\displaystyle\sum_{n=1}^{\infty} \cos\frac{1}{n}$

23. $\displaystyle\sum_{n=1}^{\infty} \frac{1+2^n}{3^n}$

24. $\displaystyle\sum_{n=1}^{\infty} \frac{1+3^n}{2^n}$

25. $\displaystyle\sum_{n=1}^{\infty} \sqrt[n]{2}$

26. $\displaystyle\sum_{k=1}^{\infty} (\cos 1)^k$

27. $\displaystyle\sum_{n=1}^{\infty} \arctan n$

28. $\displaystyle\sum_{n=1}^{\infty} [(0.8)^{n-1} - (0.3)^n]$

29. $\displaystyle\sum_{n=1}^{\infty} \left(\frac{1}{e^n} + \frac{1}{n(n+1)}\right)$

30. $\displaystyle\sum_{n=1}^{\infty} \left(\frac{3}{5^n} + \frac{2}{n}\right)$

31–34 Determine whether the series is convergent or divergent by expressing s_n as a telescoping sum (as in Example 6). If it is convergent, find its sum.

31. $\displaystyle\sum_{n=2}^{\infty} \frac{2}{n^2-1}$

32. $\displaystyle\sum_{n=1}^{\infty} \frac{2}{n^2+4n+3}$

33. $\displaystyle\sum_{n=1}^{\infty} \frac{3}{n(n+3)}$

34. $\displaystyle\sum_{n=1}^{\infty} \ln\frac{n}{n+1}$

35. Let $x = 0.99999\ldots$.
(a) Do you think that $x < 1$ or $x = 1$?
(b) Sum a geometric series to find the value of x.
(c) How many decimal representations does the number 1 have?
(d) Which numbers have more than one decimal representation?

36–40 Express the number as a ratio of integers.

36. $0.\overline{73} = 0.73737373\ldots$

37. $0.\overline{2} = 0.2222\ldots$

Graphing calculator or computer with graphing software required   CAS Computer algebra system required   **1.** Homework Hints available in TEC

38. $6.2\overline{54} = 6.2545454\ldots$

39. $1.5\overline{342}$

40. $7.\overline{12345}$

41–43 Find the values of x for which the series converges. Find the sum of the series for those values of x.

41. $\displaystyle\sum_{n=1}^{\infty} \frac{x^n}{3^n}$

42. $\displaystyle\sum_{n=0}^{\infty} \frac{(x+3)^n}{2^n}$

43. $\displaystyle\sum_{n=0}^{\infty} \frac{\cos^n x}{2^n}$

44. We have seen that the harmonic series is a divergent series whose terms approach 0. Show that

$$\sum_{n=1}^{\infty} \ln\left(1 + \frac{1}{n}\right)$$

is another series with this property.

CAS **45–46** Use the partial fraction command on your CAS to find a convenient expression for the partial sum, and then use this expression to find the sum of the series. Check your answer by using the CAS to sum the series directly.

45. $\displaystyle\sum_{n=1}^{\infty} \frac{3n^2 + 3n + 1}{(n^2+n)^3}$

46. $\displaystyle\sum_{n=2}^{\infty} \frac{1}{n^3 - n}$

47. If the nth partial sum of a series $\sum_{n=1}^{\infty} a_n$ is

$$s_n = \frac{n-1}{n+1}$$

find a_n and $\sum_{n=1}^{\infty} a_n$.

48. If the nth partial sum of a series $\sum_{n=1}^{\infty} a_n$ is $s_n = 3 - n2^{-n}$, find a_n and $\sum_{n=1}^{\infty} a_n$.

49. A patient is prescribed a drug and is told to take one 100-mg pill every eight hours. After eight hours, about 5% of the drug remains in the body.
(a) What quantity of the drug remains in the body after the patient takes three pills?
(b) What quantity remains after n pills are taken?
(c) What happens in the long run?

50. To control an agricultural pest called the medfly (Mediterranean fruit fly), N sterilized male flies are released into the general fly population every day. If s is the proportion of these sterilized flies that survive a given day, then Ns^k will survive for k days.
(a) How many sterile flies are there after n days? What happens in the long run?
(b) If $s = 0.9$ and 10,000 sterilized males are needed to control the medfly population in a given area, how many should be released every day?

51. When money is spent on goods and services, those who receive the money also spend some of it. The people receiving some of the twice-spent money will spend some of that, and so on. Economists call this chain reaction the *multiplier effect*. In a hypothetical isolated community, the local government begins the process by spending D dollars. Suppose that each recipient of spent money spends $100c\%$ and saves $100s\%$ of the money that he or she receives. The values c and s are called the *marginal propensity to consume* and the *marginal propensity to save* and, of course, $c + s = 1$.
(a) Let S_n be the total spending that has been generated after n transactions. Find an equation for S_n.
(b) Show that $\lim_{n\to\infty} S_n = kD$, where $k = 1/s$. The number k is called the *multiplier*. What is the multiplier if the marginal propensity to consume is 80%?

Note: The federal government uses this principle to justify deficit spending. Banks use this principle to justify lending a large percentage of the money that they receive in deposits.

52. A certain ball has the property that each time it falls from a height h onto a hard, level surface, it rebounds to a height rh, where $0 < r < 1$. Suppose that the ball is dropped from an initial height of H meters.
(a) Assuming that the ball continues to bounce indefinitely, find the total distance that it travels.
(b) Calculate the total time that the ball travels. (Use the fact that the ball falls $\frac{1}{2}gt^2$ meters in t seconds.)
(c) Suppose that each time the ball strikes the surface with velocity v it rebounds with velocity $-kv$, where $0 < k < 1$. How long will it take for the ball to come to rest?

53. Find the value of c if

$$\sum_{n=2}^{\infty} (1 + c)^{-n} = 2$$

54. Find the value of c such that

$$\sum_{n=0}^{\infty} e^{nc} = 10$$

55. In Example 7 we showed that the harmonic series is divergent. Here we outline another method, making use of the fact that $e^x > 1 + x$ for any $x > 0$. (See Exercise 4.3.62.)

If s_n is the nth partial sum of the harmonic series, show that $e^{s_n} > n + 1$. Why does this imply that the harmonic series is divergent?

56. Graph the curves $y = x^n$, $0 \leqslant x \leqslant 1$, for $n = 0, 1, 2, 3, 4, \ldots$ on a common screen. By finding the areas between successive curves, give a geometric demonstration of the fact, shown in Example 6, that

$$\sum_{n=1}^{\infty} \frac{1}{n(n+1)} = 1$$

57. The figure shows two circles C and D of radius 1 that touch at P. T is a common tangent line; C_1 is the circle that touches C, D, and T; C_2 is the circle that touches C, D, and C_1; C_3 is the circle that touches C, D, and C_2. This procedure can be continued indefinitely and produces an infinite sequence of circles $\{C_n\}$. Find an expression for the diameter of C_n and thus provide another geometric demonstration of Example 6.

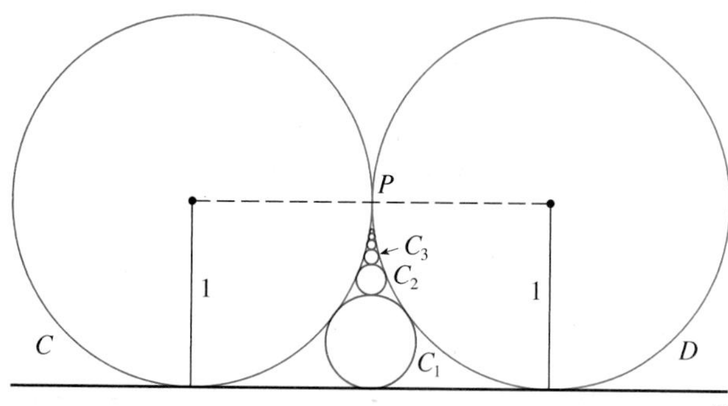

58. A right triangle ABC is given with $\angle A = \theta$ and $|AC| = b$. CD is drawn perpendicular to AB, DE is drawn perpendicular to BC, $EF \perp AB$, and this process is continued indefinitely, as shown in the figure. Find the total length of all the perpendiculars

$$|CD| + |DE| + |EF| + |FG| + \cdots$$

in terms of b and θ.

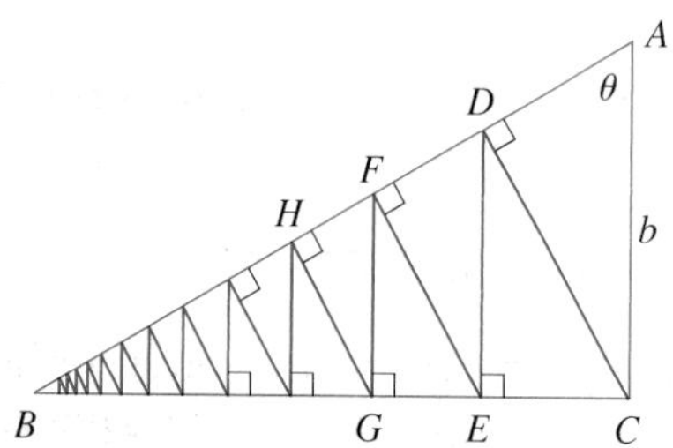

59. What is wrong with the following calculation?

$$\begin{aligned} 0 &= 0 + 0 + 0 + \cdots \\ &= (1 - 1) + (1 - 1) + (1 - 1) + \cdots \\ &= 1 - 1 + 1 - 1 + 1 - 1 + \cdots \\ &= 1 + (-1 + 1) + (-1 + 1) + (-1 + 1) + \cdots \\ &= 1 + 0 + 0 + 0 + \cdots = 1 \end{aligned}$$

(Guido Ubaldus thought that this proved the existence of God because "something has been created out of nothing.")

60. Suppose that $\sum_{n=1}^{\infty} a_n$ $(a_n \neq 0)$ is known to be a convergent series. Prove that $\sum_{n=1}^{\infty} 1/a_n$ is a divergent series.

61. If $\sum a_n$ is convergent and $\sum b_n$ is divergent, show that the series $\sum (a_n + b_n)$ is divergent. [*Hint:* Argue by contradiction.]

62. If $\sum a_n$ and $\sum b_n$ are both divergent, is $\sum (a_n + b_n)$ necessarily divergent?

63. Suppose that a series $\sum a_n$ has positive terms and its partial sums s_n satisfy the inequality $s_n \leqslant 1000$ for all n. Explain why $\sum a_n$ must be convergent.

64. The Fibonacci sequence was defined in Section 8.1 by the equations

$$f_1 = 1, \quad f_2 = 1, \quad f_n = f_{n-1} + f_{n-2} \qquad n \geqslant 3$$

Show that each of the following statements is true.

(a) $\dfrac{1}{f_{n-1} f_{n+1}} = \dfrac{1}{f_{n-1} f_n} - \dfrac{1}{f_n f_{n+1}}$

(b) $\displaystyle\sum_{n=2}^{\infty} \frac{1}{f_{n-1} f_{n+1}} = 1$

(c) $\displaystyle\sum_{n=2}^{\infty} \frac{f_n}{f_{n-1} f_{n+1}} = 2$

65. The **Cantor set**, named after the German mathematician Georg Cantor (1845–1918), is constructed as follows. We start with the closed interval $[0, 1]$ and remove the open interval $(\frac{1}{3}, \frac{2}{3})$. That leaves the two intervals $[0, \frac{1}{3}]$ and $[\frac{2}{3}, 1]$ and we remove the open middle third of each. Four intervals remain and again we remove the open middle third of each of them. We continue this procedure indefinitely, at each step removing the open middle third of every interval that remains from the preceding step. The Cantor set consists of the numbers that remain in $[0, 1]$ after all those intervals have been removed.

(a) Show that the total length of all the intervals that are removed is 1. Despite that, the Cantor set contains infinitely many numbers. Give examples of some numbers in the Cantor set.

(b) The **Sierpinski carpet** is a two-dimensional counterpart of the Cantor set. It is constructed by removing the center one-ninth of a square of side 1, then removing the centers of the eight smaller remaining squares, and so on. (The figure shows the first three steps of the construction.) Show that the sum of the areas of the removed squares is 1. This implies that the Sierpinski carpet has area 0.

66. (a) A sequence $\{a_n\}$ is defined recursively by the equation $a_n = \frac{1}{2}(a_{n-1} + a_{n-2})$ for $n \geqslant 3$, where a_1 and a_2 can be any real numbers. Experiment with various values of a_1 and a_2 and use your calculator to guess the limit of the sequence.
(b) Find $\lim_{n\to\infty} a_n$ in terms of a_1 and a_2 by expressing $a_{n+1} - a_n$ in terms of $a_2 - a_1$ and summing a series.

67. Consider the series $\sum_{n=1}^{\infty} n/(n+1)!$.
(a) Find the partial sums s_1, s_2, s_3, and s_4. Do you recognize the denominators? Use the pattern to guess a formula for s_n.
(b) Use mathematical induction to prove your guess.
(c) Show that the given infinite series is convergent, and find its sum.

68. In the figure there are infinitely many circles approaching the vertices of an equilateral triangle, each circle touching other circles and sides of the triangle. If the triangle has sides of length 1, find the total area occupied by the circles.

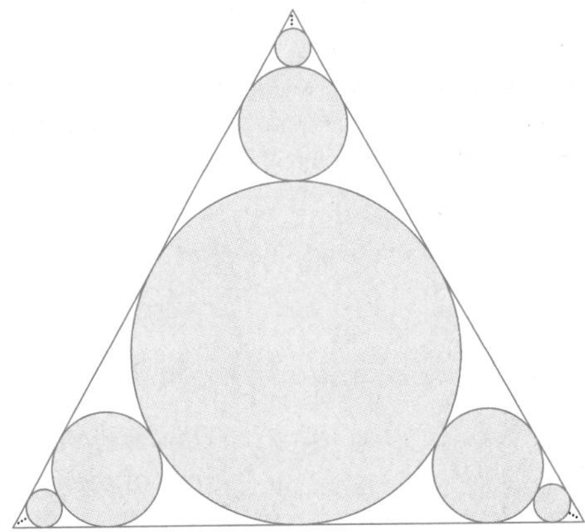

8.3 The Integral and Comparison Tests; Estimating Sums

In general, it is difficult to find the exact sum of a series. We were able to accomplish this for geometric series and the series $\Sigma\, 1/[n(n+1)]$ because in each of those cases we could find a simple formula for the nth partial sum s_n. But usually it isn't easy to compute $\lim_{n\to\infty} s_n$. Therefore in this section and the next we develop tests that enable us to determine whether a series is convergent or divergent without explicitly finding its sum. In some cases, however, our methods will enable us to find good estimates of the sum.

In this section we deal only with series with positive terms, so the partial sums are increasing. In view of the Monotonic Sequence Theorem, to decide whether a series is convergent or divergent, we need to determine whether the partial sums are bounded or not.

Testing with an Integral

Let's investigate the series whose terms are the reciprocals of the squares of the positive integers:

$$\sum_{n=1}^{\infty} \frac{1}{n^2} = \frac{1}{1^2} + \frac{1}{2^2} + \frac{1}{3^2} + \frac{1}{4^2} + \frac{1}{5^2} + \cdots$$

n	$s_n = \sum_{i=1}^{n} \frac{1}{i^2}$
5	1.4636
10	1.5498
50	1.6251
100	1.6350
500	1.6429
1000	1.6439
5000	1.6447

There's no simple formula for the sum s_n of the first n terms, but the computer-generated table of values given in the margin suggests that the partial sums are approaching a number near 1.64 as $n \to \infty$ and so it looks as if the series is convergent.

We can confirm this impression with a geometric argument. Figure 1 shows the curve $y = 1/x^2$ and rectangles that lie below the curve. The base of each rectangle is an interval of length 1; the height is equal to the value of the function $y = 1/x^2$ at the right endpoint of the interval.

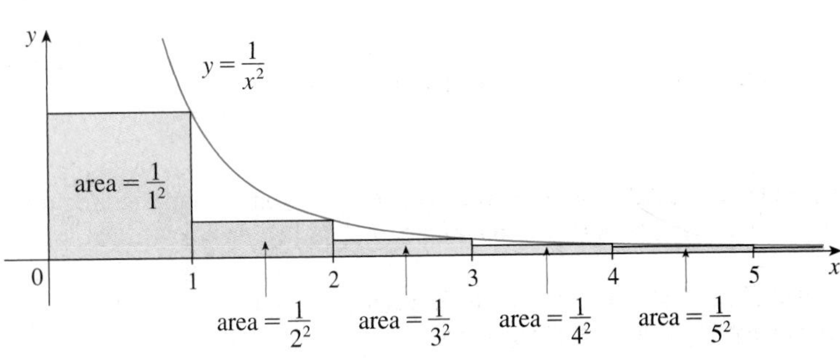

FIGURE 1

So the sum of the areas of the rectangles is

$$\frac{1}{1^2} + \frac{1}{2^2} + \frac{1}{3^2} + \frac{1}{4^2} + \frac{1}{5^2} + \cdots = \sum_{n=1}^{\infty} \frac{1}{n^2}$$

If we exclude the first rectangle, the total area of the remaining rectangles is smaller than the area under the curve $y = 1/x^2$ for $x \geqslant 1$, which is the value of the integral $\int_1^\infty (1/x^2)\,dx$. In Section 5.10 we discovered that this improper integral is convergent and has value 1. So the picture shows that all the partial sums are less than

$$\frac{1}{1^2} + \int_1^\infty \frac{1}{x^2}\,dx = 2$$

Thus the partial sums are bounded and the series converges. The sum of the series (the limit of the partial sums) is also less than 2:

$$\sum_{n=1}^{\infty} \frac{1}{n^2} = \frac{1}{1^2} + \frac{1}{2^2} + \frac{1}{3^2} + \frac{1}{4^2} + \cdots < 2$$

[The exact sum of this series was found by the Swiss mathematician Leonhard Euler (1707–1783) to be $\pi^2/6$, but the proof of this fact is beyond the scope of this book.]

Now let's look at the series

n	$s_n = \sum_{i=1}^{n} \frac{1}{\sqrt{i}}$
5	3.2317
10	5.0210
50	12.7524
100	18.5896
500	43.2834
1000	61.8010
5000	139.9681

$$\sum_{n=1}^{\infty} \frac{1}{\sqrt{n}} = \frac{1}{\sqrt{1}} + \frac{1}{\sqrt{2}} + \frac{1}{\sqrt{3}} + \frac{1}{\sqrt{4}} + \frac{1}{\sqrt{5}} + \cdots$$

The table of values of s_n suggests that the partial sums aren't approaching a finite number, so we suspect that the given series may be divergent. Again we use a picture for confirmation. Figure 2 shows the curve $y = 1/\sqrt{x}$, but this time we use rectangles whose tops lie *above* the curve.

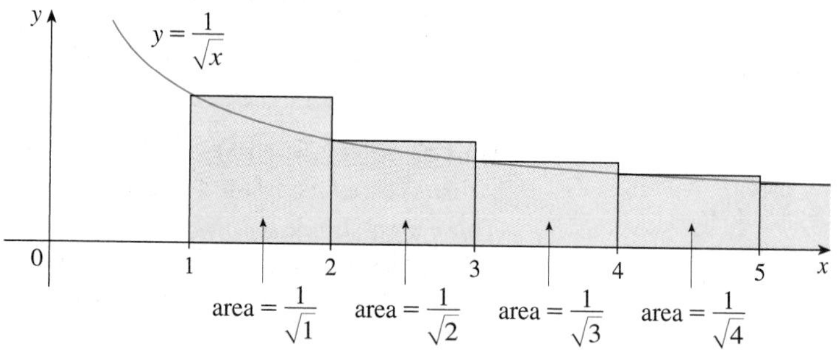

FIGURE 2

The base of each rectangle is an interval of length 1. The height is equal to the value of the function $y = 1/\sqrt{x}$ at the *left* endpoint of the interval. So the sum of the areas of all the rectangles is

$$\frac{1}{\sqrt{1}} + \frac{1}{\sqrt{2}} + \frac{1}{\sqrt{3}} + \frac{1}{\sqrt{4}} + \frac{1}{\sqrt{5}} + \cdots = \sum_{n=1}^{\infty} \frac{1}{\sqrt{n}}$$

This total area is greater than the area under the curve $y = 1/\sqrt{x}$ for $x \geqslant 1$, which is equal to the integral $\int_1^\infty (1/\sqrt{x})\,dx$. But we know from Section 5.10 that this improper integral is divergent. In other words, the area under the curve is infinite. So the sum of the series must be infinite, that is, the series is divergent.

The same sort of geometric reasoning that we used for these two series can be used to prove the following test.

The Integral Test Suppose f is a continuous, positive, decreasing function on $[1, \infty)$ and let $a_n = f(n)$. Then the series $\sum_{n=1}^{\infty} a_n$ is convergent if and only if the improper integral $\int_1^{\infty} f(x)\, dx$ is convergent. In other words:

(a) If $\displaystyle\int_1^{\infty} f(x)\, dx$ is convergent, then $\displaystyle\sum_{n=1}^{\infty} a_n$ is convergent.

(b) If $\displaystyle\int_1^{\infty} f(x)\, dx$ is divergent, then $\displaystyle\sum_{n=1}^{\infty} a_n$ is divergent.

Note: When we use the Integral Test it is not necessary to start the series or the integral at $n = 1$. For instance, in testing the series

$$\sum_{n=4}^{\infty} \frac{1}{(n-3)^2} \qquad \text{we use} \qquad \int_4^{\infty} \frac{1}{(x-3)^2}\, dx$$

Also, it is not necessary that f be always decreasing. What is important is that f be *ultimately* decreasing, that is, decreasing for x larger than some number N. Then $\sum_{n=N}^{\infty} a_n$ is convergent, so $\sum_{n=1}^{\infty} a_n$ is convergent by Note 4 of Section 8.2.

V EXAMPLE 1 Using the Integral Test

Determine whether the series $\displaystyle\sum_{n=1}^{\infty} \frac{\ln n}{n}$ converges or diverges.

SOLUTION The function $f(x) = (\ln x)/x$ is positive and continuous for $x > 1$ because the logarithm function is continuous. But it is not obvious whether or not f is decreasing, so we compute its derivative:

$$f'(x) = \frac{x(1/x) - \ln x}{x^2} = \frac{1 - \ln x}{x^2}$$

Thus $f'(x) < 0$ when $\ln x > 1$, that is, $x > e$. It follows that f is decreasing when $x > e$ and so we can apply the Integral Test:

$$\int_1^{\infty} \frac{\ln x}{x}\, dx = \lim_{t\to\infty} \int_1^t \frac{\ln x}{x}\, dx = \lim_{t\to\infty} \frac{(\ln x)^2}{2}\bigg]_1^t$$

$$= \lim_{t\to\infty} \frac{(\ln t)^2}{2} = \infty$$

Since this improper integral is divergent, the series $\Sigma\, (\ln n)/n$ is also divergent by the Integral Test.

V EXAMPLE 2 Convergence of the p-series

For what values of p is the series $\displaystyle\sum_{n=1}^{\infty} \frac{1}{n^p}$ convergent?

SOLUTION If $p < 0$, then $\lim_{n\to\infty} (1/n^p) = \infty$. If $p = 0$, then $\lim_{n\to\infty} (1/n^p) = 1$. In either case $\lim_{n\to\infty} (1/n^p) \neq 0$, so the given series diverges by the Test for Divergence [see (8.2.7)].

In order to use the Integral Test we need to be able to evaluate $\int_1^\infty f(x)\,dx$ and therefore we have to be able to find an antiderivative of f. Frequently this is difficult or impossible, so we need other tests for convergence too.

If $p > 0$, then the function $f(x) = 1/x^p$ is clearly continuous, positive, and decreasing on $[1, \infty)$. We found in Chapter 5 [see (5.10.2)] that

$$\int_1^\infty \frac{1}{x^p}\,dx \quad \text{converges if } p > 1 \text{ and diverges if } p \leqslant 1$$

It follows from the Integral Test that the series $\Sigma\, 1/n^p$ converges if $p > 1$ and diverges if $0 < p \leqslant 1$. (For $p = 1$, this series is the harmonic series discussed in Example 7 in Section 8.2.)

The series in Example 2 is called the ***p*-series**. It is important in the rest of this chapter, so we summarize the results of Example 2 for future reference as follows.

1 The p-series $\displaystyle\sum_{n=1}^{\infty} \frac{1}{n^p}$ is convergent if $p > 1$ and divergent if $p \leqslant 1$.

For instance, the series

$$\sum_{n=1}^{\infty} \frac{1}{n^3} = \frac{1}{1^3} + \frac{1}{2^3} + \frac{1}{3^3} + \frac{1}{4^3} + \cdots$$

is convergent because it is a p-series with $p = 3 > 1$. But the series

$$\sum_{n=1}^{\infty} \frac{1}{n^{1/3}} = \sum_{n=1}^{\infty} \frac{1}{\sqrt[3]{n}} = 1 + \frac{1}{\sqrt[3]{2}} + \frac{1}{\sqrt[3]{3}} + \frac{1}{\sqrt[3]{4}} + \cdots$$

is divergent because it is a p-series with $p = \frac{1}{3} < 1$.

Testing by Comparing

The series

2 $$\sum_{n=1}^{\infty} \frac{1}{2^n + 1}$$

reminds us of the series $\sum_{n=1}^{\infty} 1/2^n$, which is a geometric series with $a = \frac{1}{2}$ and $r = \frac{1}{2}$ and is therefore convergent. Because the series (2) is so similar to a convergent series, we have the feeling that it too must be convergent. Indeed, it is. The inequality

$$\frac{1}{2^n + 1} < \frac{1}{2^n}$$

shows that our given series (2) has smaller terms than those of the geometric series and therefore all its partial sums are also smaller than 1 (the sum of the geometric series). This means that its partial sums form a bounded increasing sequence, which is convergent. It also follows that the sum of the series is less than the sum of the geometric series:

$$\sum_{n=1}^{\infty} \frac{1}{2^n + 1} < 1$$

Similar reasoning can be used to prove the following test, which applies only to series whose terms are positive. The first part says that if we have a series whose terms are *smaller* than those of a known *convergent* series, then our series is also convergent. The second part says that if we start with a series whose terms are *larger* than those of a known *divergent* series, then it too is divergent.

The Comparison Test Suppose that $\Sigma\, a_n$ and $\Sigma\, b_n$ are series with positive terms.

(a) If $\Sigma\, b_n$ is convergent and $a_n \leqslant b_n$ for all n, then $\Sigma\, a_n$ is also convergent.

(b) If $\Sigma\, b_n$ is divergent and $a_n \geqslant b_n$ for all n, then $\Sigma\, a_n$ is also divergent.

Standard Series for Use with the Comparison Test

In using the Comparison Test we must, of course, have some known series $\Sigma\, b_n$ for the purpose of comparison. Most of the time we use one of these series:

- A p-series $[\Sigma\, 1/n^p$ converges if $p > 1$ and diverges if $p \leqslant 1$; see (1)$]$
- A geometric series $[\Sigma\, ar^{n-1}$ converges if $|r| < 1$ and diverges if $|r| \geqslant 1$; see (8.2.4)$]$

V EXAMPLE 3 Using the Comparison Test

Determine whether the series $\displaystyle\sum_{n=1}^{\infty} \frac{5}{2n^2 + 4n + 3}$ converges or diverges.

SOLUTION For large n the dominant term in the denominator is $2n^2$, so we compare the given series with the series $\Sigma\, 5/(2n^2)$. Observe that

$$\frac{5}{2n^2 + 4n + 3} < \frac{5}{2n^2}$$

because the left side has a bigger denominator. (In the notation of the Comparison Test, a_n is the left side and b_n is the right side.) We know that

$$\sum_{n=1}^{\infty} \frac{5}{2n^2} = \frac{5}{2} \sum_{n=1}^{\infty} \frac{1}{n^2}$$

is convergent because it's a constant times a p-series with $p = 2 > 1$. Therefore

$$\sum_{n=1}^{\infty} \frac{5}{2n^2 + 4n + 3}$$

is convergent by part (a) of the Comparison Test.

Although the condition $a_n \leqslant b_n$ or $a_n \geqslant b_n$ in the Comparison Test is given for all n, we need verify only that it holds for $n \geqslant N$, where N is some fixed integer, because the convergence of a series is not affected by a finite number of terms. This is illustrated in the next example.

V EXAMPLE 4 Test the series $\displaystyle\sum_{n=1}^{\infty} \frac{\ln n}{n}$ for convergence or divergence.

SOLUTION We used the Integral Test to test this series in Example 1, but we can also test it by comparing it with the harmonic series. Observe that $\ln n > 1$ for $n \geqslant 3$ and so

$$\frac{\ln n}{n} > \frac{1}{n} \qquad n \geqslant 3$$

We know that $\Sigma\, 1/n$ is divergent (p-series with $p = 1$). Thus the given series is divergent by the Comparison Test.

Note: The terms of the series being tested must be smaller than those of a convergent series or larger than those of a divergent series. If the terms are larger than the terms of a convergent series or smaller than those of a divergent series, then the Comparison Test doesn't apply. Consider, for instance, the series

$$\sum_{n=1}^{\infty} \frac{1}{2^n - 1}$$

The inequality

$$\frac{1}{2^n - 1} > \frac{1}{2^n}$$

is useless as far as the Comparison Test is concerned because $\Sigma\, b_n = \Sigma\left(\frac{1}{2}\right)^n$ is convergent and $a_n > b_n$. Nonetheless, we have the feeling that $\Sigma\, 1/(2^n - 1)$ ought to be convergent because it is very similar to the convergent geometric series $\Sigma\left(\frac{1}{2}\right)^n$. In such cases the following test can be used.

The Limit Comparison Test Suppose that $\Sigma\, a_n$ and $\Sigma\, b_n$ are series with positive terms. If

$$\lim_{n\to\infty} \frac{a_n}{b_n} = c$$

where c is a finite number and $c > 0$, then either both series converge or both diverge.

Although we won't prove the Limit Comparison Test, it seems reasonable because for large n, $a_n \approx cb_n$.

EXAMPLE 5 Using the Limit Comparison Test

Test the series $\displaystyle\sum_{n=1}^{\infty} \frac{1}{2^n - 1}$ for convergence or divergence.

SOLUTION We use the Limit Comparison Test with

$$a_n = \frac{1}{2^n - 1} \qquad b_n = \frac{1}{2^n}$$

and obtain

$$\lim_{n\to\infty} \frac{a_n}{b_n} = \lim_{n\to\infty} \frac{1/(2^n - 1)}{1/2^n} = \lim_{n\to\infty} \frac{2^n}{2^n - 1} = \lim_{n\to\infty} \frac{1}{1 - 1/2^n} = 1 > 0$$

Since this limit exists and $\Sigma\, 1/2^n$ is a convergent geometric series, the given series converges by the Limit Comparison Test.

Estimating the Sum of a Series

Suppose we have been able to use the Integral Test to show that a series $\Sigma\, a_n$ is convergent and we now want to find an approximation to the sum s of the series. Of course, any partial sum s_n is an approximation to s because $\lim_{n\to\infty} s_n = s$. But how good is such an approximation? To find out, we need to estimate the size of the **remainder**

$$R_n = s - s_n = a_{n+1} + a_{n+2} + a_{n+3} + \cdots$$

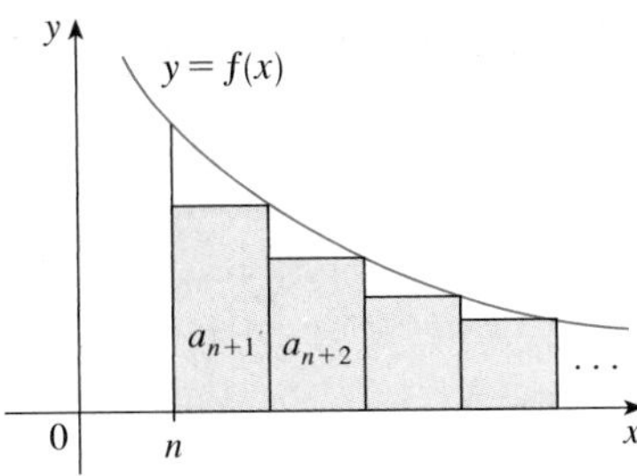

FIGURE 3

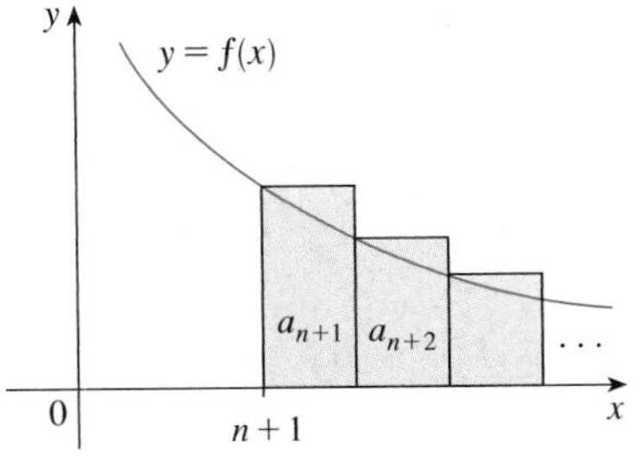

FIGURE 4

The remainder R_n is the error made when s_n, the sum of the first n terms, is used as an approximation to the total sum.

We use the same notation and ideas as in the Integral Test, assuming that f is decreasing on $[n, \infty)$. Comparing the areas of the rectangles with the area under $y = f(x)$ for $x > n$ in Figure 3, we see that

$$R_n = a_{n+1} + a_{n+2} + \cdots \leqslant \int_n^\infty f(x)\,dx$$

Similarly, we see from Figure 4 that

$$R_n = a_{n+1} + a_{n+2} + \cdots \geqslant \int_{n+1}^\infty f(x)\,dx$$

So we have proved the following error estimate.

> **3 Remainder Estimate for the Integral Test** Suppose $f(k) = a_k$, where f is a continuous, positive, decreasing function for $x \geqslant n$ and $\Sigma\, a_n$ is convergent. If $R_n = s - s_n$, then
>
> $$\int_{n+1}^\infty f(x)\,dx \leqslant R_n \leqslant \int_n^\infty f(x)\,dx$$

V EXAMPLE 6 Estimating the sum of a series

(a) Approximate the sum of the series $\Sigma\, 1/n^3$ by using the sum of the first 10 terms. Estimate the error involved in this approximation.

(b) How many terms are required to ensure that the sum is accurate to within 0.0005?

SOLUTION In both parts (a) and (b) we need to know $\int_n^\infty f(x)\,dx$. With $f(x) = 1/x^3$, which satisfies the conditions of the Integral Test, we have

$$\int_n^\infty \frac{1}{x^3}\,dx = \lim_{t\to\infty}\left[-\frac{1}{2x^2}\right]_n^t = \lim_{t\to\infty}\left(-\frac{1}{2t^2} + \frac{1}{2n^2}\right) = \frac{1}{2n^2}$$

(a) Approximating the sum of the series by the 10th partial sum, we have

$$\sum_{n=1}^\infty \frac{1}{n^3} \approx s_{10} = \frac{1}{1^3} + \frac{1}{2^3} + \frac{1}{3^3} + \cdots + \frac{1}{10^3} \approx 1.1975$$

According to the remainder estimate in (3), we have

$$R_{10} \leqslant \int_{10}^\infty \frac{1}{x^3}\,dx = \frac{1}{2(10)^2} = \frac{1}{200}$$

So the size of the error is at most 0.005.

(b) Accuracy to within 0.0005 means that we have to find a value of n such that $R_n \leqslant 0.0005$. Since

$$R_n \leqslant \int_n^\infty \frac{1}{x^3}\,dx = \frac{1}{2n^2}$$

we want

$$\frac{1}{2n^2} < 0.0005$$

Solving this inequality, we get

$$n^2 > \frac{1}{0.001} = 1000 \qquad \text{or} \qquad n > \sqrt{1000} \approx 31.6$$

We need 32 terms to ensure accuracy to within 0.0005.

If we add s_n to each side of the inequalities in (3), we get

4
$$s_n + \int_{n+1}^{\infty} f(x)\,dx \leqslant s \leqslant s_n + \int_{n}^{\infty} f(x)\,dx$$

because $s_n + R_n = s$. The inequalities in (4) give a lower bound and an upper bound for s. They provide a more accurate approximation to the sum of the series than the partial sum s_n does.

EXAMPLE 7 An improved estimate

Use (4) with $n = 10$ to estimate the sum of the series $\sum_{n=1}^{\infty} \frac{1}{n^3}$.

SOLUTION The inequalities in (4) become

$$s_{10} + \int_{11}^{\infty} \frac{1}{x^3}\,dx \leqslant s \leqslant s_{10} + \int_{10}^{\infty} \frac{1}{x^3}\,dx$$

From Example 6 we know that

$$\int_{n}^{\infty} \frac{1}{x^3}\,dx = \frac{1}{2n^2}$$

so

$$s_{10} + \frac{1}{2(11)^2} \leqslant s \leqslant s_{10} + \frac{1}{2(10)^2}$$

Using $s_{10} \approx 1.197532$, we get

$$1.201664 \leqslant s \leqslant 1.202532$$

If we approximate s by the midpoint of this interval, then the error is at most half the length of the interval. So

$$\sum_{n=1}^{\infty} \frac{1}{n^3} \approx 1.2021 \qquad \text{with error} < 0.0005$$

If we compare Example 7 with Example 6, we see that the improved estimate in (4) can be much better than the estimate $s \approx s_n$. To make the error smaller than 0.0005 we had to use 32 terms in Example 6 but only 10 terms in Example 7.

If we have used the Comparison Test to show that a series $\sum a_n$ converges by comparison with a series $\sum b_n$, then we may be able to estimate the sum $\sum a_n$ by comparing remainders, as the following example shows.

V EXAMPLE 8 Use the sum of the first 100 terms to approximate the sum of the series $\Sigma\, 1/(n^3 + 1)$. Estimate the error involved in this approximation.

SOLUTION Since

$$\frac{1}{n^3 + 1} < \frac{1}{n^3}$$

the given series is convergent by the Comparison Test. The remainder T_n for the comparison series $\Sigma\, 1/n^3$ was estimated in Example 6. There we found that

$$T_n \leqslant \int_n^\infty \frac{1}{x^3}\,dx = \frac{1}{2n^2}$$

Therefore the remainder R_n for the given series satisfies

$$R_n \leqslant T_n \leqslant \frac{1}{2n^2}$$

With $n = 100$ we have

$$R_{100} \leqslant \frac{1}{2(100)^2} = 0.00005$$

Using a programmable calculator or a computer, we find that

$$\sum_{n=1}^{\infty} \frac{1}{n^3 + 1} \approx \sum_{n=1}^{100} \frac{1}{n^3 + 1} \approx 0.6864538$$

with error less than 0.00005.

8.3 Exercises

1. Draw a picture to show that

$$\sum_{n=2}^{\infty} \frac{1}{n^{1.3}} < \int_1^\infty \frac{1}{x^{1.3}}\,dx$$

What can you conclude about the series?

2. Suppose f is a continuous positive decreasing function for $x \geqslant 1$ and $a_n = f(n)$. By drawing a picture, rank the following three quantities in increasing order:

$$\int_1^6 f(x)\,dx \qquad \sum_{i=1}^{5} a_i \qquad \sum_{i=2}^{6} a_i$$

3. Suppose $\Sigma\, a_n$ and $\Sigma\, b_n$ are series with positive terms and $\Sigma\, b_n$ is known to be convergent.
(a) If $a_n > b_n$ for all n, what can you say about $\Sigma\, a_n$? Why?
(b) If $a_n < b_n$ for all n, what can you say about $\Sigma\, a_n$? Why?

4. Suppose $\Sigma\, a_n$ and $\Sigma\, b_n$ are series with positive terms and $\Sigma\, b_n$ is known to be divergent.
(a) If $a_n > b_n$ for all n, what can you say about $\Sigma\, a_n$? Why?
(b) If $a_n < b_n$ for all n, what can you say about $\Sigma\, a_n$? Why?

5. It is important to distinguish between

$$\sum_{n=1}^{\infty} n^b \qquad \text{and} \qquad \sum_{n=1}^{\infty} b^n$$

What name is given to the first series? To the second? For what values of b does the first series converge? For what values of b does the second series converge?

6–8 Use the Integral Test to determine whether the series is convergent or divergent.

6. $\displaystyle\sum_{n=1}^{\infty} \frac{1}{n^5}$

7. $\displaystyle\sum_{n=1}^{\infty} \frac{1}{\sqrt[5]{n}}$

8. $\displaystyle\sum_{n=1}^{\infty} \frac{1}{\sqrt{n + 4}}$

9–10 Use the Comparison Test to determine whether the series is convergent or divergent.

9. $\displaystyle\sum_{n=1}^{\infty} \frac{n}{2n^3 + 1}$

10. $\displaystyle\sum_{n=2}^{\infty} \frac{n^3}{n^4 - 1}$

1. Homework Hints available in TEC

11–30 Determine whether the series is convergent or divergent.

11. $\sum_{n=1}^{\infty} \frac{2}{n^{0.85}}$

12. $\sum_{n=1}^{\infty} (n^{-1.4} + 3n^{-1.2})$

13. $1 + \frac{1}{8} + \frac{1}{27} + \frac{1}{64} + \frac{1}{125} + \cdots$

14. $1 + \frac{1}{2\sqrt{2}} + \frac{1}{3\sqrt{3}} + \frac{1}{4\sqrt{4}} + \frac{1}{5\sqrt{5}} + \cdots$

15. $\sum_{n=1}^{\infty} ne^{-n}$

16. $\sum_{n=1}^{\infty} \frac{n^2}{n^3 + 1}$

17. $\sum_{n=2}^{\infty} \frac{1}{n \ln n}$

18. $\sum_{n=1}^{\infty} \frac{1}{n^2 + 9}$

19. $\sum_{n=1}^{\infty} \frac{\cos^2 n}{n^2 + 1}$

20. $\sum_{n=1}^{\infty} \frac{n^2 - 1}{3n^4 + 1}$

21. $\sum_{n=1}^{\infty} \frac{n - 1}{n4^n}$

22. $\sum_{n=1}^{\infty} \frac{4 + 3^n}{2^n}$

23. $1 + \frac{1}{3} + \frac{1}{5} + \frac{1}{7} + \frac{1}{9} + \cdots$

24. $\frac{1}{5} + \frac{1}{8} + \frac{1}{11} + \frac{1}{14} + \frac{1}{17} + \cdots$

25. $\sum_{n=1}^{\infty} \frac{1 + 4^n}{1 + 3^n}$

26. $\sum_{n=1}^{\infty} \frac{1}{\sqrt{n^3 + 1}}$

27. $\sum_{n=1}^{\infty} \frac{2 + (-1)^n}{n\sqrt{n}}$

28. $\sum_{n=0}^{\infty} \frac{1 + \sin n}{10^n}$

29. $\sum_{n=1}^{\infty} \sin\left(\frac{1}{n}\right)$

30. $\sum_{n=1}^{\infty} \frac{n^2 - 5n}{n^3 + n + 1}$

---

31. Find the values of p for which the following series is convergent.

$$\sum_{n=2}^{\infty} \frac{1}{n(\ln n)^p}$$

32. (a) Find the partial sum s_{10} of the series $\Sigma_{n=1}^{\infty} 1/n^4$. Estimate the error in using s_{10} as an approximation to the sum of the series.
(b) Use (4) with $n = 10$ to give an improved estimate of the sum.
(c) Find a value of n so that s_n is within 0.00001 of the sum.

33. (a) Use the sum of the first 10 terms to estimate the sum of the series $\Sigma_{n=1}^{\infty} 1/n^2$. How good is this estimate?
(b) Improve this estimate using (4) with $n = 10$.
(c) Find a value of n that will ensure that the error in the approximation $s \approx s_n$ is less than 0.001.

34. Find the sum of the series $\Sigma_{n=1}^{\infty} 1/n^5$ correct to three decimal places.

35. Estimate $\Sigma_{n=1}^{\infty} (2n + 1)^{-6}$ correct to five decimal places.

36. How many terms of the series $\Sigma_{n=2}^{\infty} 1/[n(\ln n)^2]$ would you need to add to find its sum to within 0.01?

37–38 Use the sum of the first 10 terms to approximate the sum of the series. Estimate the error.

37. $\sum_{n=1}^{\infty} \frac{1}{\sqrt{n^4 + 1}}$

38. $\sum_{n=1}^{\infty} \frac{\sin^2 n}{n^3}$

---

39. (a) Use a graph of $y = 1/x$ to show that if s_n is the nth partial sum of the harmonic series, then

$$s_n \leqslant 1 + \ln n$$

(b) The harmonic series diverges, but very slowly. Use part (a) to show that the sum of the first million terms is less than 15 and the sum of the first billion terms is less than 22.

40. Show that if we want to approximate the sum of the series $\Sigma_{n=1}^{\infty} n^{-1.001}$ so that the error is less than 5 in the ninth decimal place, then we need to add more than $10^{11,301}$ terms!

41. The meaning of the decimal representation of a number $0.d_1d_2d_3\ldots$ (where the digit d_i is one of the numbers 0, 1, 2, . . . , 9) is that

$$0.d_1d_2d_3d_4\ldots = \frac{d_1}{10} + \frac{d_2}{10^2} + \frac{d_3}{10^3} + \frac{d_4}{10^4} + \cdots$$

Show that this series always converges.

42. Show that if $a_n > 0$ and $\Sigma\, a_n$ is convergent, then $\Sigma \ln(1 + a_n)$ is convergent.

43. If $\Sigma\, a_n$ is a convergent series with positive terms, is it true that $\Sigma \sin(a_n)$ is also convergent?

44. Find all positive values of b for which the series $\Sigma_{n=1}^{\infty} b^{\ln n}$ converges.

45. Show that if $a_n > 0$ and $\lim_{n\to\infty} na_n \neq 0$, then $\Sigma\, a_n$ is divergent.

46. Find all values of c for which the following series converges.

$$\sum_{n=1}^{\infty} \left(\frac{c}{n} - \frac{1}{n + 1}\right)$$

8.4 Other Convergence Tests

The convergence tests that we have looked at so far apply only to series with positive terms. In this section we learn how to deal with series whose terms are not necessarily positive.

Alternating Series

An **alternating series** is a series whose terms are alternately positive and negative. Here are two examples:

$$1 - \frac{1}{2} + \frac{1}{3} - \frac{1}{4} + \frac{1}{5} - \frac{1}{6} + \cdots = \sum_{n=1}^{\infty} (-1)^{n-1} \frac{1}{n}$$

$$-\frac{1}{2} + \frac{2}{3} - \frac{3}{4} + \frac{4}{5} - \frac{5}{6} + \frac{6}{7} - \cdots = \sum_{n=1}^{\infty} (-1)^{n} \frac{n}{n+1}$$

We see from these examples that the nth term of an alternating series is of the form

$$a_n = (-1)^{n-1} b_n \qquad \text{or} \qquad a_n = (-1)^n b_n$$

where b_n is a positive number. (In fact, $b_n = |a_n|$.)

The following test says that if the terms of an alternating series decrease to 0 in absolute value, then the series converges.

The Alternating Series Test If the alternating series

$$\sum_{n=1}^{\infty} (-1)^{n-1} b_n = b_1 - b_2 + b_3 - b_4 + b_5 - b_6 + \cdots \qquad (b_n > 0)$$

satisfies

$$\text{(i)} \quad b_{n+1} \leqslant b_n \qquad \text{for all } n$$

$$\text{(ii)} \quad \lim_{n \to \infty} b_n = 0$$

then the series is convergent.

We won't present a formal proof of this test, but Figure 1 gives a picture of the idea behind the proof.

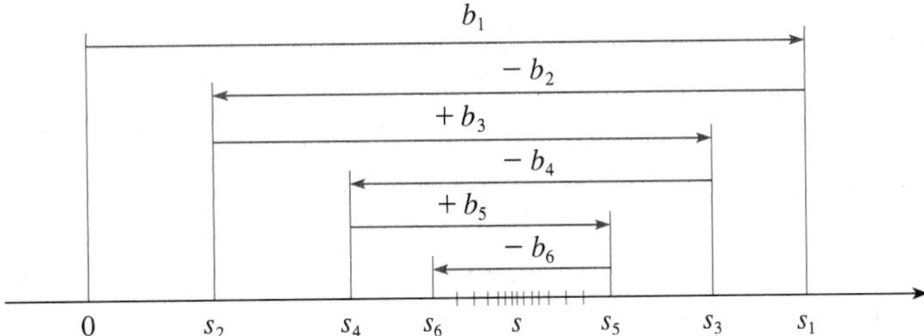

FIGURE 1

We first plot $s_1 = b_1$ on a number line. To find s_2 we subtract b_2, so s_2 is to the left of s_1. Then to find s_3 we add b_3, so s_3 is to the right of s_2. But, since $b_3 < b_2$, s_3 is to the left of s_1. Continuing in this manner, we see that the partial sums oscillate back and forth. Since $b_n \to 0$, the successive steps are becoming smaller and smaller. The even partial sums s_2, s_4, s_6, . . . are increasing and the odd partial sums s_1, s_3, s_5, . . . are decreasing. Thus it seems plausible that both are converging to some number s, which is the sum of the series.

Figure 2 illustrates Example 1 by showing the graphs of the terms $a_n = (-1)^{n-1}/n$ and the partial sums s_n. Notice how the values of s_n zigzag across the limiting value, which appears to be about 0.7. In fact, it can be proved that the exact sum of the series is $\ln 2 \approx 0.693$.

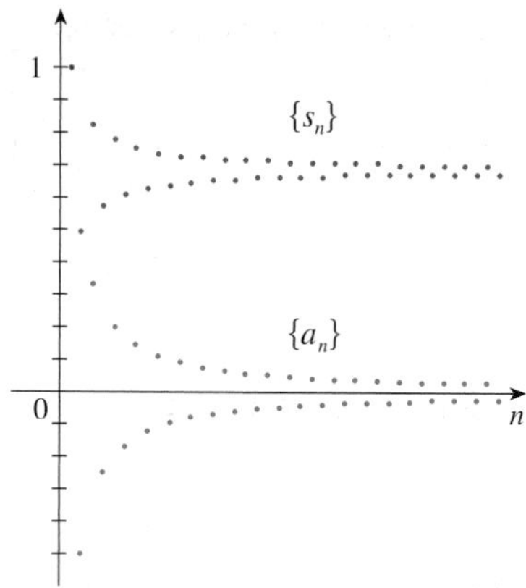

FIGURE 2

V EXAMPLE 1 Using the Alternating Series Test The alternating harmonic series

$$1 - \frac{1}{2} + \frac{1}{3} - \frac{1}{4} + \cdots = \sum_{n=1}^{\infty} \frac{(-1)^{n-1}}{n}$$

satisfies

$$\text{(i) } b_{n+1} < b_n \qquad \text{because} \qquad \frac{1}{n+1} < \frac{1}{n}$$

$$\text{(ii) } \lim_{n\to\infty} b_n = \lim_{n\to\infty} \frac{1}{n} = 0$$

so the series is convergent by the Alternating Series Test.

V EXAMPLE 2 An alternating series for which the Alternating Series Test fails

The series $\displaystyle\sum_{n=1}^{\infty} \frac{(-1)^n 3n}{4n-1}$ is alternating, but

$$\lim_{n\to\infty} b_n = \lim_{n\to\infty} \frac{3n}{4n-1} = \lim_{n\to\infty} \frac{3}{4 - \dfrac{1}{n}} = \frac{3}{4}$$

so condition (ii) is not satisfied. Instead, we look at the limit of the nth term of the series:

$$\lim_{n\to\infty} a_n = \lim_{n\to\infty} \frac{(-1)^n 3n}{4n-1}$$

This limit does not exist, so the series diverges by the Test for Divergence.

EXAMPLE 3 Test the series $\displaystyle\sum_{n=1}^{\infty} (-1)^{n+1} \frac{n^2}{n^3+1}$ for convergence or divergence.

SOLUTION The given series is alternating so we try to verify conditions (i) and (ii) of the Alternating Series Test.

Unlike the situation in Example 1, it is not obvious that the sequence given by $b_n = n^2/(n^3+1)$ is decreasing. However, if we consider the related function $f(x) = x^2/(x^3+1)$, we find that

$$f'(x) = \frac{x(2 - x^3)}{(x^3+1)^2}$$

Since we are considering only positive x, we see that $f'(x) < 0$ if $2 - x^3 < 0$, that is, $x > \sqrt[3]{2}$. Thus f is decreasing on the interval $(\sqrt[3]{2}, \infty)$. This means that $f(n+1) < f(n)$ and therefore $b_{n+1} < b_n$ when $n \geqslant 2$. (The inequality $b_2 < b_1$ can be verified directly but all that really matters is that the sequence $\{b_n\}$ is eventually decreasing.)

Instead of verifying condition (i) of the Alternating Series Test by computing a derivative, we could verify that $b_{n+1} < b_n$ directly by using the technique of Solution 1 of Example 12 in Section 8.1.

Condition (ii) is readily verified:

$$\lim_{n\to\infty} b_n = \lim_{n\to\infty} \frac{n^2}{n^3+1} = \lim_{n\to\infty} \frac{\dfrac{1}{n}}{1 + \dfrac{1}{n^3}} = 0$$

Thus the given series is convergent by the Alternating Series Test.

The error involved in using the partial sum s_n as an approximation to the total sum s is the remainder $R_n = s - s_n$. The next theorem says that for series that satisfy the conditions of the Alternating Series Test, the size of the error is smaller than b_{n+1}, which is the absolute value of the first neglected term.

Alternating Series Estimation Theorem If $s = \Sigma\,(-1)^{n-1}b_n$ is the sum of an alternating series that satisfies

$$\text{(i) } b_{n+1} \leqslant b_n \qquad \text{and} \qquad \text{(ii) } \lim_{n\to\infty} b_n = 0$$

then

$$|R_n| = |s - s_n| \leqslant b_{n+1}$$

You can see geometrically why this is true by looking at Figure 1. Notice that $s - s_4 < b_5$, $|s - s_5| < b_6$, and so on.

By definition, $0! = 1$.

V EXAMPLE 4 Using the Alternating Series Estimation Theorem

Find the sum of the series $\displaystyle\sum_{n=0}^{\infty} \frac{(-1)^n}{n!}$ correct to three decimal places.

SOLUTION We first observe that the series is convergent by the Alternating Series Test because

$$\text{(i)} \quad b_{n+1} = \frac{1}{(n+1)!} = \frac{1}{n!(n+1)} < \frac{1}{n!} = b_n$$

$$\text{(ii)} \quad 0 < \frac{1}{n!} < \frac{1}{n} \to 0 \quad \text{so} \quad b_n = \frac{1}{n!} \to 0 \text{ as } n \to \infty$$

To get a feel for how many terms we need to use in our approximation, let's write out the first few terms of the series:

$$s = \frac{1}{0!} - \frac{1}{1!} + \frac{1}{2!} - \frac{1}{3!} + \frac{1}{4!} - \frac{1}{5!} + \frac{1}{6!} - \frac{1}{7!} + \cdots$$

$$= 1 - 1 + \tfrac{1}{2} - \tfrac{1}{6} + \tfrac{1}{24} - \tfrac{1}{120} + \tfrac{1}{720} - \tfrac{1}{5040} + \cdots$$

Notice that

$$b_7 = \tfrac{1}{5040} < \tfrac{1}{5000} = 0.0002$$

and

$$s_6 = 1 - 1 + \tfrac{1}{2} - \tfrac{1}{6} + \tfrac{1}{24} - \tfrac{1}{120} + \tfrac{1}{720} \approx 0.368056$$

By the Alternating Series Estimation Theorem we know that

$$|s - s_6| \leqslant b_7 < 0.0002$$

This error of less than 0.0002 does not affect the third decimal place, so we have $s \approx 0.368$ correct to three decimal places.

In Section 8.7 we will prove that $e^x = \Sigma_{n=0}^{\infty} x^n/n!$ for all x, so what we have obtained in Example 4 is actually an approximation to the number e^{-1}.

Note: The rule that the error (in using s_n to approximate s) is smaller than the first neglected term is, in general, valid only for alternating series that satisfy the conditions of the Alternating Series Estimation Theorem. The rule does not apply to other types of series.

Absolute Convergence

Given any series $\Sigma\, a_n$, we can consider the corresponding series

$$\sum_{n=1}^{\infty} |a_n| = |a_1| + |a_2| + |a_3| + \cdots$$

whose terms are the absolute values of the terms of the original series.

We have convergence tests for series with positive terms and for alternating series. But what if the signs of the terms switch back and forth irregularly? We will see in Example 7 that the idea of absolute convergence sometimes helps in such cases.

> **Definition** A series $\Sigma\, a_n$ is called **absolutely convergent** if the series of absolute values $\Sigma\, |a_n|$ is convergent.

Notice that if $\Sigma\, a_n$ is a series with positive terms, then $|a_n| = a_n$ and so absolute convergence is the same as convergence.

EXAMPLE 5 Determining absolute convergence The series

$$\sum_{n=1}^{\infty} \frac{(-1)^{n-1}}{n^2} = 1 - \frac{1}{2^2} + \frac{1}{3^2} - \frac{1}{4^2} + \cdots$$

is absolutely convergent because

$$\sum_{n=1}^{\infty} \left| \frac{(-1)^{n-1}}{n^2} \right| = \sum_{n=1}^{\infty} \frac{1}{n^2} = 1 + \frac{1}{2^2} + \frac{1}{3^2} + \frac{1}{4^2} + \cdots$$

is a convergent p-series ($p = 2$).

EXAMPLE 6 A series that is convergent but not absolutely convergent
We know that the alternating harmonic series

$$\sum_{n=1}^{\infty} \frac{(-1)^{n-1}}{n} = 1 - \frac{1}{2} + \frac{1}{3} - \frac{1}{4} + \cdots$$

is convergent (see Example 1), but it is not absolutely convergent because the corresponding series of absolute values is

$$\sum_{n=1}^{\infty} \left| \frac{(-1)^{n-1}}{n} \right| = \sum_{n=1}^{\infty} \frac{1}{n} = 1 + \frac{1}{2} + \frac{1}{3} + \frac{1}{4} + \cdots$$

which is the harmonic series (p-series with $p = 1$) and is therefore divergent.

Example 6 shows that it is possible for a series to be convergent but not absolutely convergent. However, Theorem 1 shows that absolute convergence implies convergence.

> **1 Theorem** If a series $\Sigma\, a_n$ is absolutely convergent, then it is convergent.

To see why Theorem 1 is true, observe that the inequality

$$0 \leqslant a_n + |a_n| \leqslant 2|a_n|$$

is true because $|a_n|$ is either a_n or $-a_n$. If $\sum a_n$ is absolutely convergent, then $\sum |a_n|$ is convergent, so $\sum 2|a_n|$ is convergent. Therefore, by the Comparison Test, $\sum (a_n + |a_n|)$ is convergent. Then

$$\sum a_n = \sum (a_n + |a_n|) - \sum |a_n|$$

is the difference of two convergent series and is therefore convergent. ☐

V EXAMPLE 7 Determine whether the series

$$\sum_{n=1}^{\infty} \frac{\cos n}{n^2} = \frac{\cos 1}{1^2} + \frac{\cos 2}{2^2} + \frac{\cos 3}{3^2} + \cdots$$

is convergent or divergent.

Figure 3 shows the graphs of the terms a_n and partial sums s_n of the series in Example 7. Notice that the series is not alternating but has positive and negative terms.

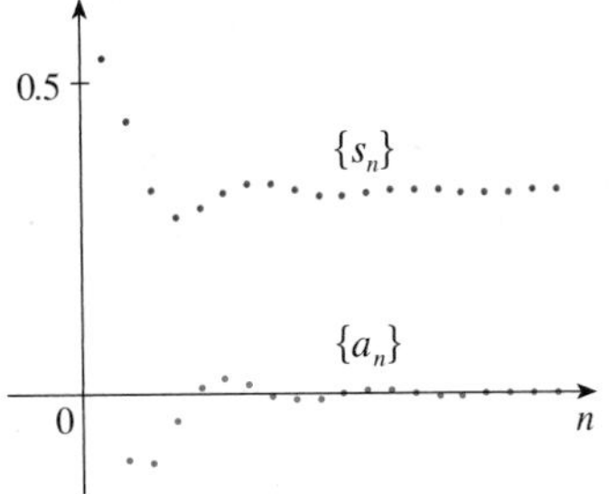

FIGURE 3

SOLUTION This series has both positive and negative terms, but it is not alternating. (The first term is positive, the next three are negative, and the following three are positive. The signs change irregularly.) We can apply the Comparison Test to the series of absolute values

$$\sum_{n=1}^{\infty} \left| \frac{\cos n}{n^2} \right| = \sum_{n=1}^{\infty} \frac{|\cos n|}{n^2}$$

Since $|\cos n| \leqslant 1$ for all n, we have

$$\frac{|\cos n|}{n^2} \leqslant \frac{1}{n^2}$$

We know that $\sum 1/n^2$ is convergent (p-series with $p = 2$) and therefore $\sum |\cos n|/n^2$ is convergent by the Comparison Test. Thus the given series $\sum (\cos n)/n^2$ is absolutely convergent and therefore convergent by Theorem 1. ■

The Ratio Test

The following test is very useful in determining whether a given series is absolutely convergent.

The Ratio Test

(i) If $\displaystyle\lim_{n\to\infty} \left| \frac{a_{n+1}}{a_n} \right| = L < 1$, then the series $\displaystyle\sum_{n=1}^{\infty} a_n$ is absolutely convergent (and therefore convergent).

(ii) If $\displaystyle\lim_{n\to\infty} \left| \frac{a_{n+1}}{a_n} \right| = L > 1$ or $\displaystyle\lim_{n\to\infty} \left| \frac{a_{n+1}}{a_n} \right| = \infty$, then the series $\displaystyle\sum_{n=1}^{\infty} a_n$ is divergent.

(iii) If $\displaystyle\lim_{n\to\infty} \left| \frac{a_{n+1}}{a_n} \right| = 1$, the Ratio Test is inconclusive; that is, no conclusion can be drawn about the convergence or divergence of $\sum a_n$.

The Ratio Test can be proved by comparing the given series to a geometric series. It's understandable that geometric series are involved because, for those series, the ratio r of consecutive terms is constant and the series converges if $|r| < 1$. In part (i) of the Ratio Test, the ratio of consecutive terms isn't constant but $|a_{n+1}/a_n| \to L$ so, for large n, $|a_{n+1}/a_n|$ is almost constant and the series converges if $L < 1$.

Note: Part (iii) of the Ratio Test says that if $\lim_{n\to\infty} |a_{n+1}/a_n| = 1$, the test gives no information. For instance, for the convergent series $\Sigma\ 1/n^2$ we have

$$\left|\frac{a_{n+1}}{a_n}\right| = \frac{\dfrac{1}{(n+1)^2}}{\dfrac{1}{n^2}} = \frac{n^2}{(n+1)^2} = \frac{1}{\left(1+\dfrac{1}{n}\right)^2} \to 1 \qquad \text{as } n \to \infty$$

whereas for the divergent series $\Sigma\ 1/n$ we have

$$\left|\frac{a_{n+1}}{a_n}\right| = \frac{\dfrac{1}{n+1}}{\dfrac{1}{n}} = \frac{n}{n+1} = \frac{1}{1+\dfrac{1}{n}} \to 1 \qquad \text{as } n \to \infty$$

Therefore, if $\lim_{n\to\infty} |a_{n+1}/a_n| = 1$, the series $\Sigma\ a_n$ might converge or it might diverge. In this case the Ratio Test fails and we must use some other test.

EXAMPLE 8 Using the Ratio Test Test the series $\displaystyle\sum_{n=1}^{\infty} (-1)^n \frac{n^3}{3^n}$ for absolute convergence.

SOLUTION We use the Ratio Test with $a_n = (-1)^n n^3/3^n$:

$$\left|\frac{a_{n+1}}{a_n}\right| = \left|\frac{\dfrac{(-1)^{n+1}(n+1)^3}{3^{n+1}}}{\dfrac{(-1)^n n^3}{3^n}}\right| = \frac{(n+1)^3}{3^{n+1}} \cdot \frac{3^n}{n^3}$$

$$= \frac{1}{3}\left(\frac{n+1}{n}\right)^3 = \frac{1}{3}\left(1+\frac{1}{n}\right)^3 \to \frac{1}{3} < 1$$

Thus, by the Ratio Test, the given series is absolutely convergent and therefore convergent.

V EXAMPLE 9 Test the convergence of the series $\displaystyle\sum_{n=1}^{\infty} \frac{n^n}{n!}$.

Series that involve factorials or other products (including a constant raised to the nth power) are often conveniently tested using the Ratio Test.

SOLUTION Since the terms $a_n = n^n/n!$ are positive, we don't need the absolute value signs.

$$\frac{a_{n+1}}{a_n} = \frac{(n+1)^{n+1}}{(n+1)!} \cdot \frac{n!}{n^n}$$

$$= \frac{(n+1)(n+1)^n}{(n+1)n!} \cdot \frac{n!}{n^n}$$

$$= \left(\frac{n+1}{n}\right)^n = \left(1+\frac{1}{n}\right)^n \to e \qquad \text{as } n \to \infty$$

(see Equation 3.7.6). Since $e > 1$, the given series is divergent by the Ratio Test.

www.stewartcalculus.com

We now have several tests for convergence of series. So, given a series, how do you know which test to use? For advice, click on *Additional Topics* and then on *Strategy for Testing Series.*

Note: Although the Ratio Test works in Example 9, another method is to use the Test for Divergence. Since

$$a_n = \frac{n^n}{n!} = \frac{n \cdot n \cdot n \cdot \cdots \cdot n}{1 \cdot 2 \cdot 3 \cdot \cdots \cdot n} \geqslant n$$

it follows that a_n does not approach 0 as $n \to \infty$. Therefore the given series is divergent by the Test for Divergence.

8.4 Exercises

1. (a) What is an alternating series?
   (b) Under what conditions does an alternating series converge?
   (c) If these conditions are satisfied, what can you say about the remainder after n terms?

2. What can you say about the series $\Sigma\, a_n$ in each of the following cases?

   (a) $\displaystyle\lim_{n\to\infty}\left|\frac{a_{n+1}}{a_n}\right| = 8$ (b) $\displaystyle\lim_{n\to\infty}\left|\frac{a_{n+1}}{a_n}\right| = 0.8$

   (c) $\displaystyle\lim_{n\to\infty}\left|\frac{a_{n+1}}{a_n}\right| = 1$

3–10 Test the series for convergence or divergence.

3. $\frac{4}{7} - \frac{4}{8} + \frac{4}{9} - \frac{4}{10} + \frac{4}{11} - \cdots$

4. $-\frac{3}{4} + \frac{5}{5} - \frac{7}{6} + \frac{9}{7} - \frac{11}{8} + \cdots$

5. $\displaystyle\sum_{n=1}^{\infty} \frac{(-1)^{n-1}}{2n+1}$

6. $\displaystyle\sum_{n=1}^{\infty} \frac{(-1)^{n-1}}{\ln(n+4)}$

7. $\displaystyle\sum_{n=1}^{\infty} (-1)^n \frac{3n-1}{2n+1}$

8. $\displaystyle\sum_{n=1}^{\infty} (-1)^n \frac{n}{\sqrt{n^3+2}}$

9. $\displaystyle\sum_{n=1}^{\infty} (-1)^{n+1} \frac{n}{n^2+9}$

10. $\displaystyle\sum_{n=1}^{\infty} (-1)^n \cos\left(\frac{\pi}{n}\right)$

11. Is the 50th partial sum s_{50} of the alternating series $\sum_{n=1}^{\infty} (-1)^{n-1}/n$ an overestimate or an underestimate of the total sum? Explain.

12. Calculate the first 10 partial sums of the series

$$\sum_{n=1}^{\infty} \frac{(-1)^{n-1}}{n^3}$$

and graph both the sequence of terms and the sequence of partial sums on the same screen. Estimate the error in using the 10th partial sum to approximate the total sum.

13. For what values of p is the following series convergent?

$$\sum_{n=1}^{\infty} \frac{(-1)^{n-1}}{n^p}$$

14–16 Show that the series is convergent. How many terms of the series do we need to add in order to find the sum to the indicated accuracy?

14. $\displaystyle\sum_{n=1}^{\infty} \frac{(-1)^n}{n\,5^n}$ $\quad(|\text{error}| < 0.0001)$

15. $\displaystyle\sum_{n=1}^{\infty} \frac{(-1)^{n+1}}{n^6}$ $\quad(|\text{error}| < 0.00005)$

16. $\displaystyle\sum_{n=1}^{\infty} (-1)^{n-1} n e^{-n}$ $\quad(|\text{error}| < 0.01)$

17–18 Graph both the sequence of terms and the sequence of partial sums on the same screen. Use the graph to make a rough estimate of the sum of the series. Then use the Alternating Series Estimation Theorem to estimate the sum correct to four decimal places.

17. $\displaystyle\sum_{n=1}^{\infty} \frac{(-0.8)^n}{n!}$

18. $\displaystyle\sum_{n=1}^{\infty} (-1)^{n-1} \frac{n}{8^n}$

19–20 Approximate the sum of the series correct to four decimal places.

19. $\displaystyle\sum_{n=1}^{\infty} \frac{(-1)^{n-1} n^2}{10^n}$

20. $\displaystyle\sum_{n=1}^{\infty} \frac{(-1)^n}{3^n n!}$

21–34 Determine whether the series is absolutely convergent.

21. $\displaystyle\sum_{n=1}^{\infty} \frac{(-3)^n}{n^3}$

22. $\displaystyle\sum_{n=1}^{\infty} \frac{n!}{100^n}$

23. $\displaystyle\sum_{n=0}^{\infty} \frac{(-10)^n}{n!}$

24. $\displaystyle\sum_{n=1}^{\infty} (-1)^{n-1} \frac{\sqrt{n}}{n+1}$

25. $\displaystyle\sum_{k=1}^{\infty} k\left(\tfrac{2}{3}\right)^k$

26. $\displaystyle\sum_{n=1}^{\infty} \frac{n^2}{2^n}$

Graphing calculator or computer with graphing software required

1. Homework Hints available in TEC

27. $\displaystyle\sum_{n=1}^{\infty} \frac{(-1)^{n-1}}{\sqrt{n}}$

28. $\displaystyle\sum_{n=1}^{\infty} (-1)^{n-1} \frac{2^n}{n^4}$

29. $\displaystyle\sum_{n=1}^{\infty} \frac{10^n}{(n+1)4^{2n+1}}$

30. $\displaystyle\sum_{n=1}^{\infty} \frac{\sin 4n}{4^n}$

31. $\displaystyle\sum_{n=1}^{\infty} \frac{(-1)^n \arctan n}{n^2}$

32. $\displaystyle\sum_{n=1}^{\infty} \frac{(-2)^n n!}{(2n)!}$

33. $1 - \dfrac{1 \cdot 3}{3!} + \dfrac{1 \cdot 3 \cdot 5}{5!} - \dfrac{1 \cdot 3 \cdot 5 \cdot 7}{7!} + \cdots + (-1)^{n-1} \dfrac{1 \cdot 3 \cdot 5 \cdot \cdots \cdot (2n-1)}{(2n-1)!} + \cdots$

34. $\dfrac{2}{5} + \dfrac{2 \cdot 6}{5 \cdot 8} + \dfrac{2 \cdot 6 \cdot 10}{5 \cdot 8 \cdot 11} + \dfrac{2 \cdot 6 \cdot 10 \cdot 14}{5 \cdot 8 \cdot 11 \cdot 14} + \cdots$

35. The terms of a series are defined recursively by the equations

$$a_1 = 2 \qquad a_{n+1} = \frac{5n+1}{4n+3} a_n$$

Determine whether $\Sigma\, a_n$ converges or diverges.

36. A series $\Sigma\, a_n$ is defined by the equations

$$a_1 = 1 \qquad a_{n+1} = \frac{2 + \cos n}{\sqrt{n}} a_n$$

Determine whether $\Sigma\, a_n$ converges or diverges.

37. For which of the following series is the Ratio Test inconclusive (that is, it fails to give a definite answer)?

(a) $\displaystyle\sum_{n=1}^{\infty} \frac{1}{n^3}$ (b) $\displaystyle\sum_{n=1}^{\infty} \frac{n}{2^n}$

(c) $\displaystyle\sum_{n=1}^{\infty} \frac{(-3)^{n-1}}{\sqrt{n}}$ (d) $\displaystyle\sum_{n=1}^{\infty} \frac{\sqrt{n}}{1+n^2}$

38–39 Let

$$\lim_{n\to\infty} \sqrt[n]{|a_n|} = L$$

The **Root Test** says the following:

(i) If $L < 1$, then $\Sigma\, a_n$ is absolutely convergent.
(ii) If $L > 1$ (or $L = \infty$), then $\Sigma\, a_n$ is divergent.
(iii) If $L = 1$, then the Root Test is inconclusive.

(Like the Ratio Test, the Root Test is proved by comparison with a geometric series.) Determine whether the given series is absolutely convergent.

38. $\displaystyle\sum_{n=2}^{\infty} \left(\frac{-2n}{n+1}\right)^{5n}$

39. $\displaystyle\sum_{n=1}^{\infty} \left(\frac{n^2+1}{2n^2+1}\right)^n$

40. For which positive integers k is the following series convergent?

$$\sum_{n=1}^{\infty} \frac{(n!)^2}{(kn)!}$$

41. (a) Show that $\Sigma_{n=0}^{\infty} x^n/n!$ converges for all x.
(b) Deduce that $\lim_{n\to\infty} x^n/n! = 0$ for all x.

42. Around 1910, the Indian mathematician Srinivasa Ramanujan discovered the formula

$$\frac{1}{\pi} = \frac{2\sqrt{2}}{9801} \sum_{n=0}^{\infty} \frac{(4n)!(1103 + 26390n)}{(n!)^4 396^{4n}}$$

William Gosper used this series in 1985 to compute the first 17 million digits of π.
(a) Verify that the series is convergent.
(b) How many correct decimal places of π do you get if you use just the first term of the series? What if you use two terms?

8.5 Power Series

A **power series** is a series of the form

$$\boxed{1} \qquad \sum_{n=0}^{\infty} c_n x^n = c_0 + c_1 x + c_2 x^2 + c_3 x^3 + \cdots$$

where x is a variable and the c_n's are constants called the **coefficients** of the series. For each fixed x, the series (1) is a series of constants that we can test for convergence or divergence. A power series may converge for some values of x and diverge for other values of x. The sum of the series is a function

$$f(x) = c_0 + c_1 x + c_2 x^2 + \cdots + c_n x^n + \cdots$$

whose domain is the set of all x for which the series converges. Notice that f resembles a polynomial. The only difference is that f has infinitely many terms.

For instance, if we take $c_n = 1$ for all n, the power series becomes the geometric series

$$\sum_{n=0}^{\infty} x^n = 1 + x + x^2 + \cdots + x^n + \cdots$$

which converges when $-1 < x < 1$ and diverges when $|x| \geqslant 1$. (See Equation 8.2.5.)

More generally, a series of the form

2 $$\sum_{n=0}^{\infty} c_n(x-a)^n = c_0 + c_1(x-a) + c_2(x-a)^2 + \cdots$$

is called a **power series in $(x - a)$** or a **power series centered at a** or a **power series about a**. Notice that in writing out the term corresponding to $n = 0$ in Equations 1 and 2 we have adopted the convention that $(x-a)^0 = 1$ even when $x = a$. Notice also that when $x = a$ all of the terms are 0 for $n \geqslant 1$ and so the power series (2) always converges when $x = a$.

Trigonometric Series

A power series is a series in which each term is a power function. A **trigonometric series**

$$\sum_{n=0}^{\infty} (a_n \cos nx + b_n \sin nx)$$

is a series whose terms are trigonometric functions. This type of series is discussed on the website

www.stewartcalculus.com

Click on *Additional Topics* and then on *Fourier Series.*

V EXAMPLE 1 A power series that converges only at its center

For what values of x is the series $\sum_{n=0}^{\infty} n!x^n$ convergent?

SOLUTION We use the Ratio Test. If we let a_n, as usual, denote the nth term of the series, then $a_n = n!x^n$. If $x \neq 0$, we have

$$\lim_{n\to\infty} \left|\frac{a_{n+1}}{a_n}\right| = \lim_{n\to\infty} \left|\frac{(n+1)!x^{n+1}}{n!x^n}\right| = \lim_{n\to\infty} (n+1)|x| = \infty$$

Notice that

$$(n+1)! = (n+1)n(n-1)\cdot\cdots\cdot 3\cdot 2\cdot 1 = (n+1)n!$$

By the Ratio Test, the series diverges when $x \neq 0$. Thus the given series converges only when $x = 0$.

V EXAMPLE 2 Using the Ratio Test to determine where a power series converges

For what values of x does the series $\sum_{n=1}^{\infty} \frac{(x-3)^n}{n}$ converge?

SOLUTION Let $a_n = (x-3)^n/n$. Then

$$\left|\frac{a_{n+1}}{a_n}\right| = \left|\frac{(x-3)^{n+1}}{n+1} \cdot \frac{n}{(x-3)^n}\right|$$

$$= \frac{1}{1+\frac{1}{n}}|x-3| \to |x-3| \quad \text{as } n \to \infty$$

By the Ratio Test, the given series is absolutely convergent, and therefore convergent, when $|x-3| < 1$ and divergent when $|x-3| > 1$. Now

$$|x-3| < 1 \iff -1 < x-3 < 1 \iff 2 < x < 4$$

so the series converges when $2 < x < 4$ and diverges when $x < 2$ or $x > 4$.

The Ratio Test gives no information when $|x-3| = 1$ so we must consider $x = 2$ and $x = 4$ separately. If we put $x = 4$ in the series, it becomes $\Sigma\, 1/n$, the harmonic series, which is divergent. If $x = 2$, the series is $\Sigma\, (-1)^n/n$, which converges by the Alternating Series Test. Thus the given power series converges for $2 \leqslant x < 4$.

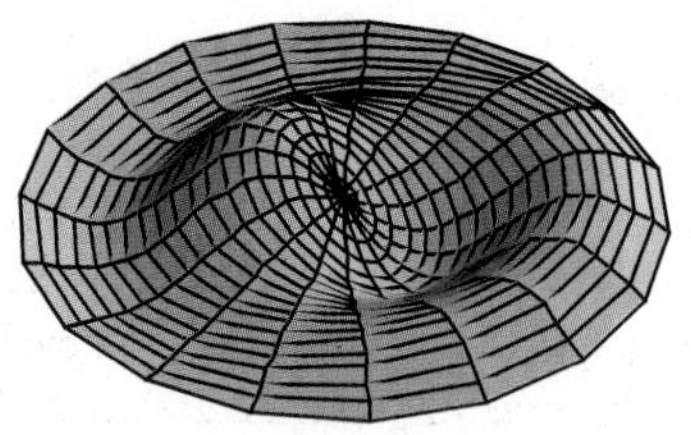

Notice how closely the computer-generated model (which involves Bessel functions and cosine functions) matches the photograph of a vibrating rubber membrane.

We will see that the main use of a power series is that it provides a way to represent some of the most important functions that arise in mathematics, physics, and chemistry. In particular, the sum of the power series in the next example is called a **Bessel function**, after the German astronomer Friedrich Bessel (1784–1846), and the function given in Exercise 29 is another example of a Bessel function. In fact, these functions first arose when Bessel solved Kepler's equation for describing planetary motion. Since that time, these functions have been applied in many different physical situations, including the temperature distribution in a circular plate and the shape of a vibrating drumhead.

EXAMPLE 3 **A power series that converges for all values of x** Find the domain of the Bessel function of order 0 defined by

$$J_0(x) = \sum_{n=0}^{\infty} \frac{(-1)^n x^{2n}}{2^{2n}(n!)^2}$$

SOLUTION Let $a_n = (-1)^n x^{2n}/[2^{2n}(n!)^2]$. Then

$$\left|\frac{a_{n+1}}{a_n}\right| = \left|\frac{(-1)^{n+1}x^{2(n+1)}}{2^{2(n+1)}[(n+1)!]^2} \cdot \frac{2^{2n}(n!)^2}{(-1)^n x^{2n}}\right|$$

$$= \frac{x^{2n+2}}{2^{2n+2}(n+1)^2(n!)^2} \cdot \frac{2^{2n}(n!)^2}{x^{2n}}$$

$$= \frac{x^2}{4(n+1)^2} \to 0 < 1 \qquad \text{for all } x$$

Thus, by the Ratio Test, the given series converges for all values of x. In other words, the domain of the Bessel function J_0 is $(-\infty, \infty) = \mathbb{R}$.

Recall that the sum of a series is equal to the limit of the sequence of partial sums. So when we define the Bessel function in Example 3 as the sum of a series we mean that, for every real number x,

$$J_0(x) = \lim_{n\to\infty} s_n(x) \qquad \text{where} \qquad s_n(x) = \sum_{i=0}^{n} \frac{(-1)^i x^{2i}}{2^{2i}(i!)^2}$$

The first few partial sums are

$$s_0(x) = 1 \qquad s_1(x) = 1 - \frac{x^2}{4} \qquad s_2(x) = 1 - \frac{x^2}{4} + \frac{x^4}{64}$$

$$s_3(x) = 1 - \frac{x^2}{4} + \frac{x^4}{64} - \frac{x^6}{2304} \qquad s_4(x) = 1 - \frac{x^2}{4} + \frac{x^4}{64} - \frac{x^6}{2304} + \frac{x^8}{147{,}456}$$

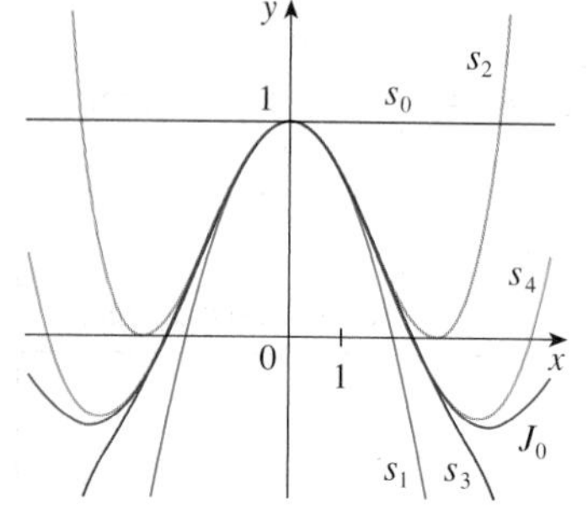

FIGURE 1
Partial sums of the Bessel function J_0

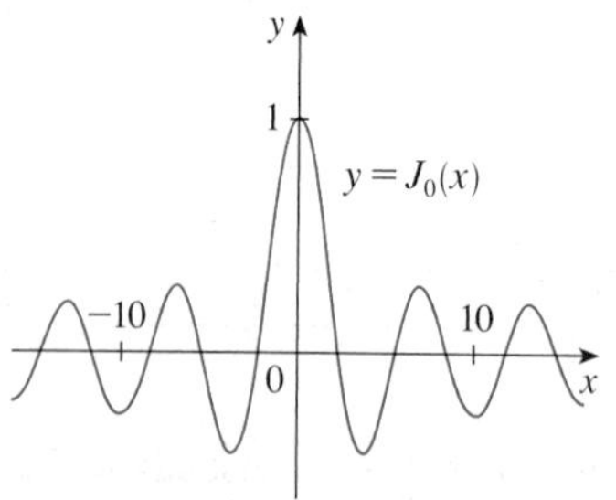

FIGURE 2

Figure 1 shows the graphs of these partial sums, which are polynomials. They are all approximations to the function J_0, but notice that the approximations become better when more terms are included. Figure 2 shows a more complete graph of the Bessel function.

For the power series that we have looked at so far, the set of values of x for which the series is convergent has always turned out to be an interval [a finite interval for the geometric series and the series in Example 2, the infinite interval $(-\infty, \infty)$ in Example 3, and a collapsed interval $[0, 0] = \{0\}$ in Example 1]. The following theorem, which we won't prove, says that this is true in general.

3 Theorem For a given power series $\sum_{n=0}^{\infty} c_n(x - a)^n$ there are only three possibilities:

(i) The series converges only when $x = a$.

(ii) The series converges for all x.

(iii) There is a positive number R such that the series converges if $|x - a| < R$ and diverges if $|x - a| > R$.

The number R in case (iii) is called the **radius of convergence** of the power series. By convention, the radius of convergence is $R = 0$ in case (i) and $R = \infty$ in case (ii). The **interval of convergence** of a power series is the interval that consists of all values of x for which the series converges. In case (i) the interval consists of just a single point a. In case (ii) the interval is $(-\infty, \infty)$. In case (iii) note that the inequality $|x - a| < R$ can be rewritten as $a - R < x < a + R$. When x is an *endpoint* of the interval, that is, $x = a \pm R$, anything can happen—the series might converge at one or both endpoints or it might diverge at both endpoints. Thus in case (iii) there are four possibilities for the interval of convergence:

$$(a - R, a + R) \qquad (a - R, a + R] \qquad [a - R, a + R) \qquad [a - R, a + R]$$

The situation is illustrated in Figure 3.

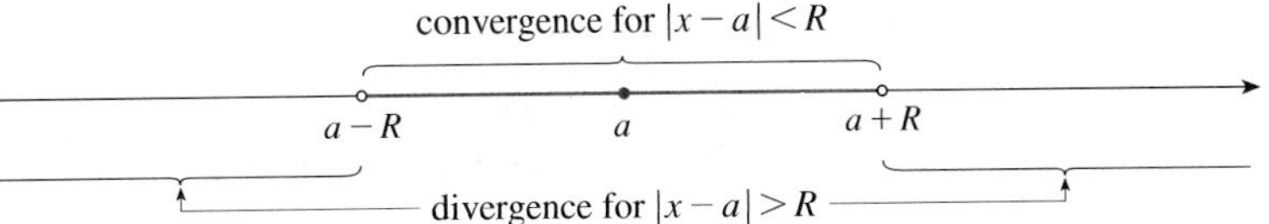

FIGURE 3

We summarize here the radius and interval of convergence for each of the examples already considered in this section.

	Series	Radius of convergence	Interval of convergence
Geometric series	$\sum_{n=0}^{\infty} x^n$	$R = 1$	$(-1, 1)$
Example 1	$\sum_{n=0}^{\infty} n!\, x^n$	$R = 0$	$\{0\}$
Example 2	$\sum_{n=1}^{\infty} \frac{(x-3)^n}{n}$	$R = 1$	$[2, 4)$
Example 3	$\sum_{n=0}^{\infty} \frac{(-1)^n x^{2n}}{2^{2n}(n!)^2}$	$R = \infty$	$(-\infty, \infty)$

The Ratio Test can be used to determine the radius of convergence R in most cases. The Ratio Test always fails when x is an endpoint of the interval of convergence, so the endpoints must be checked with some other test.

EXAMPLE 4 Find the radius of convergence and interval of convergence of the series

$$\sum_{n=0}^{\infty} \frac{(-3)^n x^n}{\sqrt{n+1}}$$

SOLUTION Let $a_n = (-3)^n x^n/\sqrt{n+1}$. Then

$$\left|\frac{a_{n+1}}{a_n}\right| = \left|\frac{(-3)^{n+1}x^{n+1}}{\sqrt{n+2}} \cdot \frac{\sqrt{n+1}}{(-3)^n x^n}\right| = \left|-3x\sqrt{\frac{n+1}{n+2}}\right|$$

$$= 3\sqrt{\frac{1+(1/n)}{1+(2/n)}}\,|x| \to 3|x| \qquad \text{as } n \to \infty$$

By the Ratio Test, the given series converges if $3|x| < 1$ and diverges if $3|x| > 1$. Thus it converges if $|x| < \frac{1}{3}$ and diverges if $|x| > \frac{1}{3}$. This means that the radius of convergence is $R = \frac{1}{3}$.

We know the series converges in the interval $\left(-\frac{1}{3}, \frac{1}{3}\right)$, but we must now test for convergence at the endpoints of this interval. If $x = -\frac{1}{3}$, the series becomes

$$\sum_{n=0}^{\infty} \frac{(-3)^n\left(-\frac{1}{3}\right)^n}{\sqrt{n+1}} = \sum_{n=0}^{\infty} \frac{1}{\sqrt{n+1}} = \frac{1}{\sqrt{1}} + \frac{1}{\sqrt{2}} + \frac{1}{\sqrt{3}} + \frac{1}{\sqrt{4}} + \cdots$$

which diverges. (Use the Integral Test or simply observe that it is a p-series with $p = \frac{1}{2} < 1$.) If $x = \frac{1}{3}$, the series is

$$\sum_{n=0}^{\infty} \frac{(-3)^n\left(\frac{1}{3}\right)^n}{\sqrt{n+1}} = \sum_{n=0}^{\infty} \frac{(-1)^n}{\sqrt{n+1}}$$

which converges by the Alternating Series Test. Therefore the given power series converges when $-\frac{1}{3} < x \leqslant \frac{1}{3}$, so the interval of convergence is $\left(-\frac{1}{3}, \frac{1}{3}\right]$.

V **EXAMPLE 5** Find the radius of convergence and interval of convergence of the series

$$\sum_{n=0}^{\infty} \frac{n(x+2)^n}{3^{n+1}}$$

SOLUTION If $a_n = n(x+2)^n/3^{n+1}$, then

$$\left|\frac{a_{n+1}}{a_n}\right| = \left|\frac{(n+1)(x+2)^{n+1}}{3^{n+2}} \cdot \frac{3^{n+1}}{n(x+2)^n}\right|$$

$$= \left(1 + \frac{1}{n}\right)\frac{|x+2|}{3} \to \frac{|x+2|}{3} \qquad \text{as } n \to \infty$$

Using the Ratio Test, we see that the series converges if $|x+2|/3 < 1$ and it diverges if $|x+2|/3 > 1$. So it converges if $|x+2| < 3$ and diverges if $|x+2| > 3$. Thus the radius of convergence is $R = 3$.

The inequality $|x+2| < 3$ can be written as $-5 < x < 1$, so we test the series at the endpoints -5 and 1. When $x = -5$, the series is

$$\sum_{n=0}^{\infty} \frac{n(-3)^n}{3^{n+1}} = \frac{1}{3}\sum_{n=0}^{\infty} (-1)^n n$$

which diverges by the Test for Divergence [$(-1)^n n$ doesn't converge to 0]. When $x = 1$, the series is

$$\sum_{n=0}^{\infty} \frac{n(3)^n}{3^{n+1}} = \frac{1}{3} \sum_{n=0}^{\infty} n$$

which also diverges by the Test for Divergence. Thus the series converges only when $-5 < x < 1$, so the interval of convergence is $(-5, 1)$.

8.5 Exercises

1. What is a power series?

2. (a) What is the radius of convergence of a power series? How do you find it?
   (b) What is the interval of convergence of a power series? How do you find it?

3–24 Find the radius of convergence and interval of convergence of the series.

3. $\displaystyle\sum_{n=1}^{\infty} \frac{x^n}{\sqrt{n}}$

4. $\displaystyle\sum_{n=0}^{\infty} \frac{(-1)^n x^n}{n+1}$

5. $\displaystyle\sum_{n=1}^{\infty} \frac{(-1)^{n-1} x^n}{n^3}$

6. $\displaystyle\sum_{n=1}^{\infty} \sqrt{n}\, x^n$

7. $\displaystyle\sum_{n=0}^{\infty} \frac{x^n}{n!}$

8. $\displaystyle\sum_{n=1}^{\infty} \frac{10^n x^n}{n^3}$

9. $\displaystyle\sum_{n=1}^{\infty} (-1)^n \frac{n^2 x^n}{2^n}$

10. $\displaystyle\sum_{n=0}^{\infty} (-1)^n \frac{x^{2n}}{(2n)!}$

11. $\displaystyle\sum_{n=1}^{\infty} \frac{(-2)^n x^n}{\sqrt[4]{n}}$

12. $\displaystyle\sum_{n=1}^{\infty} \frac{(2n)!}{2^n} x^n$

13. $\displaystyle\sum_{n=0}^{\infty} \frac{(x-2)^n}{n^2+1}$

14. $\displaystyle\sum_{n=0}^{\infty} (-1)^n \frac{(x-3)^n}{2n+1}$

15. $\displaystyle\sum_{n=1}^{\infty} \frac{3^n (x+4)^n}{\sqrt{n}}$

16. $\displaystyle\sum_{n=1}^{\infty} \frac{n}{4^n} (x+1)^n$

17. $\displaystyle\sum_{n=1}^{\infty} \frac{(4x+1)^n}{n^2}$

18. $\displaystyle\sum_{n=1}^{\infty} \frac{n(x-4)^n}{n^3+1}$

19. $\displaystyle\sum_{n=1}^{\infty} n!(2x-1)^n$

20. $\displaystyle\sum_{n=1}^{\infty} \frac{(3x-2)^n}{n\,3^n}$

21. $\displaystyle\sum_{n=1}^{\infty} \frac{n}{b^n} (x-a)^n, \quad b > 0$

22. $\displaystyle\sum_{n=2}^{\infty} \frac{x^{2n}}{n(\ln n)^2}$

23. $\displaystyle\sum_{n=1}^{\infty} \frac{x^n}{1 \cdot 3 \cdot 5 \cdot \cdots \cdot (2n-1)}$

24. $\displaystyle\sum_{n=1}^{\infty} \frac{n^2 x^n}{2 \cdot 4 \cdot 6 \cdot \cdots \cdot (2n)}$

25. If $\sum_{n=0}^{\infty} c_n 4^n$ is convergent, does it follow that the following series are convergent?
    (a) $\displaystyle\sum_{n=0}^{\infty} c_n(-2)^n$ (b) $\displaystyle\sum_{n=0}^{\infty} c_n(-4)^n$

26. Suppose that $\sum_{n=0}^{\infty} c_n x^n$ converges when $x = -4$ and diverges when $x = 6$. What can be said about the convergence or divergence of the following series?
    (a) $\displaystyle\sum_{n=0}^{\infty} c_n$ (b) $\displaystyle\sum_{n=0}^{\infty} c_n 8^n$
    (c) $\displaystyle\sum_{n=0}^{\infty} c_n(-3)^n$ (d) $\displaystyle\sum_{n=0}^{\infty} (-1)^n c_n 9^n$

27. If k is a positive integer, find the radius of convergence of the series

$$\sum_{n=0}^{\infty} \frac{(n!)^k}{(kn)!} x^n$$

28. Graph the first several partial sums $s_n(x)$ of the series $\sum_{n=0}^{\infty} x^n$, together with the sum function $f(x) = 1/(1-x)$, on a common screen. On what interval do these partial sums appear to be converging to $f(x)$?

29. The function J_1 defined by

$$J_1(x) = \sum_{n=0}^{\infty} \frac{(-1)^n x^{2n+1}}{n!(n+1)!\,2^{2n+1}}$$

is called the *Bessel function of order 1.*
    (a) Find its domain.

    (b) Graph the first several partial sums on a common screen.
CAS (c) If your CAS has built-in Bessel functions, graph J_1 on the same screen as the partial sums in part (b) and observe how the partial sums approximate J_1.

Graphing calculator or computer with graphing software required CAS Computer algebra system required **1.** Homework Hints available in TEC

30. The function A defined by

$$A(x) = 1 + \frac{x^3}{2 \cdot 3} + \frac{x^6}{2 \cdot 3 \cdot 5 \cdot 6} + \frac{x^9}{2 \cdot 3 \cdot 5 \cdot 6 \cdot 8 \cdot 9} + \cdots$$

is called the *Airy function* after the English mathematician and astronomer Sir George Airy (1801–1892).
(a) Find the domain of the Airy function.
(b) Graph the first several partial sums on a common screen.
CAS (c) If your CAS has built-in Airy functions, graph A on the same screen as the partial sums in part (b) and observe how the partial sums approximate A.

31. A function f is defined by

$$f(x) = 1 + 2x + x^2 + 2x^3 + x^4 + \cdots$$

that is, its coefficients are $c_{2n} = 1$ and $c_{2n+1} = 2$ for all $n \geqslant 0$. Find the interval of convergence of the series and find an explicit formula for $f(x)$.

32. If $f(x) = \sum_{n=0}^{\infty} c_n x^n$, where $c_{n+4} = c_n$ for all $n \geqslant 0$, find the interval of convergence of the series and a formula for $f(x)$.

33. Suppose the series $\sum c_n x^n$ has radius of convergence 2 and the series $\sum d_n x^n$ has radius of convergence 3. What is the radius of convergence of the series $\sum (c_n + d_n)x^n$?

34. Suppose that the radius of convergence of the power series $\sum c_n x^n$ is R. What is the radius of convergence of the power series $\sum c_n x^{2n}$?

35. Is it possible to find a power series whose interval of convergence is $[0, \infty)$? Explain.

36. Let p and q be real numbers with $p < q$. Find a power series whose interval of convergence is
(a) (p, q) (b) $(p, q]$
(c) $[p, q)$ (d) $[p, q]$

8.6 Representations of Functions as Power Series

In this section we learn how to represent certain types of functions as sums of power series by manipulating geometric series or by differentiating or integrating such a series. You might wonder why we would ever want to express a known function as a sum of infinitely many terms. This strategy is useful for integrating functions that don't have elementary antiderivatives, for solving differential equations, and for approximating functions by polynomials. (Scientists do this to simplify the expressions they deal with; computer scientists do this to represent functions on calculators and computers.)

We start with an equation that we have seen before:

1 $$\frac{1}{1-x} = 1 + x + x^2 + x^3 + \cdots = \sum_{n=0}^{\infty} x^n \qquad |x| < 1$$

A geometric illustration of Equation 1 is shown in Figure 1. Because the sum of a series is the limit of the sequence of partial sums, we have

$$\frac{1}{1-x} = \lim_{n\to\infty} s_n(x)$$

where

$$s_n(x) = 1 + x + x^2 + \cdots + x^n$$

is the nth partial sum. Notice that as n increases, $s_n(x)$ becomes a better approximation to $f(x)$ for $-1 < x < 1$.

We first encountered this equation in Example 5 in Section 8.2, where we obtained it by observing that the series is a geometric series with $a = 1$ and $r = x$. But here our point of view is different. We now regard Equation 1 as expressing the function $f(x) = 1/(1 - x)$ as a sum of a power series.

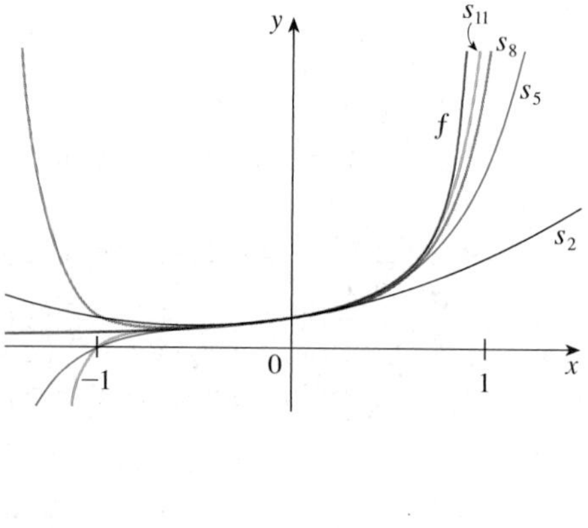

FIGURE 1
$f(x) = \dfrac{1}{1-x}$ and some partial sums

V EXAMPLE 1 Finding a new power series from an old one Express $1/(1 + x^2)$ as the sum of a power series and find the interval of convergence.

SOLUTION Replacing x by $-x^2$ in Equation 1, we have

$$\frac{1}{1+x^2} = \frac{1}{1-(-x^2)} = \sum_{n=0}^{\infty} (-x^2)^n$$

$$= \sum_{n=0}^{\infty} (-1)^n x^{2n} = 1 - x^2 + x^4 - x^6 + x^8 - \cdots$$

Because this is a geometric series, it converges when $|-x^2| < 1$, that is, $x^2 < 1$, or $|x| < 1$. Therefore the interval of convergence is $(-1, 1)$. (Of course, we could have determined the radius of convergence by applying the Ratio Test, but that much work is unnecessary here.)

EXAMPLE 2 Find a power series representation for $1/(x + 2)$.

SOLUTION In order to put this function in the form of the left side of Equation 1 we first factor a 2 from the denominator:

$$\frac{1}{2+x} = \frac{1}{2\left(1+\dfrac{x}{2}\right)} = \frac{1}{2\left[1-\left(-\dfrac{x}{2}\right)\right]}$$

$$= \frac{1}{2}\sum_{n=0}^{\infty}\left(-\frac{x}{2}\right)^n = \sum_{n=0}^{\infty}\frac{(-1)^n}{2^{n+1}}x^n$$

This series converges when $|-x/2| < 1$, that is, $|x| < 2$. So the interval of convergence is $(-2, 2)$.

EXAMPLE 3 Find a power series representation of $x^3/(x + 2)$.

SOLUTION Since this function is just x^3 times the function in Example 2, all we have to do is to multiply that series by x^3:

It's legitimate to move x^3 across the sigma sign because it doesn't depend on n. [Use Theorem 8.2.8(i) with $c = x^3$.]

$$\frac{x^3}{x+2} = x^3 \cdot \frac{1}{x+2} = x^3 \sum_{n=0}^{\infty}\frac{(-1)^n}{2^{n+1}}x^n = \sum_{n=0}^{\infty}\frac{(-1)^n}{2^{n+1}}x^{n+3}$$

$$= \tfrac{1}{2}x^3 - \tfrac{1}{4}x^4 + \tfrac{1}{8}x^5 - \tfrac{1}{16}x^6 + \cdots$$

Another way of writing this series is as follows:

$$\frac{x^3}{x+2} = \sum_{n=3}^{\infty}\frac{(-1)^{n-1}}{2^{n-2}}x^n$$

As in Example 2, the interval of convergence is $(-2, 2)$.

Differentiation and Integration of Power Series

The sum of a power series is a function $f(x) = \sum_{n=0}^{\infty} c_n(x-a)^n$ whose domain is the interval of convergence of the series. We would like to be able to differentiate and integrate such functions, and the following theorem (which we won't prove) says that we can do so by differentiating or integrating each individual term in the series, just as we would for a polynomial. This is called **term-by-term differentiation and integration**.

2 Theorem If the power series $\Sigma\, c_n(x-a)^n$ has radius of convergence $R > 0$, then the function f defined by

$$f(x) = c_0 + c_1(x-a) + c_2(x-a)^2 + \cdots = \sum_{n=0}^{\infty} c_n(x-a)^n$$

is differentiable (and therefore continuous) on the interval $(a - R, a + R)$ and

$$\text{(i)}\quad f'(x) = c_1 + 2c_2(x-a) + 3c_3(x-a)^2 + \cdots = \sum_{n=1}^{\infty} nc_n(x-a)^{n-1}$$

$$\text{(ii)}\quad \int f(x)\,dx = C + c_0(x-a) + c_1\frac{(x-a)^2}{2} + c_2\frac{(x-a)^3}{3} + \cdots$$

$$= C + \sum_{n=0}^{\infty} c_n \frac{(x-a)^{n+1}}{n+1}$$

The radii of convergence of the power series in Equations (i) and (ii) are both R.

In part (ii), $\int c_0\,dx = c_0x + C_1$ is written as $c_0(x-a) + C$, where $C = C_1 + ac_0$, so all the terms of the series have the same form.

Note 1: Equations (i) and (ii) in Theorem 2 can be rewritten in the form

$$\text{(iii)}\quad \frac{d}{dx}\left[\sum_{n=0}^{\infty} c_n(x-a)^n\right] = \sum_{n=0}^{\infty} \frac{d}{dx}\left[c_n(x-a)^n\right]$$

$$\text{(iv)}\quad \int\left[\sum_{n=0}^{\infty} c_n(x-a)^n\right]dx = \sum_{n=0}^{\infty} \int c_n(x-a)^n\,dx$$

We know that, for finite sums, the derivative of a sum is the sum of the derivatives and the integral of a sum is the sum of the integrals. Equations (iii) and (iv) assert that the same is true for infinite sums, provided we are dealing with *power series*. (For other types of series of functions the situation is not as simple; see Exercise 36.)

www.stewartcalculus.com

The idea of differentiating a power series term by term is the basis for a powerful method for solving differential equations. Click on *Additional Topics* and then on *Using Series to Solve Differential Equations*.

Note 2: Although Theorem 2 says that the radius of convergence remains the same when a power series is differentiated or integrated, this does not mean that the *interval* of convergence remains the same. It may happen that the original series converges at an endpoint, whereas the differentiated series diverges there. (See Exercise 37.)

EXAMPLE 4 Differentiating a power series In Example 3 in Section 8.5 we saw that the Bessel function

$$J_0(x) = \sum_{n=0}^{\infty} \frac{(-1)^n x^{2n}}{2^{2n}(n!)^2}$$

is defined for all x. Thus, by Theorem 2, J_0 is differentiable for all x and its derivative is found by term-by-term differentiation as follows:

$$J_0'(x) = \sum_{n=0}^{\infty} \frac{d}{dx}\frac{(-1)^n x^{2n}}{2^{2n}(n!)^2} = \sum_{n=1}^{\infty} \frac{(-1)^n 2nx^{2n-1}}{2^{2n}(n!)^2}$$

V EXAMPLE 5 Express $1/(1 - x)^2$ as a power series by differentiating Equation 1. What is the radius of convergence?

SOLUTION Differentiating each side of the equation

$$\frac{1}{1 - x} = 1 + x + x^2 + x^3 + \cdots = \sum_{n=0}^{\infty} x^n$$

we get

$$\frac{1}{(1 - x)^2} = 1 + 2x + 3x^2 + \cdots = \sum_{n=1}^{\infty} nx^{n-1}$$

If we wish, we can replace n by $n + 1$ and write the answer as

$$\frac{1}{(1 - x)^2} = \sum_{n=0}^{\infty} (n + 1)x^n$$

According to Theorem 2, the radius of convergence of the differentiated series is the same as the radius of convergence of the original series, namely, $R = 1$.

EXAMPLE 6 Finding a new power series by integrating an old one Find a power series representation for $\ln(1 + x)$ and its radius of convergence.

SOLUTION We notice that the derivative of this function is $1/(1 + x)$. From Equation 1 we have

$$\frac{1}{1 + x} = \frac{1}{1 - (-x)} = 1 - x + x^2 - x^3 + \cdots \qquad |x| < 1$$

Integrating both sides of this equation, we get

$$\ln(1 + x) = \int \frac{1}{1 + x}\, dx = \int (1 - x + x^2 - x^3 + \cdots)\, dx$$

$$= x - \frac{x^2}{2} + \frac{x^3}{3} - \frac{x^4}{4} + \cdots + C$$

$$= \sum_{n=1}^{\infty} (-1)^{n-1} \frac{x^n}{n} + C \qquad |x| < 1$$

To determine the value of C we put $x = 0$ in this equation and obtain $\ln(1 + 0) = C$. Thus $C = 0$ and

$$\ln(1 + x) = x - \frac{x^2}{2} + \frac{x^3}{3} - \frac{x^4}{4} + \cdots = \sum_{n=1}^{\infty} (-1)^{n-1} \frac{x^n}{n} \qquad |x| < 1$$

The radius of convergence is the same as for the original series: $R = 1$.

V EXAMPLE 7 Find a power series representation for $f(x) = \tan^{-1}x$.

SOLUTION We observe that $f'(x) = 1/(1 + x^2)$ and find the required series by integrating the power series for $1/(1 + x^2)$ found in Example 1.

$$\tan^{-1}x = \int \frac{1}{1 + x^2}\, dx = \int (1 - x^2 + x^4 - x^6 + \cdots)\, dx$$

$$= C + x - \frac{x^3}{3} + \frac{x^5}{5} - \frac{x^7}{7} + \cdots$$

To find C we put $x = 0$ and obtain $C = \tan^{-1} 0 = 0$. Therefore

$$\tan^{-1}x = x - \frac{x^3}{3} + \frac{x^5}{5} - \frac{x^7}{7} + \cdots = \sum_{n=0}^{\infty} (-1)^n \frac{x^{2n+1}}{2n + 1}$$

Since the radius of convergence of the series for $1/(1 + x^2)$ is 1, the radius of convergence of this series for $\tan^{-1}x$ is also 1.

The power series for $\tan^{-1}x$ obtained in Example 7 is called *Gregory's series* after the Scottish mathematician James Gregory (1638–1675), who had anticipated some of Newton's discoveries. We have shown that Gregory's series is valid when $-1 < x < 1$, but it turns out (although it isn't easy to prove) that it is also valid when $x = \pm 1$. Notice that when $x = 1$ the series becomes

$$\frac{\pi}{4} = 1 - \frac{1}{3} + \frac{1}{5} - \frac{1}{7} + \cdots$$

This beautiful result is known as the Leibniz formula for π.

EXAMPLE 8

(a) Evaluate $\int [1/(1 + x^7)]\,dx$ as a power series.

(b) Use part (a) to approximate $\int_0^{0.5} [1/(1 + x^7)]\,dx$ correct to within 10^{-7}.

SOLUTION

(a) The first step is to express the integrand, $1/(1 + x^7)$, as the sum of a power series. As in Example 1, we start with Equation 1 and replace x by $-x^7$:

$$\frac{1}{1 + x^7} = \frac{1}{1 - (-x^7)} = \sum_{n=0}^{\infty} (-x^7)^n$$

$$= \sum_{n=0}^{\infty} (-1)^n x^{7n} = 1 - x^7 + x^{14} - \cdots$$

This example demonstrates one way in which power series representations are useful. Integrating $1/(1 + x^7)$ by hand is incredibly difficult. Different computer algebra systems return different forms of the answer, but they are all extremely complicated. (If you have a CAS, try it yourself.) The infinite series answer that we obtain in Example 8(a) is actually much easier to deal with than the finite answer provided by a CAS.

Now we integrate term by term:

$$\int \frac{1}{1 + x^7}\,dx = \int \sum_{n=0}^{\infty} (-1)^n x^{7n}\,dx = C + \sum_{n=0}^{\infty} (-1)^n \frac{x^{7n+1}}{7n + 1}$$

$$= C + x - \frac{x^8}{8} + \frac{x^{15}}{15} - \frac{x^{22}}{22} + \cdots$$

This series converges for $|-x^7| < 1$, that is, for $|x| < 1$.

(b) In applying the Evaluation Theorem it doesn't matter which antiderivative we use, so let's use the antiderivative from part (a) with $C = 0$:

$$\int_0^{0.5} \frac{1}{1 + x^7}\,dx = \left[x - \frac{x^8}{8} + \frac{x^{15}}{15} - \frac{x^{22}}{22} + \cdots \right]_0^{1/2}$$

$$= \frac{1}{2} - \frac{1}{8 \cdot 2^8} + \frac{1}{15 \cdot 2^{15}} - \frac{1}{22 \cdot 2^{22}} + \cdots + \frac{(-1)^n}{(7n + 1)2^{7n+1}} + \cdots$$

This infinite series is the exact value of the definite integral, but since it is an alternating series, we can approximate the sum using the Alternating Series Estimation Theorem. If we stop adding after the term with $n = 3$, the error is smaller than the term with $n = 4$:

$$\frac{1}{29 \cdot 2^{29}} \approx 6.4 \times 10^{-11}$$

So we have

$$\int_0^{0.5} \frac{1}{1 + x^7}\,dx \approx \frac{1}{2} - \frac{1}{8 \cdot 2^8} + \frac{1}{15 \cdot 2^{15}} - \frac{1}{22 \cdot 2^{22}} \approx 0.49951374$$

8.6 Exercises

1. If the radius of convergence of the power series $\sum_{n=0}^{\infty} c_n x^n$ is 10, what is the radius of convergence of the series $\sum_{n=1}^{\infty} n c_n x^{n-1}$? Why?

2. Suppose you know that the series $\sum_{n=0}^{\infty} b_n x^n$ converges for $|x| < 2$. What can you say about the following series? Why?

$$\sum_{n=0}^{\infty} \frac{b_n}{n+1} x^{n+1}$$

3–10 Find a power series representation for the function and determine the interval of convergence.

3. $f(x) = \dfrac{1}{1+x}$

4. $f(x) = \dfrac{3}{1-x^4}$

5. $f(x) = \dfrac{2}{3-x}$

6. $f(x) = \dfrac{1}{x+10}$

7. $f(x) = \dfrac{x}{9+x^2}$

8. $f(x) = \dfrac{x}{2x^2+1}$

9. $f(x) = \dfrac{1+x}{1-x}$

10. $f(x) = \dfrac{x^2}{a^3-x^3}$

11. (a) Use differentiation to find a power series representation for

$$f(x) = \frac{1}{(1+x)^2}$$

What is the radius of convergence?

(b) Use part (a) to find a power series for

$$f(x) = \frac{1}{(1+x)^3}$$

(c) Use part (b) to find a power series for

$$f(x) = \frac{x^2}{(1+x)^3}$$

12. (a) Use Equation 1 to find a power series representation for $f(x) = \ln(1-x)$. What is the radius of convergence?
(b) Use part (a) to find a power series for $f(x) = x\ln(1-x)$.
(c) By putting $x = \frac{1}{2}$ in your result from part (a), express ln 2 as the sum of an infinite series.

13–18 Find a power series representation for the function and determine the radius of convergence.

13. $f(x) = \ln(5-x)$

14. $f(x) = x^2\tan^{-1}(x^3)$

15. $f(x) = \dfrac{x}{(1+4x)^2}$

16. $f(x) = \left(\dfrac{x}{2-x}\right)^3$

17. $f(x) = \dfrac{1+x}{(1-x)^2}$

18. $f(x) = \dfrac{x^2+x}{(1-x)^3}$

19–22 Find a power series representation for f, and graph f and several partial sums $s_n(x)$ on the same screen. What happens as n increases?

19. $f(x) = \dfrac{x}{x^2+16}$

20. $f(x) = \ln(x^2+4)$

21. $f(x) = \ln\left(\dfrac{1+x}{1-x}\right)$

22. $f(x) = \tan^{-1}(2x)$

23–26 Evaluate the indefinite integral as a power series. What is the radius of convergence?

23. $\displaystyle\int \frac{t}{1-t^8}\,dt$

24. $\displaystyle\int \frac{\ln(1-t)}{t}\,dt$

25. $\displaystyle\int \frac{x-\tan^{-1}x}{x^3}\,dx$

26. $\displaystyle\int \tan^{-1}(x^2)\,dx$

27–30 Use a power series to approximate the definite integral to six decimal places.

27. $\displaystyle\int_0^{0.2} \frac{1}{1+x^5}\,dx$

28. $\displaystyle\int_0^{0.4} \ln(1+x^4)\,dx$

29. $\displaystyle\int_0^{0.1} x\arctan(3x)\,dx$

30. $\displaystyle\int_0^{0.3} \frac{x^2}{1+x^4}\,dx$

31. Use the result of Example 7 to compute arctan 0.2 correct to five decimal places.

32. Show that the function

$$f(x) = \sum_{n=0}^{\infty} \frac{(-1)^n x^{2n}}{(2n)!}$$

is a solution of the differential equation

$$f''(x) + f(x) = 0$$

33. (a) Show that J_0 (the Bessel function of order 0 given in Example 4) satisfies the differential equation

$$x^2 J_0''(x) + xJ_0'(x) + x^2 J_0(x) = 0$$

(b) Evaluate $\int_0^1 J_0(x)\,dx$ correct to three decimal places.

34. The Bessel function of order 1 is defined by

$$J_1(x) = \sum_{n=0}^{\infty} \frac{(-1)^n x^{2n+1}}{n!\,(n+1)!\,2^{2n+1}}$$

(a) Show that J_1 satisfies the differential equation

$$x^2 J_1''(x) + xJ_1'(x) + (x^2 - 1)J_1(x) = 0$$

(b) Show that $J_0'(x) = -J_1(x)$.

35. (a) Show that the function

$$f(x) = \sum_{n=0}^{\infty} \frac{x^n}{n!}$$

is a solution of the differential equation

$$f'(x) = f(x)$$

(b) Show that $f(x) = e^x$.

36. Let $f_n(x) = (\sin nx)/n^2$. Show that the series $\Sigma f_n(x)$ converges for all values of x but the series of derivatives $\Sigma f_n'(x)$ diverges when $x = 2n\pi$, n an integer. For what values of x does the series $\Sigma f_n''(x)$ converge?

37. Let

$$f(x) = \sum_{n=1}^{\infty} \frac{x^n}{n^2}$$

Find the intervals of convergence for f, f', and f''.

38. (a) Starting with the geometric series $\Sigma_{n=0}^{\infty} x^n$, find the sum of the series

$$\sum_{n=1}^{\infty} nx^{n-1} \qquad |x| < 1$$

(b) Find the sum of each of the following series.

(i) $\displaystyle\sum_{n=1}^{\infty} nx^n, \quad |x| < 1$ (ii) $\displaystyle\sum_{n=1}^{\infty} \frac{n}{2^n}$

(c) Find the sum of each of the following series.

(i) $\displaystyle\sum_{n=2}^{\infty} n(n-1)x^n, \quad |x| < 1$

(ii) $\displaystyle\sum_{n=2}^{\infty} \frac{n^2 - n}{2^n}$ (iii) $\displaystyle\sum_{n=1}^{\infty} \frac{n^2}{2^n}$

39. Use the power series for $\tan^{-1}x$ to prove the following expression for π as the sum of an infinite series:

$$\pi = 2\sqrt{3} \sum_{n=0}^{\infty} \frac{(-1)^n}{(2n+1)3^n}$$

40. (a) By completing the square, show that

$$\int_0^{1/2} \frac{dx}{x^2 - x + 1} = \frac{\pi}{3\sqrt{3}}$$

(b) By factoring $x^3 + 1$ as a sum of cubes, rewrite the integral in part (a). Then express $1/(x^3 + 1)$ as the sum of a power series and use it to prove the following formula for π:

$$\pi = \frac{3\sqrt{3}}{4} \sum_{n=0}^{\infty} \frac{(-1)^n}{8^n} \left(\frac{2}{3n+1} + \frac{1}{3n+2} \right)$$

8.7 Taylor and Maclaurin Series

In the preceding section we were able to find power series representations for a certain restricted class of functions. Here we investigate more general problems: Which functions have power series representations? How can we find such representations?

We start by supposing that f is any function that can be represented by a power series

$$\boxed{1} \quad f(x) = c_0 + c_1(x-a) + c_2(x-a)^2 + c_3(x-a)^3 + c_4(x-a)^4 + \cdots \qquad |x-a| < R$$

Let's try to determine what the coefficients c_n must be in terms of f. To begin, notice that if we put $x = a$ in Equation 1, then all terms after the first one are 0 and we get

$$f(a) = c_0$$

By Theorem 8.6.2, we can differentiate the series in Equation 1 term by term:

$$\boxed{2} \quad f'(x) = c_1 + 2c_2(x-a) + 3c_3(x-a)^2 + 4c_4(x-a)^3 + \cdots \qquad |x-a| < R$$

and substitution of $x = a$ in Equation 2 gives

$$f'(a) = c_1$$

Now we differentiate both sides of Equation 2 and obtain

3 $$f''(x) = 2c_2 + 2 \cdot 3c_3(x - a) + 3 \cdot 4c_4(x - a)^2 + \cdots \qquad |x - a| < R$$

Again we put $x = a$ in Equation 3. The result is

$$f''(a) = 2c_2$$

Let's apply the procedure one more time. Differentiation of the series in Equation 3 gives

4 $$f'''(x) = 2 \cdot 3c_3 + 2 \cdot 3 \cdot 4c_4(x - a) + 3 \cdot 4 \cdot 5c_5(x - a)^2 + \cdots \qquad |x - a| < R$$

and substitution of $x = a$ in Equation 4 gives

$$f'''(a) = 2 \cdot 3c_3 = 3!c_3$$

By now you can see the pattern. If we continue to differentiate and substitute $x = a$, we obtain

$$f^{(n)}(a) = 2 \cdot 3 \cdot 4 \cdot \cdots \cdot nc_n = n!c_n$$

Solving this equation for the nth coefficient c_n, we get

$$c_n = \frac{f^{(n)}(a)}{n!}$$

This formula remains valid even for $n = 0$ if we adopt the conventions that $0! = 1$ and $f^{(0)} = f$. Thus we have proved the following theorem.

5 **Theorem** If f has a power series representation (expansion) at a, that is, if

$$f(x) = \sum_{n=0}^{\infty} c_n(x - a)^n \qquad |x - a| < R$$

then its coefficients are given by the formula

$$c_n = \frac{f^{(n)}(a)}{n!}$$

Substituting this formula for c_n back into the series, we see that *if* f has a power series expansion at a, then it must be of the following form.

6 $$f(x) = \sum_{n=0}^{\infty} \frac{f^{(n)}(a)}{n!}(x - a)^n$$
$$= f(a) + \frac{f'(a)}{1!}(x - a) + \frac{f''(a)}{2!}(x - a)^2 + \frac{f'''(a)}{3!}(x - a)^3 + \cdots$$

The series in Equation 6 is called the **Taylor series of the function *f* at *a*** (or **about *a*** or **centered at *a***).

Taylor and Maclaurin

The Taylor series is named after the English mathematician Brook Taylor (1685–1731) and the Maclaurin series is named in honor of the Scottish mathematician Colin Maclaurin (1698–1746) despite the fact that the Maclaurin series is really just a special case of the Taylor series. But the idea of representing particular functions as sums of power series goes back to Newton, and the general Taylor series was known to the Scottish mathematician James Gregory in 1668 and to the Swiss mathematician John Bernoulli in the 1690s. Taylor was apparently unaware of the work of Gregory and Bernoulli when he published his discoveries on series in 1715 in his book *Methodus incrementorum directa et inversa*. Maclaurin series are named after Colin Maclaurin because he popularized them in his calculus textbook *Treatise of Fluxions* published in 1742.

For the special case $a = 0$ the Taylor series becomes

$$\boxed{7} \qquad f(x) = \sum_{n=0}^{\infty} \frac{f^{(n)}(0)}{n!} x^n = f(0) + \frac{f'(0)}{1!} x + \frac{f''(0)}{2!} x^2 + \cdots$$

This case arises frequently enough that it is given the special name **Maclaurin series**.

Note: We have shown that *if* f can be represented as a power series about a, then f is equal to the sum of its Taylor series. But there exist functions that are not equal to the sum of their Taylor series. An example of such a function is given in Exercise 68.

V EXAMPLE 1 Maclaurin series for the exponential function Find the Maclaurin series of the function $f(x) = e^x$ and its radius of convergence.

SOLUTION If $f(x) = e^x$, then $f^{(n)}(x) = e^x$, so $f^{(n)}(0) = e^0 = 1$ for all n. Therefore the Taylor series for f at 0 (that is, the Maclaurin series) is

$$\sum_{n=0}^{\infty} \frac{f^{(n)}(0)}{n!} x^n = \sum_{n=0}^{\infty} \frac{x^n}{n!} = 1 + \frac{x}{1!} + \frac{x^2}{2!} + \frac{x^3}{3!} + \cdots$$

To find the radius of convergence we let $a_n = x^n/n!$. Then

$$\left| \frac{a_{n+1}}{a_n} \right| = \left| \frac{x^{n+1}}{(n+1)!} \cdot \frac{n!}{x^n} \right| = \frac{|x|}{n+1} \to 0 < 1$$

so, by the Ratio Test, the series converges for all x and the radius of convergence is $R = \infty$.

The conclusion we can draw from Theorem 5 and Example 1 is that *if* e^x has a power series expansion at 0, then

$$e^x = \sum_{n=0}^{\infty} \frac{x^n}{n!}$$

So how can we determine whether e^x *does* have a power series representation?

Let's investigate the more general question: Under what circumstances is a function equal to the sum of its Taylor series? In other words, if f has derivatives of all orders, when is it true that

$$f(x) = \sum_{n=0}^{\infty} \frac{f^{(n)}(a)}{n!} (x - a)^n$$

As with any convergent series, this means that $f(x)$ is the limit of the sequence of partial sums. In the case of the Taylor series, the partial sums are

$$T_n(x) = \sum_{i=0}^{n} \frac{f^{(i)}(a)}{i!} (x - a)^i$$

$$= f(a) + \frac{f'(a)}{1!} (x - a) + \frac{f''(a)}{2!} (x - a)^2 + \cdots + \frac{f^{(n)}(a)}{n!} (x - a)^n$$

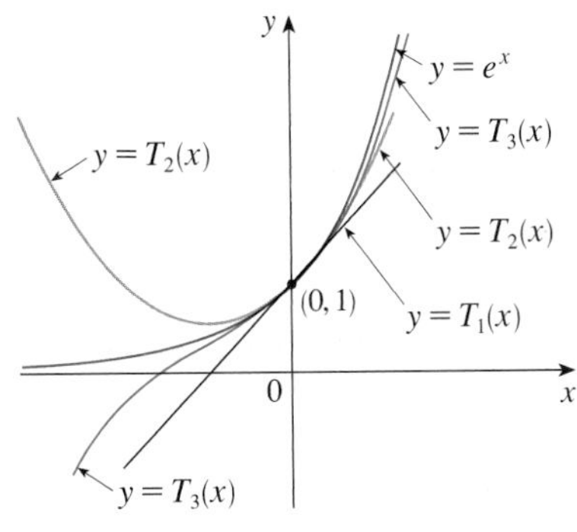

FIGURE 1

As n increases, $T_n(x)$ appears to approach e^x in Figure 1. This suggests that e^x is equal to the sum of its Taylor series.

Notice that T_n is a polynomial of degree n called the ***n*th-degree Taylor polynomial of *f* at *a***. For instance, for the exponential function $f(x) = e^x$, the result of Example 1 shows that the Taylor polynomials at 0 (or Maclaurin polynomials) with $n = 1$, 2, and 3 are

$$T_1(x) = 1 + x \qquad T_2(x) = 1 + x + \frac{x^2}{2!} \qquad T_3(x) = 1 + x + \frac{x^2}{2!} + \frac{x^3}{3!}$$

The graphs of the exponential function and these three Taylor polynomials are drawn in Figure 1.

In general, $f(x)$ is the sum of its Taylor series if

$$f(x) = \lim_{n \to \infty} T_n(x)$$

If we let

$$R_n(x) = f(x) - T_n(x) \qquad \text{so that} \qquad f(x) = T_n(x) + R_n(x)$$

then $R_n(x)$ is called the **remainder** of the Taylor series. If we can somehow show that $\lim_{n \to \infty} R_n(x) = 0$, then it follows that

$$\lim_{n \to \infty} T_n(x) = \lim_{n \to \infty} [f(x) - R_n(x)] = f(x) - \lim_{n \to \infty} R_n(x) = f(x)$$

We have therefore proved the following.

8 Theorem If $f(x) = T_n(x) + R_n(x)$, where T_n is the nth-degree Taylor polynomial of f at a and

$$\lim_{n \to \infty} R_n(x) = 0$$

for $|x - a| < R$, then f is equal to the sum of its Taylor series on the interval $|x - a| < R$.

In trying to show that $\lim_{n \to \infty} R_n(x) = 0$ for a specific function f, we usually use the following fact.

9 Taylor's Inequality If $|f^{(n+1)}(x)| \leqslant M$ for $|x - a| \leqslant d$, then the remainder $R_n(x)$ of the Taylor series satisfies the inequality

$$|R_n(x)| \leqslant \frac{M}{(n + 1)!} |x - a|^{n+1} \qquad \text{for } |x - a| \leqslant d$$

To see why this is true for $n = 1$, we assume that $|f''(x)| \leqslant M$. In particular, we have $f''(x) \leqslant M$, so for $a \leqslant x \leqslant a + d$ we have

$$\int_a^x f''(t)\, dt \leqslant \int_a^x M\, dt$$

An antiderivative of f'' is f', so by the Evaluation Theorem, we have

$$f'(x) - f'(a) \leqslant M(x - a) \qquad \text{or} \qquad f'(x) \leqslant f'(a) + M(x - a)$$

Formulas for the Taylor Remainder Term

As alternatives to Taylor's Inequality, we have the following formulas for the remainder term. If $f^{(n+1)}$ is continuous on an interval I and $x \in I$, then

$$R_n(x) = \frac{1}{n!}\int_a^x (x - t)^n f^{(n+1)}(t)\, dt$$

This is called the *integral form of the remainder term.* Another formula, called *Lagrange's form of the remainder term,* states that there is a number z between x and a such that

$$R_n(x) = \frac{f^{(n+1)}(z)}{(n+1)!}(x - a)^{n+1}$$

This version is an extension of the Mean Value Theorem (which is the case $n = 0$).

Proofs of these formulas, together with discussions of how to use them to solve the examples of Sections 8.7 and 8.8, are given on the website

www.stewartcalculus.com

Click on *Additional Topics* and then on *Formulas for the Remainder Term in Taylor series.*

Thus
$$\int_a^x f'(t)\, dt \leqslant \int_a^x [f'(a) + M(t - a)]\, dt$$

$$f(x) - f(a) \leqslant f'(a)(x - a) + M\frac{(x - a)^2}{2}$$

$$f(x) - f(a) - f'(a)(x - a) \leqslant \frac{M}{2}(x - a)^2$$

But $R_1(x) = f(x) - T_1(x) = f(x) - f(a) - f'(a)(x - a)$. So

$$R_1(x) \leqslant \frac{M}{2}(x - a)^2$$

A similar argument, using $f''(x) \geqslant -M$, shows that

$$R_1(x) \geqslant -\frac{M}{2}(x - a)^2$$

So
$$|R_1(x)| \leqslant \frac{M}{2}|x - a|^2$$

Although we have assumed that $x > a$, similar calculations show that this inequality is also true for $x < a$.

This proves Taylor's Inequality for the case where $n = 1$. The result for any n is proved in a similar way by integrating $n + 1$ times. (See Exercise 67 for the case $n = 2$.)

Note: In Section 8.8 we will explore the use of Taylor's Inequality in approximating functions. Our immediate use of it is in conjunction with Theorem 8.

In applying Theorems 8 and 9 it is often helpful to make use of the following fact.

10
$$\lim_{n \to \infty} \frac{x^n}{n!} = 0 \qquad \text{for every real number } x$$

This is true because we know from Example 1 that the series $\Sigma\, x^n/n!$ converges for all x and so its nth term approaches 0.

V EXAMPLE 2 Prove that e^x is equal to the sum of its Maclaurin series.

SOLUTION If $f(x) = e^x$, then $f^{(n+1)}(x) = e^x$ for all n. If d is any positive number and $|x| \leqslant d$, then $|f^{(n+1)}(x)| = e^x \leqslant e^d$. So Taylor's Inequality, with $a = 0$ and $M = e^d$, says that

$$|R_n(x)| \leqslant \frac{e^d}{(n+1)!}|x|^{n+1} \qquad \text{for } |x| \leqslant d$$

Notice that the same constant $M = e^d$ works for every value of n. But, from Equation 10, we have

$$\lim_{n \to \infty} \frac{e^d}{(n+1)!}|x|^{n+1} = e^d \lim_{n \to \infty} \frac{|x|^{n+1}}{(n+1)!} = 0$$

It follows from the Squeeze Theorem that $\lim_{n\to\infty}|R_n(x)| = 0$ and therefore $\lim_{n\to\infty} R_n(x) = 0$ for all values of x. By Theorem 8, e^x is equal to the sum of its Maclaurin series, that is,

11 $$e^x = \sum_{n=0}^{\infty} \frac{x^n}{n!} \qquad \text{for all } x$$

In particular, if we put $x = 1$ in Equation 11, we obtain the following expression for the number e as a sum of an infinite series:

In 1748 Leonard Euler used Equation 12 to find the value of e correct to 23 digits. In 2003 Shigeru Kondo, again using the series in (12), computed e to more than 50 billion decimal places. The special techniques employed to speed up the computation are explained on the web page

numbers.computation.free.fr

12 $$e = \sum_{n=0}^{\infty} \frac{1}{n!} = 1 + \frac{1}{1!} + \frac{1}{2!} + \frac{1}{3!} + \cdots$$

EXAMPLE 3 Find the Taylor series for $f(x) = e^x$ at $a = 2$.

SOLUTION We have $f^{(n)}(2) = e^2$ and so, putting $a = 2$ in the definition of a Taylor series (6), we get

$$\sum_{n=0}^{\infty} \frac{f^{(n)}(2)}{n!}(x-2)^n = \sum_{n=0}^{\infty} \frac{e^2}{n!}(x-2)^n$$

Again it can be verified, as in Example 1, that the radius of convergence is $R = \infty$. As in Example 2 we can verify that $\lim_{n\to\infty} R_n(x) = 0$, so

13 $$e^x = \sum_{n=0}^{\infty} \frac{e^2}{n!}(x-2)^n \qquad \text{for all } x$$

We have two power series expansions for e^x, the Maclaurin series in Equation 11 and the Taylor series in Equation 13. The first is better if we are interested in values of x near 0 and the second is better if x is near 2.

EXAMPLE 4 Find the Maclaurin series for $\sin x$ and prove that it represents $\sin x$ for all x.

SOLUTION We arrange our computation in two columns as follows:

$$\begin{aligned} f(x) &= \sin x & f(0) &= 0 \\ f'(x) &= \cos x & f'(0) &= 1 \\ f''(x) &= -\sin x & f''(0) &= 0 \\ f'''(x) &= -\cos x & f'''(0) &= -1 \\ f^{(4)}(x) &= \sin x & f^{(4)}(0) &= 0 \end{aligned}$$

Since the derivatives repeat in a cycle of four, we can write the Maclaurin series as follows:

$$f(0) + \frac{f'(0)}{1!}x + \frac{f''(0)}{2!}x^2 + \frac{f'''(0)}{3!}x^3 + \cdots$$

$$= x - \frac{x^3}{3!} + \frac{x^5}{5!} - \frac{x^7}{7!} + \cdots = \sum_{n=0}^{\infty} (-1)^n \frac{x^{2n+1}}{(2n+1)!}$$

Figure 2 shows the graph of $\sin x$ together with its Taylor (or Maclaurin) polynomials

$$T_1(x) = x$$

$$T_3(x) = x - \frac{x^3}{3!}$$

$$T_5(x) = x - \frac{x^3}{3!} + \frac{x^5}{5!}$$

Notice that, as n increases, $T_n(x)$ becomes a better approximation to $\sin x$.

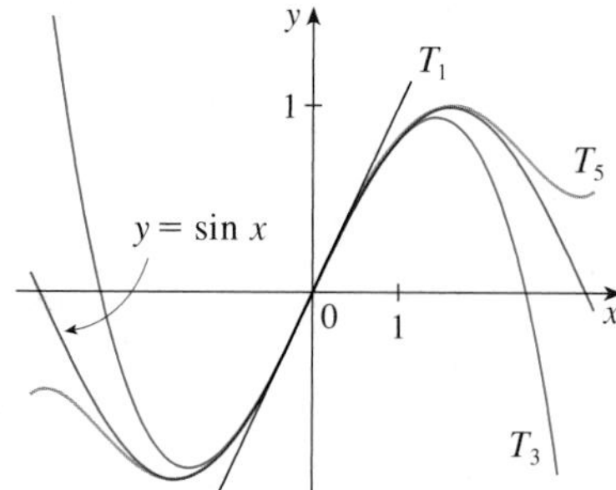

FIGURE 2

Since $f^{(n+1)}(x)$ is $\pm\sin x$ or $\pm\cos x$, we know that $|f^{(n+1)}(x)| \leqslant 1$ for all x. So we can take $M = 1$ in Taylor's Inequality:

14 $$|R_n(x)| \leqslant \frac{M}{(n+1)!}|x^{n+1}| = \frac{|x|^{n+1}}{(n+1)!}$$

By Equation 10 the right side of this inequality approaches 0 as $n \to \infty$, so $|R_n(x)| \to 0$ by the Squeeze Theorem. It follows that $R_n(x) \to 0$ as $n \to \infty$, so $\sin x$ is equal to the sum of its Maclaurin series by Theorem 8.

We state the result of Example 4 for future reference.

15 $$\sin x = x - \frac{x^3}{3!} + \frac{x^5}{5!} - \frac{x^7}{7!} + \cdots = \sum_{n=0}^{\infty} (-1)^n \frac{x^{2n+1}}{(2n+1)!} \qquad \text{for all } x$$

EXAMPLE 5 Obtaining a Maclaurin series by differentiating a known series Find the Maclaurin series for $\cos x$.

SOLUTION We could proceed directly as in Example 4, but it's easier to differentiate the Maclaurin series for $\sin x$ given by Equation 15:

$$\cos x = \frac{d}{dx}(\sin x) = \frac{d}{dx}\left(x - \frac{x^3}{3!} + \frac{x^5}{5!} - \frac{x^7}{7!} + \cdots\right)$$

$$= 1 - \frac{3x^2}{3!} + \frac{5x^4}{5!} - \frac{7x^6}{7!} + \cdots = 1 - \frac{x^2}{2!} + \frac{x^4}{4!} - \frac{x^6}{6!} + \cdots$$

The Maclaurin series for e^x, $\sin x$, and $\cos x$ that we found in Examples 2, 4, and 5 were discovered, using different methods, by Newton. These equations are remarkable because they say we know everything about each of these functions if we know all its derivatives at the single number 0.

Since the Maclaurin series for $\sin x$ converges for all x, Theorem 2 in Section 8.6 tells us that the differentiated series for $\cos x$ also converges for all x. Thus

16 $$\cos x = 1 - \frac{x^2}{2!} + \frac{x^4}{4!} - \frac{x^6}{6!} + \cdots = \sum_{n=0}^{\infty} (-1)^n \frac{x^{2n}}{(2n)!} \qquad \text{for all } x$$

EXAMPLE 6 A shortcut for obtaining a Maclaurin series Find the Maclaurin series for the function $f(x) = x\cos x$.

SOLUTION Instead of computing derivatives and substituting in Equation 7, it's easier to multiply the series for $\cos x$ (Equation 16) by x:

$$x\cos x = x\sum_{n=0}^{\infty} (-1)^n \frac{x^{2n}}{(2n)!} = \sum_{n=0}^{\infty} (-1)^n \frac{x^{2n+1}}{(2n)!}$$

The power series that we obtained by indirect methods in Examples 5 and 6 and in Section 8.6 are indeed the Taylor or Maclaurin series of the given functions because

Theorem 5 asserts that, no matter how a power series representation $f(x) = \Sigma\, c_n(x-a)^n$ is obtained, it is always true that $c_n = f^{(n)}(a)/n!$. In other words, the coefficients are uniquely determined.

EXAMPLE 7 Represent $f(x) = \sin x$ as the sum of its Taylor series centered at $\pi/3$.

SOLUTION Arranging our work in columns, we have

$$f(x) = \sin x \qquad f\left(\frac{\pi}{3}\right) = \frac{\sqrt{3}}{2}$$

$$f'(x) = \cos x \qquad f'\left(\frac{\pi}{3}\right) = \frac{1}{2}$$

$$f''(x) = -\sin x \qquad f''\left(\frac{\pi}{3}\right) = -\frac{\sqrt{3}}{2}$$

$$f'''(x) = -\cos x \qquad f'''\left(\frac{\pi}{3}\right) = -\frac{1}{2}$$

We have obtained two different series representations for $\sin x$, the Maclaurin series in Example 4 and the Taylor series in Example 7. It is best to use the Maclaurin series for values of x near 0 and the Taylor series for x near $\pi/3$. Notice that the third Taylor polynomial T_3 in Figure 3 is a good approximation to $\sin x$ near $\pi/3$ but not as good near 0. Compare it with the third Maclaurin polynomial T_3 in Figure 2, where the opposite is true.

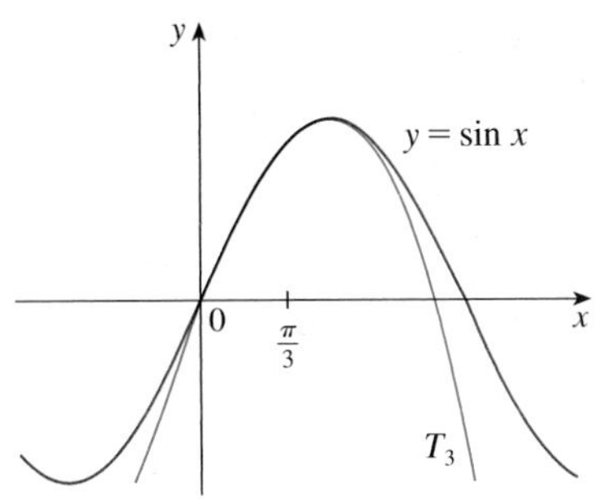

FIGURE 3

and this pattern repeats indefinitely. Therefore the Taylor series at $\pi/3$ is

$$f\left(\frac{\pi}{3}\right) + \frac{f'\left(\frac{\pi}{3}\right)}{1!}\left(x-\frac{\pi}{3}\right) + \frac{f''\left(\frac{\pi}{3}\right)}{2!}\left(x-\frac{\pi}{3}\right)^2 + \frac{f'''\left(\frac{\pi}{3}\right)}{3!}\left(x-\frac{\pi}{3}\right)^3 + \cdots$$

$$= \frac{\sqrt{3}}{2} + \frac{1}{2\cdot 1!}\left(x-\frac{\pi}{3}\right) - \frac{\sqrt{3}}{2\cdot 2!}\left(x-\frac{\pi}{3}\right)^2 - \frac{1}{2\cdot 3!}\left(x-\frac{\pi}{3}\right)^3 + \cdots$$

The proof that this series represents $\sin x$ for all x is very similar to that in Example 4. [Just replace x by $x - \pi/3$ in (14).] We can write the series in sigma notation if we separate the terms that contain $\sqrt{3}$:

$$\sin x = \sum_{n=0}^{\infty} \frac{(-1)^n\sqrt{3}}{2(2n)!}\left(x-\frac{\pi}{3}\right)^{2n} + \sum_{n=0}^{\infty} \frac{(-1)^n}{2(2n+1)!}\left(x-\frac{\pi}{3}\right)^{2n+1}$$

EXAMPLE 8 Find the Maclaurin series for $f(x) = (1+x)^k$, where k is any real number.

SOLUTION Arranging our work in columns, we have

$$f(x) = (1+x)^k \qquad f(0) = 1$$

$$f'(x) = k(1+x)^{k-1} \qquad f'(0) = k$$

$$f''(x) = k(k-1)(1+x)^{k-2} \qquad f''(0) = k(k-1)$$

$$f'''(x) = k(k-1)(k-2)(1+x)^{k-3} \qquad f'''(0) = k(k-1)(k-2)$$

$$\vdots \qquad \vdots$$

$$f^{(n)}(x) = k(k-1)\cdots(k-n+1)(1+x)^{k-n} \qquad f^{(n)}(0) = k(k-1)\cdots(k-n+1)$$

Therefore the Maclaurin series of $f(x) = (1 + x)^k$ is

$$\sum_{n=0}^{\infty} \frac{f^{(n)}(0)}{n!} x^n = \sum_{n=0}^{\infty} \frac{k(k-1)\cdots(k-n+1)}{n!} x^n$$

This series is called the **binomial series**. If its nth term is a_n, then

$$\left|\frac{a_{n+1}}{a_n}\right| = \left|\frac{k(k-1)\cdots(k-n+1)(k-n)x^{n+1}}{(n+1)!} \cdot \frac{n!}{k(k-1)\cdots(k-n+1)x^n}\right|$$

$$= \frac{|k-n|}{n+1}|x| = \frac{\left|1-\dfrac{k}{n}\right|}{1+\dfrac{1}{n}}|x| \to |x| \quad \text{as } n \to \infty$$

Thus, by the Ratio Test, the binomial series converges if $|x| < 1$ and diverges if $|x| > 1$.

The traditional notation for the coefficients in the binomial series is

$$\binom{k}{n} = \frac{k(k-1)(k-2)\cdots(k-n+1)}{n!}$$

and these numbers are called the **binomial coefficients**.

The following theorem states that $(1 + x)^k$ is equal to the sum of its Maclaurin series. It is possible to prove this by showing that the remainder term $R_n(x)$ approaches 0, but that turns out to be quite difficult. The proof outlined in Exercise 69 is much easier.

17 The Binomial Series If k is any real number and $|x| < 1$, then

$$(1+x)^k = \sum_{n=0}^{\infty} \binom{k}{n} x^n = 1 + kx + \frac{k(k-1)}{2!}x^2 + \frac{k(k-1)(k-2)}{3!}x^3 + \cdots$$

Although the binomial series always converges when $|x| < 1$, the question of whether or not it converges at the endpoints, ± 1, depends on the value of k. It turns out that the series converges at 1 if $-1 < k \leqslant 0$ and at both endpoints if $k \geqslant 0$. Notice that if k is a positive integer and $n > k$, then the expression for $\binom{k}{n}$ contains a factor $(k - k)$, so $\binom{k}{n} = 0$ for $n > k$. This means that the series terminates and reduces to the ordinary Binomial Theorem when k is a positive integer. (See Reference Page 1.)

V EXAMPLE 9 Using a binomial series to obtain a Maclaurin series

Find the Maclaurin series for the function $f(x) = \dfrac{1}{\sqrt{4-x}}$ and its radius of convergence.

SOLUTION We rewrite $f(x)$ in a form where we can use the binomial series:

$$\frac{1}{\sqrt{4-x}} = \frac{1}{\sqrt{4\left(1-\dfrac{x}{4}\right)}} = \frac{1}{2\sqrt{1-\dfrac{x}{4}}} = \frac{1}{2}\left(1-\frac{x}{4}\right)^{-1/2}$$

Using the binomial series with $k = -\frac{1}{2}$ and with x replaced by $-x/4$, we have

$$\frac{1}{\sqrt{4-x}} = \frac{1}{2}\left(1 - \frac{x}{4}\right)^{-1/2} = \frac{1}{2}\sum_{n=0}^{\infty}\binom{-\frac{1}{2}}{n}\left(-\frac{x}{4}\right)^n$$

$$= \frac{1}{2}\left[1 + \left(-\frac{1}{2}\right)\left(-\frac{x}{4}\right) + \frac{(-\frac{1}{2})(-\frac{3}{2})}{2!}\left(-\frac{x}{4}\right)^2 + \frac{(-\frac{1}{2})(-\frac{3}{2})(-\frac{5}{2})}{3!}\left(-\frac{x}{4}\right)^3\right.$$

$$\left. + \cdots + \frac{(-\frac{1}{2})(-\frac{3}{2})(-\frac{5}{2})\cdots(-\frac{1}{2} - n + 1)}{n!}\left(-\frac{x}{4}\right)^n + \cdots\right]$$

$$= \frac{1}{2}\left[1 + \frac{1}{8}x + \frac{1 \cdot 3}{2!8^2}x^2 + \frac{1 \cdot 3 \cdot 5}{3!8^3}x^3 + \cdots + \frac{1 \cdot 3 \cdot 5 \cdot \cdots \cdot (2n-1)}{n!8^n}x^n + \cdots\right]$$

We know from (17) that this series converges when $|-x/4| < 1$, that is, $|x| < 4$, so the radius of convergence is $R = 4$.

We collect in the following table, for future reference, some important Maclaurin series that we have derived in this section and the preceding one.

TABLE 1

Important Maclaurin Series and Their Radii of Convergence

Series	Radius
$\frac{1}{1-x} = \sum_{n=0}^{\infty} x^n = 1 + x + x^2 + x^3 + \cdots$	$R = 1$
$e^x = \sum_{n=0}^{\infty} \frac{x^n}{n!} = 1 + \frac{x}{1!} + \frac{x^2}{2!} + \frac{x^3}{3!} + \cdots$	$R = \infty$
$\sin x = \sum_{n=0}^{\infty} (-1)^n \frac{x^{2n+1}}{(2n+1)!} = x - \frac{x^3}{3!} + \frac{x^5}{5!} - \frac{x^7}{7!} + \cdots$	$R = \infty$
$\cos x = \sum_{n=0}^{\infty} (-1)^n \frac{x^{2n}}{(2n)!} = 1 - \frac{x^2}{2!} + \frac{x^4}{4!} - \frac{x^6}{6!} + \cdots$	$R = \infty$
$\tan^{-1}x = \sum_{n=0}^{\infty} (-1)^n \frac{x^{2n+1}}{2n+1} = x - \frac{x^3}{3} + \frac{x^5}{5} - \frac{x^7}{7} + \cdots$	$R = 1$
$\ln(1+x) = \sum_{n=1}^{\infty} (-1)^{n-1} \frac{x^n}{n} = x - \frac{x^2}{2} + \frac{x^3}{3} - \frac{x^4}{4} + \cdots$	$R = 1$
$(1+x)^k = \sum_{n=0}^{\infty} \binom{k}{n} x^n = 1 + kx + \frac{k(k-1)}{2!}x^2 + \frac{k(k-1)(k-2)}{3!}x^3 + \cdots$	$R = 1$

EXAMPLE 10 Find the sum of the series $\frac{1}{1 \cdot 2} - \frac{1}{2 \cdot 2^2} + \frac{1}{3 \cdot 2^3} - \frac{1}{4 \cdot 2^4} + \cdots$.

SOLUTION With sigma notation we can write the given series as

$$\sum_{n=1}^{\infty} (-1)^{n-1} \frac{1}{n \cdot 2^n} = \sum_{n=1}^{\infty} (-1)^{n-1} \frac{(\frac{1}{2})^n}{n}$$

Then from Table 1 we see that this series matches the entry for $\ln(1 + x)$ with $x = \frac{1}{2}$. So

$$\sum_{n=1}^{\infty} (-1)^{n-1} \frac{1}{n \cdot 2^n} = \ln\left(1 + \tfrac{1}{2}\right) = \ln \tfrac{3}{2}$$

TEC Module 8.7/8.8 enables you to see how successive Taylor polynomials approach the original function.

One reason that Taylor series are important is that they enable us to integrate functions that we couldn't previously handle. In fact, in the introduction to this chapter we mentioned that Newton often integrated functions by first expressing them as power series and then integrating the series term by term. The function $f(x) = e^{-x^2}$ can't be integrated by techniques discussed so far because its antiderivative is not an elementary function (see Section 5.8). In the following example we use Newton's idea to integrate this function.

V EXAMPLE 11 Using a series to evaluate an integral

(a) Evaluate $\int e^{-x^2}\,dx$ as an infinite series.

(b) Evaluate $\int_0^1 e^{-x^2}\,dx$ correct to within an error of 0.001.

SOLUTION

(a) First we find the Maclaurin series for $f(x) = e^{-x^2}$. Although it's possible to use the direct method, let's find it simply by replacing x with $-x^2$ in the series for e^x given in Table 1. Thus, for all values of x,

$$e^{-x^2} = \sum_{n=0}^{\infty} \frac{(-x^2)^n}{n!} = \sum_{n=0}^{\infty} (-1)^n \frac{x^{2n}}{n!} = 1 - \frac{x^2}{1!} + \frac{x^4}{2!} - \frac{x^6}{3!} + \cdots$$

Now we integrate term by term:

$$\int e^{-x^2}\,dx = \int \left(1 - \frac{x^2}{1!} + \frac{x^4}{2!} - \frac{x^6}{3!} + \cdots + (-1)^n \frac{x^{2n}}{n!} + \cdots\right) dx$$

$$= C + x - \frac{x^3}{3 \cdot 1!} + \frac{x^5}{5 \cdot 2!} - \frac{x^7}{7 \cdot 3!} + \cdots + (-1)^n \frac{x^{2n+1}}{(2n + 1)n!} + \cdots$$

This series converges for all x because the original series for e^{-x^2} converges for all x.

(b) The Evaluation Theorem gives

We can take $C = 0$ in the antiderivative in part (a).

$$\int_0^1 e^{-x^2}\,dx = \left[x - \frac{x^3}{3 \cdot 1!} + \frac{x^5}{5 \cdot 2!} - \frac{x^7}{7 \cdot 3!} + \frac{x^9}{9 \cdot 4!} - \cdots\right]_0^1$$

$$= 1 - \tfrac{1}{3} + \tfrac{1}{10} - \tfrac{1}{42} + \tfrac{1}{216} - \cdots$$

$$\approx 1 - \tfrac{1}{3} + \tfrac{1}{10} - \tfrac{1}{42} + \tfrac{1}{216} \approx 0.7475$$

The Alternating Series Estimation Theorem shows that the error involved in this approximation is less than

$$\frac{1}{11 \cdot 5!} = \frac{1}{1320} < 0.001$$

Another use of Taylor series is illustrated in the next example. The limit could be found with l'Hospital's Rule, but instead we use a series.

EXAMPLE 12 Using a series to evaluate a limit Evaluate $\lim_{x \to 0} \dfrac{e^x - 1 - x}{x^2}$.

SOLUTION Using the Maclaurin series for e^x, we have

$$\lim_{x \to 0} \frac{e^x - 1 - x}{x^2} = \lim_{x \to 0} \frac{\left(1 + \dfrac{x}{1!} + \dfrac{x^2}{2!} + \dfrac{x^3}{3!} + \cdots\right) - 1 - x}{x^2}$$

$$= \lim_{x \to 0} \frac{\dfrac{x^2}{2!} + \dfrac{x^3}{3!} + \dfrac{x^4}{4!} + \cdots}{x^2}$$

$$= \lim_{x \to 0} \left(\frac{1}{2} + \frac{x}{3!} + \frac{x^2}{4!} + \frac{x^3}{5!} + \cdots\right) = \frac{1}{2}$$

Some computer algebra systems compute limits in this way.

because power series are continuous functions.

Multiplication and Division of Power Series

If power series are added or subtracted, they behave like polynomials (Theorem 8.2.8 shows this). In fact, as the following example illustrates, they can also be multiplied and divided like polynomials. We find only the first few terms because the calculations for the later terms become tedious and the initial terms are the most important ones.

EXAMPLE 13 Finding Maclaurin series by multiplication and division Find the first three nonzero terms in the Maclaurin series for (a) $e^x \sin x$ and (b) $\tan x$.

SOLUTION

(a) Using the Maclaurin series for e^x and $\sin x$ in Table 1, we have

$$e^x \sin x = \left(1 + \frac{x}{1!} + \frac{x^2}{2!} + \frac{x^3}{3!} + \cdots\right)\left(x - \frac{x^3}{3!} + \cdots\right)$$

We multiply these expressions, collecting like terms just as for polynomials:

$$\begin{array}{rl} & 1 + x + \tfrac{1}{2}x^2 + \tfrac{1}{6}x^3 + \cdots \\ \times & x \qquad\quad - \tfrac{1}{6}x^3 + \cdots \\ \hline & x + x^2 + \tfrac{1}{2}x^3 + \tfrac{1}{6}x^4 + \cdots \\ + & \qquad - \tfrac{1}{6}x^3 - \tfrac{1}{6}x^4 - \cdots \\ \hline & x + x^2 + \tfrac{1}{3}x^3 + \cdots \end{array}$$

Thus $$e^x \sin x = x + x^2 + \tfrac{1}{3}x^3 + \cdots$$

(b) Using the Maclaurin series in Table 1, we have

$$\tan x = \frac{\sin x}{\cos x} = \frac{x - \dfrac{x^3}{3!} + \dfrac{x^5}{5!} - \cdots}{1 - \dfrac{x^2}{2!} + \dfrac{x^4}{4!} - \cdots}$$

We use a procedure like long division:

$$
\begin{array}{r|l}
 & x + \frac{1}{3}x^3 + \frac{2}{15}x^5 + \cdots \\
\hline
1 - \frac{1}{2}x^2 + \frac{1}{24}x^4 - \cdots & x - \frac{1}{6}x^3 + \frac{1}{120}x^5 - \cdots \\
 & x - \frac{1}{2}x^3 + \frac{1}{24}x^5 - \cdots \\
\cline{2-2}
 & \frac{1}{3}x^3 - \frac{1}{30}x^5 + \cdots \\
 & \frac{1}{3}x^3 - \frac{1}{6}x^5 + \cdots \\
\cline{2-2}
 & \frac{2}{15}x^5 + \cdots
\end{array}
$$

Thus
$$\tan x = x + \tfrac{1}{3}x^3 + \tfrac{2}{15}x^5 + \cdots$$

Although we have not attempted to justify the formal manipulations used in Example 13, they are legitimate. There is a theorem which states that if both $f(x) = \Sigma\, c_n x^n$ and $g(x) = \Sigma\, b_n x^n$ converge for $|x| < R$ and the series are multiplied as if they were polynomials, then the resulting series also converges for $|x| < R$ and represents $f(x)g(x)$. For division we require $b_0 \neq 0$; the resulting series converges for sufficiently small $|x|$.

8.7 Exercises

1. If $f(x) = \sum_{n=0}^{\infty} b_n(x - 5)^n$ for all x, write a formula for b_8.

2. The graph of f is shown.

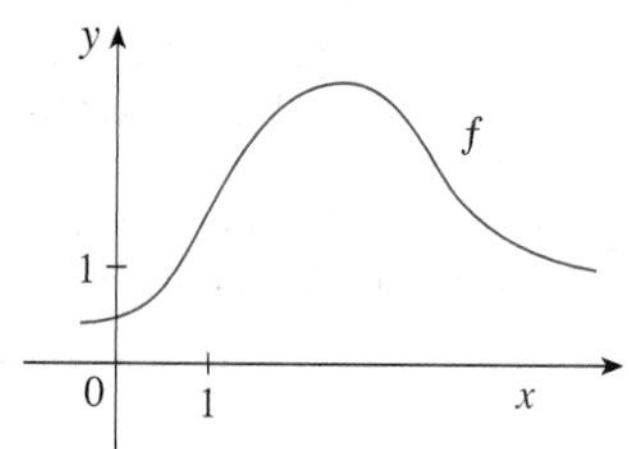

(a) Explain why the series

$$1.6 - 0.8(x - 1) + 0.4(x - 1)^2 - 0.1(x - 1)^3 + \cdots$$

is *not* the Taylor series of f centered at 1.

(b) Explain why the series

$$2.8 + 0.5(x - 2) + 1.5(x - 2)^2 - 0.1(x - 2)^3 + \cdots$$

is *not* the Taylor series of f centered at 2.

3. If $f^{(n)}(0) = (n + 1)!$ for $n = 0, 1, 2, \ldots$, find the Maclaurin series for f and its radius of convergence.

4. Find the Taylor series for f centered at 4 if

$$f^{(n)}(4) = \frac{(-1)^n n!}{3^n(n + 1)}$$

What is the radius of convergence of the Taylor series?

5–10 Find the Maclaurin series for $f(x)$ using the definition of a Maclaurin series. [Assume that f has a power series expansion. Do not show that $R_n(x) \to 0$.] Also find the associated radius of convergence.

5. $f(x) = (1 - x)^{-2}$ **6.** $f(x) = \ln(1 + x)$

7. $f(x) = \sin \pi x$ **8.** $f(x) = \cos 3x$

9. $f(x) = e^{5x}$ **10.** $f(x) = xe^x$

11–18 Find the Taylor series for $f(x)$ centered at the given value of a. [Assume that f has a power series expansion. Do not show that $R_n(x) \to 0$.]

11. $f(x) = x^4 - 3x^2 + 1, \quad a = 1$

12. $f(x) = x - x^3, \quad a = -2$

13. $f(x) = e^x, \quad a = 3$ **14.** $f(x) = 1/x, \quad a = -3$

15. $f(x) = \cos x, \quad a = \pi$ **16.** $f(x) = \sin x, \quad a = \pi/2$

17. $f(x) = 1/\sqrt{x}, \quad a = 9$ **18.** $f(x) = x^{-2}, \quad a = 1$

19. Prove that the series obtained in Exercise 7 represents $\sin \pi x$ for all x.

20. Prove that the series obtained in Exercise 16 represents $\sin x$ for all x.

Graphing calculator or computer with graphing software required **1.** Homework Hints available in TEC

21–24 Use the binomial series to expand the function as a power series. State the radius of convergence.

21. $\sqrt{1+x}$

22. $\dfrac{1}{(1+x)^4}$

23. $\dfrac{1}{(2+x)^3}$

24. $(1-x)^{2/3}$

25–34 Use a Maclaurin series in Table 1 to obtain the Maclaurin series for the given function.

25. $f(x) = \sin \pi x$

26. $f(x) = \cos(\pi x/2)$

27. $f(x) = e^x + e^{2x}$

28. $f(x) = e^x + 2e^{-x}$

29. $f(x) = x\cos(\frac{1}{2}x^2)$

30. $f(x) = x^2 \ln(1 + x^3)$

31. $f(x) = \dfrac{x}{\sqrt{4+x^2}}$

32. $f(x) = \dfrac{x^2}{\sqrt{2+x}}$

33. $f(x) = \sin^2 x$ $\left[\textit{Hint:} \text{ Use } \sin^2 x = \frac{1}{2}(1 - \cos 2x).\right]$

34. $f(x) = \begin{cases} \dfrac{x - \sin x}{x^3} & \text{if } x \neq 0 \\ \frac{1}{6} & \text{if } x = 0 \end{cases}$

35–38 Find the Maclaurin series of f (by any method) and its radius of convergence. Graph f and its first few Taylor polynomials on the same screen. What do you notice about the relationship between these polynomials and f?

35. $f(x) = \cos(x^2)$

36. $f(x) = e^{-x^2} + \cos x$

37. $f(x) = xe^{-x}$

38. $f(x) = \ln(1 + x^2)$

39. Use the Maclaurin series for e^x to calculate $e^{-0.2}$ correct to five decimal places.

40. Use the Maclaurin series for $\sin x$ to compute $\sin 3°$ correct to five decimal places.

41. (a) Use the binomial series to expand $1/\sqrt{1-x^2}$.
(b) Use part (a) to find the Maclaurin series for $\sin^{-1}x$.

42. (a) Expand $1/\sqrt[4]{1+x}$ as a power series.
(b) Use part (a) to estimate $1/\sqrt[4]{1.1}$ correct to three decimal places.

43–46 Evaluate the indefinite integral as an infinite series.

43. $\int x\cos(x^3)\,dx$

44. $\int \dfrac{e^x - 1}{x}\,dx$

45. $\int \dfrac{\cos x - 1}{x}\,dx$

46. $\int \arctan(x^2)\,dx$

47–50 Use series to approximate the definite integral to within the indicated accuracy.

47. $\int_0^1 x\cos(x^3)\,dx$ (three decimal places)

48. $\int_0^{0.2} [\tan^{-1}(x^3) + \sin(x^3)]\,dx$ (five decimal places)

49. $\int_0^{0.4} \sqrt{1+x^4}\,dx$ $(|\text{error}| < 5 \times 10^{-6})$

50. $\int_0^{0.5} x^2 e^{-x^2}\,dx$ $(|\text{error}| < 0.001)$

51–53 Use series to evaluate the limit.

51. $\lim\limits_{x\to 0} \dfrac{x - \ln(1+x)}{x^2}$

52. $\lim\limits_{x\to 0} \dfrac{1 - \cos x}{1 + x - e^x}$

53. $\lim\limits_{x\to 0} \dfrac{\sin x - x + \frac{1}{6}x^3}{x^5}$

54. Use the series in Example 13(b) to evaluate

$$\lim_{x\to 0} \frac{\tan x - x}{x^3}$$

We found this limit in Example 4 in Section 4.5 using l'Hospital's Rule three times. Which method do you prefer?

55–58 Use multiplication or division of power series to find the first three nonzero terms in the Maclaurin series for each function.

55. $y = e^{-x^2}\cos x$

56. $y = \sec x$

57. $y = \dfrac{x}{\sin x}$

58. $y = e^x \ln(1 + x)$

59–66 Find the sum of the series.

59. $\displaystyle\sum_{n=0}^{\infty} (-1)^n \frac{x^{4n}}{n!}$

60. $\displaystyle\sum_{n=0}^{\infty} \frac{(-1)^n \pi^{2n}}{6^{2n}(2n)!}$

61. $\displaystyle\sum_{n=1}^{\infty} (-1)^{n-1} \frac{3^n}{n\,5^n}$

62. $\displaystyle\sum_{n=0}^{\infty} \frac{3^n}{5^n n!}$

63. $\displaystyle\sum_{n=0}^{\infty} \frac{(-1)^n \pi^{2n+1}}{4^{2n+1}(2n+1)!}$

64. $1 - \ln 2 + \dfrac{(\ln 2)^2}{2!} - \dfrac{(\ln 2)^3}{3!} + \cdots$

65. $3 + \dfrac{9}{2!} + \dfrac{27}{3!} + \dfrac{81}{4!} + \cdots$

66. $\dfrac{1}{1 \cdot 2} - \dfrac{1}{3 \cdot 2^3} + \dfrac{1}{5 \cdot 2^5} - \dfrac{1}{7 \cdot 2^7} + \cdots$

67. Prove Taylor's Inequality for $n = 2$, that is, prove that if $|f'''(x)| \leq M$ for $|x - a| \leq d$, then

$$|R_2(x)| \leq \frac{M}{6}|x - a|^3 \qquad \text{for } |x - a| \leq d$$

68. (a) Show that the function defined by

$$f(x) = \begin{cases} e^{-1/x^2} & \text{if } x \neq 0 \\ 0 & \text{if } x = 0 \end{cases}$$

is not equal to its Maclaurin series.

(b) Graph the function in part (a) and comment on its behavior near the origin.

69. Use the following steps to prove (17).

(a) Let $g(x) = \sum_{n=0}^{\infty} \binom{k}{n} x^n$. Differentiate this series to show that

$$g'(x) = \frac{kg(x)}{1 + x} \qquad -1 < x < 1$$

(b) Let $h(x) = (1 + x)^{-k} g(x)$ and show that $h'(x) = 0$.

(c) Deduce that $g(x) = (1 + x)^k$.

70. In Exercise 31 in Section 6.4 it was shown that the length of the ellipse $x = a \sin \theta$, $y = b \cos \theta$, where $a > b > 0$, is

$$L = 4a \int_0^{\pi/2} \sqrt{1 - e^2 \sin^2 \theta}\, d\theta$$

where $e = \sqrt{a^2 - b^2}/a$ is the eccentricity of the ellipse. Expand the integrand as a binomial series and use the result of Exercise 38 in Section 5.6 to express L as a series in powers of the eccentricity up to the term in e^6.

LABORATORY PROJECT — CAS An Elusive Limit

This project deals with the function

$$f(x) = \frac{\sin(\tan x) - \tan(\sin x)}{\arcsin(\arctan x) - \arctan(\arcsin x)}$$

1. Use your computer algebra system to evaluate $f(x)$ for $x = 1, 0.1, 0.01, 0.001$, and 0.0001. Does it appear that f has a limit as $x \to 0$?
2. Use the CAS to graph f near $x = 0$. Does it appear that f has a limit as $x \to 0$?
3. Try to evaluate $\lim_{x \to 0} f(x)$ with l'Hospital's Rule, using the CAS to find derivatives of the numerator and denominator. What do you discover? How many applications of l'Hospital's Rule are required?
4. Evaluate $\lim_{x \to 0} f(x)$ by using the CAS to find sufficiently many terms in the Taylor series of the numerator and denominator. (Use the command `taylor` in Maple or `Series` in Mathematica.)
5. Use the limit command on your CAS to find $\lim_{x \to 0} f(x)$ directly. (Most computer algebra systems use the method of Problem 4 to compute limits.)
6. In view of the answers to Problems 4 and 5, how do you explain the results of Problems 1 and 2?

CAS Computer algebra system required

WRITING PROJECT — How Newton Discovered the Binomial Series

The Binomial Theorem, which gives the expansion of $(a + b)^k$, was known to Chinese mathematicians many centuries before the time of Newton for the case where the exponent k is a positive integer. In 1665, when he was 22, Newton was the first to discover the infinite series expansion of $(a + b)^k$ when k is a fractional exponent (positive or negative). He didn't publish his discovery, but he stated it and gave examples of how to use it in a letter (now called the *epistola prior*) dated June 13, 1676, that he sent to Henry Oldenburg, secretary of the Royal Society of London, to transmit to Leibniz. When Leibniz replied, he asked how Newton had discovered the binomial series. Newton wrote a second letter, the *epistola posterior* of October 24, 1676, in which he explained in great detail how he arrived at his discovery by a very indirect route. He was investigating the areas under the curves $y = (1 - x^2)^{n/2}$ from 0 to x for $n = 0, 1, 2, 3, 4, \ldots$. These are easy to calculate if n is even. By observing patterns and interpolating, Newton was able to guess the answers for odd values of n. Then he realized he could get the same answers by expressing $(1 - x^2)^{n/2}$ as an infinite series.

Write a report on Newton's discovery of the binomial series. Start by giving the statement of the binomial series in Newton's notation (see the *epistola prior* on page 285 of [4] or page 402 of [2]). Explain why Newton's version is equivalent to Theorem 17 on page 612. Then read Newton's *epistola posterior* (page 287 in [4] or page 404 in [2]) and explain the patterns that Newton discovered in the areas under the curves $y = (1 - x^2)^{n/2}$. Show how he was able to guess the areas under the remaining curves and how he verified his answers. Finally, explain how these discoveries led to the binomial series. The books by Edwards [1] and Katz [3] contain commentaries on Newton's letters.

1. C. H. Edwards, *The Historical Development of the Calculus* (New York: Springer-Verlag, 1979), pp. 178–187.

2. John Fauvel and Jeremy Gray, eds., *The History of Mathematics: A Reader* (London: MacMillan Press, 1987).

3. Victor Katz, *A History of Mathematics: An Introduction* (New York: HarperCollins, 1993), pp. 463–466.

4. D. J. Struik, ed., *A Sourcebook in Mathematics, 1200–1800* (Princeton, NJ: Princeton University Press, 1969).

8.8 Applications of Taylor Polynomials

In this section we explore two types of applications of Taylor polynomials. First we look at how they are used to approximate functions—computer scientists like them because polynomials are the simplest of functions. Then we investigate how physicists and engineers use them in such fields as relativity, optics, blackbody radiation, electric dipoles, and building highways across a desert.

Approximating Functions by Polynomials

Suppose that $f(x)$ is equal to the sum of its Taylor series at a:

$$f(x) = \sum_{n=0}^{\infty} \frac{f^{(n)}(a)}{n!}(x - a)^n$$

In Section 8.7 we introduced the notation $T_n(x)$ for the nth partial sum of this series and called it the nth-degree Taylor polynomial of f at a. Thus

$$\begin{aligned} T_n(x) &= \sum_{i=0}^{n} \frac{f^{(i)}(a)}{i!}(x - a)^i \\ &= f(a) + \frac{f'(a)}{1!}(x - a) + \frac{f''(a)}{2!}(x - a)^2 + \cdots + \frac{f^{(n)}(a)}{n!}(x - a)^n \end{aligned}$$

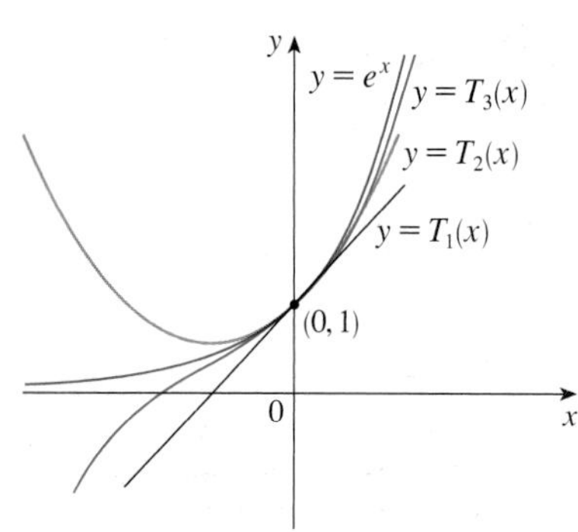

FIGURE 1

	$x = 0.2$	$x = 3.0$
$T_2(x)$	1.220000	8.500000
$T_4(x)$	1.221400	16.375000
$T_6(x)$	1.221403	19.412500
$T_8(x)$	1.221403	20.009152
$T_{10}(x)$	1.221403	20.079665
e^x	1.221403	20.085537

Since f is the sum of its Taylor series, we know that $T_n(x) \to f(x)$ as $n \to \infty$ and so T_n can be used as an approximation to f: $f(x) \approx T_n(x)$.

Notice that the first-degree Taylor polynomial

$$T_1(x) = f(a) + f'(a)(x - a)$$

is the same as the linearization of f at a that we discussed in Section 3.9. Notice also that T_1 and its derivative have the same values at a that f and f' have. In general, it can be shown that the derivatives of T_n at a agree with those of f up to and including derivatives of order n.

To illustrate these ideas let's take another look at the graphs of $y = e^x$ and its first few Taylor polynomials, as shown in Figure 1. The graph of T_1 is the tangent line to $y = e^x$ at $(0, 1)$; this tangent line is the best linear approximation to e^x near $(0, 1)$. The graph of T_2 is the parabola $y = 1 + x + x^2/2$, and the graph of T_3 is the cubic curve $y = 1 + x + x^2/2 + x^3/6$, which is a closer fit to the exponential curve $y = e^x$ than T_2. The next Taylor polynomial T_4 would be an even better approximation, and so on.

The values in the table give a numerical demonstration of the convergence of the Taylor polynomials $T_n(x)$ to the function $y = e^x$. We see that when $x = 0.2$ the convergence is very rapid, but when $x = 3$ it is somewhat slower. In fact, the farther x is from 0, the more slowly $T_n(x)$ converges to e^x.

When using a Taylor polynomial T_n to approximate a function f, we have to ask the questions: How good an approximation is it? How large should we take n to be in order to achieve a desired accuracy? To answer these questions we need to look at the absolute value of the remainder:

$$|R_n(x)| = |f(x) - T_n(x)|$$

There are three possible methods for estimating the size of the error:

1. If a graphing device is available, we can use it to graph $|R_n(x)|$ and thereby estimate the error.

2. If the series happens to be an alternating series, we can use the Alternating Series Estimation Theorem.

3. In all cases we can use Taylor's Inequality (Theorem 8.7.9), which says that if $|f^{(n+1)}(x)| \leqslant M$, then

$$|R_n(x)| \leqslant \frac{M}{(n + 1)!} |x - a|^{n+1}$$

V EXAMPLE 1 Approximating a root function by a quadratic function
(a) Approximate the function $f(x) = \sqrt[3]{x}$ by a Taylor polynomial of degree 2 at $a = 8$.
(b) How accurate is this approximation when $7 \leqslant x \leqslant 9$?

SOLUTION

(a)

$$f(x) = \sqrt[3]{x} = x^{1/3} \qquad f(8) = 2$$

$$f'(x) = \tfrac{1}{3}x^{-2/3} \qquad f'(8) = \tfrac{1}{12}$$

$$f''(x) = -\tfrac{2}{9}x^{-5/3} \qquad f''(8) = -\tfrac{1}{144}$$

$$f'''(x) = \tfrac{10}{27}x^{-8/3}$$

Thus the second-degree Taylor polynomial is

$$\begin{aligned} T_2(x) &= f(8) + \frac{f'(8)}{1!}(x-8) + \frac{f''(8)}{2!}(x-8)^2 \\ &= 2 + \tfrac{1}{12}(x-8) - \tfrac{1}{288}(x-8)^2 \end{aligned}$$

The desired approximation is

$$\sqrt[3]{x} \approx T_2(x) = 2 + \tfrac{1}{12}(x-8) - \tfrac{1}{288}(x-8)^2$$

(b) The Taylor series is not alternating when $x < 8$, so we can't use the Alternating Series Estimation Theorem in this example. But we can use Taylor's Inequality with $n = 2$ and $a = 8$:

$$|R_2(x)| \leqslant \frac{M}{3!}|x-8|^3$$

where $|f'''(x)| \leqslant M$. Because $x \geqslant 7$, we have $x^{8/3} \geqslant 7^{8/3}$ and so

$$f'''(x) = \frac{10}{27} \cdot \frac{1}{x^{8/3}} \leqslant \frac{10}{27} \cdot \frac{1}{7^{8/3}} < 0.0021$$

Therefore we can take $M = 0.0021$. Also $7 \leqslant x \leqslant 9$, so $-1 \leqslant x - 8 \leqslant 1$ and $|x - 8| \leqslant 1$. Then Taylor's Inequality gives

$$|R_2(x)| \leqslant \frac{0.0021}{3!} \cdot 1^3 = \frac{0.0021}{6} < 0.0004$$

Thus, if $7 \leqslant x \leqslant 9$, the approximation in part (a) is accurate to within 0.0004. ■

FIGURE 2

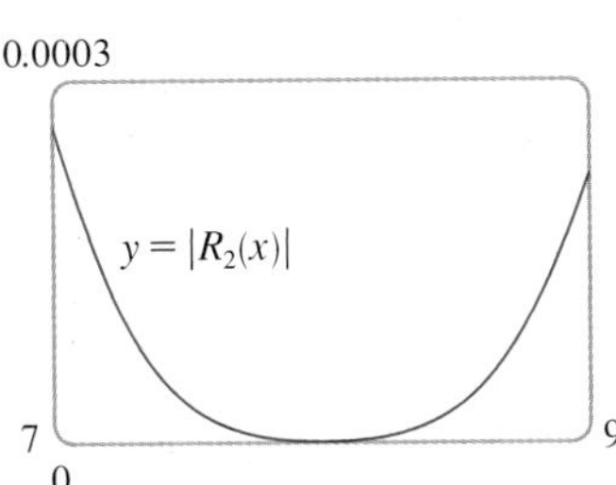

FIGURE 3

Let's use a graphing device to check the calculation in Example 1. Figure 2 shows that the graphs of $y = \sqrt[3]{x}$ and $y = T_2(x)$ are very close to each other when x is near 8. Figure 3 shows the graph of $|R_2(x)|$ computed from the expression

$$|R_2(x)| = |\sqrt[3]{x} - T_2(x)|$$

We see from the graph that

$$|R_2(x)| < 0.0003$$

when $7 \leqslant x \leqslant 9$. Thus the error estimate from graphical methods is slightly better than the error estimate from Taylor's Inequality in this case.

V EXAMPLE 2 Approximating $\sin x$ by a fifth-degree Taylor polynomial
(a) What is the maximum error possible in using the approximation

$$\sin x \approx x - \frac{x^3}{3!} + \frac{x^5}{5!}$$

when $-0.3 \leqslant x \leqslant 0.3$? Use this approximation to find $\sin 12°$ correct to six decimal places.
(b) For what values of x is this approximation accurate to within 0.00005?

SOLUTION

(a) Notice that the Maclaurin series

$$\sin x = x - \frac{x^3}{3!} + \frac{x^5}{5!} - \frac{x^7}{7!} + \cdots$$

is alternating for all nonzero values of x, and the successive terms decrease in size because $|x| < 1$, so we can use the Alternating Series Estimation Theorem. The error in approximating $\sin x$ by the first three terms of its Maclaurin series is at most

$$\left|\frac{x^7}{7!}\right| = \frac{|x|^7}{5040}$$

If $-0.3 \leqslant x \leqslant 0.3$, then $|x| \leqslant 0.3$, so the error is smaller than

$$\frac{(0.3)^7}{5040} \approx 4.3 \times 10^{-8}$$

To find $\sin 12°$ we first convert to radian measure:

$$\sin 12° = \sin\left(\frac{12\pi}{180}\right) = \sin\left(\frac{\pi}{15}\right)$$

$$\approx \frac{\pi}{15} - \left(\frac{\pi}{15}\right)^3 \frac{1}{3!} + \left(\frac{\pi}{15}\right)^5 \frac{1}{5!} \approx 0.20791169$$

Thus, correct to six decimal places, $\sin 12° \approx 0.207912$.

(b) The error will be smaller than 0.00005 if

$$\frac{|x|^7}{5040} < 0.00005$$

TEC Module 8.7/8.8 graphically shows the remainders in Taylor polynomial approximations.

Solving this inequality for x, we get

$$|x|^7 < 0.252 \qquad \text{or} \qquad |x| < (0.252)^{1/7} \approx 0.821$$

So the given approximation is accurate to within 0.00005 when $|x| < 0.82$.

What if we use Taylor's Inequality to solve Example 2? Since $f^{(7)}(x) = -\cos x$, we have $|f^{(7)}(x)| \leqslant 1$ and so

$$|R_6(x)| \leqslant \frac{1}{7!}|x|^7$$

So we get the same estimates as with the Alternating Series Estimation Theorem.

What about graphical methods? Figure 4 shows the graph of

$$|R_6(x)| = \left|\sin x - \left(x - \tfrac{1}{6}x^3 + \tfrac{1}{120}x^5\right)\right|$$

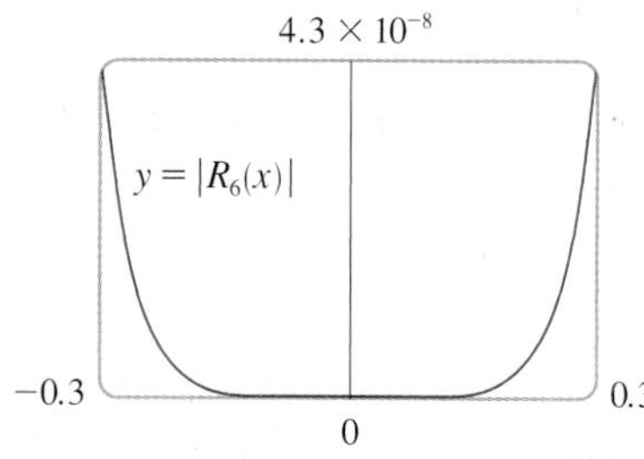

FIGURE 4

and we see from it that $|R_6(x)| < 4.3 \times 10^{-8}$ when $|x| \leqslant 0.3$. This is the same estimate that we obtained in Example 2. For part (b) we want $|R_6(x)| < 0.00005$, so we graph both $y = |R_6(x)|$ and $y = 0.00005$ in Figure 5. By placing the cursor on the right intersection point we find that the inequality is satisfied when $|x| < 0.82$. Again this is the same estimate that we obtained in the solution to Example 2.

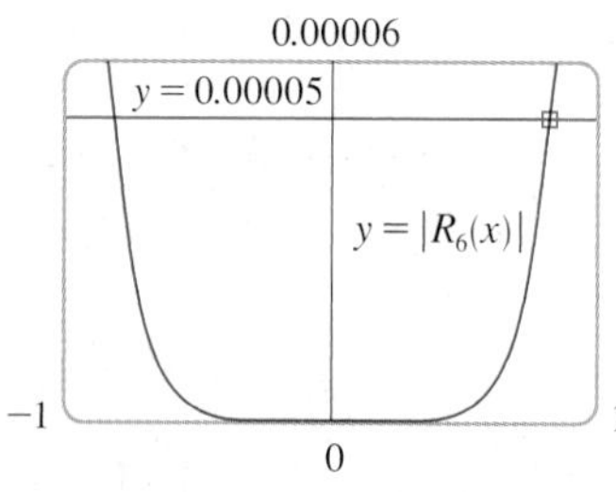

FIGURE 5

If we had been asked to approximate $\sin 72°$ instead of $\sin 12°$ in Example 2, it would have been wise to use the Taylor polynomials at $a = \pi/3$ (instead of $a = 0$) because they are better approximations to $\sin x$ for values of x close to $\pi/3$. Notice that 72° is close to 60° (or $\pi/3$ radians) and the derivatives of $\sin x$ are easy to compute at $\pi/3$.

Figure 6 shows the graphs of the Maclaurin polynomial approximations

$$T_1(x) = x \qquad T_3(x) = x - \frac{x^3}{3!}$$

$$T_5(x) = x - \frac{x^3}{3!} + \frac{x^5}{5!} \qquad T_7(x) = x - \frac{x^3}{3!} + \frac{x^5}{5!} - \frac{x^7}{7!}$$

to the sine curve. You can see that as n increases, $T_n(x)$ is a good approximation to $\sin x$ on a larger and larger interval.

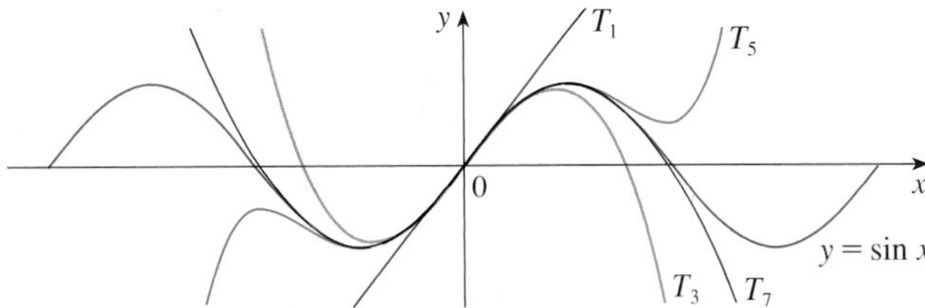

FIGURE 6

One use of the type of calculation done in Examples 1 and 2 occurs in calculators and computers. For instance, when you press the sin or e^x key on your calculator, or when a computer programmer uses a subroutine for a trigonometric or exponential or Bessel function, in many machines a polynomial approximation is calculated. The polynomial is often a Taylor polynomial that has been modified so that the error is spread more evenly throughout an interval.

Applications to Physics

Taylor polynomials are also used frequently in physics. In order to gain insight into an equation, a physicist often simplifies a function by considering only the first two or three terms in its Taylor series. In other words, the physicist uses a Taylor polynomial as an approximation to the function. Taylor's Inequality can then be used to gauge the accuracy of the approximation. The following example shows one way in which this idea is used in special relativity.

V **EXAMPLE 3** **Using Taylor to compare Einstein and Newton** In Einstein's theory of special relativity the mass of an object moving with velocity v is

$$m = \frac{m_0}{\sqrt{1 - v^2/c^2}}$$

where m_0 is the mass of the object when at rest and c is the speed of light. The kinetic energy of the object is the difference between its total energy and its energy at rest:

$$K = mc^2 - m_0c^2$$

(a) Show that when v is very small compared with c, this expression for K agrees with classical Newtonian physics: $K = \frac{1}{2}m_0v^2$.

(b) Use Taylor's Inequality to estimate the difference in these expressions for K when $|v| \leqslant 100$ m/s.

SOLUTION

(a) Using the expressions given for K and m, we get

$$K = mc^2 - m_0c^2 = \frac{m_0c^2}{\sqrt{1 - v^2/c^2}} - m_0c^2 = m_0c^2\left[\left(1 - \frac{v^2}{c^2}\right)^{-1/2} - 1\right]$$

The upper curve in Figure 7 is the graph of the expression for the kinetic energy K of an object with velocity v in special relativity. The lower curve shows the function used for K in classical Newtonian physics. When v is much smaller than the speed of light, the curves are practically identical.

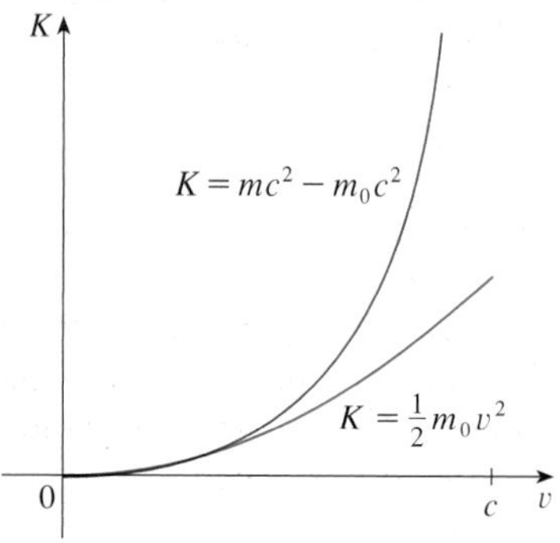

FIGURE 7

With $x = -v^2/c^2$, the Maclaurin series for $(1 + x)^{-1/2}$ is most easily computed as a binomial series with $k = -\frac{1}{2}$. (Notice that $|x| < 1$ because $v < c$.) Therefore we have

$$(1 + x)^{-1/2} = 1 - \tfrac{1}{2}x + \frac{(-\frac{1}{2})(-\frac{3}{2})}{2!}x^2 + \frac{(-\frac{1}{2})(-\frac{3}{2})(-\frac{5}{2})}{3!}x^3 + \cdots$$

$$= 1 - \tfrac{1}{2}x + \tfrac{3}{8}x^2 - \tfrac{5}{16}x^3 + \cdots$$

and

$$K = m_0c^2\left[\left(1 + \frac{1}{2}\frac{v^2}{c^2} + \frac{3}{8}\frac{v^4}{c^4} + \frac{5}{16}\frac{v^6}{c^6} + \cdots\right) - 1\right]$$

$$= m_0c^2\left(\frac{1}{2}\frac{v^2}{c^2} + \frac{3}{8}\frac{v^4}{c^4} + \frac{5}{16}\frac{v^6}{c^6} + \cdots\right)$$

If v is much smaller than c, then all terms after the first are very small when compared with the first term. If we omit them, we get

$$K \approx m_0c^2\left(\frac{1}{2}\frac{v^2}{c^2}\right) = \tfrac{1}{2}m_0v^2$$

(b) If $x = -v^2/c^2$, $f(x) = m_0c^2[(1 + x)^{-1/2} - 1]$, and M is a number such that $|f''(x)| \leq M$, then we can use Taylor's Inequality to write

$$|R_1(x)| \leq \frac{M}{2!}x^2$$

We have $f''(x) = \frac{3}{4}m_0c^2(1 + x)^{-5/2}$ and we are given that $|v| \leq 100$ m/s, so

$$|f''(x)| = \frac{3m_0c^2}{4(1 - v^2/c^2)^{5/2}} \leq \frac{3m_0c^2}{4(1 - 100^2/c^2)^{5/2}} \quad (= M)$$

Thus, with $c = 3 \times 10^8$ m/s,

$$|R_1(x)| \leq \frac{1}{2} \cdot \frac{3m_0c^2}{4(1 - 100^2/c^2)^{5/2}} \cdot \frac{100^4}{c^4} < (4.17 \times 10^{-10})m_0$$

So when $|v| \leq 100$ m/s, the magnitude of the error in using the Newtonian expression for kinetic energy is at most $(4.2 \times 10^{-10})m_0$.

Another application to physics occurs in optics. Figure 8 is adapted from *Optics*, 4th ed., by Eugene Hecht (San Francisco, 2002), page 153. It depicts a wave from the point source S meeting a spherical interface of radius R centered at C. The ray SA is refracted toward P.

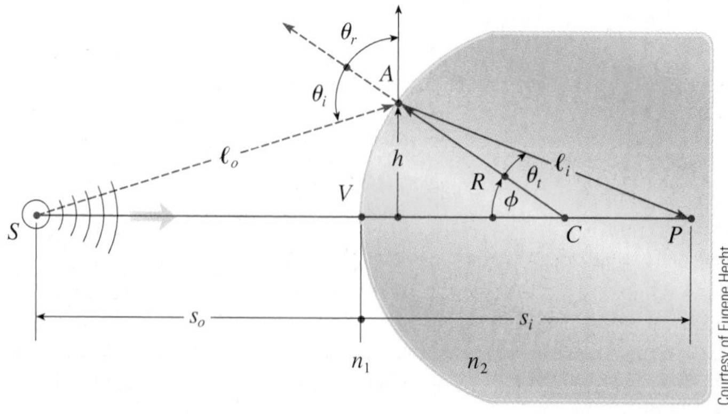

FIGURE 8
Refraction at a spherical interface

Using Fermat's principle that light travels so as to minimize the time taken, Hecht derives the equation

$$\boxed{1} \qquad \frac{n_1}{\ell_o} + \frac{n_2}{\ell_i} = \frac{1}{R}\left(\frac{n_2 s_i}{\ell_i} - \frac{n_1 s_o}{\ell_o}\right)$$

where n_1 and n_2 are indexes of refraction and ℓ_o, ℓ_i, s_o, and s_i are the distances indicated in Figure 8. By the Law of Cosines, applied to triangles ACS and ACP, we have

Here we use the identity

$$\cos(\pi - \phi) = -\cos\phi$$

$$\boxed{2} \qquad \ell_o = \sqrt{R^2 + (s_o + R)^2 - 2R(s_o + R)\cos\phi}$$

$$\ell_i = \sqrt{R^2 + (s_i - R)^2 + 2R(s_i - R)\cos\phi}$$

Because Equation 1 is cumbersome to work with, Gauss, in 1841, simplified it by using the linear approximation $\cos\phi \approx 1$ for small values of ϕ. (This amounts to using the Taylor polynomial of degree 1.) Then Equation 1 becomes the following simpler equation [as you are asked to show in Exercise 28(a)]:

$$\boxed{3} \qquad \frac{n_1}{s_o} + \frac{n_2}{s_i} = \frac{n_2 - n_1}{R}$$

The resulting optical theory is known as *Gaussian optics,* or *first-order optics,* and has become the basic theoretical tool used to design lenses.

A more accurate theory is obtained by approximating $\cos\phi$ by its Taylor polynomial of degree 3 (which is the same as the Taylor polynomial of degree 2). This takes into account rays for which ϕ is not so small, that is, rays that strike the surface at greater distances h above the axis. In Exercise 28(b) you are asked to use this approximation to derive the more accurate equation

$$\boxed{4} \qquad \frac{n_1}{s_o} + \frac{n_2}{s_i} = \frac{n_2 - n_1}{R} + h^2\left[\frac{n_1}{2s_o}\left(\frac{1}{s_o} + \frac{1}{R}\right)^2 + \frac{n_2}{2s_i}\left(\frac{1}{R} - \frac{1}{s_i}\right)^2\right]$$

The resulting optical theory is known as *third-order optics.*

Other applications of Taylor polynomials to physics and engineering are explored in Exercises 29–32 and in the Applied Project on page 627.

8.8 Exercises

1. (a) Find the Taylor polynomials up to degree 6 for $f(x) = \cos x$ centered at $a = 0$. Graph f and these polynomials on a common screen.
(b) Evaluate f and these polynomials at $x = \pi/4$, $\pi/2$, and π.
(c) Comment on how the Taylor polynomials converge to $f(x)$.

2. (a) Find the Taylor polynomials up to degree 3 for $f(x) = 1/x$ centered at $a = 1$. Graph f and these polynomials on a common screen.
(b) Evaluate f and these polynomials at $x = 0.9$ and 1.3.
(c) Comment on how the Taylor polynomials converge to $f(x)$.

3–8 Find the Taylor polynomial $T_3(x)$ for the function f at the number a. Graph f and T_3 on the same screen.

3. $f(x) = 1/x, \quad a = 2$

4. $f(x) = x + e^{-x}, \quad a = 0$

5. $f(x) = \cos x, \quad a = \pi/2$

6. $f(x) = \dfrac{\ln x}{x}, \quad a = 1$

7. $f(x) = xe^{-2x}, \quad a = 0$

8. $f(x) = \tan^{-1}x, \quad a = 1$

Graphing calculator or computer with graphing software required   CAS Computer algebra system required   1. Homework Hints available in TEC

CAS **9–10** Use a computer algebra system to find the Taylor polynomials T_n centered at a for $n = 2, 3, 4, 5$. Then graph these polynomials and f on the same screen.

9. $f(x) = \cot x, \quad a = \pi/4$

10. $f(x) = \sqrt[3]{1 + x^2}, \quad a = 0$

11–18

(a) Approximate f by a Taylor polynomial with degree n at the number a.

(b) Use Taylor's Inequality to estimate the accuracy of the approximation $f(x) \approx T_n(x)$ when x lies in the given interval.

(c) Check your result in part (b) by graphing $|R_n(x)|$.

11. $f(x) = \sqrt{x}, \quad a = 4, \quad n = 2, \quad 4 \leqslant x \leqslant 4.2$

12. $f(x) = x^{-2}, \quad a = 1, \quad n = 2, \quad 0.9 \leqslant x \leqslant 1.1$

13. $f(x) = x^{2/3}, \quad a = 1, \quad n = 3, \quad 0.8 \leqslant x \leqslant 1.2$

14. $f(x) = \sin x, \quad a = \pi/6, \quad n = 4, \quad 0 \leqslant x \leqslant \pi/3$

15. $f(x) = e^{x^2}, \quad a = 0, \quad n = 3, \quad 0 \leqslant x \leqslant 0.1$

16. $f(x) = \ln(1 + 2x), \quad a = 1, \quad n = 3, \quad 0.5 \leqslant x \leqslant 1.5$

17. $f(x) = x \sin x, \quad a = 0, \quad n = 4, \quad -1 \leqslant x \leqslant 1$

18. $f(x) = x \ln x, \quad a = 1, \quad n = 3, \quad 0.5 \leqslant x \leqslant 1.5$

---

19. Use the information from Exercise 5 to estimate cos 80° correct to five decimal places.

20. Use the information from Exercise 14 to estimate sin 38° correct to five decimal places.

21. Use Taylor's Inequality to determine the number of terms of the Maclaurin series for e^x that should be used to estimate $e^{0.1}$ to within 0.00001.

22. How many terms of the Maclaurin series for $\ln(1 + x)$ do you need to use to estimate ln 1.4 to within 0.001?

23–25 Use the Alternating Series Estimation Theorem or Taylor's Inequality to estimate the range of values of x for which the given approximation is accurate to within the stated error. Check your answer graphically.

23. $\sin x \approx x - \dfrac{x^3}{6} \quad (|\text{error}| < 0.01)$

24. $\cos x \approx 1 - \dfrac{x^2}{2} + \dfrac{x^4}{24} \quad (|\text{error}| < 0.005)$

25. $\arctan x \approx x - \dfrac{x^3}{3} + \dfrac{x^5}{5} \quad (|\text{error}| < 0.05)$

---

26. Suppose you know that

$$f^{(n)}(4) = \frac{(-1)^n n!}{3^n(n + 1)}$$

and the Taylor series of f centered at 4 converges to $f(x)$ for all x in the interval of convergence. Show that the fifth-degree Taylor polynomial approximates $f(5)$ with error less than 0.0002.

27. A car is moving with speed 20 m/s and acceleration 2 m/s^2 at a given instant. Using a second-degree Taylor polynomial, estimate how far the car moves in the next second. Would it be reasonable to use this polynomial to estimate the distance traveled during the next minute?

28. (a) Derive Equation 3 for Gaussian optics from Equation 1 by approximating $\cos \phi$ in Equation 2 by its first-degree Taylor polynomial.

(b) Show that if $\cos \phi$ is replaced by its third-degree Taylor polynomial in Equation 2, then Equation 1 becomes Equation 4 for third-order optics. [*Hint:* Use the first two terms in the binomial series for ℓ_o^{-1} and ℓ_i^{-1}. Also, use $\phi \approx \sin \phi$.]

29. An electric dipole consists of two electric charges of equal magnitude and opposite sign. If the charges are q and $-q$ and are located at a distance d from each other, then the electric field E at the point P in the figure is

$$E = \frac{q}{D^2} - \frac{q}{(D + d)^2}$$

By expanding this expression for E as a series in powers of d/D, show that E is approximately proportional to $1/D^3$ when P is far away from the dipole.

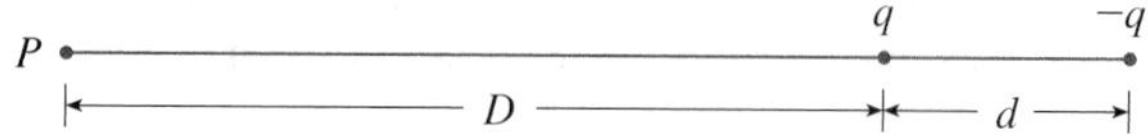

30. The resistivity ρ of a conducting wire is the reciprocal of the conductivity and is measured in units of ohm-meters (Ω-m). The resistivity of a given metal depends on the temperature according to the equation

$$\rho(t) = \rho_{20}e^{\alpha(t-20)}$$

where t is the temperature in °C. There are tables that list the values of α (called the temperature coefficient) and ρ_{20} (the resistivity at 20°C) for various metals. Except at very low temperatures, the resistivity varies almost linearly with temperature and so it is common to approximate the expression for $\rho(t)$ by its first- or second-degree Taylor polynomial at $t = 20$.

(a) Find expressions for these linear and quadratic approximations.

(b) For copper, the tables give $\alpha = 0.0039/°C$ and $\rho_{20} = 1.7 \times 10^{-8}$ Ω-m. Graph the resistivity of copper and the linear and quadratic approximations for $-250°C \leqslant t \leqslant 1000°C$.

(c) For what values of t does the linear approximation agree with the exponential expression to within one percent?

31. If a surveyor measures differences in elevation when making plans for a highway across a desert, corrections must be made for the curvature of the earth.

(a) If R is the radius of the earth and L is the length of the highway, show that the correction is

$$C = R\sec(L/R) - R$$

(b) Use a Taylor polynomial to show that

$$C \approx \frac{L^2}{2R} + \frac{5L^4}{24R^3}$$

(c) Compare the corrections given by the formulas in parts (a) and (b) for a highway that is 100 km long. (Take the radius of the earth to be 6370 km.)

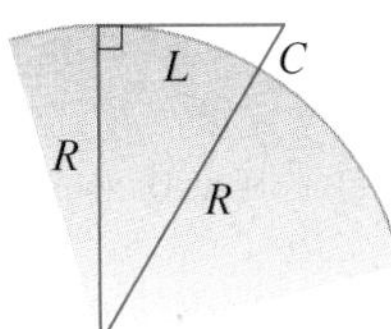

32. The period of a pendulum with length L that makes a maximum angle θ_0 with the vertical is

$$T = 4\sqrt{\frac{L}{g}}\int_0^{\pi/2} \frac{dx}{\sqrt{1 - k^2\sin^2 x}}$$

where $k = \sin(\frac{1}{2}\theta_0)$ and g is the acceleration due to gravity. (In Exercise 34 in Section 5.9 we approximated this integral using Simpson's Rule.)

(a) Expand the integrand as a binomial series and use the result of Exercise 38 in Section 5.6 to show that

$$T = 2\pi\sqrt{\frac{L}{g}}\left[1 + \frac{1^2}{2^2}k^2 + \frac{1^2 3^2}{2^2 4^2}k^4 + \frac{1^2 3^2 5^2}{2^2 4^2 6^2}k^6 + \cdots\right]$$

If θ_0 is not too large, the approximation $T \approx 2\pi\sqrt{L/g}$, obtained by using only the first term in the series, is often used. A better approximation is obtained by using two terms:

$$T \approx 2\pi\sqrt{\frac{L}{g}}\left(1 + \tfrac{1}{4}k^2\right)$$

(b) Notice that all the terms in the series after the first one have coefficients that are at most $\frac{1}{4}$. Use this fact to compare this series with a geometric series and show that

$$2\pi\sqrt{\frac{L}{g}}\left(1 + \tfrac{1}{4}k^2\right) \leqslant T \leqslant 2\pi\sqrt{\frac{L}{g}}\,\frac{4 - 3k^2}{4 - 4k^2}$$

(c) Use the inequalities in part (b) to estimate the period of a pendulum with $L = 1$ meter and $\theta_0 = 10°$. How does it compare with the estimate $T \approx 2\pi\sqrt{L/g}$? What if $\theta_0 = 42°$?

33. In Section 4.7 we considered Newton's method for approximating a root r of the equation $f(x) = 0$, and from an initial approximation x_1 we obtained successive approximations $x_2, x_3, \ldots$, where

$$x_{n+1} = x_n - \frac{f(x_n)}{f'(x_n)}$$

Use Taylor's Inequality with $n = 1$, $a = x_n$, and $x = r$ to show that if $f''(x)$ exists on an interval I containing r, x_n, and x_{n+1}, and $|f''(x)| \leqslant M$, $|f'(x)| \geqslant K$ for all $x \in I$, then

$$|x_{n+1} - r| \leqslant \frac{M}{2K}|x_n - r|^2$$

[This means that if x_n is accurate to d decimal places, then x_{n+1} is accurate to about $2d$ decimal places. More precisely, if the error at stage n is at most 10^{-m}, then the error at stage $n + 1$ is at most $(M/2K)10^{-2m}$.]

APPLIED PROJECT Radiation from the Stars

Any object emits radiation when heated. A *blackbody* is a system that absorbs all the radiation that falls on it. For instance, a matte black surface or a large cavity with a small hole in its wall (like a blastfurnace) is a blackbody and emits blackbody radiation. Even the radiation from the sun is close to being blackbody radiation.

Proposed in the late 19th century, the Rayleigh-Jeans Law expresses the energy density of blackbody radiation of wavelength λ as

$$f(\lambda) = \frac{8\pi kT}{\lambda^4}$$

where λ is measured in meters, T is the temperature in kelvins (K), and k is Boltzmann's constant. The Rayleigh-Jeans Law agrees with experimental measurements for long wavelengths

Graphing calculator or computer with graphing software required

but disagrees drastically for short wavelengths. [The law predicts that $f(\lambda) \to \infty$ as $\lambda \to 0^+$ but experiments have shown that $f(\lambda) \to 0$.] This fact is known as the *ultraviolet catastrophe*.

In 1900 Max Planck found a better model (known now as Planck's Law) for blackbody radiation:

$$f(\lambda) = \frac{8\pi hc\lambda^{-5}}{e^{hc/(\lambda kT)} - 1}$$

where λ is measured in meters, T is the temperature (in kelvins), and

$$h = \text{Planck's constant} = 6.6262 \times 10^{-34} \text{ J·s}$$

$$c = \text{speed of light} = 2.997925 \times 10^{8} \text{ m/s}$$

$$k = \text{Boltzmann's constant} = 1.3807 \times 10^{-23} \text{ J/K}$$

1. Use l'Hospital's Rule to show that

$$\lim_{\lambda \to 0^+} f(\lambda) = 0 \qquad \text{and} \qquad \lim_{\lambda \to \infty} f(\lambda) = 0$$

for Planck's Law. So this law models blackbody radiation better than the Rayleigh-Jeans Law for short wavelengths.

2. Use a Taylor polynomial to show that, for large wavelengths, Planck's Law gives approximately the same values as the Rayleigh-Jeans Law.

3. Graph f as given by both laws on the same screen and comment on the similarities and differences. Use $T = 5700$ K (the temperature of the sun). (You may want to change from meters to the more convenient unit of micrometers: 1 μm $= 10^{-6}$ m.)

4. Use your graph in Problem 3 to estimate the value of λ for which $f(\lambda)$ is a maximum under Planck's Law.

5. Investigate how the graph of f changes as T varies. (Use Planck's Law.) In particular, graph f for the stars Betelgeuse ($T = 3400$ K), Procyon ($T = 6400$ K), and Sirius ($T = 9200$ K), as well as the sun. How does the total radiation emitted (the area under the curve) vary with T? Use the graph to comment on why Sirius is known as a blue star and Betelgeuse as a red star.

8 Review

Concept Check

1. (a) What is a convergent sequence?
(b) What is a convergent series?
(c) What does $\lim_{n\to\infty} a_n = 3$ mean?
(d) What does $\Sigma_{n=1}^{\infty} a_n = 3$ mean?

2. (a) What is a bounded sequence?
(b) What is a monotonic sequence?
(c) What can you say about a bounded monotonic sequence?

3. (a) What is a geometric series? Under what circumstances is it convergent? What is its sum?
(b) What is a p-series? Under what circumstances is it convergent?

4. Suppose $\Sigma a_n = 3$ and s_n is the nth partial sum of the series. What is $\lim_{n\to\infty} a_n$? What is $\lim_{n\to\infty} s_n$?

5. State the following.
(a) The Test for Divergence
(b) The Integral Test
(c) The Comparison Test
(d) The Limit Comparison Test
(e) The Alternating Series Test
(f) The Ratio Test

6. (a) What is an absolutely convergent series?
(b) What can you say about such a series?

7. (a) If a series is convergent by the Integral Test, how do you estimate its sum?
(b) If a series is convergent by the Comparison Test, how do you estimate its sum?

(c) If a series is convergent by the Alternating Series Test, how do you estimate its sum?

8. (a) Write the general form of a power series.
(b) What is the radius of convergence of a power series?
(c) What is the interval of convergence of a power series?

9. Suppose $f(x)$ is the sum of a power series with radius of convergence R.
(a) How do you differentiate f? What is the radius of convergence of the series for f'?
(b) How do you integrate f? What is the radius of convergence of the series for $\int f(x)\,dx$?

10. (a) Write an expression for the nth-degree Taylor polynomial of f centered at a.
(b) Write an expression for the Taylor series of f centered at a.
(c) Write an expression for the Maclaurin series of f.
(d) How do you show that $f(x)$ is equal to the sum of its Taylor series?
(e) State Taylor's Inequality.

11. Write the Maclaurin series and the interval of convergence for each of the following functions.
(a) $1/(1-x)$ (b) e^x
(c) $\sin x$ (d) $\cos x$
(e) $\tan^{-1}x$ (f) $\ln(1+x)$

12. Write the binomial series expansion of $(1+x)^k$. What is the radius of convergence of this series?

True-False Quiz

Determine whether the statement is true or false. If it is true, explain why. If it is false, explain why or give an example that disproves the statement.

1. If $\lim_{n\to\infty} a_n = 0$, then $\Sigma\, a_n$ is convergent.
2. The series $\Sigma_{n=1}^{\infty} n^{-\sin 1}$ is convergent.
3. If $\lim_{n\to\infty} a_n = L$, then $\lim_{n\to\infty} a_{2n+1} = L$.
4. If $\Sigma\, c_n 6^n$ is convergent, then $\Sigma\, c_n(-2)^n$ is convergent.
5. If $\Sigma\, c_n 6^n$ is convergent, then $\Sigma\, c_n(-6)^n$ is convergent.
6. If $\Sigma\, c_n x^n$ diverges when $x = 6$, then it diverges when $x = 10$.
7. The Ratio Test can be used to determine whether $\Sigma\, 1/n^3$ converges.
8. The Ratio Test can be used to determine whether $\Sigma\, 1/n!$ converges.
9. If $0 \leqslant a_n \leqslant b_n$ and $\Sigma\, b_n$ diverges, then $\Sigma\, a_n$ diverges.
10. $\displaystyle\sum_{n=0}^{\infty} \frac{(-1)^n}{n!} = \frac{1}{e}$
11. If $-1 < \alpha < 1$, then $\lim_{n\to\infty} \alpha^n = 0$.
12. If $\Sigma\, a_n$ is divergent, then $\Sigma\, |a_n|$ is divergent.
13. If $f(x) = 2x - x^2 + \frac{1}{3}x^3 - \cdots$ converges for all x, then $f'''(0) = 2$.
14. If $\{a_n\}$ and $\{b_n\}$ are divergent, then $\{a_n + b_n\}$ is divergent.
15. If $\{a_n\}$ and $\{b_n\}$ are divergent, then $\{a_n b_n\}$ is divergent.
16. If $\{a_n\}$ is decreasing and $a_n > 0$ for all n, then $\{a_n\}$ is convergent.
17. If $a_n > 0$ and $\Sigma\, a_n$ converges, then $\Sigma\, (-1)^n a_n$ converges.
18. If $a_n > 0$ and $\lim_{n\to\infty} (a_{n+1}/a_n) < 1$, then $\lim_{n\to\infty} a_n = 0$.
19. $0.99999\ldots = 1$
20. If $\displaystyle\lim_{n\to\infty} a_n = 2$, then $\displaystyle\lim_{n\to\infty} (a_{n+3} - a_n) = 0$.

Exercises

1–7 Determine whether the sequence is convergent or divergent. If it is convergent, find its limit.

1. $a_n = \dfrac{2+n^3}{1+2n^3}$
2. $a_n = \dfrac{9^{n+1}}{10^n}$
3. $a_n = \dfrac{n^3}{1+n^2}$
4. $a_n = \cos(n\pi/2)$
5. $a_n = \dfrac{n \sin n}{n^2+1}$
6. $a_n = \dfrac{\ln n}{\sqrt{n}}$
7. $\{(1 + 3/n)^{4n}\}$

8. A sequence is defined recursively by the equations $a_1 = 1$, $a_{n+1} = \frac{1}{3}(a_n + 4)$. Show that $\{a_n\}$ is increasing and $a_n < 2$ for all n. Deduce that $\{a_n\}$ is convergent and find its limit.

9–18 Determine whether the series is convergent or divergent.

9. $\displaystyle\sum_{n=1}^{\infty} \frac{n}{n^3+1}$
10. $\displaystyle\sum_{n=1}^{\infty} \frac{n^2+1}{n^3+1}$
11. $\displaystyle\sum_{n=1}^{\infty} \frac{n^3}{5^n}$
12. $\displaystyle\sum_{n=1}^{\infty} \frac{(-1)^n}{\sqrt{n+1}}$
13. $\displaystyle\sum_{n=2}^{\infty} \frac{1}{n\sqrt{\ln n}}$
14. $\displaystyle\sum_{n=1}^{\infty} \ln\left(\frac{n}{3n+1}\right)$

Graphing calculator or computer with graphing software required

15. $\displaystyle\sum_{n=1}^{\infty} (-1)^{n-1} \frac{\sqrt{n}}{n+1}$

16. $\displaystyle\sum_{n=1}^{\infty} \frac{\cos 3n}{1 + (1.2)^n}$

17. $\displaystyle\sum_{n=1}^{\infty} \frac{1 \cdot 3 \cdot 5 \cdot \cdots \cdot (2n-1)}{5^n n!}$

18. $\displaystyle\sum_{n=1}^{\infty} \frac{(-5)^{2n}}{n^2 9^n}$

19–22 Find the sum of the series.

19. $\displaystyle\sum_{n=1}^{\infty} \frac{(-3)^{n-1}}{2^{3n}}$

20. $\displaystyle\sum_{n=0}^{\infty} \frac{(-1)^n \pi^n}{3^{2n}(2n)!}$

21. $\displaystyle\sum_{n=1}^{\infty} [\tan^{-1}(n+1) - \tan^{-1} n]$

22. $1 - e + \dfrac{e^2}{2!} - \dfrac{e^3}{3!} + \dfrac{e^4}{4!} - \cdots$

23. Express the repeating decimal $1.2345345345\ldots$ as a fraction.

24. For what values of x does the series $\sum_{n=1}^{\infty} (\ln x)^n$ converge?

25. Find the sum of the series $\displaystyle\sum_{n=1}^{\infty} \frac{(-1)^{n+1}}{n^5}$ correct to four decimal places.

26. (a) Find the partial sum s_5 of the series $\sum_{n=1}^{\infty} 1/n^6$ and estimate the error in using it as an approximation to the sum of the series.
(b) Find the sum of this series correct to five decimal places.

27. Use the sum of the first eight terms to approximate the sum of the series $\sum_{n=1}^{\infty} (2 + 5^n)^{-1}$. Estimate the error involved in this approximation.

28. (a) Show that the series $\displaystyle\sum_{n=1}^{\infty} \frac{n^n}{(2n)!}$ is convergent.
(b) Deduce that $\displaystyle\lim_{n \to \infty} \frac{n^n}{(2n)!} = 0$.

29. Prove that if the series $\sum_{n=1}^{\infty} a_n$ is absolutely convergent, then the series

$$\sum_{n=1}^{\infty} \left(\frac{n+1}{n}\right) a_n$$

is also absolutely convergent.

30–33 Find the radius of convergence and interval of convergence of the series.

30. $\displaystyle\sum_{n=1}^{\infty} (-1)^n \frac{x^n}{n^2 5^n}$

31. $\displaystyle\sum_{n=1}^{\infty} \frac{(x+2)^n}{n 4^n}$

32. $\displaystyle\sum_{n=1}^{\infty} \frac{2^n (x-2)^n}{(n+2)!}$

33. $\displaystyle\sum_{n=0}^{\infty} \frac{2^n (x-3)^n}{\sqrt{n+3}}$

34. Find the radius of convergence of the series

$$\sum_{n=1}^{\infty} \frac{(2n)!}{(n!)^2} x^n$$

35. Find the Taylor series of $f(x) = \sin x$ at $a = \pi/6$.

36. Find the Taylor series of $f(x) = \cos x$ at $a = \pi/3$.

37–44 Find the Maclaurin series for f and its radius of convergence. You may use either the direct method (definition of a Maclaurin series) or known series such as geometric series, binomial series, or the Maclaurin series for e^x, $\sin x$, and $\tan^{-1}x$.

37. $f(x) = \dfrac{x^2}{1+x}$

38. $f(x) = \tan^{-1}(x^2)$

39. $f(x) = \ln(4 - x)$

40. $f(x) = xe^{2x}$

41. $f(x) = \sin(x^4)$

42. $f(x) = 10^x$

43. $f(x) = 1/\sqrt[4]{16 - x}$

44. $f(x) = (1 - 3x)^{-5}$

45. Evaluate $\displaystyle\int \frac{e^x}{x}\,dx$ as an infinite series.

46. Use series to approximate $\int_0^1 \sqrt{1 + x^4}\,dx$ correct to two decimal places.

47–48
(a) Approximate f by a Taylor polynomial with degree n at the number a.
(b) Graph f and T_n on a common screen.
(c) Use Taylor's Inequality to estimate the accuracy of the approximation $f(x) \approx T_n(x)$ when x lies in the given interval.
(d) Check your result in part (c) by graphing $|R_n(x)|$.

47. $f(x) = \sqrt{x}$, $a = 1$, $n = 3$, $0.9 \leqslant x \leqslant 1.1$

48. $f(x) = \sec x$, $a = 0$, $n = 2$, $0 \leqslant x \leqslant \pi/6$

49. Use series to evaluate the following limit.

$$\lim_{x \to 0} \frac{\sin x - x}{x^3}$$

50. The force due to gravity on an object with mass m at a height h above the surface of the earth is

$$F = \frac{mgR^2}{(R+h)^2}$$

where R is the radius of the earth and g is the acceleration due to gravity.
(a) Express F as a series in powers of h/R.
(b) Observe that if we approximate F by the first term in the series, we get the expression $F \approx mg$ that is usually used when h is much smaller than R. Use the Alternating Series Estimation Theorem to estimate the range of values of h for which the approximation $F \approx mg$ is accurate to within one percent. (Use $R = 6400$ km.)

Focus on Problem Solving

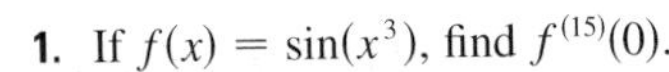

1. If $f(x) = \sin(x^3)$, find $f^{(15)}(0)$.

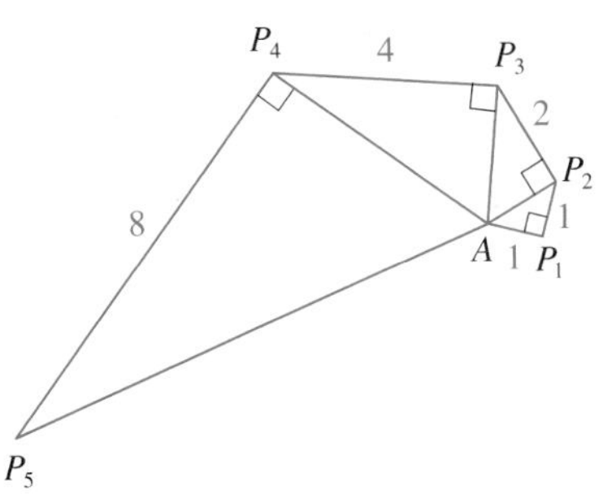

FIGURE FOR PROBLEM 2

2. Let $\{P_n\}$ be a sequence of points determined as in the figure. Thus $|AP_1| = 1$, $|P_nP_{n+1}| = 2^{n-1}$, and angle AP_nP_{n+1} is a right angle. Find $\lim_{n\to\infty} \angle P_nAP_{n+1}$.

3. To construct the **snowflake curve**, start with an equilateral triangle with sides of length 1. Step 1 in the construction is to divide each side into three equal parts, construct an equilateral triangle on the middle part, and then delete the middle part (see the figure). Step 2 is to repeat step 1 for each side of the resulting polygon. This process is repeated at each succeeding step. The snowflake curve is the curve that results from repeating this process indefinitely.

(a) Let s_n, l_n, and p_n represent the number of sides, the length of a side, and the total length of the nth approximating curve (the curve obtained after step n of the construction), respectively. Find formulas for s_n, l_n, and p_n.

(b) Show that $p_n \to \infty$ as $n \to \infty$.

(c) Sum an infinite series to find the area enclosed by the snowflake curve.

Note: Parts (b) and (c) show that the snowflake curve is infinitely long but encloses only a finite area.

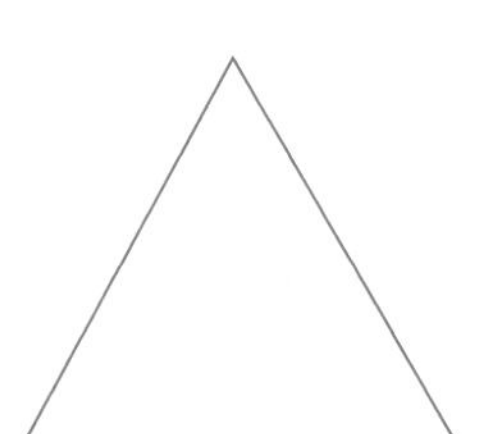

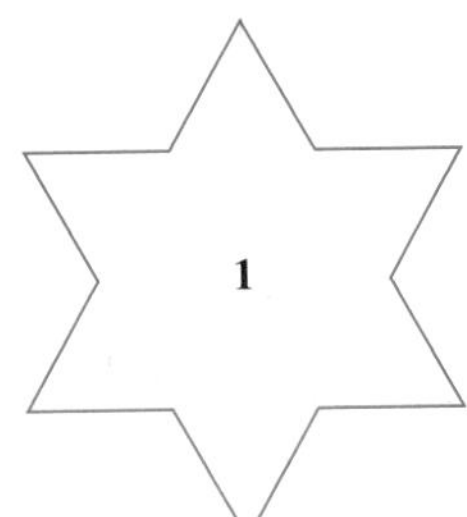

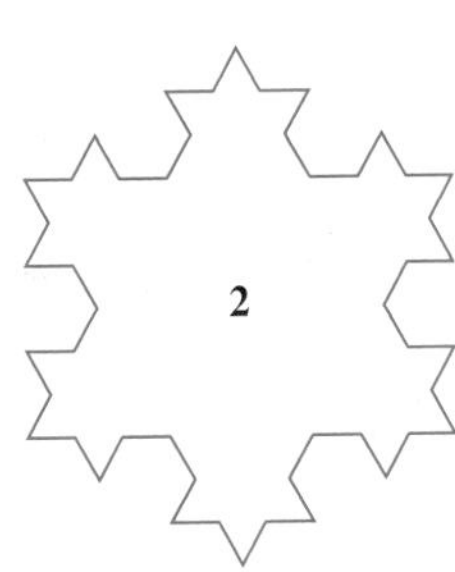

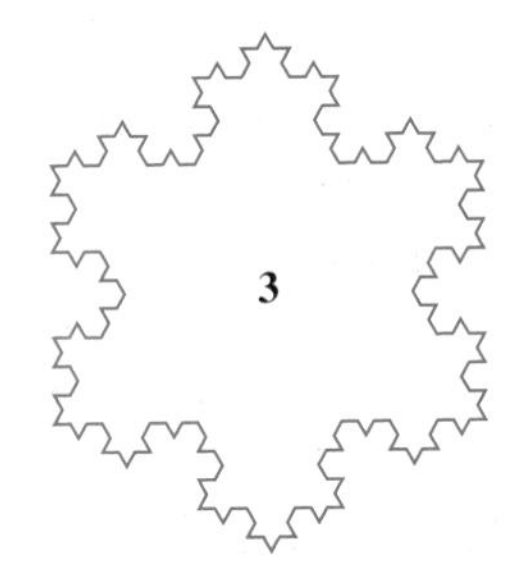

4. Find the sum of the series

$$1 + \frac{1}{2} + \frac{1}{3} + \frac{1}{4} + \frac{1}{6} + \frac{1}{8} + \frac{1}{9} + \frac{1}{12} + \cdots$$

where the terms are the reciprocals of the positive integers whose only prime factors are 2s and 3s.

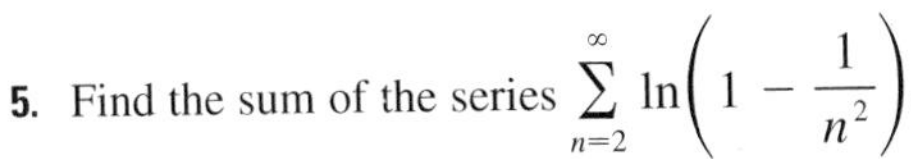

5. Find the sum of the series $\sum_{n=2}^{\infty} \ln\left(1 - \frac{1}{n^2}\right)$.

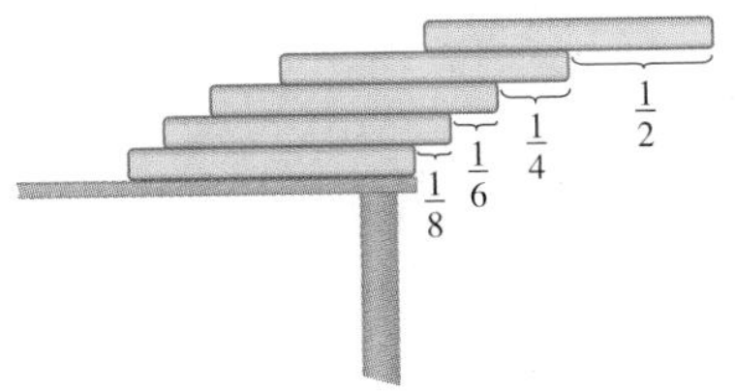

FIGURE FOR PROBLEM 6

6. Suppose you have a large supply of books, all the same size, and you stack them at the edge of a table, with each book extending farther beyond the edge of the table than the one beneath it. Show that it is possible to do this so that the top book extends entirely beyond the table. In fact, show that the top book can extend any distance at all beyond the edge of the table if the stack is high enough. Use the following method of stacking: The top book extends half its length beyond the second book. The second book extends a quarter of its length beyond the third. The third extends one-sixth of its length beyond the fourth, and so on. (Try it yourself with a deck of cards.) Consider centers of mass.

7. Let

$$u = 1 + \frac{x^3}{3!} + \frac{x^6}{6!} + \frac{x^9}{9!} + \cdots$$

$$v = x + \frac{x^4}{4!} + \frac{x^7}{7!} + \frac{x^{10}}{10!} + \cdots$$

$$w = \frac{x^2}{2!} + \frac{x^5}{5!} + \frac{x^8}{8!} + \cdots$$

Show that $u^3 + v^3 + w^3 - 3uvw = 1$.

8. If $p > 1$, evaluate the expression

$$\frac{1 + \dfrac{1}{2^p} + \dfrac{1}{3^p} + \dfrac{1}{4^p} + \cdots}{1 - \dfrac{1}{2^p} + \dfrac{1}{3^p} - \dfrac{1}{4^p} + \cdots}$$

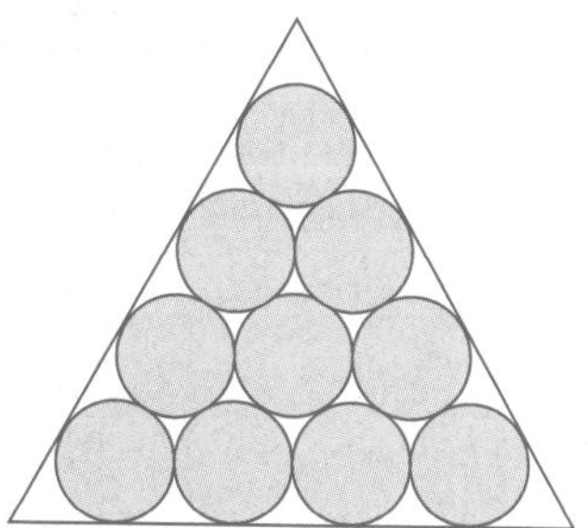

FIGURE FOR PROBLEM 9

9. Suppose that circles of equal diameter are packed tightly in n rows inside an equilateral triangle. (The figure illustrates the case $n = 4$.) If A is the area of the triangle and A_n is the total area occupied by the n rows of circles, show that

$$\lim_{n\to\infty} \frac{A_n}{A} = \frac{\pi}{2\sqrt{3}}$$

10. A sequence $\{a_n\}$ is defined recursively by the equations

$$a_0 = a_1 = 1 \qquad n(n-1)a_n = (n-1)(n-2)a_{n-1} - (n-3)a_{n-2}$$

Find the sum of the series $\Sigma_{n=0}^{\infty} a_n$.

11. Find the sum of the series $\displaystyle\sum_{n=1}^{\infty} \frac{(-1)^n}{(2n+1)3^n}$.

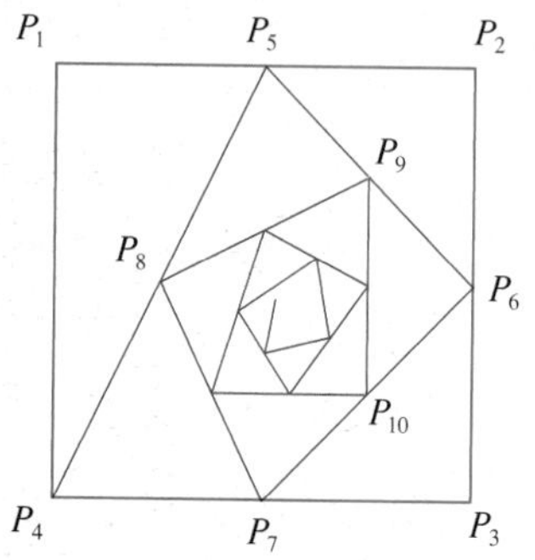

FIGURE FOR PROBLEM 12

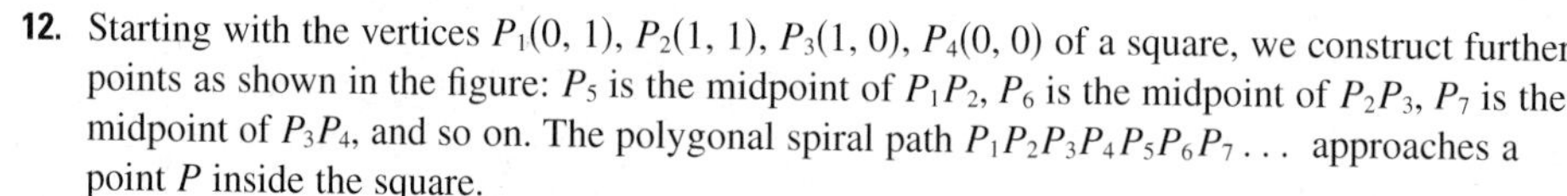

12. Starting with the vertices $P_1(0, 1)$, $P_2(1, 1)$, $P_3(1, 0)$, $P_4(0, 0)$ of a square, we construct further points as shown in the figure: P_5 is the midpoint of P_1P_2, P_6 is the midpoint of P_2P_3, P_7 is the midpoint of P_3P_4, and so on. The polygonal spiral path $P_1P_2P_3P_4P_5P_6P_7\ldots$ approaches a point P inside the square.

(a) If the coordinates of P_n are (x_n, y_n), show that $\frac{1}{2}x_n + x_{n+1} + x_{n+2} + x_{n+3} = 2$ and find a similar equation for the y-coordinates.

(b) Find the coordinates of P.

13. Find all the solutions of the equation

$$1 + \frac{x}{2!} + \frac{x^2}{4!} + \frac{x^3}{6!} + \frac{x^4}{8!} + \cdots = 0$$

Hint: Consider the cases $x \geqslant 0$ and $x < 0$ separately.

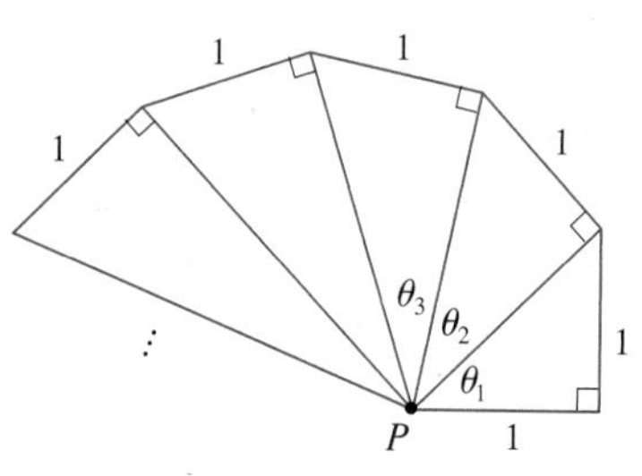

FIGURE FOR PROBLEM 14

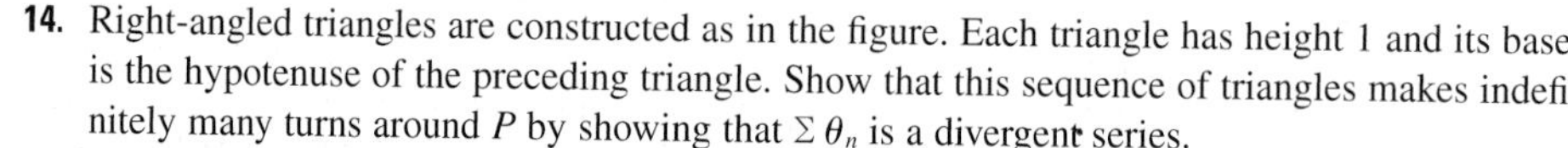

14. Right-angled triangles are constructed as in the figure. Each triangle has height 1 and its base is the hypotenuse of the preceding triangle. Show that this sequence of triangles makes indefinitely many turns around P by showing that $\Sigma\,\theta_n$ is a divergent series.

15. Consider the series whose terms are the reciprocals of the positive integers that can be written in base 10 notation without using the digit 0. Show that this series is convergent and the sum is less than 90.

16. (a) Show that the Maclaurin series of the function

$$f(x) = \frac{x}{1 - x - x^2} \qquad \text{is} \qquad \sum_{n=1}^{\infty} f_n x^n$$

where f_n is the nth Fibonacci number, that is, $f_1 = 1$, $f_2 = 1$, and $f_n = f_{n-1} + f_{n-2}$ for $n \geqslant 3$. [*Hint:* Write $x/(1 - x - x^2) = c_0 + c_1x + c_2x^2 + \cdots$ and multiply both sides of this equation by $1 - x - x^2$.]

(b) By writing $f(x)$ as a sum of partial fractions and thereby obtaining the Maclaurin series in a different way, find an explicit formula for the nth Fibonacci number.

thomasmayerarchive.com

9 Vectors and the Geometry of Space

In this chapter we introduce vectors and coordinate systems for three-dimensional space. This is the setting for the study of functions of two variables because the graph of such a function is a surface in space. Vectors provide particularly simple descriptions of lines and planes in space as well as velocities and accelerations of objects that move in space.

9.1 Three-Dimensional Coordinate Systems

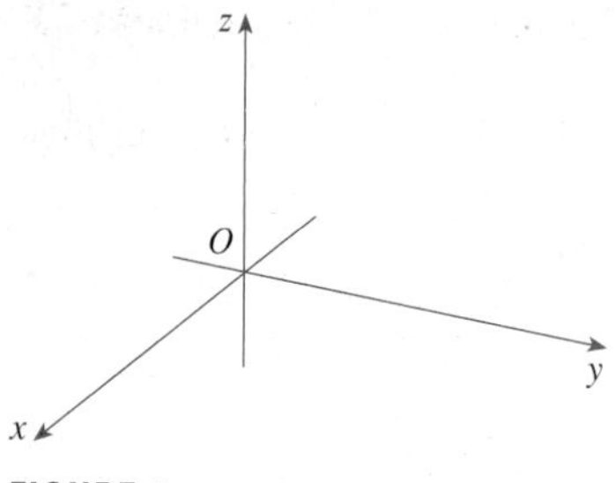

FIGURE 1
Coordinate axes

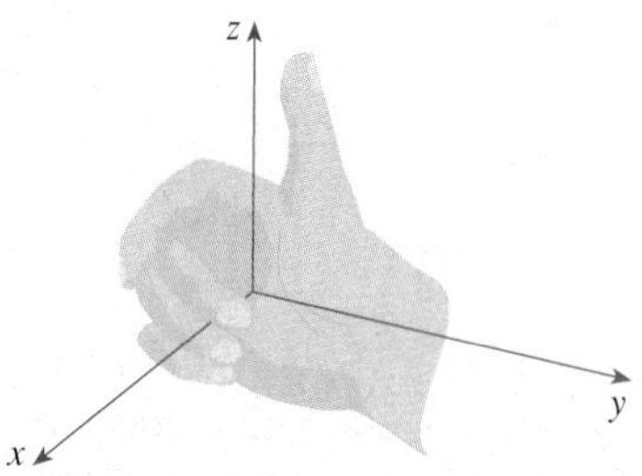

FIGURE 2
Right-hand rule

To locate a point in a plane, two numbers are necessary. We know that any point in the plane can be represented as an ordered pair (a, b) of real numbers, where a is the x-coordinate and b is the y-coordinate. For this reason, a plane is called two-dimensional. To locate a point in space, three numbers are required. We represent any point in space by an ordered triple (a, b, c) of real numbers.

In order to represent points in space, we first choose a fixed point O (the origin) and three directed lines through O that are perpendicular to each other, called the **coordinate axes** and labeled the x-axis, y-axis, and z-axis. Usually we think of the x- and y-axes as being horizontal and the z-axis as being vertical, and we draw the orientation of the axes as in Figure 1. The direction of the z-axis is determined by the **right-hand rule** as illustrated in Figure 2: If you curl the fingers of your right hand around the z-axis in the direction of a $90°$ counterclockwise rotation from the positive x-axis to the positive y-axis, then your thumb points in the positive direction of the z-axis.

The three coordinate axes determine the three **coordinate planes** illustrated in Figure 3(a). The xy-plane is the plane that contains the x- and y-axes; the yz-plane contains the y- and z-axes; the xz-plane contains the x- and z-axes. These three coordinate planes divide space into eight parts, called **octants**. The **first octant**, in the foreground, is determined by the positive axes.

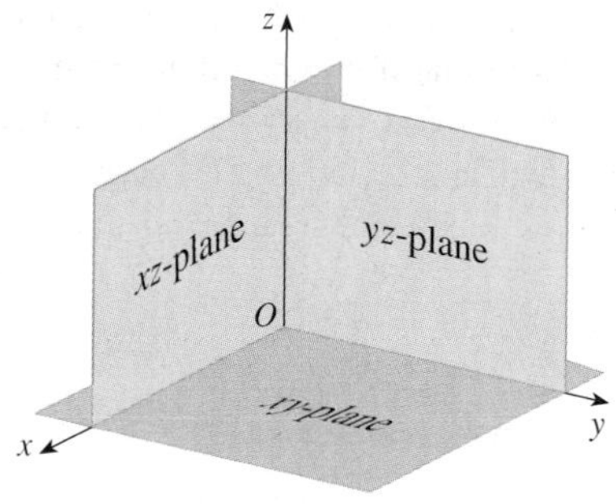

(a) Coordinate planes

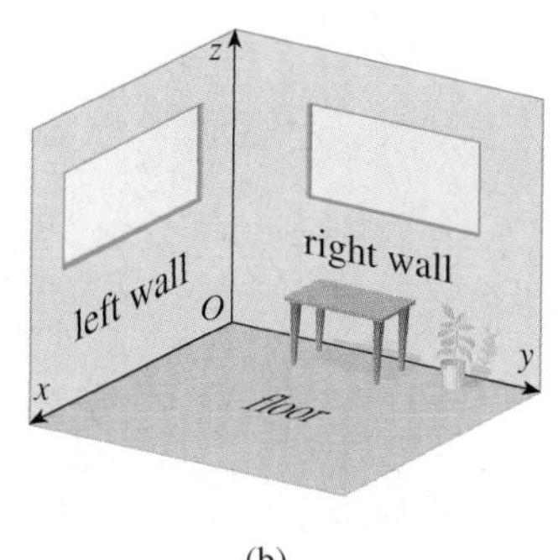

(b)

FIGURE 3

Because many people have some difficulty visualizing diagrams of three-dimensional figures, you may find it helpful to do the following [see Figure 3(b)]. Look at any bottom corner of a room and call the corner the origin. The wall on your left is in the xz-plane, the wall on your right is in the yz-plane, and the floor is in the xy-plane. The x-axis runs along the intersection of the floor and the left wall. The y-axis runs along the intersection of the floor and the right wall. The z-axis runs up from the floor toward the ceiling along the intersection of the two walls. You are situated in the first octant, and you can now imagine seven other rooms situated in the other seven octants (three on the same floor and four on the floor below), all connected by the common corner point O.

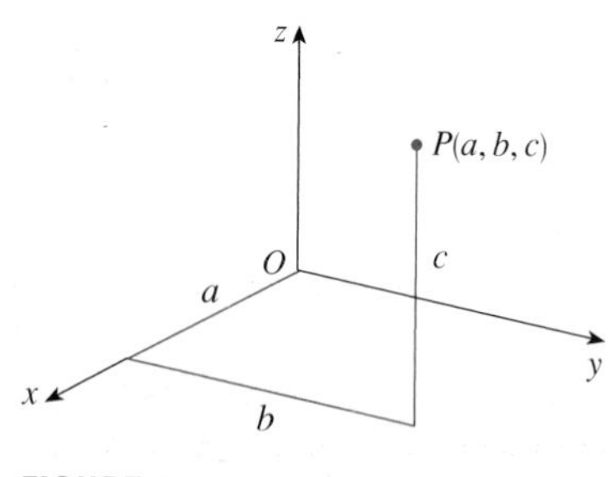

FIGURE 4

Now if P is any point in space, let a be the (directed) distance from the yz-plane to P, let b be the distance from the xz-plane to P, and let c be the distance from the xy-plane to P. We represent the point P by the ordered triple (a, b, c) of real numbers and we call a, b, and c the **coordinates** of P; a is the x-coordinate, b is the y-coordinate, and c is the z-coordinate. Thus, to locate the point (a, b, c), we can start at the origin O and move a units along the x-axis, then b units parallel to the y-axis, and then c units parallel to the z-axis as in Figure 4.

The point $P(a, b, c)$ determines a rectangular box as in Figure 5. If we drop a perpendicular from P to the xy-plane, we get a point Q with coordinates $(a, b, 0)$ called the **projection** of P onto the xy-plane. Similarly, $R(0, b, c)$ and $S(a, 0, c)$ are the projections of P onto the yz-plane and xz-plane, respectively.

As numerical illustrations, the points $(-4, 3, -5)$ and $(3, -2, -6)$ are plotted in Figure 6.

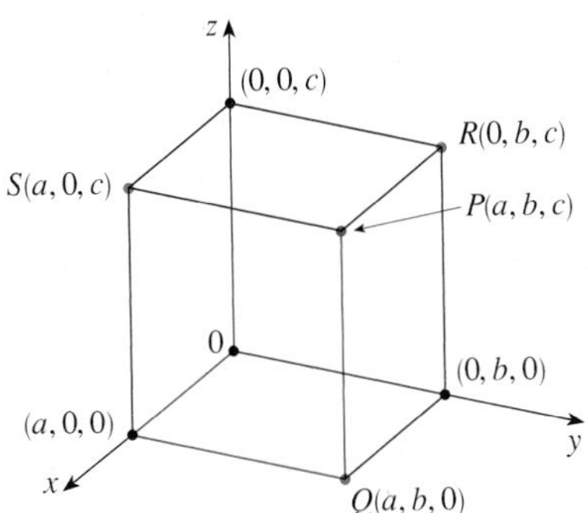

FIGURE 5

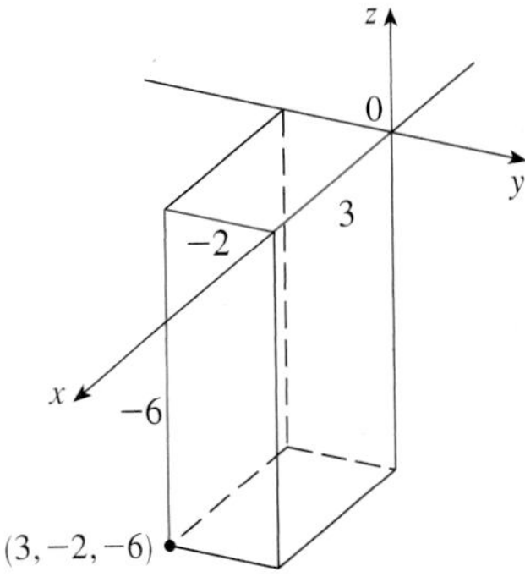

FIGURE 6

The Cartesian product $\mathbb{R} \times \mathbb{R} \times \mathbb{R} = \{(x, y, z) \mid x, y, z \in \mathbb{R}\}$ is the set of all ordered triples of real numbers and is denoted by $\mathbb{R}^3$. We have given a one-to-one correspondence between points P in space and ordered triples (a, b, c) in $\mathbb{R}^3$. It is called a **three-dimensional rectangular coordinate system**. Notice that, in terms of coordinates, the first octant can be described as the set of points whose coordinates are all positive.

In two-dimensional analytic geometry, the graph of an equation involving x and y is a curve in $\mathbb{R}^2$. In three-dimensional analytic geometry, an equation in x, y, and z represents a *surface* in $\mathbb{R}^3$.

V EXAMPLE 1 Graphing equations

What surfaces in $\mathbb{R}^3$ are represented by the following equations?

(a) $z = 3$ (b) $y = 5$

SOLUTION

(a) The equation $z = 3$ represents the set $\{(x, y, z) \mid z = 3\}$, which is the set of all points in $\mathbb{R}^3$ whose z-coordinate is 3. This is the horizontal plane that is parallel to the xy-plane and three units above it as in Figure 7(a).

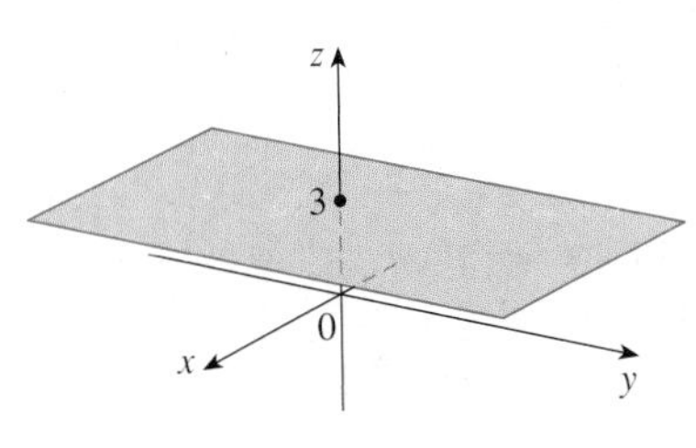

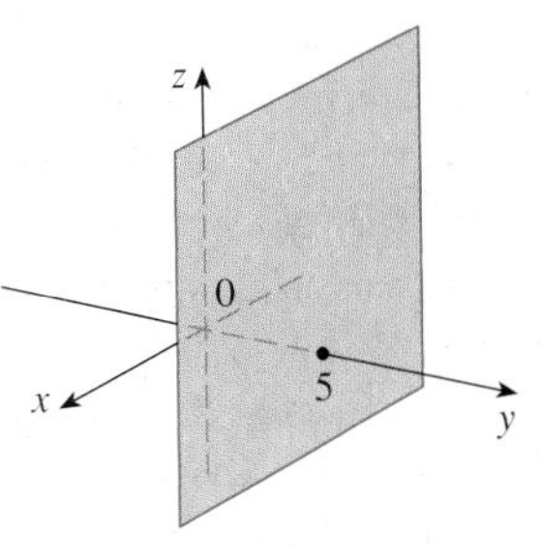

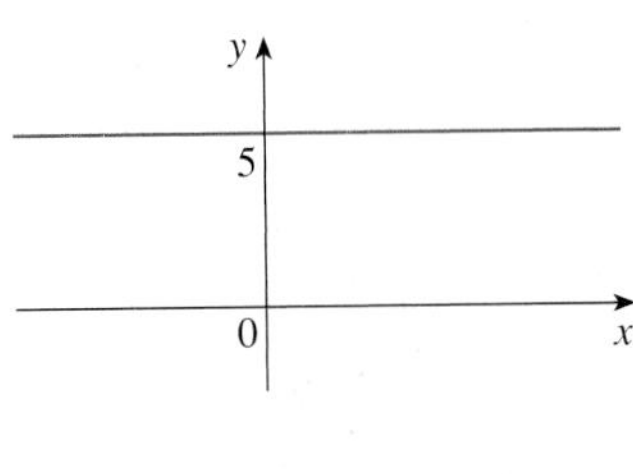

FIGURE 7 (a) $z = 3$, a plane in $\mathbb{R}^3$ (b) $y = 5$, a plane in $\mathbb{R}^3$ (c) $y = 5$, a line in $\mathbb{R}^2$

(b) The equation $y = 5$ represents the set of all points in $\mathbb{R}^3$ whose y-coordinate is 5. This is the vertical plane that is parallel to the xz-plane and five units to the right of it as in Figure 7(b).

Note: When an equation is given, we must understand from the context whether it represents a curve in $\mathbb{R}^2$ or a surface in $\mathbb{R}^3$. In Example 1, $y = 5$ represents a plane in $\mathbb{R}^3$, but of course $y = 5$ can also represent a line in $\mathbb{R}^2$ if we are dealing with two-dimensional analytic geometry. See Figure 7(b) and (c).

In general, if k is a constant, then $x = k$ represents a plane parallel to the yz-plane, $y = k$ is a plane parallel to the xz-plane, and $z = k$ is a plane parallel to the xy-plane. In Figure 5, the faces of the rectangular box are formed by the three coordinate planes $x = 0$ (the yz-plane), $y = 0$ (the xz-plane), and $z = 0$ (the xy-plane), and the planes $x = a$, $y = b$, and $z = c$.

EXAMPLE 2 Describing regions represented by equations

(a) Which points (x, y, z) satisfy the equations

$$x^2 + y^2 = 1 \qquad \text{and} \qquad z = 3$$

(b) What does the equation $x^2 + y^2 = 1$ represent as a surface in $\mathbb{R}^3$?

SOLUTION

(a) Because $z = 3$, the points lie in the horizontal plane $z = 3$ from Example 1(a). Because $x^2 + y^2 = 1$, the points lie on the circle with radius 1 and center on the z-axis. See Figure 8.

(b) Given that $x^2 + y^2 = 1$, with no restrictions on z, we see that the point (x, y, z) could lie on a circle in any horizontal plane $z = k$. So the surface $x^2 + y^2 = 1$ in $\mathbb{R}^3$ consists of all possible horizontal circles $x^2 + y^2 = 1$, $z = k$, and is therefore the circular cylinder with radius 1 whose axis is the z-axis. See Figure 9.

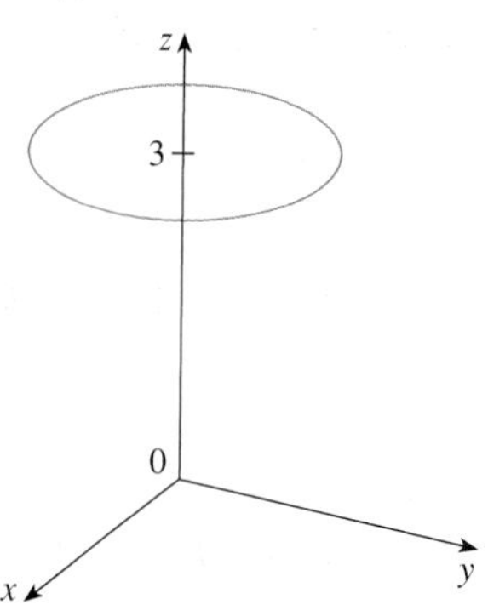

FIGURE 8
The circle $x^2 + y^2 = 1$, $z = 3$

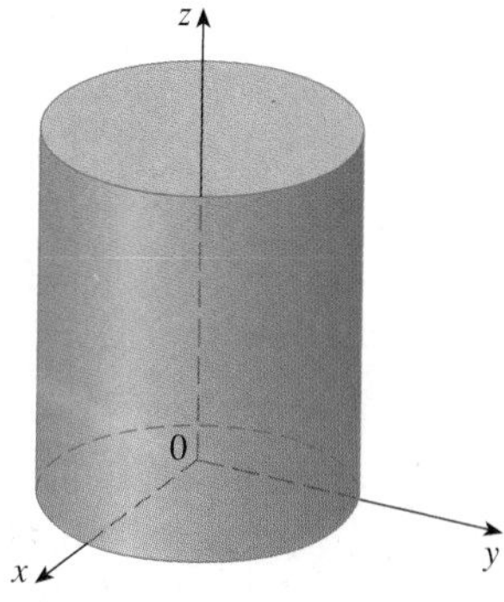

FIGURE 9
The cylinder $x^2 + y^2 = 1$

EXAMPLE 3 Describe and sketch the surface in $\mathbb{R}^3$ represented by the equation $y = x$.

SOLUTION The equation represents the set of all points in $\mathbb{R}^3$ whose x- and y-coordinates are equal, that is, $\{(x, x, z) \mid x \in \mathbb{R}, z \in \mathbb{R}\}$. This is a vertical plane that intersects the xy-plane in the line $y = x$, $z = 0$. The portion of this plane that lies in the first octant is sketched in Figure 10.

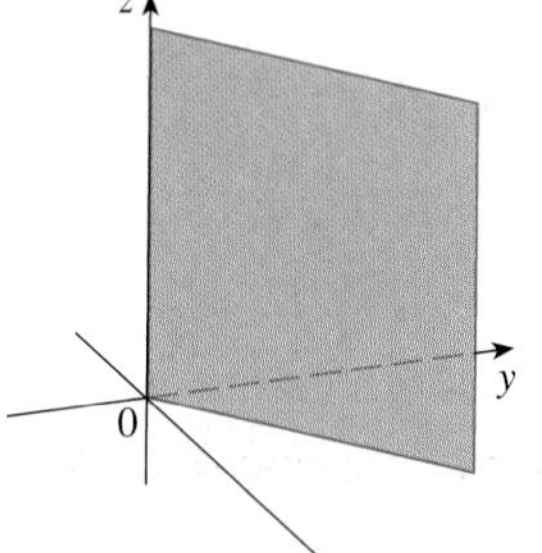

FIGURE 10
The plane $y = x$

The familiar formula for the distance between two points in a plane is easily extended to the following three-dimensional formula.

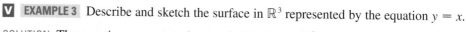

Distance Formula in Three Dimensions The distance $|P_1P_2|$ between the points $P_1(x_1, y_1, z_1)$ and $P_2(x_2, y_2, z_2)$ is

$$|P_1P_2| = \sqrt{(x_2 - x_1)^2 + (y_2 - y_1)^2 + (z_2 - z_1)^2}$$

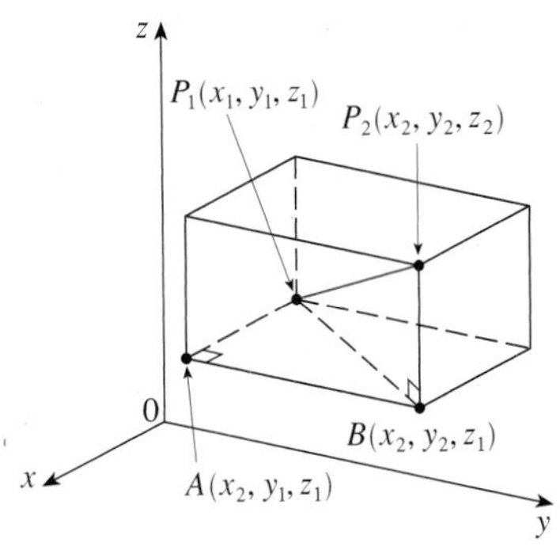

FIGURE 11

To see why this formula is true, we construct a rectangular box as in Figure 11, where P_1 and P_2 are opposite vertices and the faces of the box are parallel to the coordinate planes. If $A(x_2, y_1, z_1)$ and $B(x_2, y_2, z_1)$ are the vertices of the box indicated in the figure, then

$$|P_1A| = |x_2 - x_1| \qquad |AB| = |y_2 - y_1| \qquad |BP_2| = |z_2 - z_1|$$

Because triangles P_1BP_2 and P_1AB are both right-angled, two applications of the Pythagorean Theorem give

$$|P_1P_2|^2 = |P_1B|^2 + |BP_2|^2$$

and

$$|P_1B|^2 = |P_1A|^2 + |AB|^2$$

Combining these equations, we get

$$\begin{aligned} |P_1P_2|^2 &= |P_1A|^2 + |AB|^2 + |BP_2|^2 \\ &= |x_2 - x_1|^2 + |y_2 - y_1|^2 + |z_2 - z_1|^2 \\ &= (x_2 - x_1)^2 + (y_2 - y_1)^2 + (z_2 - z_1)^2 \end{aligned}$$

Therefore

$$|P_1P_2| = \sqrt{(x_2 - x_1)^2 + (y_2 - y_1)^2 + (z_2 - z_1)^2}$$

EXAMPLE 4 The distance from the point $P(2, -1, 7)$ to the point $Q(1, -3, 5)$ is

$$|PQ| = \sqrt{(1 - 2)^2 + (-3 + 1)^2 + (5 - 7)^2} = \sqrt{1 + 4 + 4} = 3$$

V EXAMPLE 5 Find an equation of a sphere with radius r and center $C(h, k, l)$.

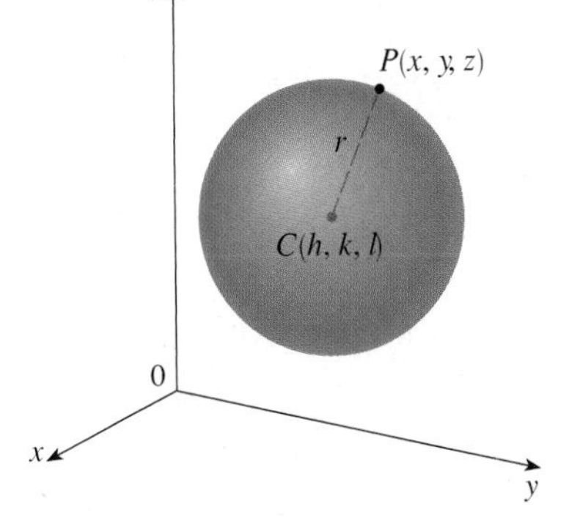

FIGURE 12

SOLUTION By definition, a sphere is the set of all points $P(x, y, z)$ whose distance from C is r. (See Figure 12.) Thus P is on the sphere if and only if $|PC| = r$. Squaring both sides, we have $|PC|^2 = r^2$ or

$$(x - h)^2 + (y - k)^2 + (z - l)^2 = r^2$$

The result of Example 5 is worth remembering.

Equation of a Sphere An equation of a sphere with center $C(h, k, l)$ and radius r is

$$(x - h)^2 + (y - k)^2 + (z - l)^2 = r^2$$

In particular, if the center is the origin O, then an equation of the sphere is

$$x^2 + y^2 + z^2 = r^2$$

EXAMPLE 6 Finding the center and radius of a sphere

Show that $x^2 + y^2 + z^2 + 4x - 6y + 2z + 6 = 0$ is the equation of a sphere, and find its center and radius.

SOLUTION We can rewrite the given equation in the form of an equation of a sphere if we complete squares:

$$\begin{aligned} (x^2 + 4x + 4) + (y^2 - 6y + 9) + (z^2 + 2z + 1) &= -6 + 4 + 9 + 1 \\ (x + 2)^2 + (y - 3)^2 + (z + 1)^2 &= 8 \end{aligned}$$

Comparing this equation with the standard form, we see that it is the equation of a sphere with center $(-2, 3, -1)$ and radius $\sqrt{8} = 2\sqrt{2}$.

EXAMPLE 7 What region in $\mathbb{R}^3$ is represented by the following inequalities?

$$1 \leqslant x^2 + y^2 + z^2 \leqslant 4 \qquad z \leqslant 0$$

SOLUTION The inequalities

$$1 \leqslant x^2 + y^2 + z^2 \leqslant 4$$

can be rewritten as

$$1 \leqslant \sqrt{x^2 + y^2 + z^2} \leqslant 2$$

so they represent the points (x, y, z) whose distance from the origin is at least 1 and at most 2. But we are also given that $z \leqslant 0$, so the points lie on or below the xy-plane. Thus the given inequalities represent the region that lies between (or on) the spheres $x^2 + y^2 + z^2 = 1$ and $x^2 + y^2 + z^2 = 4$ and beneath (or on) the xy-plane. It is sketched in Figure 13.

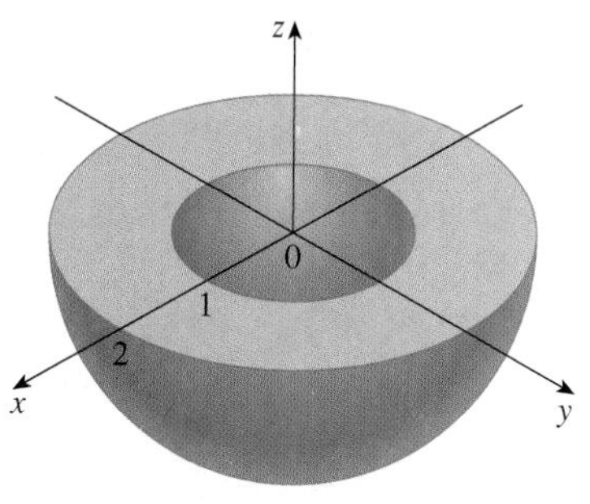

FIGURE 13

9.1 Exercises

1. Suppose you start at the origin, move along the x-axis a distance of 4 units in the positive direction, and then move downward a distance of 3 units. What are the coordinates of your position?

2. Sketch the points $(0, 5, 2)$, $(4, 0, -1)$, $(2, 4, 6)$, and $(1, -1, 2)$ on a single set of coordinate axes.

3. Which of the points $P(6, 2, 3)$, $Q(-5, -1, 4)$, and $R(0, 3, 8)$ is closest to the xz-plane? Which point lies in the yz-plane?

4. What are the projections of the point $(2, 3, 5)$ on the xy-, yz-, and xz-planes? Draw a rectangular box with the origin and $(2, 3, 5)$ as opposite vertices and with its faces parallel to the coordinate planes. Label all vertices of the box. Find the length of the diagonal of the box.

5. Describe and sketch the surface in $\mathbb{R}^3$ represented by the equation $x + y = 2$.

6. (a) What does the equation $x = 4$ represent in $\mathbb{R}^2$? What does it represent in $\mathbb{R}^3$? Illustrate with sketches.
   (b) What does the equation $y = 3$ represent in $\mathbb{R}^3$? What does $z = 5$ represent? What does the pair of equations $y = 3$, $z = 5$ represent? In other words, describe the set of points (x, y, z) such that $y = 3$ and $z = 5$. Illustrate with a sketch.

7. Find the lengths of the sides of the triangle PQR. Is it a right triangle? Is it an isosceles triangle?
   (a) $P(3, -2, -3)$, $Q(7, 0, 1)$, $R(1, 2, 1)$
   (b) $P(2, -1, 0)$, $Q(4, 1, 1)$, $R(4, -5, 4)$

8. Find the distance from $(3, 7, -5)$ to each of the following.
   (a) The xy-plane (b) The yz-plane
   (c) The xz-plane (d) The x-axis
   (e) The y-axis (f) The z-axis

9. Determine whether the points lie on straight line.
   (a) $A(2, 4, 2)$, $B(3, 7, -2)$, $C(1, 3, 3)$
   (b) $D(0, -5, 5)$, $E(1, -2, 4)$, $F(3, 4, 2)$

10. Find an equation of the sphere with center $(2, -6, 4)$ and radius 5. Describe its intersection with each of the coordinate planes.

11. Find an equation of the sphere that passes through the point $(4, 3, -1)$ and has center $(3, 8, 1)$.

12. Find an equation of the sphere that passes through the origin and whose center is $(1, 2, 3)$.

13–16 Show that the equation represents a sphere, and find its center and radius.

13. $x^2 + y^2 + z^2 - 6x + 4y - 2z = 11$

14. $x^2 + y^2 + z^2 + 8x - 6y + 2z + 17 = 0$

15. $2x^2 + 2y^2 + 2z^2 = 8x - 24z + 1$

16. $3x^2 + 3y^2 + 3z^2 = 10 + 6y + 12z$

1. Homework Hints available in TEC

17. (a) Prove that the midpoint of the line segment from $P_1(x_1, y_1, z_1)$ to $P_2(x_2, y_2, z_2)$ is

$$\left(\frac{x_1 + x_2}{2}, \frac{y_1 + y_2}{2}, \frac{z_1 + z_2}{2}\right)$$

(b) Find the lengths of the medians of the triangle with vertices $A(1, 2, 3)$, $B(-2, 0, 5)$, and $C(4, 1, 5)$.

18. Find an equation of a sphere if one of its diameters has endpoints $(2, 1, 4)$ and $(4, 3, 10)$.

19. Find equations of the spheres with center $(2, -3, 6)$ that touch (a) the xy-plane, (b) the yz-plane, (c) the xz-plane.

20. Find an equation of the largest sphere with center $(5, 4, 9)$ that is contained in the first octant.

21–32 Describe in words the region of $\mathbb{R}^3$ represented by the equations or inequalities.

21. $x = 5$

22. $y = -2$

23. $y < 8$

24. $x \geqslant -3$

25. $0 \leqslant z \leqslant 6$

26. $z^2 = 1$

27. $x^2 + y^2 = 4, \quad z = -1$

28. $y^2 + z^2 = 16$

29. $x^2 + y^2 + z^2 \leqslant 3$

30. $x = z$

31. $x^2 + z^2 \leqslant 9$

32. $x^2 + y^2 + z^2 > 2z$

33–36 Write inequalities to describe the region.

33. The region between the yz-plane and the vertical plane $x = 5$

34. The solid cylinder that lies on or below the plane $z = 8$ and on or above the disk in the xy-plane with center the origin and radius 2

35. The region consisting of all points between (but not on) the spheres of radius r and R centered at the origin, where $r < R$

36. The solid upper hemisphere of the sphere of radius 2 centered at the origin

37. The figure shows a line L_1 in space and a second line L_2, which is the projection of L_1 on the xy-plane. (In other words, the points on L_2 are directly beneath, or above, the points on L_1.)

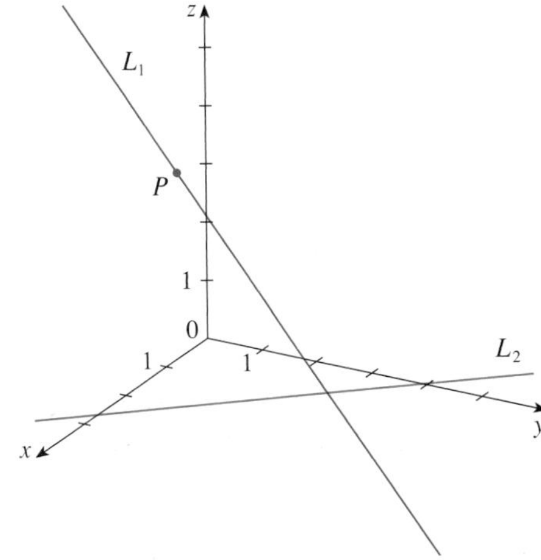

(a) Find the coordinates of the point P on the line L_1.

(b) Locate on the diagram the points A, B, and C, where the line L_1 intersects the xy-plane, the yz-plane, and the xz-plane, respectively.

38. Consider the points P such that the distance from P to $A(-1, 5, 3)$ is twice the distance from P to $B(6, 2, -2)$. Show that the set of all such points is a sphere, and find its center and radius.

39. Find an equation of the set of all points equidistant from the points $A(-1, 5, 3)$ and $B(6, 2, -2)$. Describe the set.

40. Find the volume of the solid that lies inside both of the spheres

$$x^2 + y^2 + z^2 + 4x - 2y + 4z + 5 = 0$$

and
$$x^2 + y^2 + z^2 = 4$$

41. Find the distance between the spheres $x^2 + y^2 + z^2 = 4$ and $x^2 + y^2 + z^2 = 4x + 4y + 4z - 11$.

42. Describe and sketch a solid with the following properties. When illuminated by rays parallel to the z-axis, its shadow is a circular disk. If the rays are parallel to the y-axis, its shadow is a square. If the rays are parallel to the x-axis, its shadow is an isosceles triangle.

9.2 Vectors

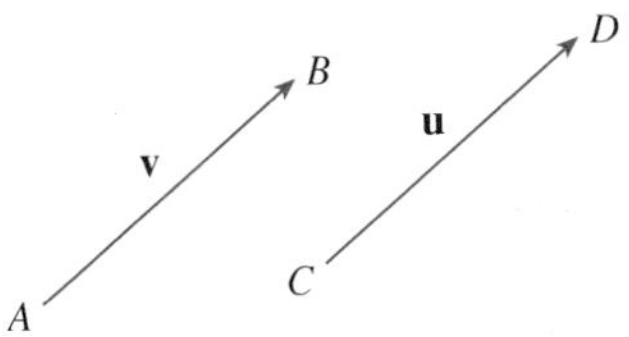

FIGURE 1
Equivalent vectors

The term **vector** is used by scientists to indicate a quantity (such as displacement or velocity or force) that has both magnitude and direction. A vector is often represented by an arrow or a directed line segment. The length of the arrow represents the magnitude of the vector and the arrow points in the direction of the vector. We denote a vector by printing a letter in boldface (**v**) or by putting an arrow above the letter ($\vec{v}$).

For instance, suppose a particle moves along a line segment from point A to point B. The corresponding **displacement vector v**, shown in Figure 1, has **initial point** A (the tail) and **terminal point** B (the tip) and we indicate this by writing $\mathbf{v} = \overrightarrow{AB}$. Notice that the vector $\mathbf{u} = \overrightarrow{CD}$ has the same length and the same direction as $\mathbf{v}$ even though it is in a different position. We say that $\mathbf{u}$ and $\mathbf{v}$ are **equivalent** (or **equal**) and we write $\mathbf{u} = \mathbf{v}$. The **zero vector**, denoted by $\mathbf{0}$, has length 0. It is the only vector with no specific direction.

Combining Vectors

C

B

A

FIGURE 2

Suppose a particle moves from A to B, so its displacement vector is $\overrightarrow{AB}$. Then the particle changes direction and moves from B to C, with displacement vector $\overrightarrow{BC}$ as in Figure 2. The combined effect of these displacements is that the particle has moved from A to C. The resulting displacement vector $\overrightarrow{AC}$ is called the *sum* of $\overrightarrow{AB}$ and $\overrightarrow{BC}$ and we write

$$\overrightarrow{AC} = \overrightarrow{AB} + \overrightarrow{BC}$$

In general, if we start with vectors $\mathbf{u}$ and $\mathbf{v}$, we first move $\mathbf{v}$ so that its tail coincides with the tip of $\mathbf{u}$ and define the sum of $\mathbf{u}$ and $\mathbf{v}$ as follows.

> **Definition of Vector Addition** If $\mathbf{u}$ and $\mathbf{v}$ are vectors positioned so the initial point of $\mathbf{v}$ is at the terminal point of $\mathbf{u}$, then the **sum** $\mathbf{u} + \mathbf{v}$ is the vector from the initial point of $\mathbf{u}$ to the terminal point of $\mathbf{v}$.

The definition of vector addition is illustrated in Figure 3. You can see why this definition is sometimes called the **Triangle Law**.

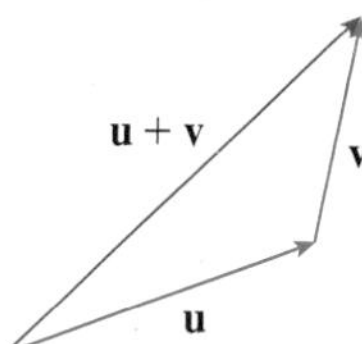

FIGURE 3 The Triangle Law

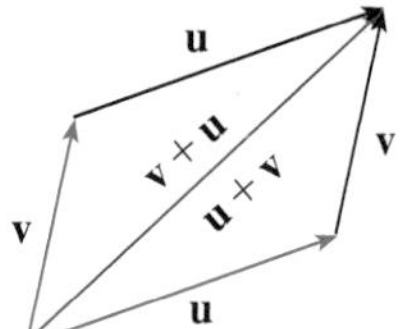

FIGURE 4 The Parallelogram Law

In Figure 4 we start with the same vectors $\mathbf{u}$ and $\mathbf{v}$ as in Figure 3 and draw another copy of $\mathbf{v}$ with the same initial point as $\mathbf{u}$. Completing the parallelogram, we see that $\mathbf{u} + \mathbf{v} = \mathbf{v} + \mathbf{u}$. This also gives another way to construct the sum: If we place $\mathbf{u}$ and $\mathbf{v}$ so they start at the same point, then $\mathbf{u} + \mathbf{v}$ lies along the diagonal of the parallelogram with $\mathbf{u}$ and $\mathbf{v}$ as sides. (This is called the **Parallelogram Law**.)

FIGURE 5

V EXAMPLE 1 Draw the sum of the vectors $\mathbf{a}$ and $\mathbf{b}$ shown in Figure 5.

SOLUTION First we translate $\mathbf{b}$ and place its tail at the tip of $\mathbf{a}$, being careful to draw a copy of $\mathbf{b}$ that has the same length and direction. Then we draw the vector $\mathbf{a} + \mathbf{b}$ [see Figure 6(a)] starting at the initial point of $\mathbf{a}$ and ending at the terminal point of the copy of $\mathbf{b}$.

Alternatively, we could place $\mathbf{b}$ so it starts where $\mathbf{a}$ starts and construct $\mathbf{a} + \mathbf{b}$ by the Parallelogram Law as in Figure 6(b).

TEC Visual 9.2 shows how the Triangle and Parallelogram Laws work for various vectors **a** and **b**.

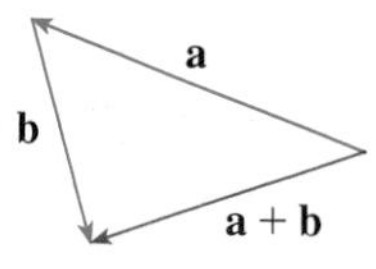

(a)

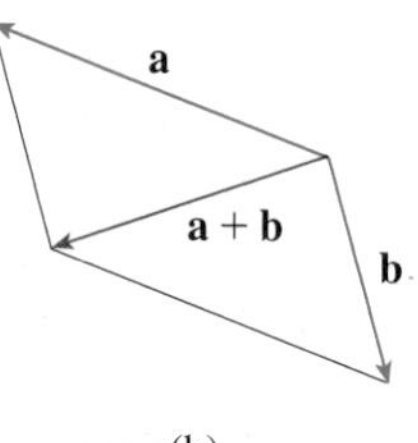

(b)

FIGURE 6

It is possible to multiply a vector by a real number c. (In this context we call the real number c a **scalar** to distinguish it from a vector.) For instance, we want $2\mathbf{v}$ to be the same vector as $\mathbf{v} + \mathbf{v}$, which has the same direction as $\mathbf{v}$ but is twice as long. In general, we multiply a vector by a scalar as follows.

> **Definition of Scalar Multiplication** If c is a scalar and $\mathbf{v}$ is a vector, then the **scalar multiple** $c\mathbf{v}$ is the vector whose length is $|c|$ times the length of $\mathbf{v}$ and whose direction is the same as $\mathbf{v}$ if $c > 0$ and is opposite to $\mathbf{v}$ if $c < 0$. If $c = 0$ or $\mathbf{v} = \mathbf{0}$, then $c\mathbf{v} = \mathbf{0}$.

v 2v $\frac{1}{2}$v

−v −1.5v

FIGURE 7
Scalar multiples of **v**

This definition is illustrated in Figure 7. We see that real numbers work like scaling factors here; that's why we call them scalars. Notice that two nonzero vectors are **parallel** if they are scalar multiples of one another. In particular, the vector $-\mathbf{v} = (-1)\mathbf{v}$ has the same length as $\mathbf{v}$ but points in the opposite direction. We call it the **negative** of $\mathbf{v}$.

By the **difference u − v** of two vectors we mean

$$\mathbf{u} - \mathbf{v} = \mathbf{u} + (-\mathbf{v})$$

So we can construct $\mathbf{u} - \mathbf{v}$ by first drawing the negative of $\mathbf{v}$, $-\mathbf{v}$, and then adding it to $\mathbf{u}$ by the Parallelogram Law as in Figure 8(a). Alternatively, since $\mathbf{v} + (\mathbf{u} - \mathbf{v}) = \mathbf{u}$, the vector $\mathbf{u} - \mathbf{v}$, when added to $\mathbf{v}$, gives $\mathbf{u}$. So we could construct $\mathbf{u} - \mathbf{v}$ as in Figure 8(b) by means of the Triangle Law.

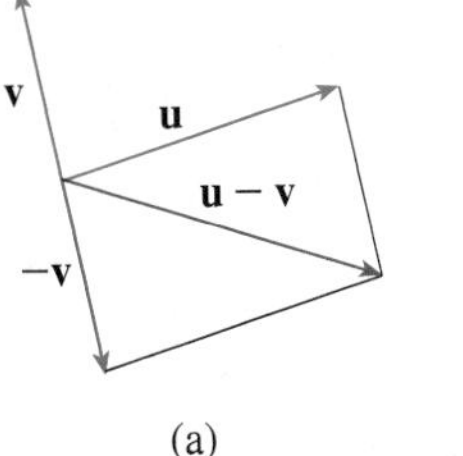

(a)

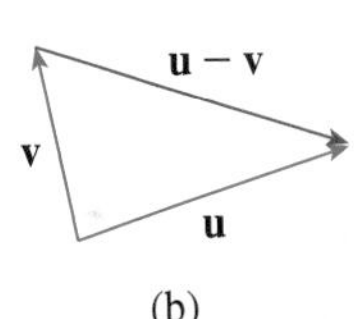

(b)

FIGURE 8
Drawing **u** − **v**

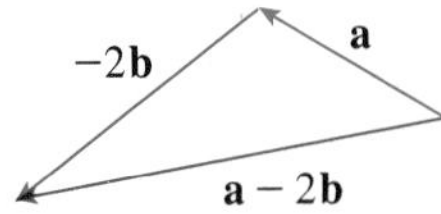

FIGURE 9

EXAMPLE 2 If **a** and **b** are the vectors shown in Figure 9, draw $\mathbf{a} - 2\mathbf{b}$.

SOLUTION We first draw the vector $-2\mathbf{b}$ pointing in the direction opposite to $\mathbf{b}$ and twice as long. We place it with its tail at the tip of $\mathbf{a}$ and then use the Triangle Law to draw $\mathbf{a} + (-2\mathbf{b})$ as in Figure 10.

−2b a
a − 2b

FIGURE 10

Components

For some purposes it's best to introduce a coordinate system and treat vectors algebraically. If we place the initial point of a vector $\mathbf{a}$ at the origin of a rectangular coordinate system, then the terminal point of $\mathbf{a}$ has coordinates of the form (a_1, a_2) or (a_1, a_2, a_3), depending on whether our coordinate system is two- or three-dimensional (see Figure 11).

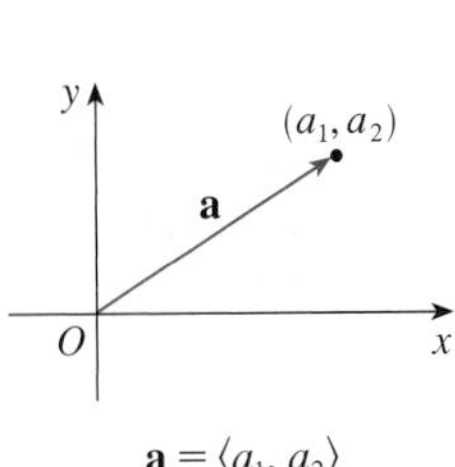

$\mathbf{a} = \langle a_1, a_2 \rangle$

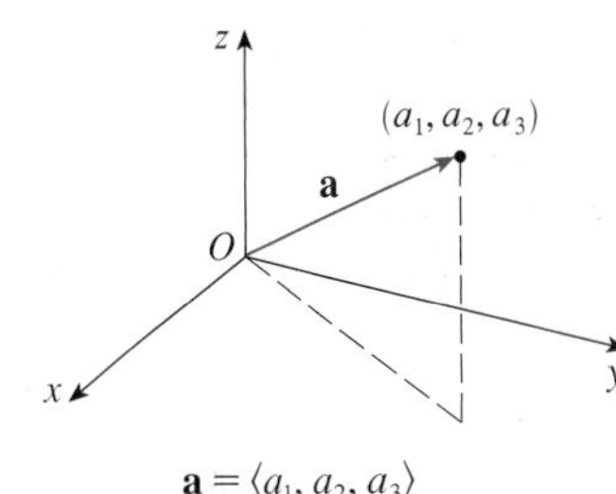

$\mathbf{a} = \langle a_1, a_2, a_3 \rangle$

FIGURE 11

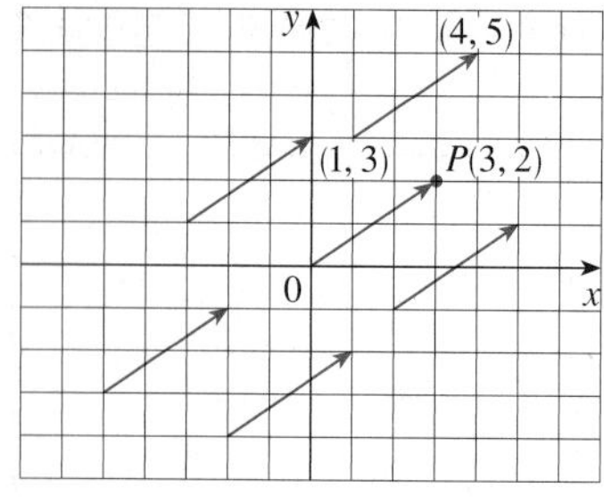

FIGURE 12
Representations of the vector $\mathbf{a} = \langle 3, 2 \rangle$

These coordinates are called the **components** of $\mathbf{a}$ and we write

$$\mathbf{a} = \langle a_1, a_2 \rangle \qquad \text{or} \qquad \mathbf{a} = \langle a_1, a_2, a_3 \rangle$$

We use the notation $\langle a_1, a_2 \rangle$ for the ordered pair that refers to a vector so as not to confuse it with the ordered pair (a_1, a_2) that refers to a point in the plane.

For instance, the vectors shown in Figure 12 are all equivalent to the vector $\overrightarrow{OP} = \langle 3, 2 \rangle$ whose terminal point is $P(3, 2)$. What they have in common is that the terminal point is reached from the initial point by a displacement of three units to the right and two upward. We can think of all these geometric vectors as **representations** of the algebraic vector $\mathbf{a} = \langle 3, 2 \rangle$. The particular representation $\overrightarrow{OP}$ from the origin to the point $P(3, 2)$ is called the **position vector** of the point P.

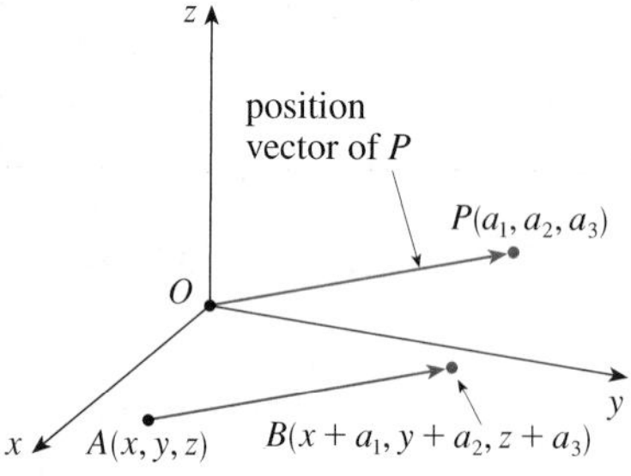

FIGURE 13
Representations of $\mathbf{a} = \langle a_1, a_2, a_3 \rangle$

In three dimensions, the vector $\mathbf{a} = \overrightarrow{OP} = \langle a_1, a_2, a_3 \rangle$ is the **position vector** of the point $P(a_1, a_2, a_3)$. (See Figure 13.) Let's consider any other representation $\overrightarrow{AB}$ of $\mathbf{a}$, where the initial point is $A(x_1, y_1, z_1)$ and the terminal point is $B(x_2, y_2, z_2)$. Then we must have $x_1 + a_1 = x_2$, $y_1 + a_2 = y_2$, and $z_1 + a_3 = z_2$ and so $a_1 = x_2 - x_1$, $a_2 = y_2 - y_1$, and $a_3 = z_2 - z_1$. Thus we have the following result.

1 Given the points $A(x_1, y_1, z_1)$ and $B(x_2, y_2, z_2)$, the vector $\mathbf{a}$ with representation $\overrightarrow{AB}$ is

$$\mathbf{a} = \langle x_2 - x_1, y_2 - y_1, z_2 - z_1 \rangle$$

V EXAMPLE 3 Representing the displacement vector from one point to another
Find the vector represented by the directed line segment with initial point $A(2, -3, 4)$ and terminal point $B(-2, 1, 1)$.

SOLUTION By (1), the vector corresponding to $\overrightarrow{AB}$ is

$$\mathbf{a} = \langle -2 - 2, 1 - (-3), 1 - 4 \rangle = \langle -4, 4, -3 \rangle$$

The **magnitude** or **length** of the vector $\mathbf{v}$ is the length of any of its representations and is denoted by the symbol $|\mathbf{v}|$ or $\|\mathbf{v}\|$. By using the distance formula to compute the length of a segment OP, we obtain the following formulas.

The length of the two-dimensional vector $\mathbf{a} = \langle a_1, a_2 \rangle$ is

$$|\mathbf{a}| = \sqrt{a_1^2 + a_2^2}$$

The length of the three-dimensional vector $\mathbf{a} = \langle a_1, a_2, a_3 \rangle$ is

$$|\mathbf{a}| = \sqrt{a_1^2 + a_2^2 + a_3^2}$$

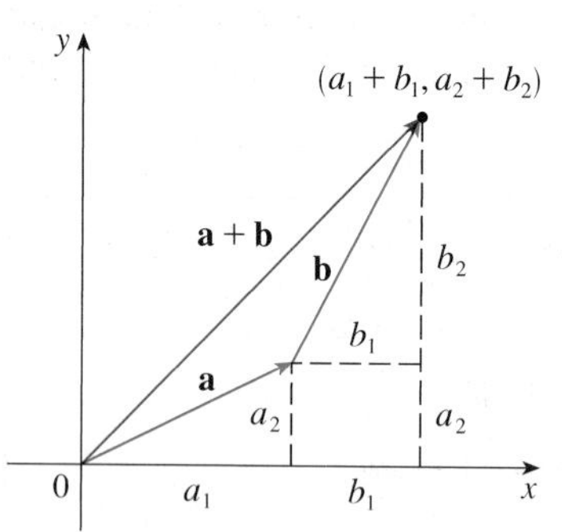

FIGURE 14

How do we add vectors algebraically? Figure 14 shows that if $\mathbf{a} = \langle a_1, a_2 \rangle$ and $\mathbf{b} = \langle b_1, b_2 \rangle$, then the sum is $\mathbf{a} + \mathbf{b} = \langle a_1 + b_1, a_2 + b_2 \rangle$, at least for the case where the components are positive. In other words, *to add algebraic vectors we add their components*. Similarly, *to subtract vectors we subtract components*. From the similar triangles in

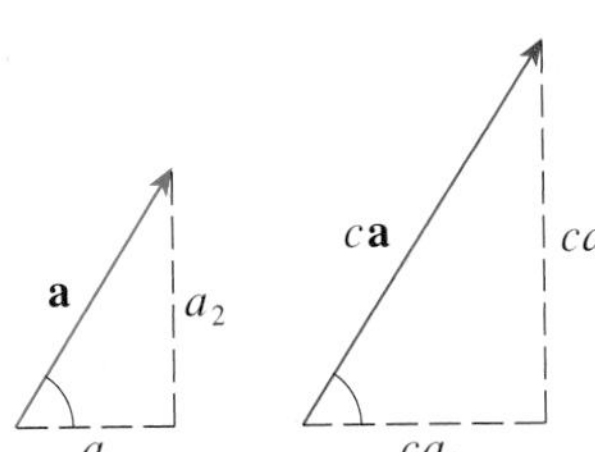

FIGURE 15

Figure 15 we see that the components of $c\mathbf{a}$ are ca_1 and ca_2. So *to multiply a vector by a scalar we multiply each component by that scalar.*

> If $\mathbf{a} = \langle a_1, a_2 \rangle$ and $\mathbf{b} = \langle b_1, b_2 \rangle$, then
>
> $$\mathbf{a} + \mathbf{b} = \langle a_1 + b_1, a_2 + b_2 \rangle \qquad \mathbf{a} - \mathbf{b} = \langle a_1 - b_1, a_2 - b_2 \rangle$$
>
> $$c\mathbf{a} = \langle ca_1, ca_2 \rangle$$
>
> Similarly, for three-dimensional vectors,
>
> $$\langle a_1, a_2, a_3 \rangle + \langle b_1, b_2, b_3 \rangle = \langle a_1 + b_1, a_2 + b_2, a_3 + b_3 \rangle$$
>
> $$\langle a_1, a_2, a_3 \rangle - \langle b_1, b_2, b_3 \rangle = \langle a_1 - b_1, a_2 - b_2, a_3 - b_3 \rangle$$
>
> $$c\langle a_1, a_2, a_3 \rangle = \langle ca_1, ca_2, ca_3 \rangle$$

V **EXAMPLE 4** **Operations on vectors** If $\mathbf{a} = \langle 4, 0, 3 \rangle$ and $\mathbf{b} = \langle -2, 1, 5 \rangle$, find $|\mathbf{a}|$ and the vectors $\mathbf{a} + \mathbf{b}$, $\mathbf{a} - \mathbf{b}$, $3\mathbf{b}$, and $2\mathbf{a} + 5\mathbf{b}$.

SOLUTION

$$|\mathbf{a}| = \sqrt{4^2 + 0^2 + 3^2} = \sqrt{25} = 5$$

$$\begin{aligned}
\mathbf{a} + \mathbf{b} &= \langle 4, 0, 3 \rangle + \langle -2, 1, 5 \rangle \\
&= \langle 4 + (-2), 0 + 1, 3 + 5 \rangle = \langle 2, 1, 8 \rangle \\
\mathbf{a} - \mathbf{b} &= \langle 4, 0, 3 \rangle - \langle -2, 1, 5 \rangle \\
&= \langle 4 - (-2), 0 - 1, 3 - 5 \rangle = \langle 6, -1, -2 \rangle \\
3\mathbf{b} &= 3\langle -2, 1, 5 \rangle = \langle 3(-2), 3(1), 3(5) \rangle = \langle -6, 3, 15 \rangle \\
2\mathbf{a} + 5\mathbf{b} &= 2\langle 4, 0, 3 \rangle + 5\langle -2, 1, 5 \rangle \\
&= \langle 8, 0, 6 \rangle + \langle -10, 5, 25 \rangle = \langle -2, 5, 31 \rangle
\end{aligned}$$

We denote by V_2 the set of all two-dimensional vectors and by V_3 the set of all three-dimensional vectors. More generally, we will later need to consider the set V_n of all n-dimensional vectors. An n-dimensional vector is an ordered n-tuple:

$$\mathbf{a} = \langle a_1, a_2, \ldots, a_n \rangle$$

where $a_1, a_2, \ldots, a_n$ are real numbers that are called the components of $\mathbf{a}$. Addition and scalar multiplication are defined in terms of components just as for the cases $n = 2$ and $n = 3$.

Vectors in n dimensions are used to list various quantities in an organized way. For instance, the components of a six-dimensional vector

$$\mathbf{p} = \langle p_1, p_2, p_3, p_4, p_5, p_6 \rangle$$

might represent the prices of six different ingredients required to make a particular product. Four-dimensional vectors $\langle x, y, z, t \rangle$ are used in relativity theory, where the first three components specify a position in space and the fourth represents time.

> **Properties of Vectors** If $\mathbf{a}$, $\mathbf{b}$, and $\mathbf{c}$ are vectors in V_n and c and d are scalars, then
>
> 1. $\mathbf{a} + \mathbf{b} = \mathbf{b} + \mathbf{a}$
> 2. $\mathbf{a} + (\mathbf{b} + \mathbf{c}) = (\mathbf{a} + \mathbf{b}) + \mathbf{c}$
> 3. $\mathbf{a} + \mathbf{0} = \mathbf{a}$
> 4. $\mathbf{a} + (-\mathbf{a}) = \mathbf{0}$
> 5. $c(\mathbf{a} + \mathbf{b}) = c\mathbf{a} + c\mathbf{b}$
> 6. $(c + d)\mathbf{a} = c\mathbf{a} + d\mathbf{a}$
> 7. $(cd)\mathbf{a} = c(d\mathbf{a})$
> 8. $1\mathbf{a} = \mathbf{a}$

These eight properties of vectors can be readily verified either geometrically or algebraically. For instance, Property 1 can be seen from Figure 4 (it's equivalent to the Parallelogram Law) or as follows for the case $n = 2$:

$$\begin{aligned} \mathbf{a} + \mathbf{b} &= \langle a_1, a_2 \rangle + \langle b_1, b_2 \rangle = \langle a_1 + b_1, a_2 + b_2 \rangle \\ &= \langle b_1 + a_1, b_2 + a_2 \rangle = \langle b_1, b_2 \rangle + \langle a_1, a_2 \rangle \\ &= \mathbf{b} + \mathbf{a} \end{aligned}$$

Q
c
(a + b) + c
= a + (b + c)
a + b
b
b + c
P
a

FIGURE 16

We can see why Property 2 (the associative law) is true by looking at Figure 16 and applying the Triangle Law several times: The vector $\overrightarrow{PQ}$ is obtained either by first constructing $\mathbf{a} + \mathbf{b}$ and then adding $\mathbf{c}$ or by adding $\mathbf{a}$ to the vector $\mathbf{b} + \mathbf{c}$.

Three vectors in V_3 play a special role. Let

$$\mathbf{i} = \langle 1, 0, 0 \rangle \qquad \mathbf{j} = \langle 0, 1, 0 \rangle \qquad \mathbf{k} = \langle 0, 0, 1 \rangle$$

Then $\mathbf{i}$, $\mathbf{j}$, and $\mathbf{k}$ are vectors that have length 1 and point in the directions of the positive x-, y-, and z-axes. Similarly, in two dimensions we define $\mathbf{i} = \langle 1, 0 \rangle$ and $\mathbf{j} = \langle 0, 1 \rangle$. (See Figure 17.)

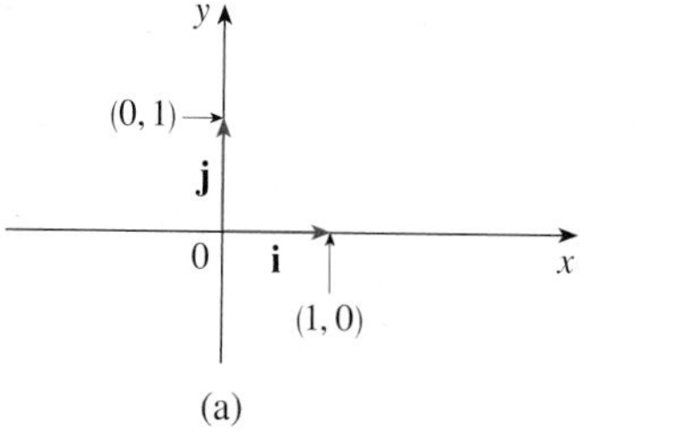

(a)

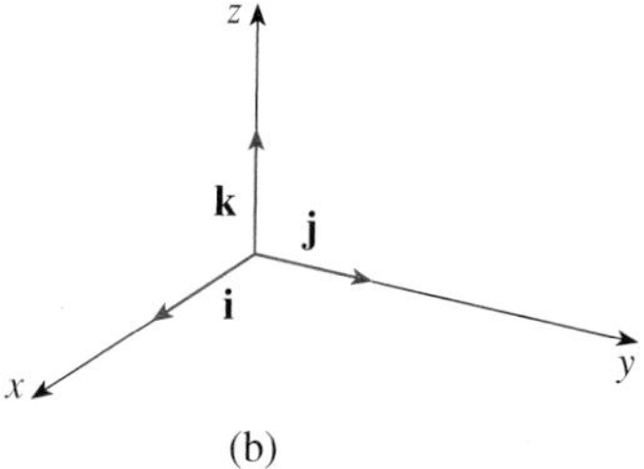

(b)

FIGURE 17
Standard basis vectors in V_2 and V_3

If $\mathbf{a} = \langle a_1, a_2, a_3 \rangle$, then we can write

$$\begin{aligned} \mathbf{a} &= \langle a_1, a_2, a_3 \rangle = \langle a_1, 0, 0 \rangle + \langle 0, a_2, 0 \rangle + \langle 0, 0, a_3 \rangle \\ &= a_1 \langle 1, 0, 0 \rangle + a_2 \langle 0, 1, 0 \rangle + a_3 \langle 0, 0, 1 \rangle \end{aligned}$$

2 $$\mathbf{a} = a_1 \mathbf{i} + a_2 \mathbf{j} + a_3 \mathbf{k}$$

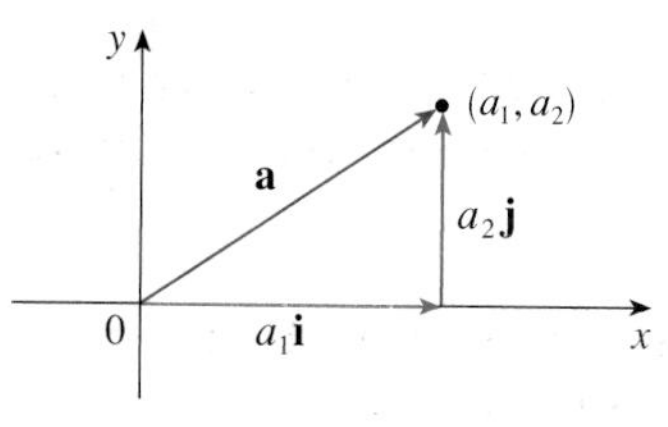

(a) $\mathbf{a} = a_1\mathbf{i} + a_2\mathbf{j}$

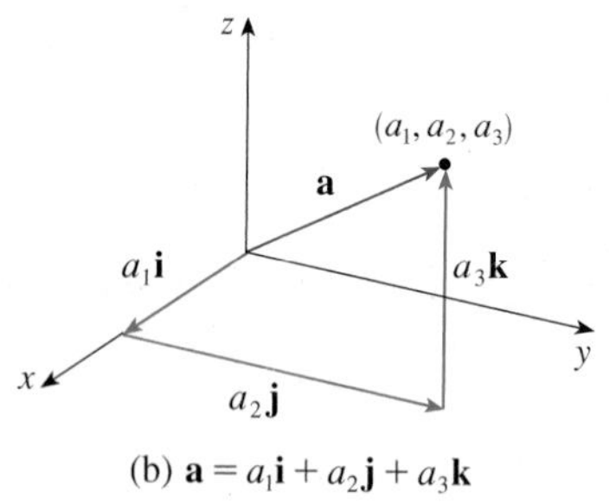

(b) $\mathbf{a} = a_1\mathbf{i} + a_2\mathbf{j} + a_3\mathbf{k}$

FIGURE 18

Thus any vector in V_3 can be expressed in terms of the **standard basis vectors $\mathbf{i}$, $\mathbf{j}$, and $\mathbf{k}$**. For instance,

$$\langle 1, -2, 6 \rangle = \mathbf{i} - 2\mathbf{j} + 6\mathbf{k}$$

Similarly, in two dimensions, we can write

3 $$\mathbf{a} = \langle a_1, a_2 \rangle = a_1 \mathbf{i} + a_2 \mathbf{j}$$

See Figure 18 for the geometric interpretation of Equations 3 and 2 and compare with Figure 17.

EXAMPLE 5 If $\mathbf{a} = \mathbf{i} + 2\mathbf{j} - 3\mathbf{k}$ and $\mathbf{b} = 4\mathbf{i} + 7\mathbf{k}$, express the vector $2\mathbf{a} + 3\mathbf{b}$ in terms of $\mathbf{i}$, $\mathbf{j}$, and $\mathbf{k}$.

SOLUTION Using Properties 1, 2, 5, 6, and 7 of vectors, we have

$$\begin{aligned} 2\mathbf{a} + 3\mathbf{b} &= 2(\mathbf{i} + 2\mathbf{j} - 3\mathbf{k}) + 3(4\mathbf{i} + 7\mathbf{k}) \\ &= 2\mathbf{i} + 4\mathbf{j} - 6\mathbf{k} + 12\mathbf{i} + 21\mathbf{k} = 14\mathbf{i} + 4\mathbf{j} + 15\mathbf{k} \end{aligned}$$

A **unit vector** is a vector whose length is 1. For instance, $\mathbf{i}$, $\mathbf{j}$, and $\mathbf{k}$ are all unit vectors. In general, if $\mathbf{a} \neq \mathbf{0}$, then the unit vector that has the same direction as $\mathbf{a}$ is

4
$$\mathbf{u} = \frac{1}{|\mathbf{a}|}\mathbf{a} = \frac{\mathbf{a}}{|\mathbf{a}|}$$

In order to verify this, we let $c = 1/|\mathbf{a}|$. Then $\mathbf{u} = c\mathbf{a}$ and c is a positive scalar, so $\mathbf{u}$ has the same direction as $\mathbf{a}$. Also

$$|\mathbf{u}| = |c\mathbf{a}| = |c||\mathbf{a}| = \frac{1}{|\mathbf{a}|}|\mathbf{a}| = 1$$

EXAMPLE 6 Find the unit vector in the direction of the vector $2\mathbf{i} - \mathbf{j} - 2\mathbf{k}$.

SOLUTION The given vector has length

$$|2\mathbf{i} - \mathbf{j} - 2\mathbf{k}| = \sqrt{2^2 + (-1)^2 + (-2)^2} = \sqrt{9} = 3$$

so, by Equation 4, the unit vector with the same direction is

$$\tfrac{1}{3}(2\mathbf{i} - \mathbf{j} - 2\mathbf{k}) = \tfrac{2}{3}\mathbf{i} - \tfrac{1}{3}\mathbf{j} - \tfrac{2}{3}\mathbf{k}$$

Applications

Vectors are useful in many aspects of physics and engineering. In Chapter 10 we will see how they describe the velocity and acceleration of objects moving in space. Here we look at forces.

A force is represented by a vector because it has both a magnitude (measured in pounds or newtons) and a direction. If several forces are acting on an object, the **resultant force** experienced by the object is the vector sum of these forces.

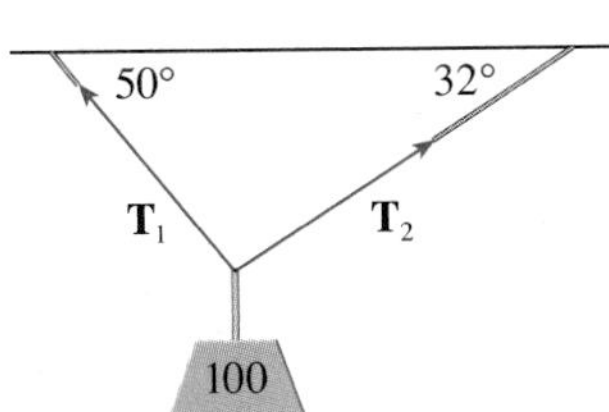

FIGURE 19

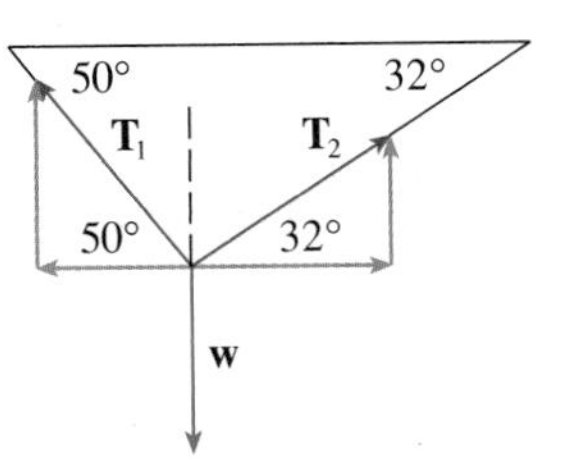

FIGURE 20

EXAMPLE 7 A 100-lb weight hangs from two wires as shown in Figure 19. Find the tensions (forces) $\mathbf{T}_1$ and $\mathbf{T}_2$ in both wires and the magnitudes of the tensions.

SOLUTION We first express $\mathbf{T}_1$ and $\mathbf{T}_2$ in terms of their horizontal and vertical components. From Figure 20 we see that

5
$$\mathbf{T}_1 = -|\mathbf{T}_1|\cos 50°\,\mathbf{i} + |\mathbf{T}_1|\sin 50°\,\mathbf{j}$$

6
$$\mathbf{T}_2 = |\mathbf{T}_2|\cos 32°\,\mathbf{i} + |\mathbf{T}_2|\sin 32°\,\mathbf{j}$$

The resultant $\mathbf{T}_1 + \mathbf{T}_2$ of the tensions counterbalances the weight $\mathbf{w}$ and so we must have

$$\mathbf{T}_1 + \mathbf{T}_2 = -\mathbf{w} = 100\mathbf{j}$$

Thus

$$\left(-|\mathbf{T}_1|\cos 50° + |\mathbf{T}_2|\cos 32°\right)\mathbf{i} + \left(|\mathbf{T}_1|\sin 50° + |\mathbf{T}_2|\sin 32°\right)\mathbf{j} = 100\mathbf{j}$$

Equating components, we get

$$-|\mathbf{T}_1|\cos 50^\circ + |\mathbf{T}_2|\cos 32^\circ = 0$$

$$|\mathbf{T}_1|\sin 50^\circ + |\mathbf{T}_2|\sin 32^\circ = 100$$

Solving the first of these equations for $|\mathbf{T}_2|$ and substituting into the second, we get

$$|\mathbf{T}_1|\sin 50^\circ + \frac{|\mathbf{T}_1|\cos 50^\circ}{\cos 32^\circ}\sin 32^\circ = 100$$

So the magnitudes of the tensions are

$$|\mathbf{T}_1| = \frac{100}{\sin 50^\circ + \tan 32^\circ \cos 50^\circ} \approx 85.64 \text{ lb}$$

and $$|\mathbf{T}_2| = \frac{|\mathbf{T}_1|\cos 50^\circ}{\cos 32^\circ} \approx 64.91 \text{ lb}$$

Substituting these values in (5) and (6), we obtain the tension vectors

$$\mathbf{T}_1 \approx -55.05\,\mathbf{i} + 65.60\,\mathbf{j} \qquad \mathbf{T}_2 \approx 55.05\,\mathbf{i} + 34.40\,\mathbf{j}$$

9.2 Exercises

1. Are the following quantities vectors or scalars? Explain.
   (a) The cost of a theater ticket
   (b) The current in a river
   (c) The initial flight path from Houston to Dallas
   (d) The population of the world

2. What is the relationship between the point (4, 7) and the vector $\langle 4, 7\rangle$? Illustrate with a sketch.

3. Name all the equal vectors in the parallelogram shown.

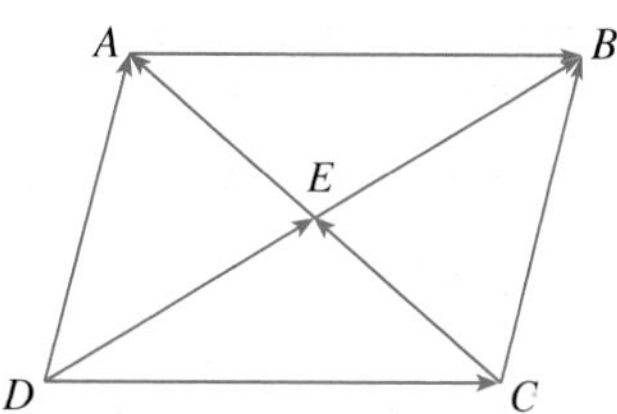

4. Write each combination of vectors as a single vector.
   (a) $\overrightarrow{PQ} + \overrightarrow{QR}$ (b) $\overrightarrow{RP} + \overrightarrow{PS}$
   (c) $\overrightarrow{QS} - \overrightarrow{PS}$ (d) $\overrightarrow{RS} + \overrightarrow{SP} + \overrightarrow{PQ}$

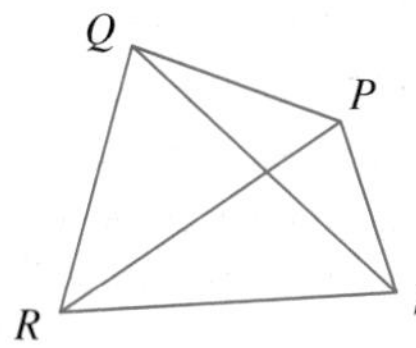

5. Copy the vectors in the figure and use them to draw the following vectors.
   (a) $\mathbf{u} + \mathbf{v}$ (b) $\mathbf{u} - \mathbf{v}$
   (c) $\mathbf{v} + \mathbf{w}$ (d) $\mathbf{w} + \mathbf{v} + \mathbf{u}$

6. Copy the vectors in the figure and use them to draw the following vectors.
   (a) $\mathbf{a} + \mathbf{b}$ (b) $\mathbf{a} - \mathbf{b}$
   (c) $\frac{1}{2}\mathbf{a}$ (d) $-3\mathbf{b}$
   (e) $\mathbf{a} + 2\mathbf{b}$ (f) $2\mathbf{b} - \mathbf{a}$

7–10 Find a vector $\mathbf{a}$ with representation given by the directed line segment $\overrightarrow{AB}$. Draw $\overrightarrow{AB}$ and the equivalent representation starting at the origin.

7. $A(-1, 3)$, $B(2, 2)$
8. $A(2, 1)$, $B(0, 6)$
9. $A(0, 3, 1)$, $B(2, 3, -1)$
10. $A(4, 0, -2)$, $B(4, 2, 1)$

1. Homework Hints available in TEC

11–14 Find the sum of the given vectors and illustrate geometrically.

11. $\langle -1, 4 \rangle$, $\langle 6, -2 \rangle$

12. $\langle -2, -1 \rangle$, $\langle 5, 7 \rangle$

13. $\langle 0, 1, 2 \rangle$, $\langle 0, 0, -3 \rangle$

14. $\langle -1, 0, 2 \rangle$, $\langle 0, 4, 0 \rangle$

15–18 Find $\mathbf{a} + \mathbf{b}$, $2\mathbf{a} + 3\mathbf{b}$, $|\mathbf{a}|$, and $|\mathbf{a} - \mathbf{b}|$.

15. $\mathbf{a} = \langle 5, -12 \rangle$, $\mathbf{b} = \langle -3, -6 \rangle$

16. $\mathbf{a} = 4\,\mathbf{i} + \mathbf{j}$, $\mathbf{b} = \mathbf{i} - 2\,\mathbf{j}$

17. $\mathbf{a} = \mathbf{i} + 2\,\mathbf{j} - 3\,\mathbf{k}$, $\mathbf{b} = -2\,\mathbf{i} - \mathbf{j} + 5\,\mathbf{k}$

18. $\mathbf{a} = 2\,\mathbf{i} - 4\,\mathbf{j} + 4\,\mathbf{k}$, $\mathbf{b} = 2\,\mathbf{j} - \mathbf{k}$

19–21 Find a unit vector that has the same direction as the given vector.

19. $-3\,\mathbf{i} + 7\,\mathbf{j}$

20. $\langle -4, 2, 4 \rangle$

21. $8\,\mathbf{i} - \mathbf{j} + 4\,\mathbf{k}$

---

22. Find a vector that has the same direction as $\langle -2, 4, 2 \rangle$ but has length 6.

23. If $\mathbf{v}$ lies in the first quadrant and makes an angle $\pi/3$ with the positive x-axis and $|\mathbf{v}| = 4$, find $\mathbf{v}$ in component form.

24. If a child pulls a sled through the snow on a level path with a force of 50 N exerted at an angle of 38° above the horizontal, find the horizontal and vertical components of the force.

25. A quarterback throws a football with angle of elevation 40° and speed 60 ft/s. Find the horizontal and vertical components of the velocity vector.

26–27 Find the magnitude of the resultant force and the angle it makes with the positive x-axis.

26.

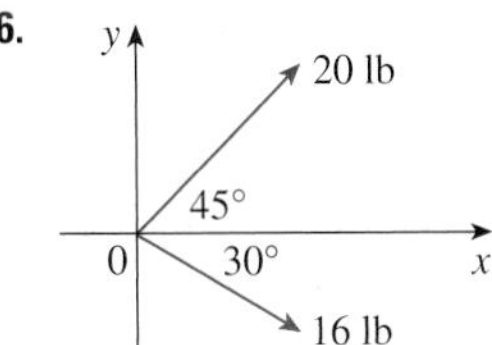

27.

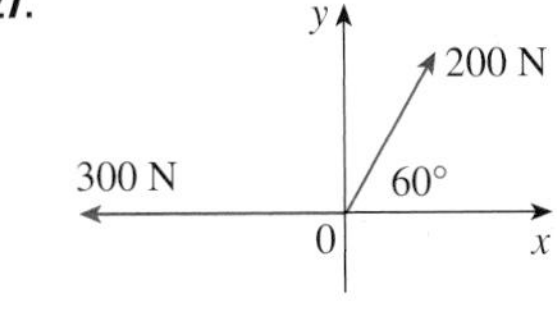

---

28. The magnitude of a velocity vector is called *speed.* Suppose that a wind is blowing from the direction N45°W at a speed of 50 km/h. (This means that the direction from which the wind blows is 45° west of the northerly direction.) A pilot is steering a plane in the direction N60°E at an airspeed (speed in still air) of 250 km/h. The *true course,* or *track,* of the plane is the direction of the resultant of the velocity vectors of the plane and the wind. The *ground speed* of the plane is the magnitude of the resultant. Find the true course and the ground speed of the plane.

29. A woman walks due west on the deck of a ship at 3 mi/h. The ship is moving north at a speed of 22 mi/h. Find the speed and direction of the woman relative to the surface of the water.

30. Ropes 3 m and 5 m in length are fastened to a holiday decoration that is suspended over a town square. The decoration has a mass of 5 kg. The ropes, fastened at different heights, make angles of 52° and 40° with the horizontal. Find the tension in each wire and the magnitude of each tension.

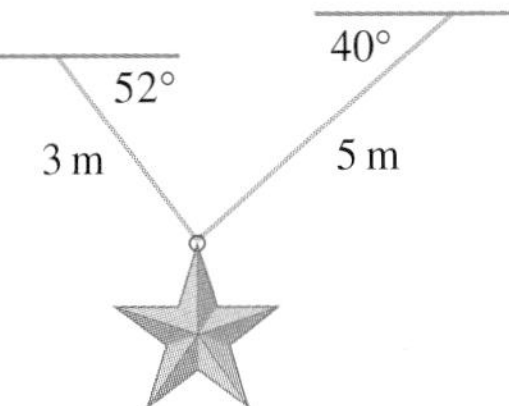

31. A clothesline is tied between two poles, 8 m apart. The line is quite taut and has negligible sag. When a wet shirt with a mass of 0.8 kg is hung at the middle of the line, the midpoint is pulled down 8 cm. Find the tension in each half of the clothesline.

32. The tension $\mathbf{T}$ at each end of the chain has magnitude 25 N (see the figure). What is the weight of the chain?

33. Find the unit vectors that are parallel to the tangent line to the parabola $y = x^2$ at the point (2, 4).

34. (a) Find the unit vectors that are parallel to the tangent line to the curve $y = 2 \sin x$ at the point $(\pi/6, 1)$.
(b) Find the unit vectors that are perpendicular to the tangent line.
(c) Sketch the curve $y = 2 \sin x$ and the vectors in parts (a) and (b), all starting at $(\pi/6, 1)$.

35. (a) Draw the vectors $\mathbf{a} = \langle 3, 2 \rangle$, $\mathbf{b} = \langle 2, -1 \rangle$, and $\mathbf{c} = \langle 7, 1 \rangle$.
(b) Show, by means of a sketch, that there are scalars s and t such that $\mathbf{c} = s\mathbf{a} + t\mathbf{b}$.
(c) Use the sketch to estimate the values of s and t.
(d) Find the exact values of s and t.

36. Suppose that $\mathbf{a}$ and $\mathbf{b}$ are nonzero vectors that are not parallel and $\mathbf{c}$ is any vector in the plane determined by $\mathbf{a}$ and $\mathbf{b}$. Give a geometric argument to show that $\mathbf{c}$ can be written as $\mathbf{c} = s\mathbf{a} + t\mathbf{b}$ for suitable scalars s and t. Then give an argument using components.

37. Suppose $\mathbf{a}$ is a three-dimensional unit vector in the first octant that starts at the origin and makes angles of 60° and 72° with the positive x- and y-axes, respectively. Express $\mathbf{a}$ in terms of its components.

38. Suppose a vector **a** makes angles α, β, and γ with the positive x-, y-, and z-axes, respectively. Find the components of **a** and show that

$$\cos^2\alpha + \cos^2\beta + \cos^2\gamma = 1$$

(The numbers $\cos\alpha$, $\cos\beta$, and $\cos\gamma$ are called the *direction cosines* of **a**.)

39. If $\mathbf{r} = \langle x, y, z\rangle$ and $\mathbf{r}_0 = \langle x_0, y_0, z_0\rangle$, describe the set of all points (x, y, z) such that $|\mathbf{r} - \mathbf{r}_0| = 1$.

40. If $\mathbf{r} = \langle x, y\rangle$, $\mathbf{r}_1 = \langle x_1, y_1\rangle$, and $\mathbf{r}_2 = \langle x_2, y_2\rangle$, describe the set of all points (x, y) such that $|\mathbf{r} - \mathbf{r}_1| + |\mathbf{r} - \mathbf{r}_2| = k$, where $k > |\mathbf{r}_1 - \mathbf{r}_2|$.

41. Figure 16 gives a geometric demonstration of Property 2 of vectors. Use components to give an algebraic proof of this fact for the case $n = 2$.

42. Prove Property 5 of vectors algebraically for the case $n = 3$. Then use similar triangles to give a geometric proof.

43. Use vectors to prove that the line joining the midpoints of two sides of a triangle is parallel to the third side and half its length.

44. Suppose the three coordinate planes are all mirrored and a light ray given by the vector $\mathbf{a} = \langle a_1, a_2, a_3\rangle$ first strikes the xz-plane, as shown in the figure. Use the fact that the angle of incidence equals the angle of reflection to show that the direction of the reflected ray is given by $\mathbf{b} = \langle a_1, -a_2, a_3\rangle$. Deduce that, after being reflected by all three mutually perpendicular mirrors, the resulting ray is parallel to the initial ray. (American space scientists used this principle, together with laser beams and an array of corner mirrors on the moon, to calculate very precisely the distance from the earth to the moon.)

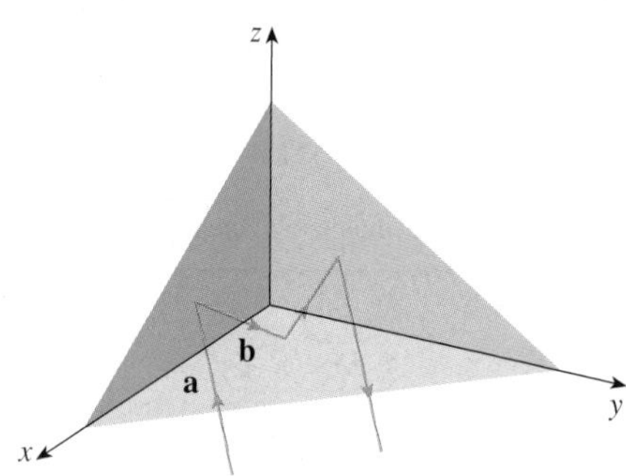

9.3 The Dot Product

So far we have added two vectors and multiplied a vector by a scalar. The question arises: Is it possible to multiply two vectors so that their product is a useful quantity? One such product is the dot product, which we consider in this section. Another is the cross product, which is discussed in the next section.

Work and the Dot Product

An example of a situation in physics and engineering where we need to combine two vectors occurs in calculating the work done by a force. In Section 6.5 we defined the work done by a constant force F in moving an object through a distance d as $W = Fd$, but this applies only when the force is directed along the line of motion of the object. Suppose, however, that the constant force is a vector $\mathbf{F} = \overrightarrow{PR}$ pointing in some other direction, as in Figure 1. If the force moves the object from P to Q, then the **displacement vector** is $\mathbf{D} = \overrightarrow{PQ}$. So here we have two vectors: the force **F** and the displacement **D**. The **work** done by **F** is defined as the magnitude of the displacement, $|\mathbf{D}|$, multiplied by the magnitude of the applied force in the direction of the motion, which, from Figure 1, is

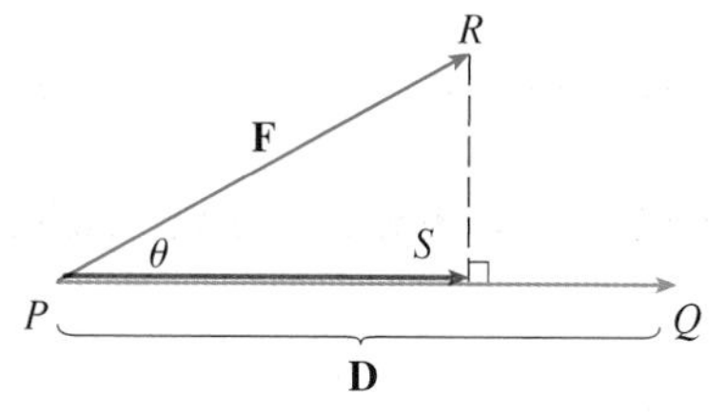

FIGURE 1

$$|\overrightarrow{PS}| = |\mathbf{F}|\cos\theta$$

So the work done by **F** is defined to be

$$W = |\mathbf{D}|(|\mathbf{F}|\cos\theta) = |\mathbf{F}||\mathbf{D}|\cos\theta \tag{1}$$

Notice that work is a scalar quantity; it has no direction. But its value depends on the angle θ between the force and displacement vectors.

We use the expression in Equation 1 to define the dot product of two vectors even when they don't represent force or displacement.

Definition The **dot product** of two nonzero vectors **a** and **b** is the number

$$\mathbf{a} \cdot \mathbf{b} = |\mathbf{a}||\mathbf{b}| \cos \theta$$

where θ is the angle between **a** and **b**, $0 \leqslant \theta \leqslant \pi$. (So θ is the smaller angle between the vectors when they are drawn with the same initial point.) If either **a** or **b** is **0**, we define $\mathbf{a} \cdot \mathbf{b} = 0$.

This product is called the **dot product** because of the dot in the notation $\mathbf{a} \cdot \mathbf{b}$. The result of computing $\mathbf{a} \cdot \mathbf{b}$ is not a vector. It is a real number, that is, a scalar. For this reason, the dot product is sometimes called the **scalar product**.

In the example of finding the work done by a force **F** in moving an object through a displacement $\mathbf{D} = \overrightarrow{PQ}$ by calculating $\mathbf{F} \cdot \mathbf{D} = |\mathbf{F}||\mathbf{D}| \cos \theta$, it makes no sense for the angle θ between **F** and **D** to be $\pi/2$ or larger because movement from P to Q couldn't take place. We make no such restriction in our general definition of $\mathbf{a} \cdot \mathbf{b}$, however, and allow θ to be any angle from 0 to π.

EXAMPLE 1 **Computing a dot product from lengths and the contained angle** If the vectors **a** and **b** have lengths 4 and 6, and the angle between them is $\pi/3$, find $\mathbf{a} \cdot \mathbf{b}$.

SOLUTION According to the definition,

$$\mathbf{a} \cdot \mathbf{b} = |\mathbf{a}||\mathbf{b}| \cos(\pi/3) = 4 \cdot 6 \cdot \tfrac{1}{2} = 12$$

EXAMPLE 2 A wagon is pulled a distance of 100 m along a horizontal path by a constant force of 70 N. The handle of the wagon is held at an angle of 35° above the horizontal. Find the work done by the force.

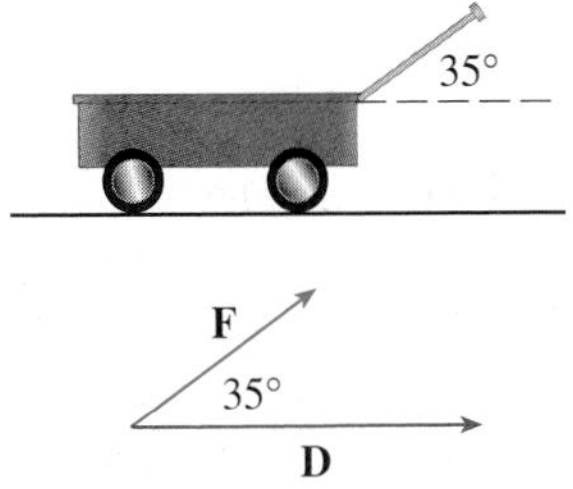

FIGURE 2

SOLUTION If **F** and **D** are the force and displacement vectors, as pictured in Figure 2, then the work done is

$$W = \mathbf{F} \cdot \mathbf{D} = |\mathbf{F}||\mathbf{D}| \cos 35°$$

$$= (70)(100) \cos 35° \approx 5734 \text{ N·m} = 5734 \text{ J}$$

Two nonzero vectors **a** and **b** are called **perpendicular** or **orthogonal** if the angle between them is $\theta = \pi/2$. For such vectors we have

$$\mathbf{a} \cdot \mathbf{b} = |\mathbf{a}||\mathbf{b}| \cos(\pi/2) = 0$$

and conversely if $\mathbf{a} \cdot \mathbf{b} = 0$, then $\cos \theta = 0$, so $\theta = \pi/2$. The zero vector **0** is considered to be perpendicular to all vectors. Therefore

2 Two vectors **a** and **b** are orthogonal if and only if $\mathbf{a} \cdot \mathbf{b} = 0$.

Because $\cos \theta > 0$ if $0 \leqslant \theta < \pi/2$ and $\cos \theta < 0$ if $\pi/2 < \theta \leqslant \pi$, we see that $\mathbf{a} \cdot \mathbf{b}$ is positive for $\theta < \pi/2$ and negative for $\theta > \pi/2$. We can think of $\mathbf{a} \cdot \mathbf{b}$ as measuring the extent to which **a** and **b** point in the same direction. The dot product $\mathbf{a} \cdot \mathbf{b}$ is positive if **a**

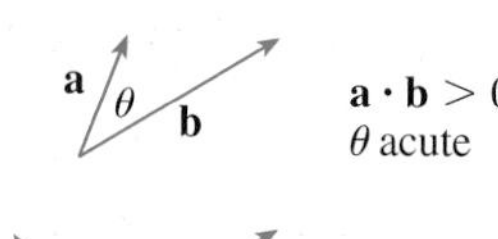

$\mathbf{a} \cdot \mathbf{b} > 0$
θ acute

$\mathbf{a} \cdot \mathbf{b} = 0$
$\theta = \pi/2$

$\mathbf{a} \cdot \mathbf{b} < 0$
θ obtuse

FIGURE 3

TEC Visual 9.3A shows an animation of Figure 3.

and $\mathbf{b}$ point in the same general direction, 0 if they are perpendicular, and negative if they point in generally opposite directions (see Figure 3). In the extreme case where $\mathbf{a}$ and $\mathbf{b}$ point in exactly the same direction, we have $\theta = 0$, so $\cos\theta = 1$ and

$$\mathbf{a} \cdot \mathbf{b} = |\mathbf{a}|\,|\mathbf{b}|$$

If $\mathbf{a}$ and $\mathbf{b}$ point in exactly opposite directions, then $\theta = \pi$ and so $\cos\theta = -1$ and $\mathbf{a} \cdot \mathbf{b} = -|\mathbf{a}|\,|\mathbf{b}|$.

The Dot Product in Component Form

Suppose we are given two vectors in component form:

$$\mathbf{a} = \langle a_1, a_2, a_3 \rangle \qquad \mathbf{b} = \langle b_1, b_2, b_3 \rangle$$

We want to find a convenient expression for $\mathbf{a} \cdot \mathbf{b}$ in terms of these components. If we apply the Law of Cosines to the triangle in Figure 4, we get

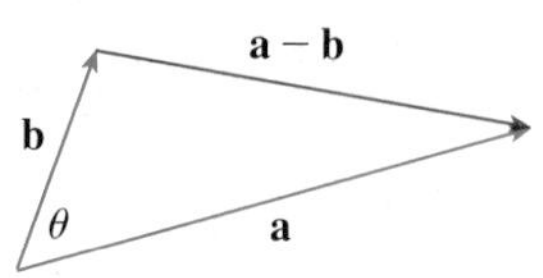

FIGURE 4

$$|\mathbf{a} - \mathbf{b}|^2 = |\mathbf{a}|^2 + |\mathbf{b}|^2 - 2|\mathbf{a}|\,|\mathbf{b}|\cos\theta = |\mathbf{a}|^2 + |\mathbf{b}|^2 - 2\mathbf{a} \cdot \mathbf{b}$$

Solving for the dot product, we obtain

$$\begin{aligned}\mathbf{a} \cdot \mathbf{b} &= \tfrac{1}{2}\left(|\mathbf{a}|^2 + |\mathbf{b}|^2 - |\mathbf{a} - \mathbf{b}|^2\right)\\ &= \tfrac{1}{2}\left[a_1^2 + a_2^2 + a_3^2 + b_1^2 + b_2^2 + b_3^2 - (a_1 - b_1)^2 - (a_2 - b_2)^2 - (a_3 - b_3)^2\right]\\ &= a_1b_1 + a_2b_2 + a_3b_3\end{aligned}$$

> The dot product of $\mathbf{a} = \langle a_1, a_2, a_3 \rangle$ and $\mathbf{b} = \langle b_1, b_2, b_3 \rangle$ is
>
> $$\mathbf{a} \cdot \mathbf{b} = a_1b_1 + a_2b_2 + a_3b_3$$

Thus, to find the dot product of $\mathbf{a}$ and $\mathbf{b}$, we multiply corresponding components and add. The dot product of two-dimensional vectors is found in a similar fashion:

$$\langle a_1, a_2 \rangle \cdot \langle b_1, b_2 \rangle = a_1b_1 + a_2b_2$$

V EXAMPLE 3 Computing dot products from components

$$\langle 2, 4 \rangle \cdot \langle 3, -1 \rangle = 2(3) + 4(-1) = 2$$

$$\langle -1, 7, 4 \rangle \cdot \left\langle 6, 2, -\tfrac{1}{2} \right\rangle = (-1)(6) + 7(2) + 4\left(-\tfrac{1}{2}\right) = 6$$

$$(\mathbf{i} + 2\mathbf{j} - 3\mathbf{k}) \cdot (2\mathbf{j} - \mathbf{k}) = 1(0) + 2(2) + (-3)(-1) = 7$$

EXAMPLE 4 Testing for orthogonality Show that $2\mathbf{i} + 2\mathbf{j} - \mathbf{k}$ is perpendicular to $5\mathbf{i} - 4\mathbf{j} + 2\mathbf{k}$.

SOLUTION Since

$$(2\mathbf{i} + 2\mathbf{j} - \mathbf{k}) \cdot (5\mathbf{i} - 4\mathbf{j} + 2\mathbf{k}) = 2(5) + 2(-4) + (-1)(2) = 0$$

these vectors are perpendicular by (2).

V EXAMPLE 5 Find the angle between the vectors $\mathbf{a} = \langle 2, 2, -1 \rangle$ and $\mathbf{b} = \langle 5, -3, 2 \rangle$.

SOLUTION Let θ be the required angle. Since

$$|\mathbf{a}| = \sqrt{2^2 + 2^2 + (-1)^2} = 3 \qquad \text{and} \qquad |\mathbf{b}| = \sqrt{5^2 + (-3)^2 + 2^2} = \sqrt{38}$$

and since

$$\mathbf{a} \cdot \mathbf{b} = 2(5) + 2(-3) + (-1)(2) = 2$$

we have, from the definition of the dot product

$$\cos \theta = \frac{\mathbf{a} \cdot \mathbf{b}}{|\mathbf{a}||\mathbf{b}|} = \frac{2}{3\sqrt{38}}$$

So the angle between **a** and **b** is

$$\theta = \cos^{-1}\left(\frac{2}{3\sqrt{38}}\right) \approx 1.46 \quad (\text{or } 84°)$$

EXAMPLE 6 A force is given by a vector $\mathbf{F} = 3\mathbf{i} + 4\mathbf{j} + 5\mathbf{k}$ and moves a particle from the point $P(2, 1, 0)$ to the point $Q(4, 6, 2)$. Find the work done.

SOLUTION The displacement vector is $\mathbf{D} = \overrightarrow{PQ} = \langle 2, 5, 2 \rangle$, so the work done is

$$W = \mathbf{F} \cdot \mathbf{D} = \langle 3, 4, 5 \rangle \cdot \langle 2, 5, 2 \rangle = 6 + 20 + 10 = 36$$

If the unit of length is meters and the magnitude of the force is measured in newtons, then the work done is 36 J.

The dot product obeys many of the laws that hold for ordinary products of real numbers. These are stated in the following theorem.

Properties of the Dot Product If **a**, **b**, and **c** are vectors in V_3 and c is a scalar, then

1. $\mathbf{a} \cdot \mathbf{a} = |\mathbf{a}|^2$
2. $\mathbf{a} \cdot \mathbf{b} = \mathbf{b} \cdot \mathbf{a}$
3. $\mathbf{a} \cdot (\mathbf{b} + \mathbf{c}) = \mathbf{a} \cdot \mathbf{b} + \mathbf{a} \cdot \mathbf{c}$
4. $(c\mathbf{a}) \cdot \mathbf{b} = c(\mathbf{a} \cdot \mathbf{b}) = \mathbf{a} \cdot (c\mathbf{b})$
5. $\mathbf{0} \cdot \mathbf{a} = 0$

Properties 1, 2, and 5 are immediate consequences of the definition of a dot product. Property 3 is best proved using components:

$$\begin{aligned} \mathbf{a} \cdot (\mathbf{b} + \mathbf{c}) &= \langle a_1, a_2, a_3 \rangle \cdot \langle b_1 + c_1, b_2 + c_2, b_3 + c_3 \rangle \\ &= a_1(b_1 + c_1) + a_2(b_2 + c_2) + a_3(b_3 + c_3) \\ &= a_1 b_1 + a_1 c_1 + a_2 b_2 + a_2 c_2 + a_3 b_3 + a_3 c_3 \\ &= (a_1 b_1 + a_2 b_2 + a_3 b_3) + (a_1 c_1 + a_2 c_2 + a_3 c_3) \\ &= \mathbf{a} \cdot \mathbf{b} + \mathbf{a} \cdot \mathbf{c} \end{aligned}$$

The proof of Property 4 is left as Exercise 47.

Projections

TEC Visual 9.3B shows how Figure 5 changes when we vary **a** and **b**.

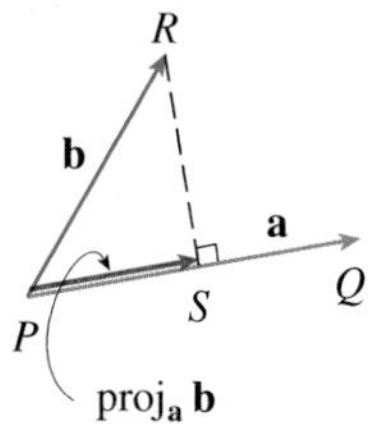

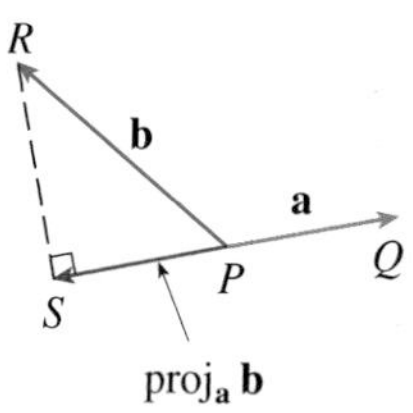

FIGURE 5
Vector projections

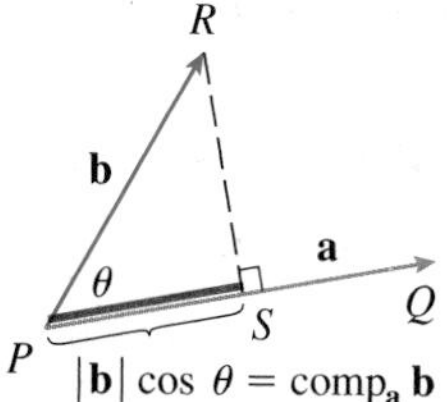

FIGURE 6
Scalar projection

Figure 5 shows representations $\overrightarrow{PQ}$ and $\overrightarrow{PR}$ of two vectors **a** and **b** with the same initial point P. If S is the foot of the perpendicular from R to the line containing $\overrightarrow{PQ}$, then the vector with representation $\overrightarrow{PS}$ is called the **vector projection** of **b** onto **a** and is denoted by $\text{proj}_{\mathbf{a}}\,\mathbf{b}$. (You can think of it as a shadow of **b**).

The **scalar projection** of **b** onto **a** (also called the **component of b along a**) is defined to be the signed magnitude of the vector projection, which is the number $|\mathbf{b}|\cos\theta$, where θ is the angle between **a** and **b**. (See Figure 6.) This is denoted by $\text{comp}_{\mathbf{a}}\,\mathbf{b}$. Observe that it is negative if $\pi/2 < \theta \leqslant \pi$. (Note that we used the component of the force **F** along the displacement **D**, $\text{comp}_{\mathbf{D}}\,\mathbf{F}$, at the beginning of this section.)

The equation

$$\mathbf{a}\cdot\mathbf{b} = |\mathbf{a}|\,|\mathbf{b}|\cos\theta = |\mathbf{a}|(|\mathbf{b}|\cos\theta)$$

shows that the dot product of **a** and **b** can be interpreted as the length of **a** times the scalar projection of **b** onto **a**. Since

$$|\mathbf{b}|\cos\theta = \frac{\mathbf{a}\cdot\mathbf{b}}{|\mathbf{a}|} = \frac{\mathbf{a}}{|\mathbf{a}|}\cdot\mathbf{b}$$

the component of **b** along **a** can be computed by taking the dot product of **b** with the unit vector in the direction of **a**. We summarize these ideas as follows.

Scalar projection of **b** onto **a**:	$\text{comp}_{\mathbf{a}}\,\mathbf{b} = \dfrac{\mathbf{a}\cdot\mathbf{b}}{|\mathbf{a}|}$
Vector projection of **b** onto **a**:	$\text{proj}_{\mathbf{a}}\,\mathbf{b} = \left(\dfrac{\mathbf{a}\cdot\mathbf{b}}{|\mathbf{a}|}\right)\dfrac{\mathbf{a}}{|\mathbf{a}|} = \dfrac{\mathbf{a}\cdot\mathbf{b}}{|\mathbf{a}|^2}\,\mathbf{a}$

V EXAMPLE 7 Find the scalar projection and vector projection of $\mathbf{b} = \langle 1, 1, 2\rangle$ onto $\mathbf{a} = \langle -2, 3, 1\rangle$.

SOLUTION Since $|\mathbf{a}| = \sqrt{(-2)^2 + 3^2 + 1^2} = \sqrt{14}$, the scalar projection of **b** onto **a** is

$$\text{comp}_{\mathbf{a}}\,\mathbf{b} = \frac{\mathbf{a}\cdot\mathbf{b}}{|\mathbf{a}|} = \frac{(-2)(1) + 3(1) + 1(2)}{\sqrt{14}} = \frac{3}{\sqrt{14}}$$

The vector projection is this scalar projection times the unit vector in the direction of **a**:

$$\text{proj}_{\mathbf{a}}\,\mathbf{b} = \frac{3}{\sqrt{14}}\frac{\mathbf{a}}{|\mathbf{a}|} = \frac{3}{14}\mathbf{a} = \left\langle -\frac{3}{7}, \frac{9}{14}, \frac{3}{14}\right\rangle$$

At the beginning of this section we saw one use of projections in physics—we used a scalar projection of a force vector in defining work. Other uses of projections occur in three-dimensional geometry. In Exercise 41 you are asked to use a projection to find the distance from a point to a line, and in Section 9.5 we use a projection to find the distance from a point to a plane.

9.3 Exercises

1. Which of the following expressions are meaningful? Which are meaningless? Explain.
(a) $(\mathbf{a} \cdot \mathbf{b}) \cdot \mathbf{c}$
(b) $(\mathbf{a} \cdot \mathbf{b})\mathbf{c}$
(c) $|\mathbf{a}|(\mathbf{b} \cdot \mathbf{c})$
(d) $\mathbf{a} \cdot (\mathbf{b} + \mathbf{c})$
(e) $\mathbf{a} \cdot \mathbf{b} + \mathbf{c}$
(f) $|\mathbf{a}| \cdot (\mathbf{b} + \mathbf{c})$

2–10 Find $\mathbf{a} \cdot \mathbf{b}$.

2. $|\mathbf{a}| = 3$, $|\mathbf{b}| = \sqrt{6}$, the angle between $\mathbf{a}$ and $\mathbf{b}$ is $45°$

3. $|\mathbf{a}| = 6$, $|\mathbf{b}| = 5$, the angle between $\mathbf{a}$ and $\mathbf{b}$ is $2\pi/3$

4. $\mathbf{a} = \langle -2, 3 \rangle$, $\mathbf{b} = \langle 0.7, 1.2 \rangle$

5. $\mathbf{a} = \langle -2, \frac{1}{3} \rangle$, $\mathbf{b} = \langle -5, 12 \rangle$

6. $\mathbf{a} = \langle 6, -2, 3 \rangle$, $\mathbf{b} = \langle 2, 5, -1 \rangle$

7. $\mathbf{a} = \langle 4, 1, \frac{1}{4} \rangle$, $\mathbf{b} = \langle 6, -3, -8 \rangle$

8. $\mathbf{a} = \langle p, -p, 2p \rangle$, $\mathbf{b} = \langle 2q, q, -q \rangle$

9. $\mathbf{a} = 2\mathbf{i} + \mathbf{j}$, $\mathbf{b} = \mathbf{i} - \mathbf{j} + \mathbf{k}$

10. $\mathbf{a} = 3\mathbf{i} + 2\mathbf{j} - \mathbf{k}$, $\mathbf{b} = 4\mathbf{i} + 5\mathbf{k}$

11–12 If $\mathbf{u}$ is a unit vector, find $\mathbf{u} \cdot \mathbf{v}$ and $\mathbf{u} \cdot \mathbf{w}$.

11.

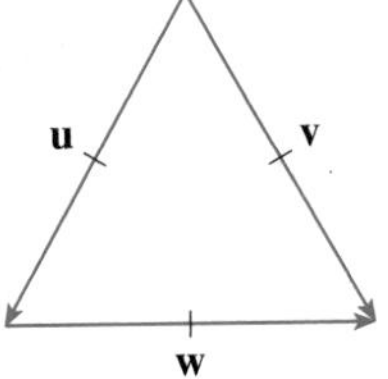

12.

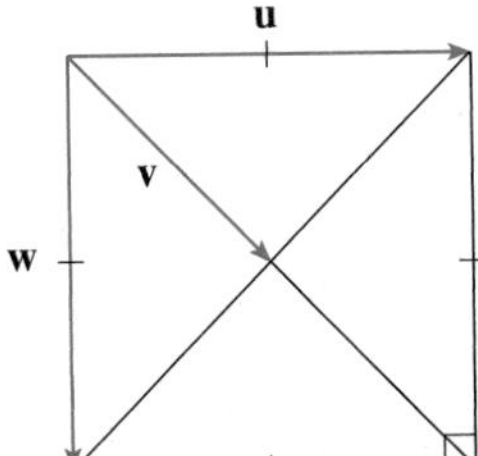

13. (a) Show that $\mathbf{i} \cdot \mathbf{j} = \mathbf{j} \cdot \mathbf{k} = \mathbf{k} \cdot \mathbf{i} = 0$.
(b) Show that $\mathbf{i} \cdot \mathbf{i} = \mathbf{j} \cdot \mathbf{j} = \mathbf{k} \cdot \mathbf{k} = 1$.

14. A street vendor sells a hamburgers, b hot dogs, and c soft drinks on a given day. He charges \$2 for a hamburger, \$1.50 for a hot dog, and \$1 for a soft drink. If $\mathbf{A} = \langle a, b, c \rangle$ and $\mathbf{P} = \langle 2, 1.5, 1 \rangle$, what is the meaning of the dot product $\mathbf{A} \cdot \mathbf{P}$?

15–18 Find the angle between the vectors. (First find an exact expression and then approximate to the nearest degree.)

15. $\mathbf{a} = \langle -8, 6 \rangle$, $\mathbf{b} = \langle \sqrt{7}, 3 \rangle$

16. $\mathbf{a} = \langle \sqrt{3}, 1 \rangle$, $\mathbf{b} = \langle 0, 5 \rangle$

17. $\mathbf{a} = \mathbf{j} + \mathbf{k}$, $\mathbf{b} = \mathbf{i} + 2\mathbf{j} - 3\mathbf{k}$

18. $\mathbf{a} = \mathbf{i} + 2\mathbf{j} - 2\mathbf{k}$, $\mathbf{b} = 4\mathbf{i} - 3\mathbf{k}$

19–20 Find, correct to the nearest degree, the three angles of the triangle with the given vertices.

19. $A(1, 0)$, $B(3, 6)$, $C(-1, 4)$

20. $D(0, 1, 1)$, $E(-2, 4, 3)$, $F(1, 2, -1)$

21–22 Determine whether the given vectors are orthogonal, parallel, or neither.

21. (a) $\mathbf{a} = \langle -5, 3, 7 \rangle$, $\mathbf{b} = \langle 6, -8, 2 \rangle$
(b) $\mathbf{a} = \langle 4, 6 \rangle$, $\mathbf{b} = \langle -3, 2 \rangle$
(c) $\mathbf{a} = -\mathbf{i} + 2\mathbf{j} + 5\mathbf{k}$, $\mathbf{b} = 3\mathbf{i} + 4\mathbf{j} - \mathbf{k}$
(d) $\mathbf{a} = 2\mathbf{i} + 6\mathbf{j} - 4\mathbf{k}$, $\mathbf{b} = -3\mathbf{i} - 9\mathbf{j} + 6\mathbf{k}$

22. (a) $\mathbf{u} = \langle -3, 9, 6 \rangle$, $\mathbf{v} = \langle 4, -12, -8 \rangle$
(b) $\mathbf{u} = \mathbf{i} - \mathbf{j} + 2\mathbf{k}$, $\mathbf{v} = 2\mathbf{i} - \mathbf{j} + \mathbf{k}$
(c) $\mathbf{u} = \langle a, b, c \rangle$, $\mathbf{v} = \langle -b, a, 0 \rangle$

23. Use vectors to decide whether the triangle with vertices $P(1, -3, -2)$, $Q(2, 0, -4)$, and $R(6, -2, -5)$ is right-angled.

24. For what values of b are the vectors $\langle -6, b, 2 \rangle$ and $\langle b, b^2, b \rangle$ orthogonal?

25. Find a unit vector that is orthogonal to both $\mathbf{i} + \mathbf{j}$ and $\mathbf{i} + \mathbf{k}$.

26. Find two unit vectors that make an angle of $60°$ with $\mathbf{v} = \langle 3, 4 \rangle$.

27–28 Find the acute angle between the lines.

27. $2x - y = 3$, $3x + y = 7$

28. $x + 2y = 7$, $5x - y = 2$

29–32 Find the scalar and vector projections of $\mathbf{b}$ onto $\mathbf{a}$.

29. $\mathbf{a} = \langle 3, -4 \rangle$, $\mathbf{b} = \langle 5, 0 \rangle$

30. $\mathbf{a} = \langle 1, 2 \rangle$, $\mathbf{b} = \langle -4, 1 \rangle$

31. $\mathbf{a} = 2\mathbf{i} - \mathbf{j} + 4\mathbf{k}$, $\mathbf{b} = \mathbf{j} + \frac{1}{2}\mathbf{k}$

32. $\mathbf{a} = \mathbf{i} + \mathbf{j} + \mathbf{k}$, $\mathbf{b} = \mathbf{i} - \mathbf{j} + \mathbf{k}$

33. Show that the vector $\text{orth}_{\mathbf{a}} \mathbf{b} = \mathbf{b} - \text{proj}_{\mathbf{a}} \mathbf{b}$ is orthogonal to $\mathbf{a}$. (It is called an **orthogonal projection** of $\mathbf{b}$.)

34. For the vectors in Exercise 30, find $\text{orth}_{\mathbf{a}} \mathbf{b}$ and illustrate by drawing the vectors $\mathbf{a}$, $\mathbf{b}$, $\text{proj}_{\mathbf{a}} \mathbf{b}$, and $\text{orth}_{\mathbf{a}} \mathbf{b}$.

35. If $\mathbf{a} = \langle 3, 0, -1 \rangle$, find a vector $\mathbf{b}$ such that $\text{comp}_{\mathbf{a}} \mathbf{b} = 2$.

36. Suppose that $\mathbf{a}$ and $\mathbf{b}$ are nonzero vectors.
(a) Under what circumstances is $\text{comp}_{\mathbf{a}} \mathbf{b} = \text{comp}_{\mathbf{b}} \mathbf{a}$?
(b) Under what circumstances is $\text{proj}_{\mathbf{a}} \mathbf{b} = \text{proj}_{\mathbf{b}} \mathbf{a}$?

1. Homework Hints available in TEC

37. Find the work done by a force $\mathbf{F} = 8\mathbf{i} - 6\mathbf{j} + 9\mathbf{k}$ that moves an object from the point $(0, 10, 8)$ to the point $(6, 12, 20)$ along a straight line. The distance is measured in meters and the force in newtons.

38. A tow truck drags a stalled car along a road. The chain makes an angle of $30°$ with the road and the tension in the chain is 1500 N. How much work is done by the truck in pulling the car 1 km?

39. A sled is pulled along a level path through snow by a rope. A 30-lb force acting at an angle of $40°$ above the horizontal moves the sled 80 ft. Find the work done by the force.

40. A boat sails south with the help of a wind blowing in the direction S36°E with magnitude 400 lb. Find the work done by the wind as the boat moves 120 ft.

41. Use a scalar projection to show that the distance from a point $P_1(x_1, y_1)$ to the line $ax + by + c = 0$ is

$$\frac{|ax_1 + by_1 + c|}{\sqrt{a^2 + b^2}}$$

Use this formula to find the distance from the point $(-2, 3)$ to the line $3x - 4y + 5 = 0$.

42. If $\mathbf{r} = \langle x, y, z \rangle$, $\mathbf{a} = \langle a_1, a_2, a_3 \rangle$, and $\mathbf{b} = \langle b_1, b_2, b_3 \rangle$, show that the vector equation $(\mathbf{r} - \mathbf{a}) \cdot (\mathbf{r} - \mathbf{b}) = 0$ represents a sphere, and find its center and radius.

43. Find the angle between a diagonal of a cube and one of its edges.

44. Find the angle between a diagonal of a cube and a diagonal of one of its faces.

45. A molecule of methane, CH_4, is structured with the four hydrogen atoms at the vertices of a regular tetrahedron and the carbon atom at the centroid. The *bond angle* is the angle formed by the H—C—H combination; it is the angle between the lines that join the carbon atom to two of the hydrogen atoms. Show that the bond angle is about $109.5°$. [*Hint:* Take the vertices of the tetrahedron to be the points $(1, 0, 0)$, $(0, 1, 0)$, $(0, 0, 1)$, and $(1, 1, 1)$, as shown in the figure. Then the centroid is $\left(\frac{1}{2}, \frac{1}{2}, \frac{1}{2}\right)$.]

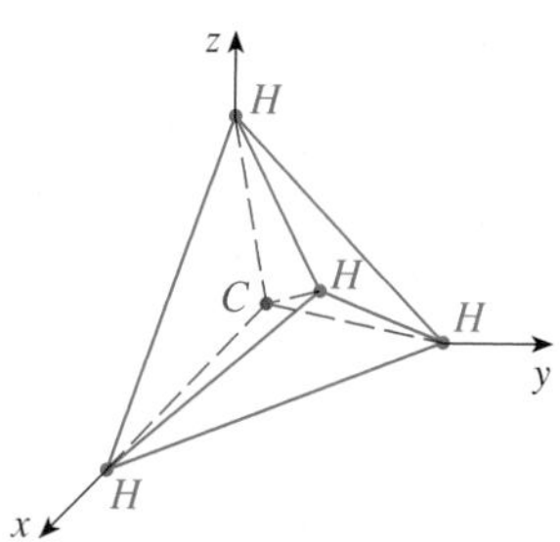

46. If $\mathbf{c} = |\mathbf{a}|\mathbf{b} + |\mathbf{b}|\mathbf{a}$, where $\mathbf{a}$, $\mathbf{b}$, and $\mathbf{c}$ are all nonzero vectors, show that $\mathbf{c}$ bisects the angle between $\mathbf{a}$ and $\mathbf{b}$.

47. Prove Property 4 of the dot product. Use either the definition of a dot product (considering the cases $c > 0$, $c = 0$, and $c < 0$ separately) or the component form.

48. Suppose that all sides of a quadrilateral are equal in length and opposite sides are parallel. Use vector methods to show that the diagonals are perpendicular.

49. Prove the Cauchy-Schwarz Inequality:

$$|\mathbf{a} \cdot \mathbf{b}| \leqslant |\mathbf{a}||\mathbf{b}|$$

50. The Triangle Inequality for vectors is

$$|\mathbf{a} + \mathbf{b}| \leqslant |\mathbf{a}| + |\mathbf{b}|$$

(a) Give a geometric interpretation of the Triangle Inequality.
(b) Use the Cauchy-Schwarz Inequality from Exercise 49 to prove the Triangle Inequality. [*Hint:* Use the fact that $|\mathbf{a} + \mathbf{b}|^2 = (\mathbf{a} + \mathbf{b}) \cdot (\mathbf{a} + \mathbf{b})$ and use Property 3 of the dot product.]

51. The Parallelogram Law states that

$$|\mathbf{a} + \mathbf{b}|^2 + |\mathbf{a} - \mathbf{b}|^2 = 2|\mathbf{a}|^2 + 2|\mathbf{b}|^2$$

(a) Give a geometric interpretation of the Parallelogram Law.
(b) Prove the Parallelogram Law. (See the hint in Exercise 50.)

52. Show that if $\mathbf{u} + \mathbf{v}$ and $\mathbf{u} - \mathbf{v}$ are orthogonal, then the vectors $\mathbf{u}$ and $\mathbf{v}$ must have the same length.

9.4 The Cross Product

The **cross product** $\mathbf{a} \times \mathbf{b}$ of two vectors $\mathbf{a}$ and $\mathbf{b}$, unlike the dot product, is a vector. For this reason it is also called the **vector product**. We will see that $\mathbf{a} \times \mathbf{b}$ is useful in geometry because it is perpendicular to both $\mathbf{a}$ and $\mathbf{b}$. But we introduce this product by looking at a situation where it arises in physics and engineering.

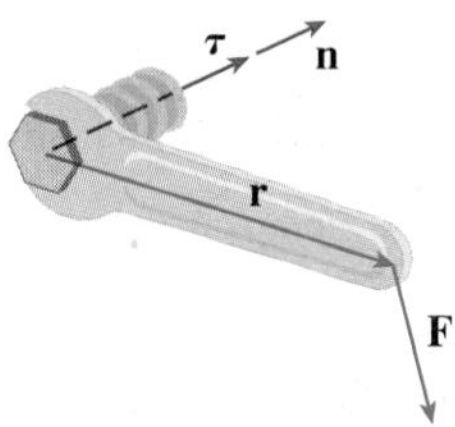

FIGURE 1

Torque and the Cross Product

If we tighten a bolt by applying a force to a wrench as in Figure 1, we produce a turning effect called a *torque* $\boldsymbol{\tau}$. The magnitude of the torque depends on two things:

- The distance from the axis of the bolt to the point where the force is applied. This is $|\mathbf{r}|$, the length of the position vector $\mathbf{r}$.

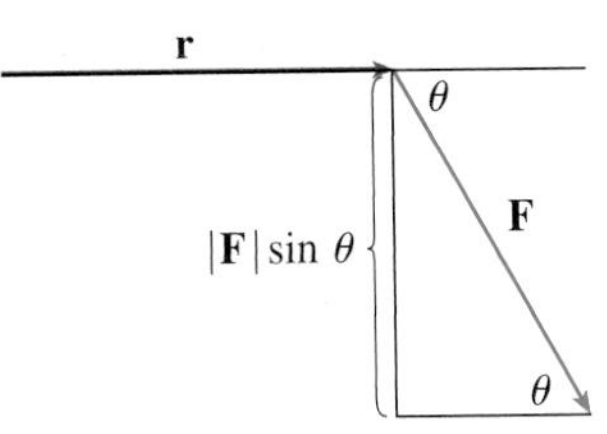

FIGURE 2

- The scalar component of the force **F** in the direction perpendicular to **r**. This is the only component that can cause a rotation and, from Figure 2, we see that it is

$$|\mathbf{F}| \sin \theta$$

where θ is the angle between the vectors **r** and **F**.

We define the magnitude of the torque vector to be the product of these two factors:

$$|\boldsymbol{\tau}| = |\mathbf{r}||\mathbf{F}| \sin \theta$$

The direction is along the axis of rotation. If **n** is a unit vector that points in the direction in which a right-threaded bolt moves (see Figure 1), we define the **torque** to be the vector

1 $$\boldsymbol{\tau} = (|\mathbf{r}||\mathbf{F}| \sin \theta)\,\mathbf{n}$$

We denote this torque vector by $\boldsymbol{\tau} = \mathbf{r} \times \mathbf{F}$ and we call it the *cross product* or *vector product* of **r** and **F**.

The type of expression in Equation 1 occurs so frequently in the study of fluid flow, planetary motion, and other areas of physics and engineering, that we define and study the cross product of *any* pair of three-dimensional vectors **a** and **b**.

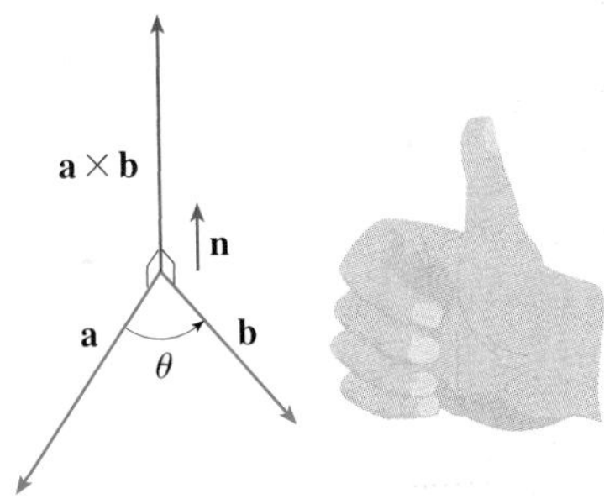

FIGURE 3
The right-hand rule gives the direction of $\mathbf{a} \times \mathbf{b}$.

Definition If **a** and **b** are nonzero three-dimensional vectors, the **cross product** of **a** and **b** is the vector

$$\mathbf{a} \times \mathbf{b} = (|\mathbf{a}||\mathbf{b}| \sin \theta)\,\mathbf{n}$$

where θ is the angle between **a** and **b**, $0 \leqslant \theta \leqslant \pi$, and **n** is a unit vector perpendicular to both **a** and **b** and whose direction is given by the **right-hand rule**: If the fingers of your right hand curl through the angle θ from **a** to **b**, then your thumb points in the direction of **n**. (See Figure 3.)

TEC Visual 9.4 shows how $\mathbf{a} \times \mathbf{b}$ changes as **b** changes.

If either **a** or **b** is **0**, then we define $\mathbf{a} \times \mathbf{b}$ to be **0**.

Because $\mathbf{a} \times \mathbf{b}$ is a scalar multiple of **n**, it has the same direction as **n** and so

> $\mathbf{a} \times \mathbf{b}$ is orthogonal to both **a** and **b**.

Notice that two nonzero vectors **a** and **b** are parallel if and only if the angle between them is 0 or π. In either case, $\sin \theta = 0$ and so $\mathbf{a} \times \mathbf{b} = \mathbf{0}$.

In particular, any vector **a** is parallel to itself, so

$$\mathbf{a} \times \mathbf{a} = \mathbf{0}$$

> Two nonzero vectors **a** and **b** are parallel if and only if $\mathbf{a} \times \mathbf{b} = \mathbf{0}$.

This makes sense in the torque interpretation: If we pull or push the wrench in the direction of its handle (so **F** is parallel to **r**), we produce no torque.

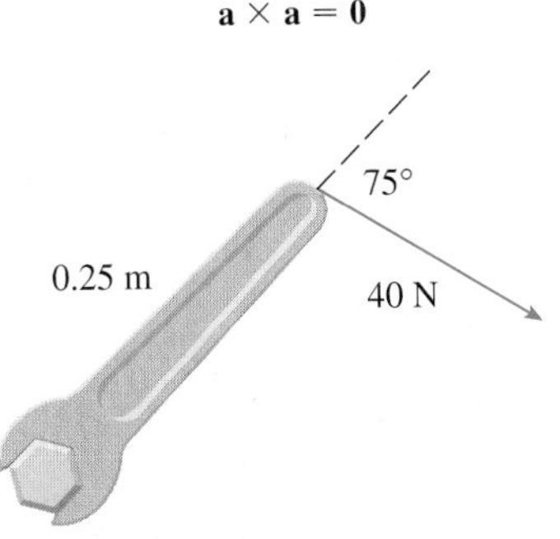

FIGURE 4

EXAMPLE 1 A bolt is tightened by applying a 40-N force to a 0.25-m wrench, as shown in Figure 4. Find the magnitude of the torque about the center of the bolt.

SOLUTION The magnitude of the torque vector is

$$|\boldsymbol{\tau}| = |\mathbf{r} \times \mathbf{F}| = |\mathbf{r}||\mathbf{F}| \sin 75^\circ |\mathbf{n}| = (0.25)(40) \sin 75^\circ$$
$$= 10 \sin 75^\circ \approx 9.66 \text{ N}\cdot\text{m}$$

If the bolt is right-threaded, then the torque vector itself is

$$\boldsymbol{\tau} = |\boldsymbol{\tau}|\,\mathbf{n} \approx 9.66\,\mathbf{n}$$

where **n** is a unit vector directed down into the page.

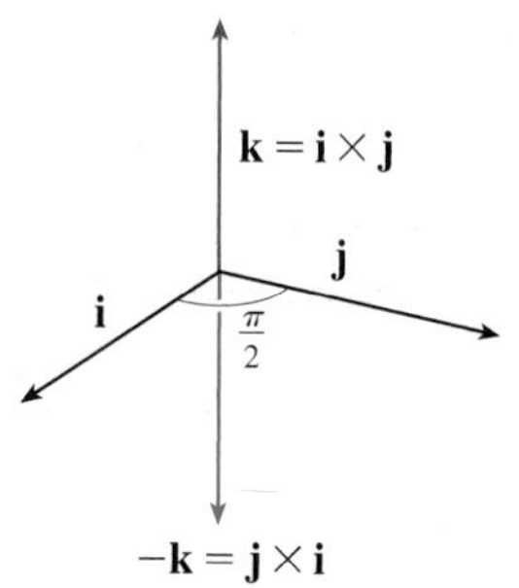

FIGURE 5

EXAMPLE 2 Cross product of standard basis vectors Find $\mathbf{i} \times \mathbf{j}$ and $\mathbf{j} \times \mathbf{i}$.

SOLUTION The standard basis vectors **i** and **j** both have length 1 and the angle between them is $\pi/2$. By the right-hand rule, the unit vector perpendicular to **i** and **j** is $\mathbf{n} = \mathbf{k}$ (see Figure 5), so

$$\mathbf{i} \times \mathbf{j} = \big(|\mathbf{i}||\mathbf{j}|\sin(\pi/2)\big)\mathbf{k} = \mathbf{k}$$

But if we apply the right-hand rule to the vectors **j** and **i** (in that order), we see that **n** points downward and so $\mathbf{n} = -\mathbf{k}$. Thus

$$\mathbf{j} \times \mathbf{i} = -\mathbf{k}$$

From Example 2 we see that

$$\mathbf{i} \times \mathbf{j} \neq \mathbf{j} \times \mathbf{i}$$

so the cross product is not commutative. Similar reasoning shows that

$$\mathbf{j} \times \mathbf{k} = \mathbf{i} \qquad \mathbf{k} \times \mathbf{j} = -\mathbf{i}$$

$$\mathbf{k} \times \mathbf{i} = \mathbf{j} \qquad \mathbf{i} \times \mathbf{k} = -\mathbf{j}$$

In general, the right-hand rule shows that

$$\mathbf{b} \times \mathbf{a} = -\mathbf{a} \times \mathbf{b}$$

Another algebraic law that fails for the cross product is the associative law for multiplication; that is, in general,

$$(\mathbf{a} \times \mathbf{b}) \times \mathbf{c} \neq \mathbf{a} \times (\mathbf{b} \times \mathbf{c})$$

For instance, if $\mathbf{a} = \mathbf{i}$, $\mathbf{b} = \mathbf{i}$, and $\mathbf{c} = \mathbf{j}$, then

$$(\mathbf{i} \times \mathbf{i}) \times \mathbf{j} = \mathbf{0} \times \mathbf{j} = \mathbf{0}$$

whereas

$$\mathbf{i} \times (\mathbf{i} \times \mathbf{j}) = \mathbf{i} \times \mathbf{k} = -\mathbf{j}$$

However, some of the usual laws of algebra *do* hold for cross products:

Properties of the Cross Product If **a**, **b**, and **c** are vectors and c is a scalar, then

1. $\mathbf{a} \times \mathbf{b} = -\mathbf{b} \times \mathbf{a}$
2. $(c\mathbf{a}) \times \mathbf{b} = c(\mathbf{a} \times \mathbf{b}) = \mathbf{a} \times (c\mathbf{b})$
3. $\mathbf{a} \times (\mathbf{b} + \mathbf{c}) = \mathbf{a} \times \mathbf{b} + \mathbf{a} \times \mathbf{c}$
4. $(\mathbf{a} + \mathbf{b}) \times \mathbf{c} = \mathbf{a} \times \mathbf{c} + \mathbf{b} \times \mathbf{c}$

Property 2 is proved by applying the definition of a cross product to each of the three expressions. Properties 3 and 4 (the Vector Distributive Laws) are more difficult to establish (see Exercise 41).

A geometric interpretation of the length of the cross product can be seen by looking at Figure 6. If **a** and **b** are represented by directed line segments with the same initial point, then they determine a parallelogram with base $|\mathbf{a}|$, altitude $|\mathbf{b}|\sin\theta$, and area

$$A = |\mathbf{a}|\left(|\mathbf{b}|\sin\theta\right) = |\mathbf{a} \times \mathbf{b}|$$

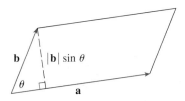

b

$|\mathbf{b}|\sin\theta$

θ

a

FIGURE 6

> The length of the cross product $\mathbf{a} \times \mathbf{b}$ is equal to the area of the parallelogram determined by **a** and **b**.

The Cross Product in Component Form

Suppose **a** and **b** are given in component form:

$$\mathbf{a} = a_1\mathbf{i} + a_2\mathbf{j} + a_3\mathbf{k} \qquad \mathbf{b} = b_1\mathbf{i} + b_2\mathbf{j} + b_3\mathbf{k}$$

We can express $\mathbf{a} \times \mathbf{b}$ in component form by using the Vector Distributive Laws together with the results from Example 2:

$$\begin{aligned}
\mathbf{a} \times \mathbf{b} &= (a_1\mathbf{i} + a_2\mathbf{j} + a_3\mathbf{k}) \times (b_1\mathbf{i} + b_2\mathbf{j} + b_3\mathbf{k}) \\
&= a_1b_1\mathbf{i} \times \mathbf{i} + a_1b_2\mathbf{i} \times \mathbf{j} + a_1b_3\mathbf{i} \times \mathbf{k} \\
&\qquad + a_2b_1\mathbf{j} \times \mathbf{i} + a_2b_2\mathbf{j} \times \mathbf{j} + a_2b_3\mathbf{j} \times \mathbf{k} \\
&\qquad + a_3b_1\mathbf{k} \times \mathbf{i} + a_3b_2\mathbf{k} \times \mathbf{j} + a_3b_3\mathbf{k} \times \mathbf{k} \\
&= a_1b_2\mathbf{k} + a_1b_3(-\mathbf{j}) + a_2b_1(-\mathbf{k}) + a_2b_3\mathbf{i} + a_3b_1\mathbf{j} + a_3b_2(-\mathbf{i}) \\
&= (a_2b_3 - a_3b_2)\mathbf{i} + (a_3b_1 - a_1b_3)\mathbf{j} + (a_1b_2 - a_2b_1)\mathbf{k}
\end{aligned}$$

Note that

$\mathbf{i} \times \mathbf{i} = \mathbf{0} \quad \mathbf{j} \times \mathbf{j} = \mathbf{0} \quad \mathbf{k} \times \mathbf{k} = \mathbf{0}$

> **2** If $\mathbf{a} = \langle a_1, a_2, a_3 \rangle$ and $\mathbf{b} = \langle b_1, b_2, b_3 \rangle$, then
>
> $$\mathbf{a} \times \mathbf{b} = \langle a_2b_3 - a_3b_2, a_3b_1 - a_1b_3, a_1b_2 - a_2b_1 \rangle$$

In order to make this expression for $\mathbf{a} \times \mathbf{b}$ easier to remember, we use the notation of determinants. A **determinant of order 2** is defined by

$$\begin{vmatrix} a & b \\ c & d \end{vmatrix} = ad - bc$$

For example,

$$\begin{vmatrix} 2 & 1 \\ -6 & 4 \end{vmatrix} = 2(4) - 1(-6) = 14$$

A **determinant of order 3** can be defined in terms of second-order determinants as follows:

3
$$\begin{vmatrix} a_1 & a_2 & a_3 \\ b_1 & b_2 & b_3 \\ c_1 & c_2 & c_3 \end{vmatrix} = a_1 \begin{vmatrix} b_2 & b_3 \\ c_2 & c_3 \end{vmatrix} - a_2 \begin{vmatrix} b_1 & b_3 \\ c_1 & c_3 \end{vmatrix} + a_3 \begin{vmatrix} b_1 & b_2 \\ c_1 & c_2 \end{vmatrix}$$

Observe that each term on the right side of Equation 3 involves a number a_i in the first row of the determinant, and a_i is multiplied by the second-order determinant obtained from the left side by deleting the row and column in which a_i appears. Notice also the minus sign in the second term. For example,

$$\begin{vmatrix} 1 & 2 & -1 \\ 3 & 0 & 1 \\ -5 & 4 & 2 \end{vmatrix} = 1 \begin{vmatrix} 0 & 1 \\ 4 & 2 \end{vmatrix} - 2 \begin{vmatrix} 3 & 1 \\ -5 & 2 \end{vmatrix} + (-1) \begin{vmatrix} 3 & 0 \\ -5 & 4 \end{vmatrix}$$

$$= 1(0 - 4) - 2(6 + 5) + (-1)(12 - 0) = -38$$

If we now rewrite the expression for $\mathbf{a} \times \mathbf{b}$ in (2) using second-order determinants and the standard basis vectors $\mathbf{i}$, $\mathbf{j}$, and $\mathbf{k}$, we see that the cross product of the vectors $\mathbf{a} = a_1\mathbf{i} + a_2\mathbf{j} + a_3\mathbf{k}$ and $\mathbf{b} = b_1\mathbf{i} + b_2\mathbf{j} + b_3\mathbf{k}$ is

4
$$\mathbf{a} \times \mathbf{b} = \begin{vmatrix} a_2 & a_3 \\ b_2 & b_3 \end{vmatrix} \mathbf{i} - \begin{vmatrix} a_1 & a_3 \\ b_1 & b_3 \end{vmatrix} \mathbf{j} + \begin{vmatrix} a_1 & a_2 \\ b_1 & b_2 \end{vmatrix} \mathbf{k}$$

In view of the similarity between Equations 3 and 4, we often write

5
$$\mathbf{a} \times \mathbf{b} = \begin{vmatrix} \mathbf{i} & \mathbf{j} & \mathbf{k} \\ a_1 & a_2 & a_3 \\ b_1 & b_2 & b_3 \end{vmatrix}$$

Although the first row of the symbolic determinant in Equation 5 consists of vectors, if we expand it as if it were an ordinary determinant using the rule in Equation 3, we obtain Equation 4. The symbolic formula in Equation 5 is probably the easiest way of remembering and computing cross products.

V EXAMPLE 3 Cross product of vectors in component form
If $\mathbf{a} = \langle 1, 3, 4 \rangle$ and $\mathbf{b} = \langle 2, 7, -5 \rangle$, then, from Equation 5, we have

$$\mathbf{a} \times \mathbf{b} = \begin{vmatrix} \mathbf{i} & \mathbf{j} & \mathbf{k} \\ 1 & 3 & 4 \\ 2 & 7 & -5 \end{vmatrix}$$

$$= \begin{vmatrix} 3 & 4 \\ 7 & -5 \end{vmatrix} \mathbf{i} - \begin{vmatrix} 1 & 4 \\ 2 & -5 \end{vmatrix} \mathbf{j} + \begin{vmatrix} 1 & 3 \\ 2 & 7 \end{vmatrix} \mathbf{k}$$

$$= (-15 - 28)\,\mathbf{i} - (-5 - 8)\,\mathbf{j} + (7 - 6)\,\mathbf{k} = -43\mathbf{i} + 13\mathbf{j} + \mathbf{k}$$

EXAMPLE 4 Find a vector perpendicular to the plane that passes through the points $P(1, 4, 6)$, $Q(-2, 5, -1)$, and $R(1, -1, 1)$.

SOLUTION The vector $\overrightarrow{PQ} \times \overrightarrow{PR}$ is perpendicular to both $\overrightarrow{PQ}$ and $\overrightarrow{PR}$ and is therefore perpendicular to the plane through P, Q, and R. We know from (9.2.1) that

$$\overrightarrow{PQ} = (-2 - 1)\mathbf{i} + (5 - 4)\mathbf{j} + (-1 - 6)\mathbf{k} = -3\mathbf{i} + \mathbf{j} - 7\mathbf{k}$$

$$\overrightarrow{PR} = (1 - 1)\mathbf{i} + (-1 - 4)\mathbf{j} + (1 - 6)\mathbf{k} = -5\mathbf{j} - 5\mathbf{k}$$

We compute the cross product of these vectors:

$$\overrightarrow{PQ} \times \overrightarrow{PR} = \begin{vmatrix} \mathbf{i} & \mathbf{j} & \mathbf{k} \\ -3 & 1 & -7 \\ 0 & -5 & -5 \end{vmatrix}$$

$$= (-5 - 35)\mathbf{i} - (15 - 0)\mathbf{j} + (15 - 0)\mathbf{k} = -40\mathbf{i} - 15\mathbf{j} + 15\mathbf{k}$$

So the vector $\langle -40, -15, 15 \rangle$ is perpendicular to the given plane. Any nonzero scalar multiple of this vector, such as $\langle -8, -3, 3 \rangle$, is also perpendicular to the plane.

EXAMPLE 5 Find the area of the triangle with vertices $P(1, 4, 6)$, $Q(-2, 5, -1)$, and $R(1, -1, 1)$.

SOLUTION In Example 4 we computed that $\overrightarrow{PQ} \times \overrightarrow{PR} = \langle -40, -15, 15 \rangle$. The area of the parallelogram with adjacent sides PQ and PR is the length of this cross product:

$$|\overrightarrow{PQ} \times \overrightarrow{PR}| = \sqrt{(-40)^2 + (-15)^2 + 15^2} = 5\sqrt{82}$$

The area A of the triangle PQR is half the area of this parallelogram, that is, $\frac{5}{2}\sqrt{82}$.

Triple Products

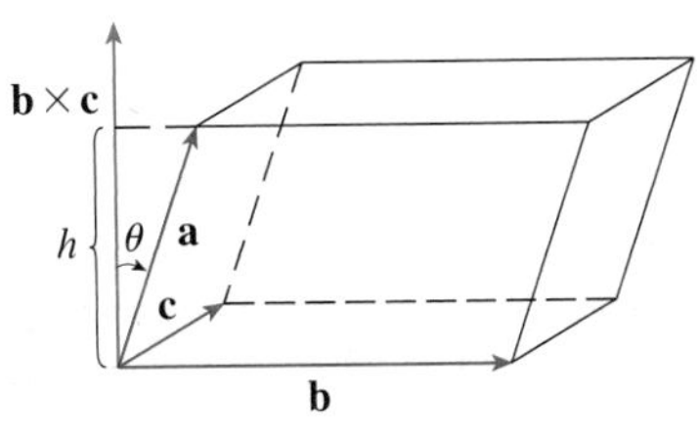

FIGURE 7

The product $\mathbf{a} \cdot (\mathbf{b} \times \mathbf{c})$ is called the **scalar triple product** of the vectors **a**, **b**, and **c**. Its geometric significance can be seen by considering the parallelepiped determined by the vectors **a**, **b**, and **c**. (See Figure 7.) The area of the base parallelogram is $A = |\mathbf{b} \times \mathbf{c}|$. If θ is the angle between the vectors **a** and $\mathbf{b} \times \mathbf{c}$, then the height h of the parallelepiped is $h = |\mathbf{a}||\cos\theta|$. (We must use $|\cos\theta|$ instead of $\cos\theta$ in case $\theta > \pi/2$.) Thus the volume of the parallelepiped is

$$V = Ah = |\mathbf{b} \times \mathbf{c}||\mathbf{a}||\cos\theta| = |\mathbf{a} \cdot (\mathbf{b} \times \mathbf{c})|$$

Therefore we have proved the following:

> The volume of the parallelepiped determined by the vectors **a**, **b**, and **c** is the magnitude of their scalar triple product:
>
> $$V = |\mathbf{a} \cdot (\mathbf{b} \times \mathbf{c})|$$

Instead of thinking of the parallelepiped as having its base parallelogram determined by **b** and **c**, we can think of it with base parallelogram determined by **a** and **b**. In this way, we see that

$$\mathbf{a} \cdot (\mathbf{b} \times \mathbf{c}) = \mathbf{c} \cdot (\mathbf{a} \times \mathbf{b})$$

But the dot product is commutative, so we can write

6 $$\mathbf{a} \cdot (\mathbf{b} \times \mathbf{c}) = (\mathbf{a} \times \mathbf{b}) \cdot \mathbf{c}$$

Suppose that **a**, **b**, and **c** are given in component form:

$$\mathbf{a} = a_1\mathbf{i} + a_2\mathbf{j} + a_3\mathbf{k} \qquad \mathbf{b} = b_1\mathbf{i} + b_2\mathbf{j} + b_3\mathbf{k} \qquad \mathbf{c} = c_1\mathbf{i} + c_2\mathbf{j} + c_3\mathbf{k}$$

Then

$$\mathbf{a} \cdot (\mathbf{b} \times \mathbf{c}) = \mathbf{a} \cdot \left[\begin{vmatrix} b_2 & b_3 \\ c_2 & c_3 \end{vmatrix} \mathbf{i} - \begin{vmatrix} b_1 & b_3 \\ c_1 & c_3 \end{vmatrix} \mathbf{j} + \begin{vmatrix} b_1 & b_2 \\ c_1 & c_2 \end{vmatrix} \mathbf{k} \right]$$

$$= a_1 \begin{vmatrix} b_2 & b_3 \\ c_2 & c_3 \end{vmatrix} - a_2 \begin{vmatrix} b_1 & b_3 \\ c_1 & c_3 \end{vmatrix} + a_3 \begin{vmatrix} b_1 & b_2 \\ c_1 & c_2 \end{vmatrix}$$

This shows that we can write the scalar triple product of **a**, **b**, and **c** as the determinant whose rows are the components of these vectors:

7 $$\mathbf{a} \cdot (\mathbf{b} \times \mathbf{c}) = \begin{vmatrix} a_1 & a_2 & a_3 \\ b_1 & b_2 & b_3 \\ c_1 & c_2 & c_3 \end{vmatrix}$$

V EXAMPLE 6 Coplanar vectors Use the scalar triple product to show that the vectors $\mathbf{a} = \langle 1, 4, -7 \rangle$, $\mathbf{b} = \langle 2, -1, 4 \rangle$, and $\mathbf{c} = \langle 0, -9, 18 \rangle$ are coplanar; that is, they lie in the same plane.

SOLUTION We use Equation 7 to compute their scalar triple product:

$$\mathbf{a} \cdot (\mathbf{b} \times \mathbf{c}) = \begin{vmatrix} 1 & 4 & -7 \\ 2 & -1 & 4 \\ 0 & -9 & 18 \end{vmatrix}$$

$$= 1 \begin{vmatrix} -1 & 4 \\ -9 & 18 \end{vmatrix} - 4 \begin{vmatrix} 2 & 4 \\ 0 & 18 \end{vmatrix} - 7 \begin{vmatrix} 2 & -1 \\ 0 & -9 \end{vmatrix}$$

$$= 1(18) - 4(36) - 7(-18) = 0$$

Therefore the volume of the parallelepiped determined by **a**, **b**, and **c** is 0. This means that **a**, **b**, and **c** are coplanar.

The product $\mathbf{a} \times (\mathbf{b} \times \mathbf{c})$ is called the **vector triple product** of **a**, **b**, and **c**. The proof of the following formula for the vector triple product is left as Exercise 36.

8 $$\mathbf{a} \times (\mathbf{b} \times \mathbf{c}) = (\mathbf{a} \cdot \mathbf{c})\mathbf{b} - (\mathbf{a} \cdot \mathbf{b})\mathbf{c}$$

Formula 8 will be used to derive Kepler's First Law of planetary motion in Chapter 10.

9.4 Exercises

1. State whether each expression is meaningful. If not, explain why. If so, state whether it is a vector or a scalar.
   (a) $\mathbf{a} \cdot (\mathbf{b} \times \mathbf{c})$ (b) $\mathbf{a} \times (\mathbf{b} \cdot \mathbf{c})$
   (c) $\mathbf{a} \times (\mathbf{b} \times \mathbf{c})$ (d) $(\mathbf{a} \cdot \mathbf{b}) \times \mathbf{c}$
   (e) $(\mathbf{a} \cdot \mathbf{b}) \times (\mathbf{c} \cdot \mathbf{d})$ (f) $(\mathbf{a} \times \mathbf{b}) \cdot (\mathbf{c} \times \mathbf{d})$

2–3 Find $|\mathbf{u} \times \mathbf{v}|$ and determine whether $\mathbf{u} \times \mathbf{v}$ is directed into the page or out of the page.

2.

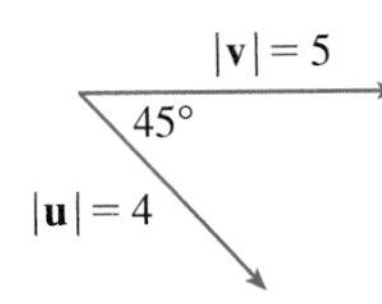

3.

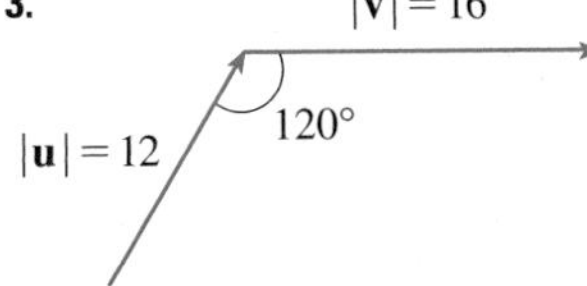

4. The figure shows a vector $\mathbf{a}$ in the xy-plane and a vector $\mathbf{b}$ in the direction of $\mathbf{k}$. Their lengths are $|\mathbf{a}| = 3$ and $|\mathbf{b}| = 2$.
   (a) Find $|\mathbf{a} \times \mathbf{b}|$.
   (b) Use the right-hand rule to decide whether the components of $\mathbf{a} \times \mathbf{b}$ are positive, negative, or 0.

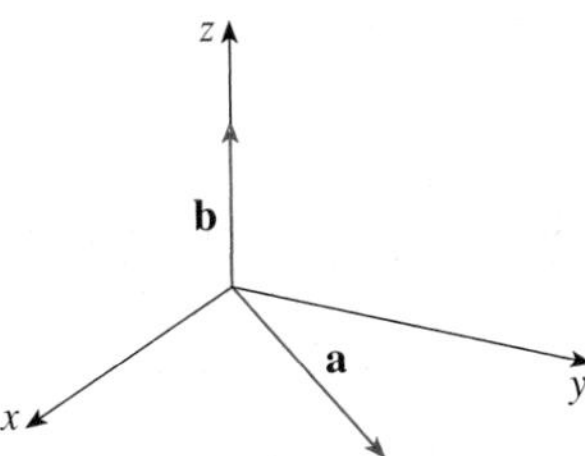

5. A bicycle pedal is pushed by a foot with a 60-N force as shown. The shaft of the pedal is 18 cm long. Find the magnitude of the torque about P.

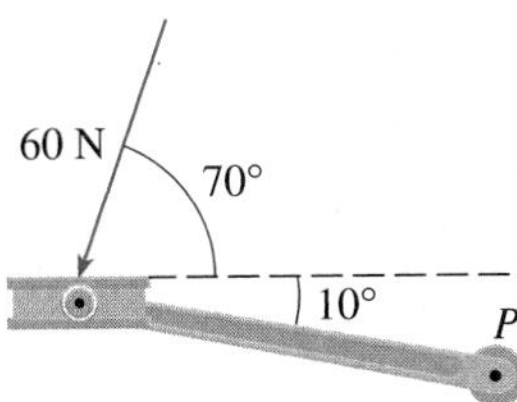

6. Find the magnitude of the torque about P if a 36-lb force is applied as shown.

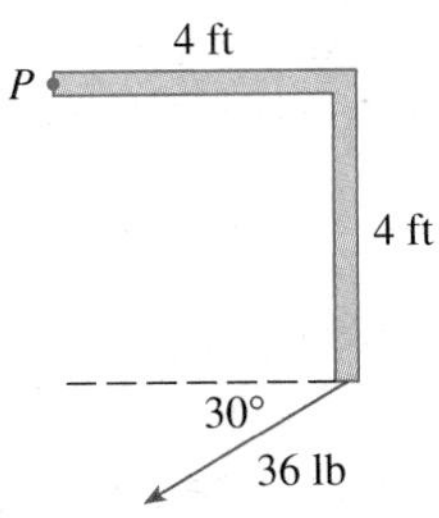

7–13 Find the cross product $\mathbf{a} \times \mathbf{b}$ and verify that it is orthogonal to both $\mathbf{a}$ and $\mathbf{b}$.

7. $\mathbf{a} = \langle 6, 0, -2 \rangle, \quad \mathbf{b} = \langle 0, 8, 0 \rangle$
8. $\mathbf{a} = \langle 1, 1, -1 \rangle, \quad \mathbf{b} = \langle 2, 4, 6 \rangle$
9. $\mathbf{a} = \mathbf{i} + 3\mathbf{j} - 2\mathbf{k}, \quad \mathbf{b} = -\mathbf{i} + 5\mathbf{k}$
10. $\mathbf{a} = \mathbf{j} + 7\mathbf{k}, \quad \mathbf{b} = 2\mathbf{i} - \mathbf{j} + 4\mathbf{k}$
11. $\mathbf{a} = \mathbf{i} - \mathbf{j} - \mathbf{k}, \quad \mathbf{b} = \frac{1}{2}\mathbf{i} + \mathbf{j} + \frac{1}{2}\mathbf{k}$
12. $\mathbf{a} = \mathbf{i} + e^t\mathbf{j} + e^{-t}\mathbf{k}, \quad \mathbf{b} = 2\mathbf{i} + e^t\mathbf{j} - e^{-t}\mathbf{k}$
13. $\mathbf{a} = \langle t, t^2, t^3 \rangle, \quad \mathbf{b} = \langle 1, 2t, 3t^2 \rangle$

14. If $\mathbf{a} = \mathbf{i} - 2\mathbf{k}$ and $\mathbf{b} = \mathbf{j} + \mathbf{k}$, find $\mathbf{a} \times \mathbf{b}$. Sketch $\mathbf{a}$, $\mathbf{b}$, and $\mathbf{a} \times \mathbf{b}$ as vectors starting at the origin.

15–18 Find the vector, not with determinants, but by using properties of cross products.

15. $(\mathbf{i} \times \mathbf{j}) \times \mathbf{k}$
16. $\mathbf{k} \times (\mathbf{i} - 2\mathbf{j})$
17. $(\mathbf{j} - \mathbf{k}) \times (\mathbf{k} - \mathbf{i})$
18. $(\mathbf{i} + \mathbf{j}) \times (\mathbf{i} - \mathbf{j})$

19. Find two unit vectors orthogonal to both $\langle 1, -1, 1 \rangle$ and $\langle 0, 4, 4 \rangle$.
20. Find two unit vectors orthogonal to both $\mathbf{i} + \mathbf{j} + \mathbf{k}$ and $2\mathbf{i} + \mathbf{k}$.
21. Find the area of the parallelogram with vertices $A(-2, 1)$, $B(0, 4)$, $C(4, 2)$, and $D(2, -1)$.
22. Find the area of the parallelogram with vertices $K(1, 2, 3)$, $L(1, 3, 6)$, $M(3, 8, 6)$, and $N(3, 7, 3)$.

23–24 (a) Find a nonzero vector orthogonal to the plane through the points P, Q, and R, and (b) find the area of triangle PQR.

23. $P(0, -2, 0), \quad Q(4, 1, -2), \quad R(5, 3, 1)$
24. $P(-1, 3, 1), \quad Q(0, 5, 2), \quad R(4, 3, -1)$

25. A wrench 30 cm long lies along the positive y-axis and grips a bolt at the origin. A force is applied in the direction $\langle 0, 3, -4 \rangle$ at the end of the wrench. Find the magnitude of the force needed to supply 100 N·m of torque to the bolt.
26. Let $\mathbf{v} = 5\mathbf{j}$ and let $\mathbf{u}$ be a vector with length 3 that starts at the origin and rotates in the xy-plane. Find the maximum and minimum values of the length of the vector $\mathbf{u} \times \mathbf{v}$. In what direction does $\mathbf{u} \times \mathbf{v}$ point?

27–28 Find the volume of the parallelepiped determined by the vectors $\mathbf{a}$, $\mathbf{b}$, and $\mathbf{c}$.

27. $\mathbf{a} = \langle 6, 3, -1 \rangle, \quad \mathbf{b} = \langle 0, 1, 2 \rangle, \quad \mathbf{c} = \langle 4, -2, 5 \rangle$
28. $\mathbf{a} = \mathbf{i} + \mathbf{j} - \mathbf{k}, \quad \mathbf{b} = \mathbf{i} - \mathbf{j} + \mathbf{k}, \quad \mathbf{c} = -\mathbf{i} + \mathbf{j} + \mathbf{k}$

1. Homework Hints available in TEC

29–30 Find the volume of the parallelepiped with adjacent edges PQ, PR, and PS.

29. $P(2, 0, -1)$, $Q(4, 1, 0)$, $R(3, -1, 1)$, $S(2, -2, 2)$

30. $P(3, 0, 1)$, $Q(-1, 2, 5)$, $R(5, 1, -1)$, $S(0, 4, 2)$

---

31. Use the scalar triple product to verify that the vectors $\mathbf{u} = \mathbf{i} + 5\mathbf{j} - 2\mathbf{k}$, $\mathbf{v} = 3\mathbf{i} - \mathbf{j}$, and $\mathbf{w} = 5\mathbf{i} + 9\mathbf{j} - 4\mathbf{k}$ are coplanar.

32. Use the scalar triple product to determine whether the points $A(1, 3, 2)$, $B(3, -1, 6)$, $C(5, 2, 0)$, and $D(3, 6, -4)$ lie in the same plane.

33. (a) Let P be a point not on the line L that passes through the points Q and R. Show that the distance d from the point P to the line L is

$$d = \frac{|\mathbf{a} \times \mathbf{b}|}{|\mathbf{a}|}$$

where $\mathbf{a} = \overrightarrow{QR}$ and $\mathbf{b} = \overrightarrow{QP}$.

(b) Use the formula in part (a) to find the distance from the point $P(1, 1, 1)$ to the line through $Q(0, 6, 8)$ and $R(-1, 4, 7)$.

34. (a) Let P be a point not on the plane that passes through the points Q, R, and S. Show that the distance d from P to the plane is

$$d = \frac{|\mathbf{a} \cdot (\mathbf{b} \times \mathbf{c})|}{|\mathbf{a} \times \mathbf{b}|}$$

where $\mathbf{a} = \overrightarrow{QR}$, $\mathbf{b} = \overrightarrow{QS}$, and $\mathbf{c} = \overrightarrow{QP}$.

(b) Use the formula in part (a) to find the distance from the point $P(2, 1, 4)$ to the plane through the points $Q(1, 0, 0)$, $R(0, 2, 0)$, and $S(0, 0, 3)$.

35. Prove that $(\mathbf{a} - \mathbf{b}) \times (\mathbf{a} + \mathbf{b}) = 2(\mathbf{a} \times \mathbf{b})$.

36. Prove the following formula (8) for the vector triple product:

$$\mathbf{a} \times (\mathbf{b} \times \mathbf{c}) = (\mathbf{a} \cdot \mathbf{c})\mathbf{b} - (\mathbf{a} \cdot \mathbf{b})\mathbf{c}$$

37. Use Exercise 36 to prove that

$$\mathbf{a} \times (\mathbf{b} \times \mathbf{c}) + \mathbf{b} \times (\mathbf{c} \times \mathbf{a}) + \mathbf{c} \times (\mathbf{a} \times \mathbf{b}) = \mathbf{0}$$

38. Prove that

$$(\mathbf{a} \times \mathbf{b}) \cdot (\mathbf{c} \times \mathbf{d}) = \begin{vmatrix} \mathbf{a} \cdot \mathbf{c} & \mathbf{b} \cdot \mathbf{c} \\ \mathbf{a} \cdot \mathbf{d} & \mathbf{b} \cdot \mathbf{d} \end{vmatrix}$$

39. Suppose that $\mathbf{a} \neq \mathbf{0}$.

(a) If $\mathbf{a} \cdot \mathbf{b} = \mathbf{a} \cdot \mathbf{c}$, does it follow that $\mathbf{b} = \mathbf{c}$?

(b) If $\mathbf{a} \times \mathbf{b} = \mathbf{a} \times \mathbf{c}$, does it follow that $\mathbf{b} = \mathbf{c}$?

(c) If $\mathbf{a} \cdot \mathbf{b} = \mathbf{a} \cdot \mathbf{c}$ and $\mathbf{a} \times \mathbf{b} = \mathbf{a} \times \mathbf{c}$, does it follow that $\mathbf{b} = \mathbf{c}$?

40. (a) If $\mathbf{u}$ is a unit vector and $\mathbf{a}$ is orthogonal to $\mathbf{u}$, show that

$$\mathbf{u} \times (\mathbf{u} \times \mathbf{a}) = -\mathbf{a}$$

(b) If $\mathbf{u}$ is a unit vector and $\mathbf{v}$ is any vector in V_3, show that

$$\mathbf{u} \times (\mathbf{u} \times (\mathbf{u} \times (\mathbf{u} \times \mathbf{v}))) = -\mathbf{u} \times (\mathbf{u} \times \mathbf{v})$$

41. (a) If $\mathbf{u} \cdot \mathbf{r} = \mathbf{v} \cdot \mathbf{r}$ for every vector $\mathbf{r}$ in V_3, show that $\mathbf{u} = \mathbf{v}$.

(b) Prove Property 3 of the cross product

$$\mathbf{a} \times (\mathbf{b} + \mathbf{c}) = \mathbf{a} \times \mathbf{b} + \mathbf{a} \times \mathbf{c}$$

by showing that

$$[\mathbf{a} \times (\mathbf{b} + \mathbf{c})] \cdot \mathbf{r} = [\mathbf{a} \times \mathbf{b} + \mathbf{a} \times \mathbf{c}] \cdot \mathbf{r}$$

for every vector $\mathbf{r}$ in V_3.

42. If $\mathbf{v}_1$, $\mathbf{v}_2$, and $\mathbf{v}_3$ are noncoplanar vectors, let

$$\mathbf{k}_1 = \frac{\mathbf{v}_2 \times \mathbf{v}_3}{\mathbf{v}_1 \cdot (\mathbf{v}_2 \times \mathbf{v}_3)} \qquad \mathbf{k}_2 = \frac{\mathbf{v}_3 \times \mathbf{v}_1}{\mathbf{v}_1 \cdot (\mathbf{v}_2 \times \mathbf{v}_3)}$$

$$\mathbf{k}_3 = \frac{\mathbf{v}_1 \times \mathbf{v}_2}{\mathbf{v}_1 \cdot (\mathbf{v}_2 \times \mathbf{v}_3)}$$

(These vectors occur in the study of crystallography. Vectors of the form $n_1\mathbf{v}_1 + n_2\mathbf{v}_2 + n_3\mathbf{v}_3$, where each n_i is an integer, form a *lattice* for a crystal. Vectors written similarly in terms of $\mathbf{k}_1$, $\mathbf{k}_2$, and $\mathbf{k}_3$ form the *reciprocal lattice*.)

(a) Show that $\mathbf{k}_i$ is perpendicular to $\mathbf{v}_j$ if $i \neq j$.

(b) Show that $\mathbf{k}_i \cdot \mathbf{v}_i = 1$ for $i = 1, 2, 3$.

(c) Show that $\mathbf{k}_1 \cdot (\mathbf{k}_2 \times \mathbf{k}_3) = \dfrac{1}{\mathbf{v}_1 \cdot (\mathbf{v}_2 \times \mathbf{v}_3)}$.

DISCOVERY PROJECT The Geometry of a Tetrahedron

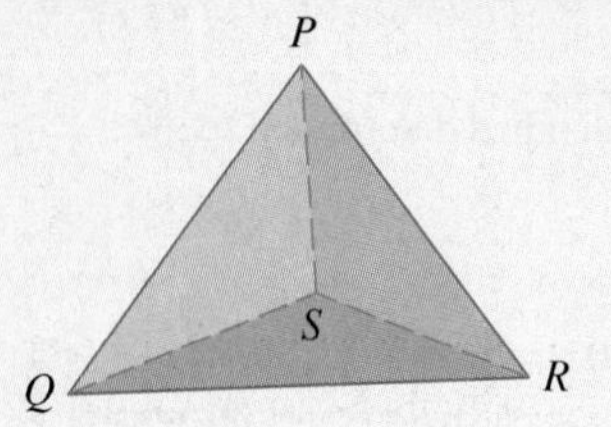

A tetrahedron is a solid with four vertices, P, Q, R, and S, and four triangular faces, as shown in the figure.

1. Let $\mathbf{v}_1$, $\mathbf{v}_2$, $\mathbf{v}_3$, and $\mathbf{v}_4$ be vectors with lengths equal to the areas of the faces opposite the vertices P, Q, R, and S, respectively, and directions perpendicular to the respective faces and pointing outward. Show that

$$\mathbf{v}_1 + \mathbf{v}_2 + \mathbf{v}_3 + \mathbf{v}_4 = \mathbf{0}$$

2. The volume V of a tetrahedron is one-third the distance from a vertex to the opposite face, times the area of that face.
   (a) Find a formula for the volume of a tetrahedron in terms of the coordinates of its vertices P, Q, R, and S.
   (b) Find the volume of the tetrahedron whose vertices are $P(1, 1, 1)$, $Q(1, 2, 3)$, $R(1, 1, 2)$, and $S(3, -1, 2)$.

3. Suppose the tetrahedron in the figure has a trirectangular vertex S. (This means that the three angles at S are all right angles.) Let A, B, and C be the areas of the three faces that meet at S, and let D be the area of the opposite face PQR. Using the result of Problem 1, or otherwise, show that

$$D^2 = A^2 + B^2 + C^2$$

(This is a three-dimensional version of the Pythagorean Theorem.)

9.5 Equations of Lines and Planes

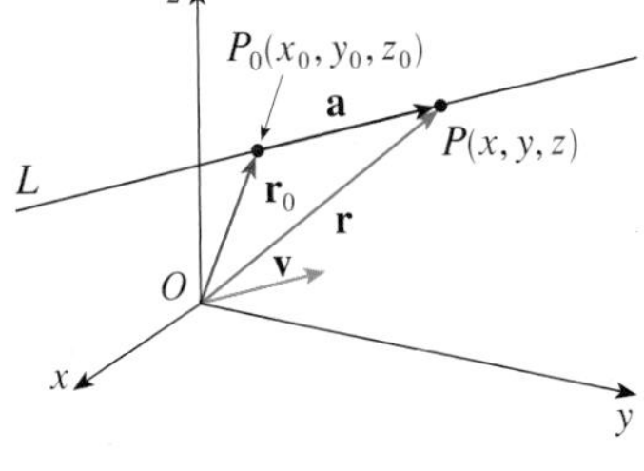

FIGURE 1

A line in the xy-plane is determined when a point on the line and the direction of the line (its slope or angle of inclination) are given. The equation of the line can then be written using the point-slope form.

Likewise, a line L in three-dimensional space is determined when we know a point $P_0(x_0, y_0, z_0)$ on L and the direction of L. In three dimensions the direction of a line is conveniently described by a vector, so we let $\mathbf{v}$ be a vector parallel to L. Let $P(x, y, z)$ be an arbitrary point on L and let $\mathbf{r}_0$ and $\mathbf{r}$ be the position vectors of P_0 and P (that is, they have representations $\overrightarrow{OP_0}$ and $\overrightarrow{OP}$). If $\mathbf{a}$ is the vector with representation $\overrightarrow{P_0P}$, as in Figure 1, then the Triangle Law for vector addition gives $\mathbf{r} = \mathbf{r}_0 + \mathbf{a}$. But, since $\mathbf{a}$ and $\mathbf{v}$ are parallel vectors, there is a scalar t such that $\mathbf{a} = t\mathbf{v}$. Thus

1 $$\mathbf{r} = \mathbf{r}_0 + t\mathbf{v}$$

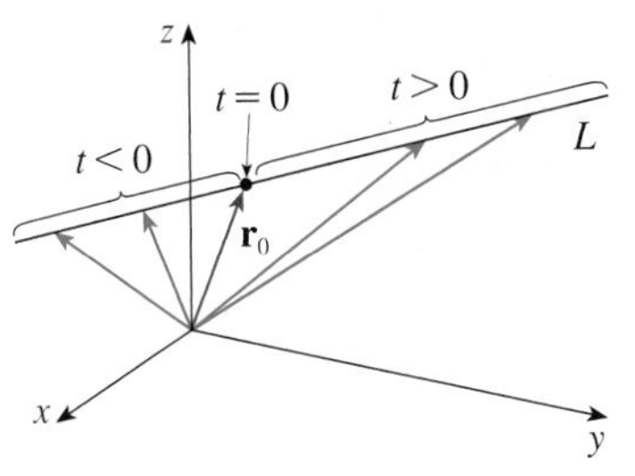

FIGURE 2

which is a **vector equation** of L. Each value of the **parameter** t gives the position vector $\mathbf{r}$ of a point on L. In other words, as t varies, the line is traced out by the tip of the vector $\mathbf{r}$. As Figure 2 indicates, positive values of t correspond to points on L that lie on one side of P_0, whereas negative values of t correspond to points that lie on the other side of P_0.

If the vector $\mathbf{v}$ that gives the direction of the line L is written in component form as $\mathbf{v} = \langle a, b, c \rangle$, then we have $t\mathbf{v} = \langle ta, tb, tc \rangle$. We can also write $\mathbf{r} = \langle x, y, z \rangle$ and $\mathbf{r}_0 = \langle x_0, y_0, z_0 \rangle$, so the vector equation (1) becomes

$$\langle x, y, z \rangle = \langle x_0 + ta, y_0 + tb, z_0 + tc \rangle$$

Two vectors are equal if and only if corresponding components are equal. Therefore we have the three scalar equations:

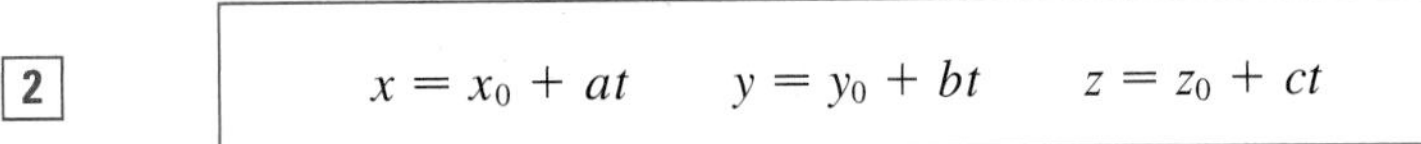

2 $$x = x_0 + at \qquad y = y_0 + bt \qquad z = z_0 + ct$$

where $t \in \mathbb{R}$. These equations are called **parametric equations** of the line L through the point $P_0(x_0, y_0, z_0)$ and parallel to the vector $\mathbf{v} = \langle a, b, c \rangle$. Each value of the parameter t gives a point (x, y, z) on L.

Figure 3 shows the line L in Example 1 and its relation to the given point and to the vector that gives its direction.

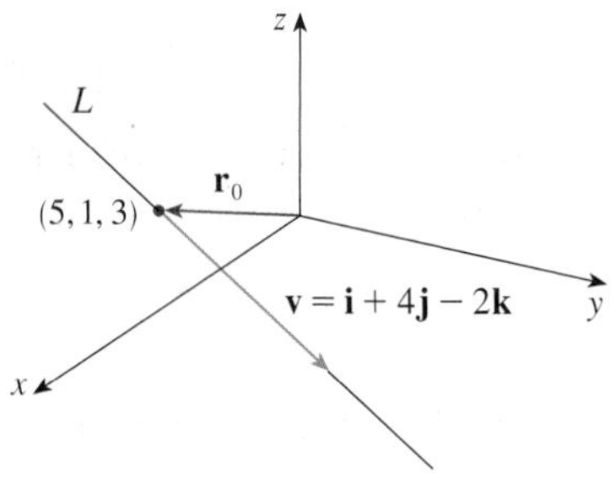

FIGURE 3

EXAMPLE 1 Equations of a line with a given direction
(a) Find a vector equation and parametric equations for the line that passes through the point (5, 1, 3) and is parallel to the vector $\mathbf{i} + 4\mathbf{j} - 2\mathbf{k}$.
(b) Find two other points on the line.

SOLUTION
(a) Here $\mathbf{r}_0 = \langle 5, 1, 3 \rangle = 5\mathbf{i} + \mathbf{j} + 3\mathbf{k}$ and $\mathbf{v} = \mathbf{i} + 4\mathbf{j} - 2\mathbf{k}$, so the vector equation (1) becomes

$$\mathbf{r} = (5\mathbf{i} + \mathbf{j} + 3\mathbf{k}) + t(\mathbf{i} + 4\mathbf{j} - 2\mathbf{k})$$

or

$$\mathbf{r} = (5 + t)\,\mathbf{i} + (1 + 4t)\,\mathbf{j} + (3 - 2t)\,\mathbf{k}$$

Parametric equations are

$$x = 5 + t \qquad y = 1 + 4t \qquad z = 3 - 2t$$

(b) Choosing the parameter value $t = 1$ gives $x = 6$, $y = 5$, and $z = 1$, so (6, 5, 1) is a point on the line. Similarly, $t = -1$ gives the point $(4, -3, 5)$.

The vector equation and parametric equations of a line are not unique. If we change the point or the parameter or choose a different parallel vector, then the equations change. For instance, if, instead of (5, 1, 3), we choose the point (6, 5, 1) in Example 1, then the parametric equations of the line become

$$x = 6 + t \qquad y = 5 + 4t \qquad z = 1 - 2t$$

Or, if we stay with the point (5, 1, 3) but choose the parallel vector $2\mathbf{i} + 8\mathbf{j} - 4\mathbf{k}$, we arrive at the equations

$$x = 5 + 2t \qquad y = 1 + 8t \qquad z = 3 - 4t$$

In general, if a vector $\mathbf{v} = \langle a, b, c \rangle$ is used to describe the direction of a line L, then the numbers a, b, and c are called **direction numbers** of L. Since any vector parallel to $\mathbf{v}$ could also be used, we see that any three numbers proportional to a, b, and c could also be used as a set of direction numbers for L.

Another way of describing a line L is to eliminate the parameter t from Equations 2. If none of a, b, or c is 0, we can solve each of these equations for t, equate the results, and obtain

3 $$\frac{x - x_0}{a} = \frac{y - y_0}{b} = \frac{z - z_0}{c}$$

These equations are called **symmetric equations** of L. Notice that the numbers a, b, and c that appear in the denominators of Equations 3 are direction numbers of L, that is, components of a vector parallel to L. If one of a, b, or c is 0, we can still eliminate t. For instance, if $a = 0$, we could write the equations of L as

$$x = x_0 \qquad \frac{y - y_0}{b} = \frac{z - z_0}{c}$$

This means that L lies in the vertical plane $x = x_0$.

Figure 4 shows the line L in Example 2 and the point P where it intersects the xy-plane.

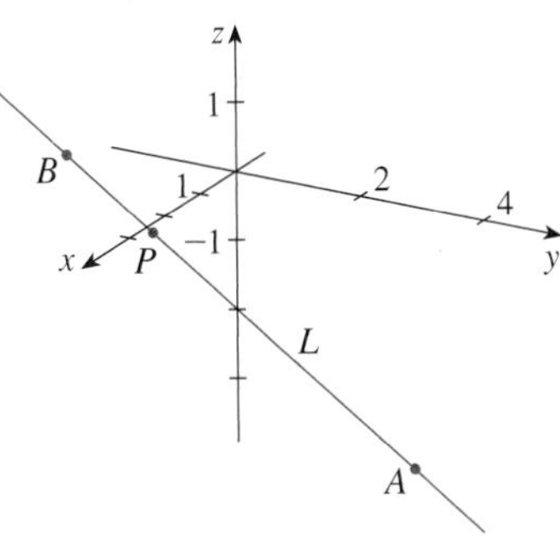

FIGURE 4

EXAMPLE 2 Equations of a line through two points
(a) Find parametric equations and symmetric equations of the line that passes through the points $A(2, 4, -3)$ and $B(3, -1, 1)$.
(b) At what point does this line intersect the xy-plane?

SOLUTION
(a) We are not explicitly given a vector parallel to the line, but observe that the vector $\mathbf{v}$ with representation $\overrightarrow{AB}$ is parallel to the line and

$$\mathbf{v} = \langle 3 - 2, -1 - 4, 1 - (-3) \rangle = \langle 1, -5, 4 \rangle$$

Thus direction numbers are $a = 1$, $b = -5$, and $c = 4$. Taking the point $(2, 4, -3)$ as P_0, we see that parametric equations (2) are

$$x = 2 + t \qquad y = 4 - 5t \qquad z = -3 + 4t$$

and symmetric equations (3) are

$$\frac{x - 2}{1} = \frac{y - 4}{-5} = \frac{z + 3}{4}$$

(b) The line intersects the xy-plane when $z = 0$, so we put $z = 0$ in the symmetric equations and obtain

$$\frac{x - 2}{1} = \frac{y - 4}{-5} = \frac{3}{4}$$

This gives $x = \frac{11}{4}$ and $y = \frac{1}{4}$, so the line intersects the xy-plane at the point $\left(\frac{11}{4}, \frac{1}{4}, 0\right)$.

In general, the procedure of Example 2 shows that direction numbers of the line L through the points $P_0(x_0, y_0, z_0)$ and $P_1(x_1, y_1, z_1)$ are $x_1 - x_0$, $y_1 - y_0$, and $z_1 - z_0$ and so symmetric equations of L are

$$\frac{x - x_0}{x_1 - x_0} = \frac{y - y_0}{y_1 - y_0} = \frac{z - z_0}{z_1 - z_0}$$

Often, we need a description, not of an entire line, but of just a line segment. How, for instance, could we describe the line segment AB in Example 2? If we put $t = 0$ in the parametric equations in Example 2(a), we get the point $(2, 4, -3)$ and if we put $t = 1$ we get $(3, -1, 1)$. So the line segment AB is described by the parametric equations

$$x = 2 + t \qquad y = 4 - 5t \qquad z = -3 + 4t \qquad 0 \leqslant t \leqslant 1$$

or by the corresponding vector equation

$$\mathbf{r}(t) = \langle 2 + t, 4 - 5t, -3 + 4t \rangle \qquad 0 \leqslant t \leqslant 1$$

In general, we know from Equation 1 that the vector equation of a line through the (tip of the) vector $\mathbf{r}_0$ in the direction of a vector $\mathbf{v}$ is $\mathbf{r} = \mathbf{r}_0 + t\mathbf{v}$. If the line also passes through (the tip of) $\mathbf{r}_1$, then we can take $\mathbf{v} = \mathbf{r}_1 - \mathbf{r}_0$ and so its vector equation is

$$\mathbf{r} = \mathbf{r}_0 + t(\mathbf{r}_1 - \mathbf{r}_0) = (1 - t)\mathbf{r}_0 + t\mathbf{r}_1$$

The line segment from $\mathbf{r}_0$ to $\mathbf{r}_1$ is given by the parameter interval $0 \leqslant t \leqslant 1$.

> **4** The line segment from $\mathbf{r}_0$ to $\mathbf{r}_1$ is given by the vector equation
>
> $$\mathbf{r}(t) = (1 - t)\mathbf{r}_0 + t\mathbf{r}_1 \qquad 0 \leqslant t \leqslant 1$$

The lines L_1 and L_2 in Example 3, shown in Figure 5, are skew lines.

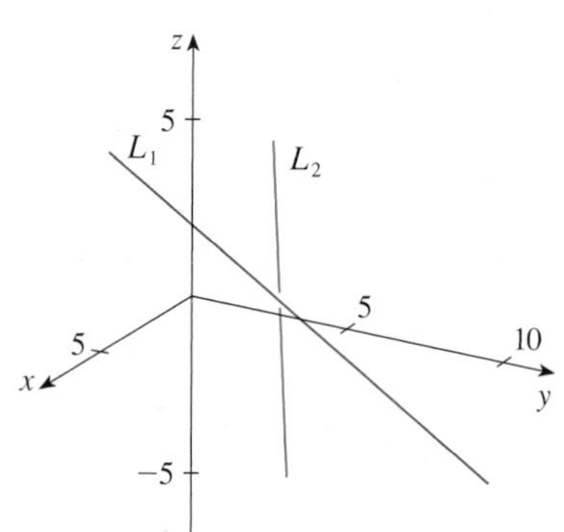

FIGURE 5

V EXAMPLE 3 Show that the lines L_1 and L_2 with parametric equations

$$x = 1 + t \qquad y = -2 + 3t \qquad z = 4 - t$$

$$x = 2s \qquad y = 3 + s \qquad z = -3 + 4s$$

are **skew lines**; that is, they do not intersect and are not parallel (and therefore do not lie in the same plane).

SOLUTION The lines are not parallel because the corresponding vectors $\langle 1, 3, -1 \rangle$ and $\langle 2, 1, 4 \rangle$ are not parallel. (Their components are not proportional.) If L_1 and L_2 had a point of intersection, there would be values of t and s such that

$$\begin{aligned} 1 + t &= 2s \\ -2 + 3t &= 3 + s \\ 4 - t &= -3 + 4s \end{aligned}$$

But if we solve the first two equations, we get $t = \frac{11}{5}$ and $s = \frac{8}{5}$, and these values don't satisfy the third equation. Therefore there are no values of t and s that satisfy the three equations, so L_1 and L_2 do not intersect. Thus L_1 and L_2 are skew lines.

Planes

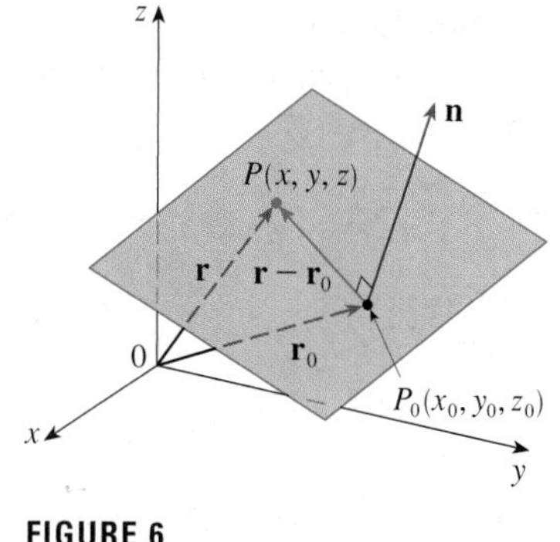

FIGURE 6

Although a line in space is determined by a point and a direction, a plane in space is more difficult to describe. A single vector parallel to a plane is not enough to convey the "direction" of the plane, but a vector perpendicular to the plane does completely specify its direction. Thus a plane in space is determined by a point $P_0(x_0, y_0, z_0)$ in the plane and a vector $\mathbf{n}$ that is orthogonal to the plane. This orthogonal vector $\mathbf{n}$ is called a **normal vector**. Let $P(x, y, z)$ be an arbitrary point in the plane, and let $\mathbf{r}_0$ and $\mathbf{r}$ be the position vectors of P_0 and P. Then the vector $\mathbf{r} - \mathbf{r}_0$ is represented by $\overrightarrow{P_0P}$. (See Figure 6.) The normal vector $\mathbf{n}$ is orthogonal to every vector in the given plane. In particular, $\mathbf{n}$ is orthogonal to $\mathbf{r} - \mathbf{r}_0$ and so we have

5
$$\mathbf{n} \cdot (\mathbf{r} - \mathbf{r}_0) = 0$$

which can be rewritten as

6
$$\mathbf{n} \cdot \mathbf{r} = \mathbf{n} \cdot \mathbf{r}_0$$

Either Equation 5 or Equation 6 is called a **vector equation of the plane**.

To obtain a scalar equation for the plane, we write $\mathbf{n} = \langle a, b, c \rangle$, $\mathbf{r} = \langle x, y, z \rangle$, and $\mathbf{r}_0 = \langle x_0, y_0, z_0 \rangle$. Then the vector equation (5) becomes

$$\langle a, b, c \rangle \cdot \langle x - x_0, y - y_0, z - z_0 \rangle = 0$$

or

$$\boxed{7} \qquad a(x - x_0) + b(y - y_0) + c(z - z_0) = 0$$

Equation 7 is the **scalar equation of the plane through $P_0(x_0, y_0, z_0)$ with normal vector $\mathbf{n} = \langle a, b, c \rangle$**.

V EXAMPLE 4 Find an equation of the plane through the point $(2, 4, -1)$ with normal vector $\mathbf{n} = \langle 2, 3, 4 \rangle$. Find the intercepts and sketch the plane.

SOLUTION Putting $a = 2$, $b = 3$, $c = 4$, $x_0 = 2$, $y_0 = 4$, and $z_0 = -1$ in Equation 7, we see that an equation of the plane is

$$2(x - 2) + 3(y - 4) + 4(z + 1) = 0$$

or

$$2x + 3y + 4z = 12$$

To find the x-intercept we set $y = z = 0$ in this equation and obtain $x = 6$. Similarly, the y-intercept is 4 and the z-intercept is 3. This enables us to sketch the portion of the plane that lies in the first octant (see Figure 7).

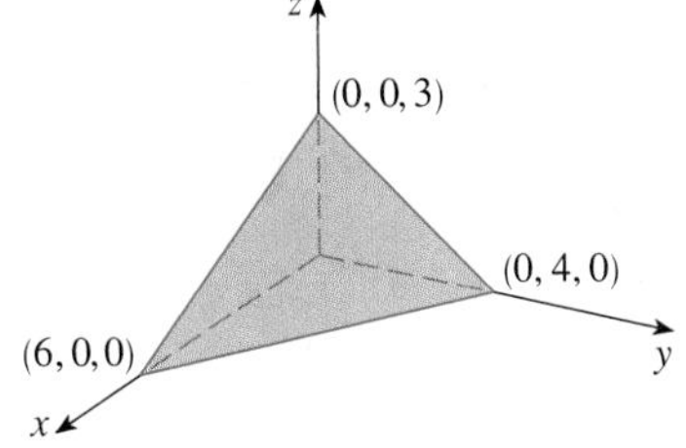

FIGURE 7

By collecting terms in Equation 7 as we did in Example 4, we can rewrite the equation of a plane as

$$\boxed{8} \qquad ax + by + cz + d = 0$$

where $d = -(ax_0 + by_0 + cz_0)$. Equation 8 is called a **linear equation** in x, y, and z. Conversely, it can be shown that if a, b, and c are not all 0, then the linear equation (8) represents a plane with normal vector $\langle a, b, c \rangle$. (See Exercise 63.)

Figure 8 shows the portion of the plane in Example 5 that is enclosed by triangle PQR.

EXAMPLE 5 The plane through three points Find an equation of the plane that passes through the points $P(1, 3, 2)$, $Q(3, -1, 6)$, and $R(5, 2, 0)$.

SOLUTION The vectors $\mathbf{a}$ and $\mathbf{b}$ corresponding to $\overrightarrow{PQ}$ and $\overrightarrow{PR}$ are

$$\mathbf{a} = \langle 2, -4, 4 \rangle \qquad \mathbf{b} = \langle 4, -1, -2 \rangle$$

Since both $\mathbf{a}$ and $\mathbf{b}$ lie in the plane, their cross product $\mathbf{a} \times \mathbf{b}$ is orthogonal to the plane and can be taken as the normal vector. Thus

$$\mathbf{n} = \mathbf{a} \times \mathbf{b} = \begin{vmatrix} \mathbf{i} & \mathbf{j} & \mathbf{k} \\ 2 & -4 & 4 \\ 4 & -1 & -2 \end{vmatrix} = 12\,\mathbf{i} + 20\,\mathbf{j} + 14\,\mathbf{k}$$

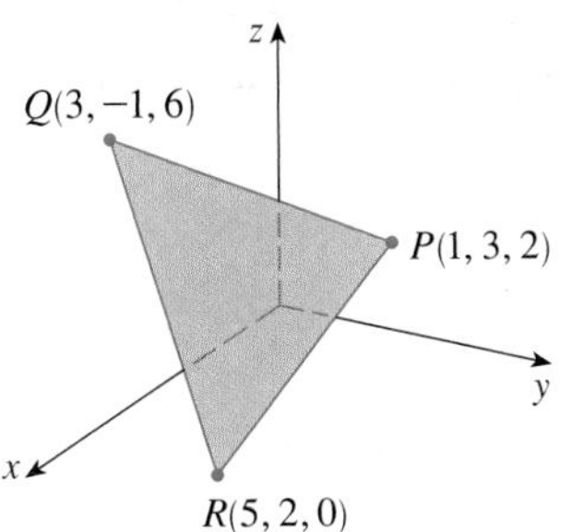

FIGURE 8

With the point $P(1, 3, 2)$ and the normal vector $\mathbf{n}$, an equation of the plane is

$$12(x - 1) + 20(y - 3) + 14(z - 2) = 0$$

or

$$6x + 10y + 7z = 50$$

EXAMPLE 6 Find the point at which the line with parametric equations $x = 2 + 3t$, $y = -4t$, $z = 5 + t$ intersects the plane $4x + 5y - 2z = 18$.

SOLUTION We substitute the expressions for x, y, and z from the parametric equations into the equation of the plane:

$$4(2 + 3t) + 5(-4t) - 2(5 + t) = 18$$

This simplifies to $-10t = 20$, so $t = -2$. Therefore the point of intersection occurs when the parameter value is $t = -2$. Then $x = 2 + 3(-2) = -4$, $y = -4(-2) = 8$, $z = 5 - 2 = 3$ and so the point of intersection is $(-4, 8, 3)$.

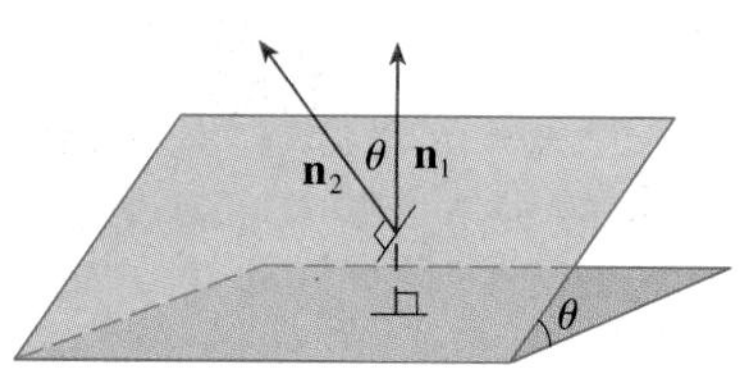

FIGURE 9

Two planes are **parallel** if their normal vectors are parallel. For instance, the planes $x + 2y - 3z = 4$ and $2x + 4y - 6z = 3$ are parallel because their normal vectors are $\mathbf{n}_1 = \langle 1, 2, -3 \rangle$ and $\mathbf{n}_2 = \langle 2, 4, -6 \rangle$ and $\mathbf{n}_2 = 2\mathbf{n}_1$. If two planes are not parallel, then they intersect in a straight line and the angle between the two planes is defined as the acute angle between their normal vectors (see angle θ in Figure 9).

V **EXAMPLE 7 Angle between planes; line of intersection of planes**

(a) Find the angle between the planes $x + y + z = 1$ and $x - 2y + 3z = 1$.
(b) Find symmetric equations for the line of intersection L of these two planes.

Figure 10 shows the planes in Example 7 and their line of intersection L.

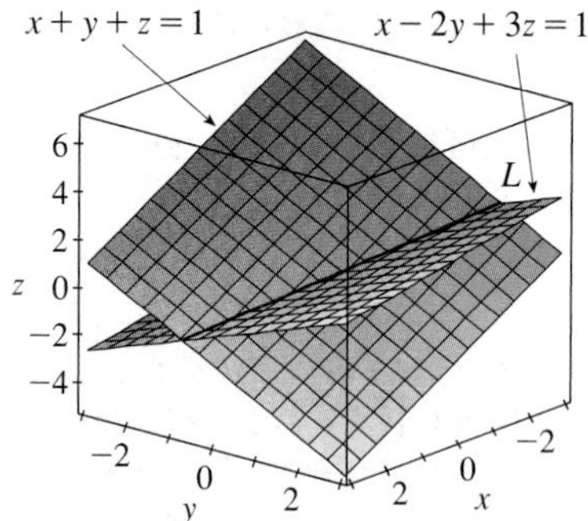

FIGURE 10

SOLUTION

(a) The normal vectors of these planes are

$$\mathbf{n}_1 = \langle 1, 1, 1 \rangle \qquad \mathbf{n}_2 = \langle 1, -2, 3 \rangle$$

and so, if θ is the angle between the planes,

$$\cos\theta = \frac{\mathbf{n}_1 \cdot \mathbf{n}_2}{|\mathbf{n}_1||\mathbf{n}_2|} = \frac{1(1) + 1(-2) + 1(3)}{\sqrt{1 + 1 + 1}\sqrt{1 + 4 + 9}} = \frac{2}{\sqrt{42}}$$

$$\theta = \cos^{-1}\left(\frac{2}{\sqrt{42}}\right) \approx 72^\circ$$

(b) We first need to find a point on L. For instance, we can find the point where the line intersects the xy-plane by setting $z = 0$ in the equations of both planes. This gives the equations $x + y = 1$ and $x - 2y = 1$, whose solution is $x = 1$, $y = 0$. So the point $(1, 0, 0)$ lies on L.

Now we observe that, since L lies in both planes, it is perpendicular to both of the normal vectors. Thus a vector $\mathbf{v}$ parallel to L is given by the cross product

Another way to find the line of intersection is to solve the equations of the planes for two of the variables in terms of the third, which can be taken as the parameter.

$$\mathbf{v} = \mathbf{n}_1 \times \mathbf{n}_2 = \begin{vmatrix} \mathbf{i} & \mathbf{j} & \mathbf{k} \\ 1 & 1 & 1 \\ 1 & -2 & 3 \end{vmatrix} = 5\mathbf{i} - 2\mathbf{j} - 3\mathbf{k}$$

and so the symmetric equations of L can be written as

$$\frac{x - 1}{5} = \frac{y}{-2} = \frac{z}{-3}$$

Note: Since a linear equation in x, y, and z represents a plane and two nonparallel planes intersect in a line, it follows that two linear equations can represent a line. The points (x, y, z) that satisfy both

$$a_1x + b_1y + c_1z + d_1 = 0 \qquad \text{and} \qquad a_2x + b_2y + c_2z + d_2 = 0$$

lie on both of these planes, and so the pair of linear equations represents the line of intersection of the planes (if they are not parallel). For instance, in Example 7 the line L was given as the line of intersection of the planes $x + y + z = 1$ and $x - 2y + 3z = 1$. The symmetric equations that we found for L could be written as

$$\frac{x-1}{5} = \frac{y}{-2} \qquad \text{and} \qquad \frac{y}{-2} = \frac{z}{-3}$$

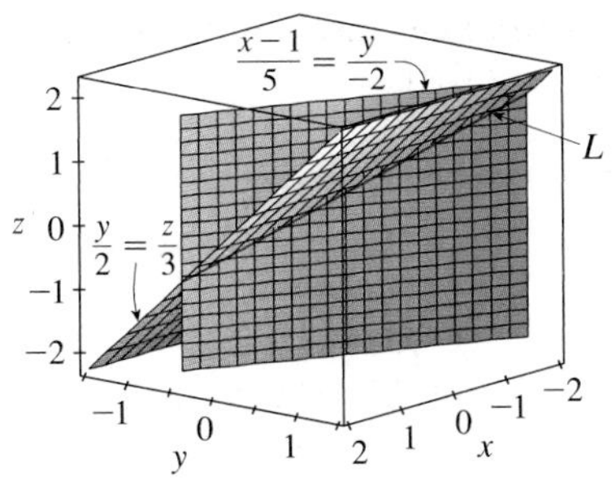

FIGURE 11

Figure 11 shows how the line L in Example 7 can also be regarded as the line of intersection of planes derived from its symmetric equations.

which is again a pair of linear equations. They exhibit L as the line of intersection of the planes $(x - 1)/5 = y/(-2)$ and $y/(-2) = z/(-3)$. (See Figure 11.)

In general, when we write the equations of a line in the symmetric form

$$\frac{x - x_0}{a} = \frac{y - y_0}{b} = \frac{z - z_0}{c}$$

we can regard the line as the line of intersection of the two planes

$$\frac{x - x_0}{a} = \frac{y - y_0}{b} \qquad \text{and} \qquad \frac{y - y_0}{b} = \frac{z - z_0}{c}$$

EXAMPLE 8 Find a formula for the distance D from a point $P_1(x_1, y_1, z_1)$ to the plane $ax + by + cz + d = 0$.

SOLUTION Let $P_0(x_0, y_0, z_0)$ be any point in the given plane and let $\mathbf{b}$ be the vector corresponding to $\overrightarrow{P_0P_1}$. Then

$$\mathbf{b} = \langle x_1 - x_0, y_1 - y_0, z_1 - z_0 \rangle$$

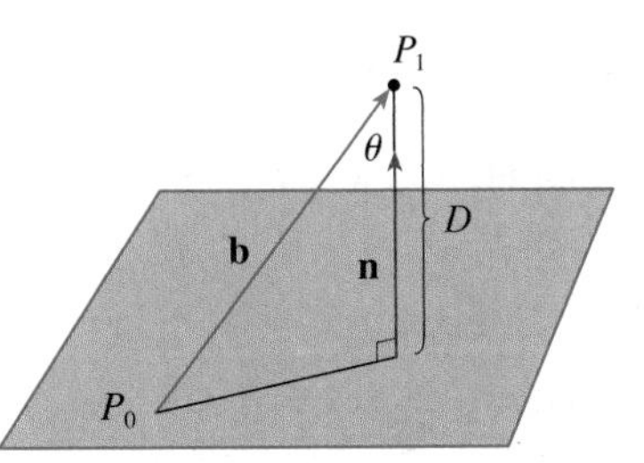

FIGURE 12

From Figure 12 you can see that the distance D from P_1 to the plane is equal to the absolute value of the scalar projection of $\mathbf{b}$ onto the normal vector $\mathbf{n} = \langle a, b, c \rangle$. (See Section 9.3.) Thus

$$\begin{aligned} D &= |\operatorname{comp}_{\mathbf{n}} \mathbf{b}| = \frac{|\mathbf{n} \cdot \mathbf{b}|}{|\mathbf{n}|} \\ &= \frac{|a(x_1 - x_0) + b(y_1 - y_0) + c(z_1 - z_0)|}{\sqrt{a^2 + b^2 + c^2}} \\ &= \frac{|(ax_1 + by_1 + cz_1) - (ax_0 + by_0 + cz_0)|}{\sqrt{a^2 + b^2 + c^2}} \end{aligned}$$

Since P_0 lies in the plane, its coordinates satisfy the equation of the plane and so we have $ax_0 + by_0 + cz_0 + d = 0$. Thus the formula for D can be written as

9 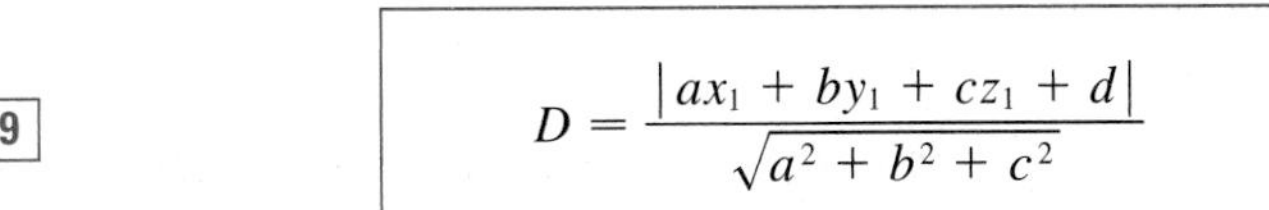

$$D = \frac{|ax_1 + by_1 + cz_1 + d|}{\sqrt{a^2 + b^2 + c^2}}$$

EXAMPLE 9 **Distance between planes** Find the distance between the parallel planes $10x + 2y - 2z = 5$ and $5x + y - z = 1$.

SOLUTION First we note that the planes are parallel because their normal vectors $\langle 10, 2, -2 \rangle$ and $\langle 5, 1, -1 \rangle$ are parallel. To find the distance D between the planes, we choose any point on one plane and calculate its distance to the other plane. In particular, if we put $y = z = 0$ in the equation of the first plane, we get $10x = 5$ and so $\left(\frac{1}{2}, 0, 0\right)$ is a point in this plane. By Formula 9, the distance between $\left(\frac{1}{2}, 0, 0\right)$ and the plane $5x + y - z - 1 = 0$ is

$$D = \frac{\left|5\left(\frac{1}{2}\right) + 1(0) - 1(0) - 1\right|}{\sqrt{5^2 + 1^2 + (-1)^2}} = \frac{\frac{3}{2}}{3\sqrt{3}} = \frac{\sqrt{3}}{6}$$

So the distance between the planes is $\sqrt{3}/6$.

EXAMPLE 10 Distance between lines In Example 3 we showed that the lines

$$L_1:\quad x = 1 + t \qquad y = -2 + 3t \qquad z = 4 - t$$

$$L_2:\quad x = 2s \qquad y = 3 + s \qquad z = -3 + 4s$$

are skew. Find the distance between them.

SOLUTION Since the two lines L_1 and L_2 are skew, they can be viewed as lying on two parallel planes P_1 and P_2. The distance between L_1 and L_2 is the same as the distance between P_1 and P_2, which can be computed as in Example 9. The common normal vector to both planes must be orthogonal to both $\mathbf{v}_1 = \langle 1, 3, -1 \rangle$ (the direction of L_1) and $\mathbf{v}_2 = \langle 2, 1, 4 \rangle$ (the direction of L_2). So a normal vector is

$$\mathbf{n} = \mathbf{v}_1 \times \mathbf{v}_2 = \begin{vmatrix} \mathbf{i} & \mathbf{j} & \mathbf{k} \\ 1 & 3 & -1 \\ 2 & 1 & 4 \end{vmatrix} = 13\mathbf{i} - 6\mathbf{j} - 5\mathbf{k}$$

If we put $s = 0$ in the equations of L_2, we get the point $(0, 3, -3)$ on L_2 and so an equation for P_2 is

$$13(x - 0) - 6(y - 3) - 5(z + 3) = 0 \qquad \text{or} \qquad 13x - 6y - 5z + 3 = 0$$

If we now set $t = 0$ in the equations for L_1, we get the point $(1, -2, 4)$ on P_1. So the distance between L_1 and L_2 is the same as the distance from $(1, -2, 4)$ to $13x - 6y - 5z + 3 = 0$. By Formula 9, this distance is

$$D = \frac{|13(1) - 6(-2) - 5(4) + 3|}{\sqrt{13^2 + (-6)^2 + (-5)^2}} = \frac{8}{\sqrt{230}} \approx 0.53$$

9.5 Exercises

1. Determine whether each statement is true or false.
   (a) Two lines parallel to a third line are parallel.
   (b) Two lines perpendicular to a third line are parallel.
   (c) Two planes parallel to a third plane are parallel.
   (d) Two planes perpendicular to a third plane are parallel.
   (e) Two lines parallel to a plane are parallel.
   (f) Two lines perpendicular to a plane are parallel.
   (g) Two planes parallel to a line are parallel.
   (h) Two planes perpendicular to a line are parallel.
   (i) Two planes either intersect or are parallel.
   (j) Two lines either intersect or are parallel.
   (k) A plane and a line either intersect or are parallel.

2–5 Find a vector equation and parametric equations for the line.

2. The line through the point $(6, -5, 2)$ and parallel to the vector $\left\langle 1, 3, -\frac{2}{3} \right\rangle$

3. The line through the point $(2, 2.4, 3.5)$ and parallel to the vector $3\mathbf{i} + 2\mathbf{j} - \mathbf{k}$

4. The line through the point $(0, 14, -10)$ and parallel to the line $x = -1 + 2t$, $y = 6 - 3t$, $z = 3 + 9t$

1. Homework Hints available in TEC

5. The line through the point (1, 0, 6) and perpendicular to the plane $x + 3y + z = 5$

6–10 Find parametric equations and symmetric equations for the line.

6. The line through the points (6, 1, −3) and (2, 4, 5)

7. The line through the points $(0, \frac{1}{2}, 1)$ and (2, 1, −3)

8. The line through (2, 1, 0) and perpendicular to both $\mathbf{i} + \mathbf{j}$ and $\mathbf{j} + \mathbf{k}$

9. The line through (1, −1, 1) and parallel to the line $x + 2 = \frac{1}{2}y = z - 3$

10. The line of intersection of the planes $x + 2y + 3z = 1$ and $x - y + z = 1$

---

11. Is the line through (−4, −6, 1) and (−2, 0, −3) parallel to the line through (10, 18, 4) and (5, 3, 14)?

12. Is the line through (4, 1, −1) and (2, 5, 3) perpendicular to the line through (−3, 2, 0) and (5, 1, 4)?

13. (a) Find symmetric equations for the line that passes through the point (1, −5, 6) and is parallel to the vector $\langle -1, 2, -3 \rangle$.
(b) Find the points in which the required line in part (a) intersects the coordinate planes.

14. (a) Find parametric equations for the line through (2, 4, 6) that is perpendicular to the plane $x - y + 3z = 7$.
(b) In what points does this line intersect the coordinate planes?

15. Find a vector equation for the line segment from (2, −1, 4) to (4, 6, 1).

16. Find parametric equations for the line segment from (10, 3, 1) to (5, 6, −3).

17–20 Determine whether the lines L_1 and L_2 are parallel, skew, or intersecting. If they intersect, find the point of intersection.

17. L_1: $x = -6t, \quad y = 1 + 9t, \quad z = -3t$

L_2: $x = 1 + 2s, \quad y = 4 - 3s, \quad z = s$

18. L_1: $x = 1 + 2t, \quad y = 3t, \quad z = 2 - t$

L_2: $x = -1 + s, \quad y = 4 + s, \quad z = 1 + 3s$

19. L_1: $\dfrac{x}{1} = \dfrac{y - 1}{2} = \dfrac{z - 2}{3}$

L_2: $\dfrac{x - 3}{-4} = \dfrac{y - 2}{-3} = \dfrac{z - 1}{2}$

20. L_1: $\dfrac{x - 1}{2} = \dfrac{y - 3}{2} = \dfrac{z - 2}{-1}$

L_2: $\dfrac{x - 2}{1} = \dfrac{y - 6}{-1} = \dfrac{z + 2}{3}$

21–32 Find an equation of the plane.

21. The plane through the point (6, 3, 2) and perpendicular to the vector $\langle -2, 1, 5 \rangle$

22. The plane through the point (4, 0, −3) and with normal vector $\mathbf{j} + 2\mathbf{k}$

23. The plane through the point (4, −2, 3) and parallel to the plane $3x - 7z = 12$

24. The plane that contains the line $x = 1 + t$, $y = 2 - t$, $z = 4 - 3t$ and is parallel to the plane $5x + 2y + z = 1$

25. The plane through the points (0, 1, 1), (1, 0, 1), and (1, 1, 0)

26. The plane through the origin and the points (2, −4, 6) and (5, 1, 3)

27. The plane that passes through the point (6, 0, −2) and contains the line $x = 4 - 2t$, $y = 3 + 5t$, $z = 7 + 4t$

28. The plane that passes through the point (1, −1, 1) and contains the line with symmetric equations $x = 2y = 3z$

29. The plane that passes through the point (−1, 2, 1) and contains the line of intersection of the planes $x + y - z = 2$ and $2x - y + 3z = 1$

30. The plane that passes through the points (0, −2, 5) and (−1, 3, 1) and is perpendicular to the plane $2z = 5x + 4y$

31. The plane that passes through the point (1, 5, 1) and is perpendicular to the planes $2x + y - 2z = 2$ and $x + 3z = 4$

32. The plane that passes through the line of intersection of the planes $x - z = 1$ and $y + 2z = 3$ and is perpendicular to the plane $x + y - 2z = 1$

33–36 Use intercepts to help sketch the plane.

33. $2x + 5y + z = 10$

34. $3x + y + 2z = 6$

35. $6x - 3y + 4z = 6$

36. $6x + 5y - 3z = 15$

---

37. Find the point at which the line $x = 3 - t$, $y = 2 + t$, $z = 5t$ intersects the plane $x - y + 2z = 9$.

38. Where does the line through (1, 0, 1) and (4, −2, 2) intersect the plane $x + y + z = 6$?

39–42 Determine whether the planes are parallel, perpendicular, or neither. If neither, find the angle between them.

39. $x + 4y - 3z = 1, \quad -3x + 6y + 7z = 0$

40. $x + 2y + 2z = 1, \quad 2x - y + 2z = 1$

41. $x + y + z = 1, \quad x - y + z = 1$

42. $2z = 4y - x, \quad 3x - 12y + 6z = 1$

43–44 (a) Find parametric equations for the line of intersection of the planes and (b) find the angle between the planes.

43. $x + y + z = 1, \quad x + 2y + 2z = 1$

44. $3x - 2y + z = 1, \quad 2x + y - 3z = 3$

45. Find symmetric equations for the line of intersection of the planes $5x - 2y - 2z = 1$ and $4x + y + z = 6$.

46. Find an equation for the plane consisting of all points that are equidistant from the points $(2, 5, 5)$ and $(-6, 3, 1)$.

47. Find an equation of the plane with x-intercept a, y-intercept b, and z-intercept c.

48. (a) Find the point at which the given lines intersect:

$$\mathbf{r} = \langle 1, 1, 0\rangle + t\langle 1, -1, 2\rangle$$

$$\mathbf{r} = \langle 2, 0, 2\rangle + s\langle -1, 1, 0\rangle$$

(b) Find an equation of the plane that contains these lines.

49. Find parametric equations for the line through the point $(0, 1, 2)$ that is parallel to the plane $x + y + z = 2$ and perpendicular to the line $x = 1 + t$, $y = 1 - t$, $z = 2t$.

50. Find parametric equations for the line through the point $(0, 1, 2)$ that is perpendicular to the line $x = 1 + t$, $y = 1 - t$, $z = 2t$ and intersects this line.

51. Which of the following four planes are parallel? Are any of them identical?

P_1: $3x + 6y - 3z = 6$ $\qquad$ P_2: $4x - 12y + 8z = 5$

P_3: $9y = 1 + 3x + 6z$ $\qquad$ P_4: $z = x + 2y - 2$

52. Which of the following four lines are parallel? Are any of them identical?

L_1: $x = 1 + 6t, \quad y = 1 - 3t, \quad z = 12t + 5$

L_2: $x = 1 + 2t, \quad y = t, \quad z = 1 + 4t$

L_3: $2x - 2 = 4 - 4y = z + 1$

L_4: $\mathbf{r} = \langle 3, 1, 5\rangle + t\langle 4, 2, 8\rangle$

53–54 Use the formula in Exercise 33 in Section 9.4 to find the distance from the point to the given line.

53. $(4, 1, -2)$; $\quad x = 1 + t, \ y = 3 - 2t, \ z = 4 - 3t$

54. $(0, 1, 3)$; $\quad x = 2t, \ y = 6 - 2t, \ z = 3 + t$

55–56 Find the distance from the point to the given plane.

55. $(1, -2, 4), \quad 3x + 2y + 6z = 5$

56. $(-6, 3, 5), \quad x - 2y - 4z = 8$

57–58 Find the distance between the given parallel planes.

57. $2x - 3y + z = 4, \quad 4x - 6y + 2z = 3$

58. $6z = 4y - 2x, \quad 9z = 1 - 3x + 6y$

59. Show that the distance between the parallel planes $ax + by + cz + d_1 = 0$ and $ax + by + cz + d_2 = 0$ is

$$D = \frac{|d_1 - d_2|}{\sqrt{a^2 + b^2 + c^2}}$$

60. Find equations of the planes that are parallel to the plane $x + 2y - 2z = 1$ and two units away from it.

61. Show that the lines with symmetric equations $x = y = z$ and $x + 1 = y/2 = z/3$ are skew, and find the distance between these lines.

62. Find the distance between the skew lines with parametric equations $x = 1 + t$, $y = 1 + 6t$, $z = 2t$, and $x = 1 + 2s$, $y = 5 + 15s$, $z = -2 + 6s$.

63. If a, b, and c are not all 0, show that the equation $ax + by + cz + d = 0$ represents a plane and $\langle a, b, c\rangle$ is a normal vector to the plane.

Hint: Suppose $a \neq 0$ and rewrite the equation in the form

$$a\left(x + \frac{d}{a}\right) + b(y - 0) + c(z - 0) = 0$$

64. Give a geometric description of each family of planes.

(a) $x + y + z = c$ $\qquad$ (b) $x + y + cz = 1$

(c) $y\cos\theta + z\sin\theta = 1$

LABORATORY PROJECT **Putting 3D in Perspective**

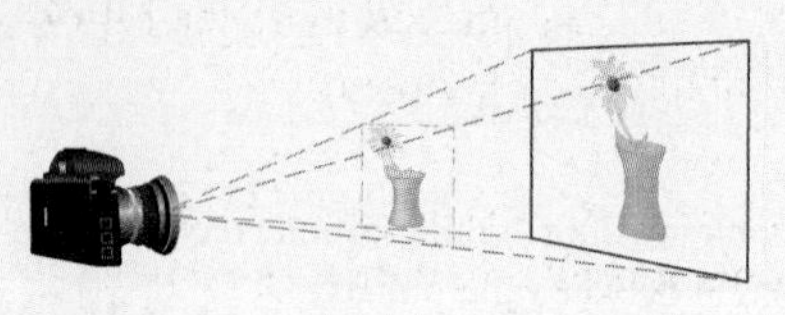

Computer graphics programmers face the same challenge as the great painters of the past: how to represent a three-dimensional scene as a flat image on a two-dimensional plane (a screen or a canvas). To create the illusion of perspective, in which closer objects appear larger than those farther away, three-dimensional objects in the computer's memory are projected onto a rectangular screen window from a viewpoint where the eye, or camera, is located. The viewing volume—the portion of space that will be visible—is the region contained by the four planes that pass through the viewpoint and an edge of the screen window. If objects in the scene extend beyond these four planes, they must be truncated before pixel data are sent to the screen. These planes are therefore called *clipping planes*.

1. Suppose the screen is represented by a rectangle in the yz-plane with vertices $(0, \pm 400, 0)$ and $(0, \pm 400, 600)$, and the camera is placed at $(1000, 0, 0)$. A line L in the scene passes through the points $(230, -285, 102)$ and $(860, 105, 264)$. At what points should L be clipped by the clipping planes?
2. If the clipped line segment is projected on the screen window, identify the resulting line segment.
3. Use parametric equations to plot the edges of the screen window, the clipped line segment, and its projection on the screen window. Then add sight lines connecting the viewpoint to each end of the clipped segments to verify that the projection is correct.
4. A rectangle with vertices $(621, -147, 206)$, $(563, 31, 242)$, $(657, -111, 86)$, and $(599, 67, 122)$ is added to the scene. The line L intersects this rectangle. To make the rectangle appear opaque, a programmer can use *hidden line rendering,* which removes portions of objects that are behind other objects. Identify the portion of L that should be removed.

9.6 Functions and Surfaces

In this section we take a first look at functions of two variables and their graphs, which are surfaces in three-dimensional space. We will give a much more thorough treatment of such functions in Chapter 11.

Functions of Two Variables

The temperature T at a point on the surface of the earth at any given time depends on the longitude x and latitude y of the point. We can think of T as being a function of the two variables x and y, or as a function of the pair (x, y). We indicate this functional dependence by writing $T = f(x, y)$.

The volume V of a circular cylinder depends on its radius r and its height h. In fact, we know that $V = \pi r^2 h$. We say that V is a function of r and h, and we write $V(r, h) = \pi r^2 h$.

Definition A **function f of two variables** is a rule that assigns to each ordered pair of real numbers (x, y) in a set D a unique real number denoted by $f(x, y)$. The set D is the **domain** of f and its **range** is the set of values that f takes on, that is, $\{f(x, y) \mid (x, y) \in D\}$.

We often write $z = f(x, y)$ to make explicit the value taken on by f at the general point (x, y). The variables x and y are **independent variables** and z is the **dependent variable**. [Compare this with the notation $y = f(x)$ for functions of a single variable.]

The domain is a subset of $\mathbb{R}^2$, the xy-plane. We can think of the domain as the set of all possible inputs and the range as the set of all possible outputs. If a function f is given by a formula and no domain is specified, then the domain of f is understood to be the set of all pairs (x, y) for which the given expression is a well-defined real number.

EXAMPLE 1 Domain and range If $f(x, y) = 4x^2 + y^2$, then $f(x, y)$ is defined for all possible ordered pairs of real numbers (x, y), so the domain is $\mathbb{R}^2$, the entire xy-plane. The range of f is the set $[0, \infty)$ of all nonnegative real numbers. [Notice that $x^2 \geqslant 0$ and $y^2 \geqslant 0$, so $f(x, y) \geqslant 0$ for all x and y.]

EXAMPLE 2 Sketching domains For each of the following functions, evaluate $f(3, 2)$ and find and sketch the domain.

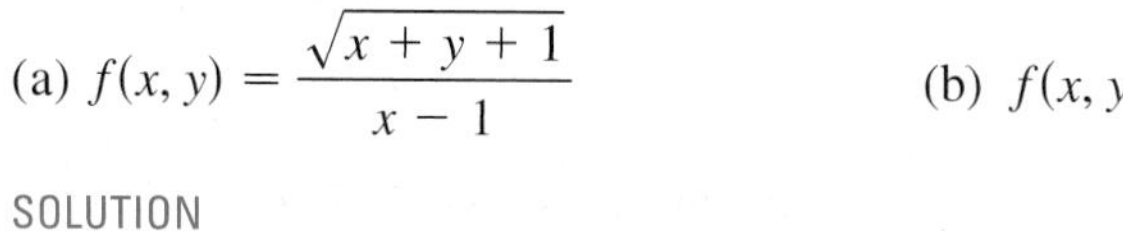

(a) $f(x, y) = \dfrac{\sqrt{x + y + 1}}{x - 1}$ (b) $f(x, y) = x \ln(y^2 - x)$

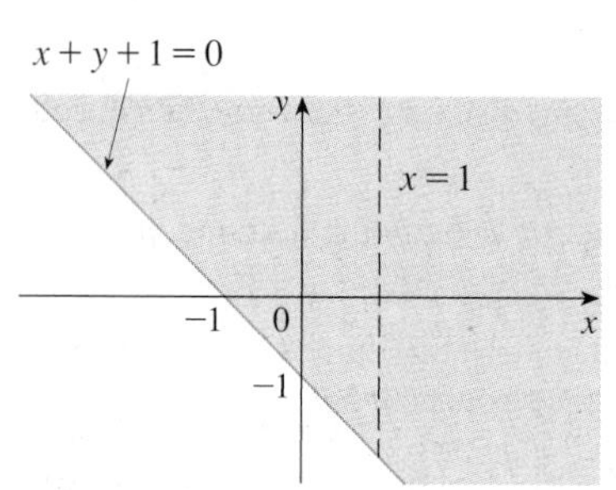

FIGURE 1
Domain of $f(x, y) = \dfrac{\sqrt{x+y+1}}{x-1}$

SOLUTION

(a)
$$f(3, 2) = \frac{\sqrt{3 + 2 + 1}}{3 - 1} = \frac{\sqrt{6}}{2}$$

The expression for f makes sense if the denominator is not 0 and the quantity under the square root sign is nonnegative. So the domain of f is

$$D = \{(x, y) \mid x + y + 1 \geqslant 0,\ x \neq 1\}$$

The inequality $x + y + 1 \geqslant 0$, or $y \geqslant -x - 1$, describes the points that lie on or above the line $y = -x - 1$, while $x \neq 1$ means that the points on the line $x = 1$ must be excluded from the domain. (See Figure 1.)

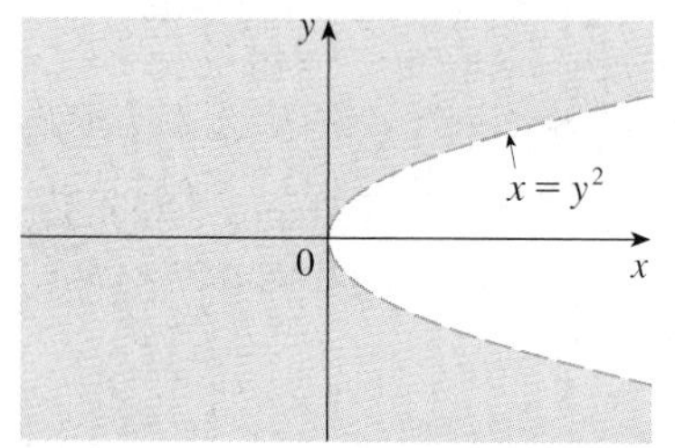

FIGURE 2
Domain of $f(x, y) = x \ln(y^2 - x)$

(b)
$$f(3, 2) = 3 \ln(2^2 - 3) = 3 \ln 1 = 0$$

Since $\ln(y^2 - x)$ is defined only when $y^2 - x > 0$, that is, $x < y^2$, the domain of f is $D = \{(x, y) \mid x < y^2\}$. This is the set of points to the left of the parabola $x = y^2$. (See Figure 2.)

Not all functions can be represented by explicit formulas. The function in the next example is described verbally and by numerical estimates of its values.

EXAMPLE 3 Wave height as a function of wind speed and time The wave heights h (in feet) in the open sea depend mainly on the speed v of the wind (in knots) and the length of time t (in hours) that the wind has been blowing at that speed. So h is a function of v and t and we can write $h = f(v, t)$. Observations and measurements have been made by meteorologists and oceanographers and are recorded in Table 1.

TABLE 1
Wave heights (in feet) produced by different wind speeds for various lengths of time

	v \ t	5	10	15	20	30	40	50
		Duration (hours)						
Wind speed (knots)	10	2	2	2	2	2	2	2
	15	4	4	5	5	5	5	5
	20	5	7	8	8	9	9	9
	30	9	13	16	17	18	19	19
	40	14	21	25	28	31	33	33
	50	19	29	36	40	45	48	50
	60	24	37	47	54	62	67	69

For instance, the table indicates that if the wind has been blowing at 50 knots for 30 hours, then the wave heights are estimated to be 45 ft, so

$$f(50, 30) \approx 45$$

The domain of this function h is given by $v \geqslant 0$ and $t \geqslant 0$. Although there is no exact formula for h in terms of v and t, we will see that the operations of calculus can still be carried out for such an experimentally defined function.

Graphs

One way of visualizing the behavior of a function of two variables is to consider its graph.

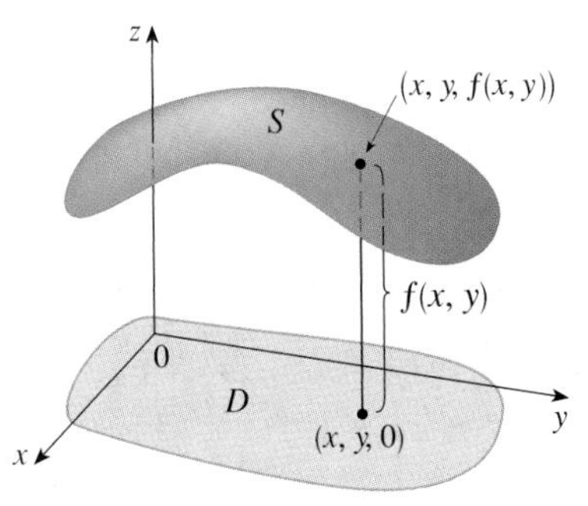

FIGURE 3

Definition If f is a function of two variables with domain D, then the **graph** of f is the set of all points (x, y, z) in $\mathbb{R}^3$ such that $z = f(x, y)$ and (x, y) is in D.

Just as the graph of a function f of one variable is a curve C with equation $y = f(x)$, so the graph of a function f of two variables is a surface S with equation $z = f(x, y)$. We can visualize the graph S of f as lying directly above or below its domain D in the xy-plane (see Figure 3).

EXAMPLE 4 Graphing a linear function Sketch the graph of the function $f(x, y) = 6 - 3x - 2y$.

SOLUTION The graph of f has the equation $z = 6 - 3x - 2y$, or $3x + 2y + z = 6$, which represents a plane. To graph the plane we first find the intercepts. Putting $y = z = 0$ in the equation, we get $x = 2$ as the x-intercept. Similarly, the y-intercept is 3 and the z-intercept is 6. This helps us sketch the portion of the graph that lies in the first octant in Figure 4.

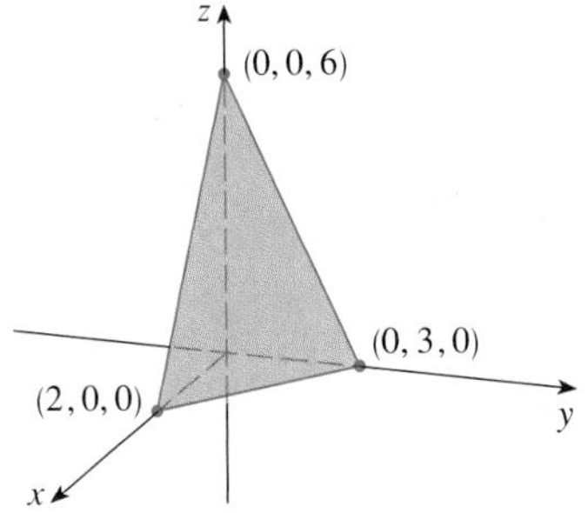

FIGURE 4

The function in Example 4 is a special case of the function

$$f(x, y) = ax + by + c$$

which is called a **linear function**. The graph of such a function has the equation

$$z = ax + by + c \qquad \text{or} \qquad ax + by - z + c = 0$$

so it is a plane. In much the same way that linear functions of one variable are important in single-variable calculus, we will see that linear functions of two variables play a central role in multivariable calculus.

V EXAMPLE 5 Sketch the graph of the function $f(x, y) = x^2$.

SOLUTION Notice that, no matter what value we give y, the value of $f(x, y)$ is always x^2. The equation of the graph is $z = x^2$, which doesn't involve y. This means that any vertical plane with equation $y = k$ (parallel to the xz-plane) intersects the graph in a curve with equation $z = x^2$, that is, a parabola. Figure 5 shows how the graph is formed by taking the parabola $z = x^2$ in the xz-plane and moving it in the direction of the y-axis. So the graph is a surface, called a **parabolic cylinder**, made up of infinitely many shifted copies of the same parabola.

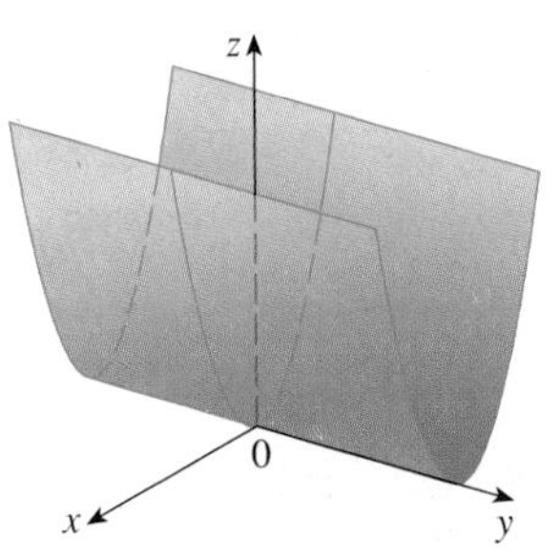

FIGURE 5
The graph of $f(x, y) = x^2$ is the parabolic cylinder $z = x^2$.

In sketching the graphs of functions of two variables, it's often useful to start by determining the shapes of cross-sections (slices) of the graph. For example, if we keep x fixed by putting $x = k$ (a constant) and letting y vary, the result is a function of one variable $z = f(k, y)$, whose graph is the curve that results when we intersect the surface $z = f(x, y)$ with the vertical plane $x = k$. In a similar fashion we can slice the surface with the vertical plane $y = k$ and look at the curves $z = f(x, k)$. We can also slice with horizontal planes $z = k$. All three types of curves are called **traces** (or cross-sections) of the surface $z = f(x, y)$.

EXAMPLE 6 Use traces to sketch the graph of the function $f(x, y) = 4x^2 + y^2$.

SOLUTION The equation of the graph is $z = 4x^2 + y^2$. If we put $x = 0$, we get $z = y^2$, so the yz-plane intersects the surface in a parabola. If we put $x = k$ (a constant), we get $z = y^2 + 4k^2$. This means that if we slice the graph with any plane parallel to the yz-plane, we obtain a parabola that opens upward. Similarly, if $y = k$, the trace is $z = 4x^2 + k^2$, which is again a parabola that opens upward. If we put $z = k$, we get the horizontal traces $4x^2 + y^2 = k$, which we recognize as a family of ellipses. Knowing the shapes of the traces, we can sketch the graph of f in Figure 6. Because of the elliptical and parabolic traces, the surface $z = 4x^2 + y^2$ is called an **elliptic paraboloid**.

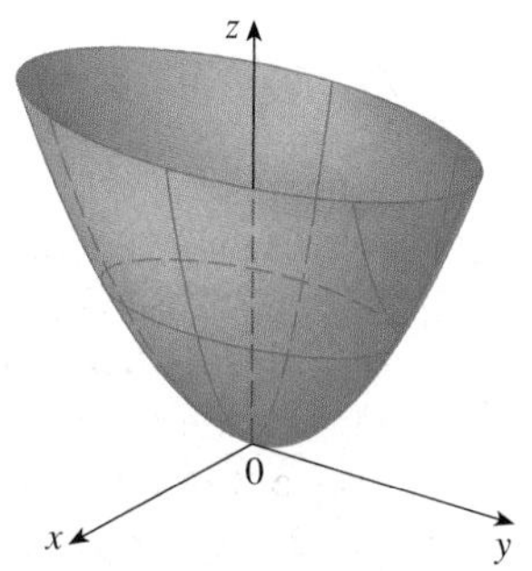

FIGURE 6
The graph of $f(x, y) = 4x^2 + y^2$ is the elliptic paraboloid $z = 4x^2 + y^2$. Horizontal traces are ellipses; vertical traces are parabolas.

V EXAMPLE 7 Sketch the graph of $f(x, y) = y^2 - x^2$.

SOLUTION The traces in the vertical planes $x = k$ are the parabolas $z = y^2 - k^2$, which open upward. The traces in $y = k$ are the parabolas $z = -x^2 + k^2$, which open downward. The horizontal traces are $y^2 - x^2 = k$, a family of hyperbolas. We draw the families of traces in Figure 7 and we show how the traces appear when placed in their correct planes in Figure 8.

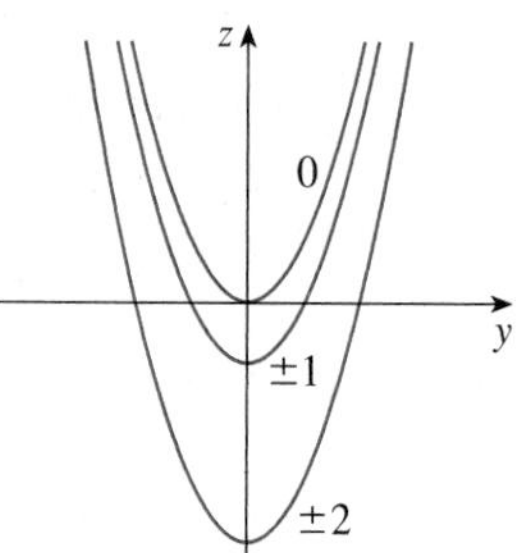

Traces in $x = k$ are $z = y^2 - k^2$

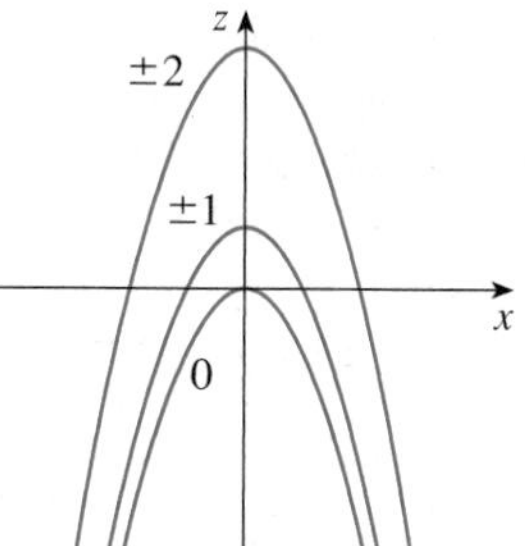

Traces in $y = k$ are $z = -x^2 + k^2$

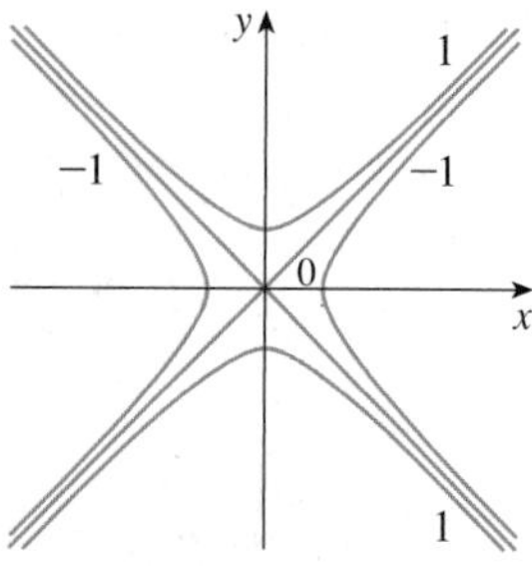

Traces in $z = k$ are $y^2 - x^2 = k$

FIGURE 7
Vertical traces are parabolas; horizontal traces are hyperbolas. All traces are labeled with the value of k.

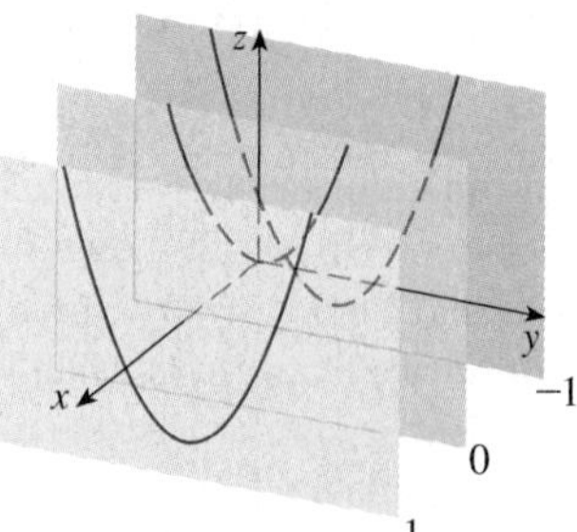

Traces in $x = k$

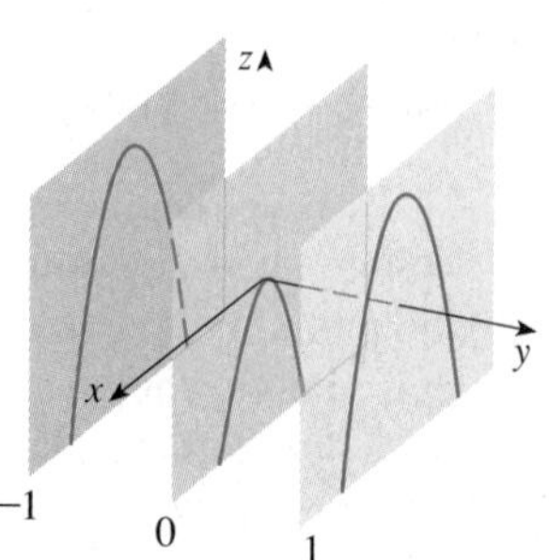

Traces in $y = k$

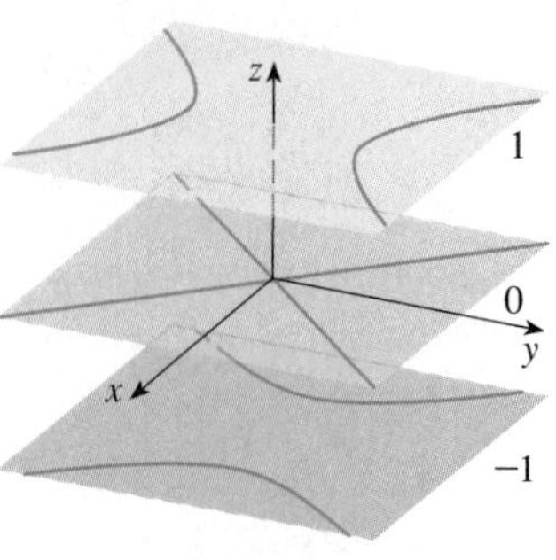

Traces in $z = k$

FIGURE 8
Traces moved to their correct planes

TEC In Module 9.6A you can investigate how traces determine the shape of a surface.

In Figure 9 we fit together the traces from Figure 8 to form the surface $z = y^2 - x^2$, a **hyperbolic paraboloid**. Notice that the shape of the surface near the origin resembles that of a saddle. This surface will be investigated further in Section 11.7 when we discuss saddle points.

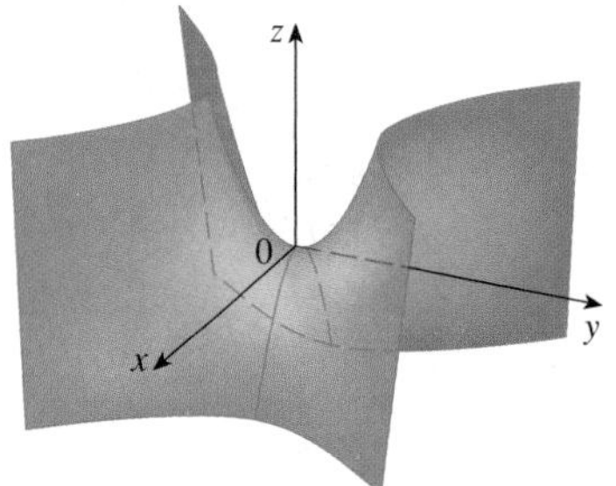

FIGURE 9
The graph of $f(x, y) = y^2 - x^2$ is the hyperbolic paraboloid $z = y^2 - x^2$.

The idea of using traces to draw a surface is employed in three-dimensional graphing software for computers. In most such software, traces in the vertical planes $x = k$ and $y = k$ are drawn for equally spaced values of k and parts of the graph are eliminated using hidden line removal. Figure 10 shows computer-generated graphs of several functions. Notice that we get an especially good picture of a function when rotation is used to give views from different vantage points. In parts (a) and (b) the graph of f is very flat and close to the xy-plane except near the origin; this is because $e^{-x^2-y^2}$ is very small when x or y is large.

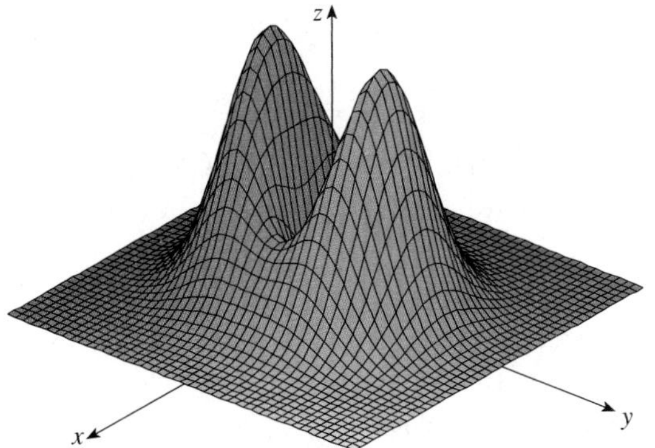

(a) $f(x, y) = (x^2 + 3y^2)e^{-x^2-y^2}$

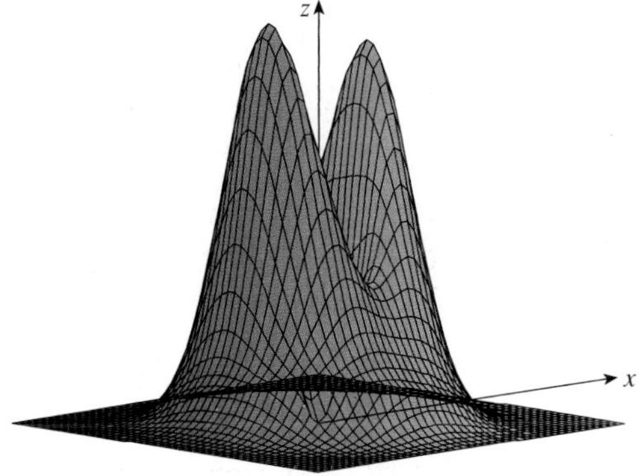

(b) $f(x, y) = (x^2 + 3y^2)e^{-x^2-y^2}$

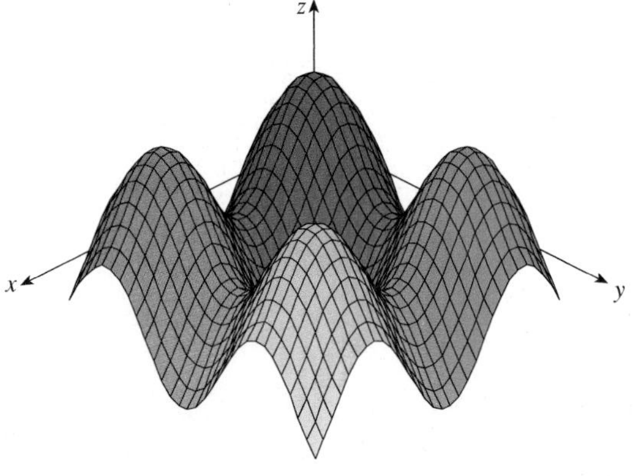

(c) $f(x, y) = \sin x + \sin y$

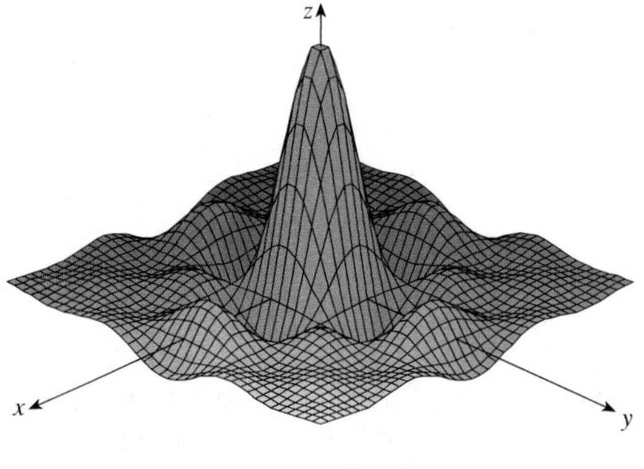

(d) $f(x, y) = \dfrac{\sin x \sin y}{xy}$

FIGURE 10

Quadric Surfaces

The graph of a second-degree equation in three variables x, y, and z is called a **quadric surface**. We have already sketched the quadric surfaces $z = 4x^2 + y^2$ (an elliptic paraboloid) and $z = y^2 - x^2$ (a hyperbolic paraboloid) in Figures 6 and 9. In the next example we investigate a quadric surface called an *ellipsoid*.

EXAMPLE 8 Sketch the quadric surface with equation

$$x^2 + \frac{y^2}{9} + \frac{z^2}{4} = 1$$

SOLUTION The trace in the xy-plane ($z = 0$) is $x^2 + y^2/9 = 1$, which we recognize as an equation of an ellipse. In general, the horizontal trace in the plane $z = k$ is

$$x^2 + \frac{y^2}{9} = 1 - \frac{k^2}{4} \qquad z = k$$

which is an ellipse, provided that $k^2 < 4$, that is, $-2 < k < 2$.

Similarly, the vertical traces are also ellipses:

$$\frac{y^2}{9} + \frac{z^2}{4} = 1 - k^2 \qquad x = k \qquad (\text{if } -1 < k < 1)$$

$$x^2 + \frac{z^2}{4} = 1 - \frac{k^2}{9} \qquad y = k \qquad (\text{if } -3 < k < 3)$$

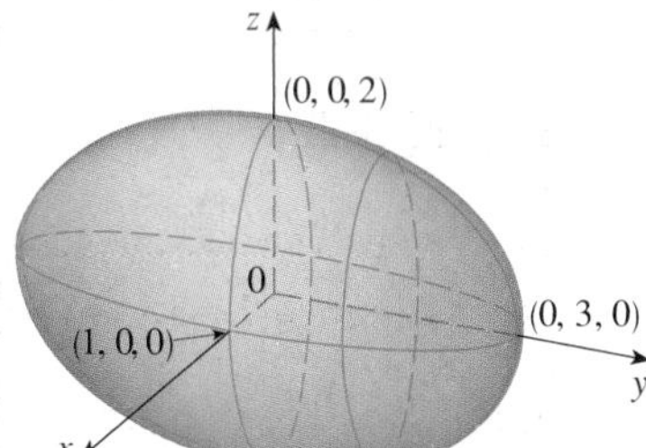

FIGURE 11

The ellipsoid $x^2 + \frac{y^2}{9} + \frac{z^2}{4} = 1$

Figure 11 shows how drawing some traces indicates the shape of the surface. It's called an **ellipsoid** because all of its traces are ellipses. Notice that it is symmetric with respect to each coordinate plane; this symmetry is a reflection of the fact that its equation involves only even powers of x, y, and z.

The ellipsoid in Example 8 is *not* the graph of a function because some vertical lines (such as the z-axis) intersect it more than once. But the top and bottom halves *are* graphs of functions. In fact, if we solve the equation of the ellipsoid for z, we get

$$z^2 = 4\left(1 - x^2 - \frac{y^2}{9}\right) \qquad z = \pm 2\sqrt{1 - x^2 - \frac{y^2}{9}}$$

So the graphs of the functions

$$f(x, y) = 2\sqrt{1 - x^2 - \frac{y^2}{9}} \qquad \text{and} \qquad g(x, y) = -2\sqrt{1 - x^2 - \frac{y^2}{9}}$$

are the top and bottom halves of the ellipsoid (see Figure 12). The domain of both f and g is the set of all points (x, y) such that

$$1 - x^2 - \frac{y^2}{9} \geqslant 0 \iff x^2 + \frac{y^2}{9} \leqslant 1$$

so the domain is the set of all points that lie on or inside the ellipse $x^2 + y^2/9 = 1$.

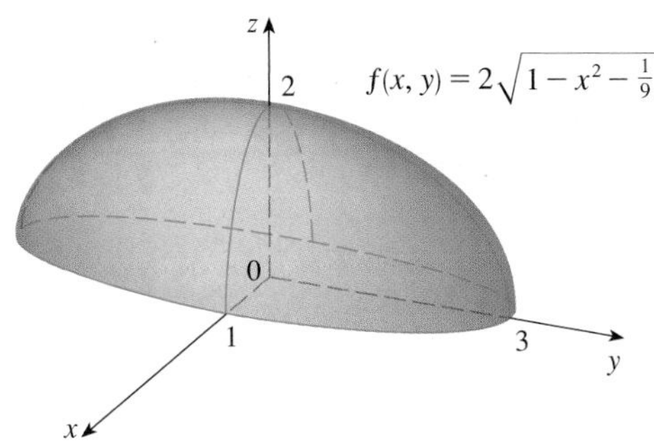

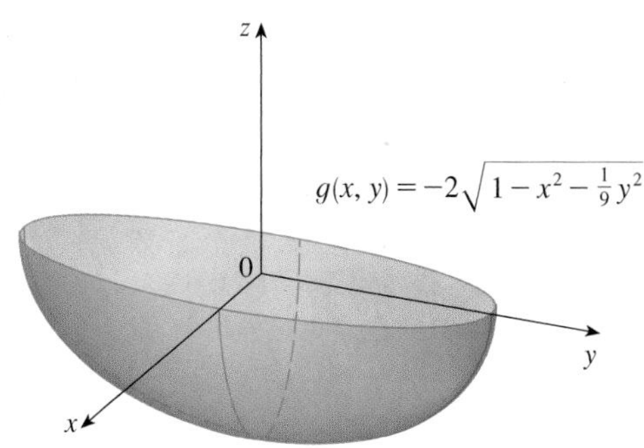

FIGURE 12

TEC In Module 9.6B you can see how changing a, b, and c in Table 2 affects the shape of the quadric surface.

Table 2 shows computer-drawn graphs of the six basic types of quadric surfaces in standard form. All surfaces are symmetric with respect to the z-axis. If a quadric surface is symmetric about a different axis, its equation changes accordingly.

TABLE 2 Graphs of quadric surfaces

Surface	Equation	Surface	Equation
Ellipsoid	$\frac{x^2}{a^2} + \frac{y^2}{b^2} + \frac{z^2}{c^2} = 1$ All traces are ellipses. If $a = b = c$, the ellipsoid is a sphere.	Cone	$\frac{z^2}{c^2} = \frac{x^2}{a^2} + \frac{y^2}{b^2}$ Horizontal traces are ellipses. Vertical traces in the planes $x = k$ and $y = k$ are hyperbolas if $k \neq 0$ but are pairs of lines if $k = 0$.
Elliptic Paraboloid	$\frac{z}{c} = \frac{x^2}{a^2} + \frac{y^2}{b^2}$ Horizontal traces are ellipses. Vertical traces are parabolas. The variable raised to the first power indicates the axis of the paraboloid.	Hyperboloid of One Sheet	$\frac{x^2}{a^2} + \frac{y^2}{b^2} - \frac{z^2}{c^2} = 1$ Horizontal traces are ellipses. Vertical traces are hyperbolas. The axis of symmetry corresponds to the variable whose coefficient is negative.
Hyperbolic Paraboloid	$\frac{z}{c} = \frac{x^2}{a^2} - \frac{y^2}{b^2}$ Horizontal traces are hyperbolas. Vertical traces are parabolas. The case where $c < 0$ is illustrated.	Hyperboloid of Two Sheets	$-\frac{x^2}{a^2} - \frac{y^2}{b^2} + \frac{z^2}{c^2} = 1$ Horizontal traces in $z = k$ are ellipses if $k > c$ or $k < -c$. Vertical traces are hyperbolas. The two minus signs indicate two sheets.

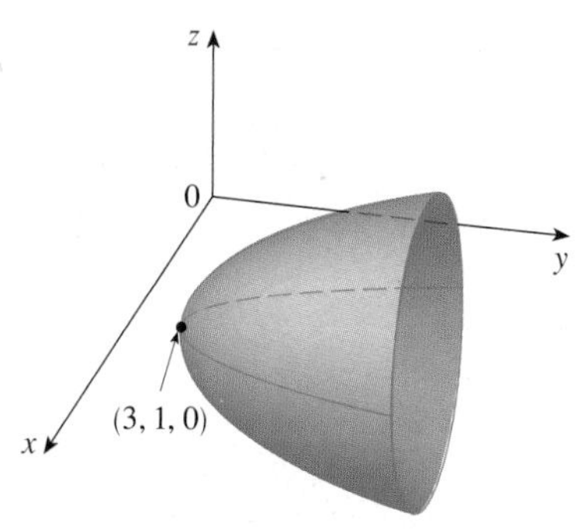

FIGURE 13
$x^2 + 2z^2 - 6x - y + 10 = 0$

EXAMPLE 9 Classify the quadric surface $x^2 + 2z^2 - 6x - y + 10 = 0$.

SOLUTION By completing the square we rewrite the equation as

$$y - 1 = (x - 3)^2 + 2z^2$$

Comparing this equation with Table 2, we see that it represents an elliptic paraboloid. Here, however, the axis of the paraboloid is parallel to the y-axis, and it has been shifted so that its vertex is the point $(3, 1, 0)$. The traces in the plane $y = k$ $(k > 1)$ are the ellipses

$$(x - 3)^2 + 2z^2 = k - 1 \qquad y = k$$

The trace in the xy-plane is the parabola with equation $y = 1 + (x - 3)^2$, $z = 0$. The paraboloid is sketched in Figure 13.

9.6 Exercises

1. In Example 3 we considered the function $h = f(v, t)$, where h is the height of waves produced by wind at speed v for a time t. Use Table 1 to answer the following questions.
(a) What is the value of $f(40, 15)$? What is its meaning?
(b) What is the meaning of the function $h = f(30, t)$? Describe the behavior of this function.
(c) What is the meaning of the function $h = f(v, 30)$? Describe the behavior of this function.

2. Let $f(x, y) = y^4 e^{x/y}$.
(a) Evaluate $f(0, 2)$.
(b) Find the domain of f.
(c) Find the range of f.

3. Let $g(x, y) = \cos(x + 2y)$.
(a) Evaluate $g(2, -1)$.
(b) Find the domain of g.
(c) Find the range of g.

4. Let $F(x, y) = 1 + \sqrt{4 - y^2}$.
(a) Evaluate $F(3, 1)$.
(b) Find and sketch the domain of F.
(c) Find the range of F.

5–8 Find and sketch the domain of the function.

5. $f(x, y) = \dfrac{\sqrt{y - x^2}}{1 - x^2}$ **6.** $f(x, y) = \sqrt{xy}$

7. $f(x, y) = \sqrt{1 - x^2} - \sqrt{1 - y^2}$

8. $f(x, y) = \ln(x^2 + y^2 - 2)$

9–13 Sketch the graph of the function.

9. $f(x, y) = 3$ **10.** $f(x, y) = y$

11. $f(x, y) = 6 - 3x - 2y$ **12.** $f(x, y) = \cos x$

13. $f(x, y) = y^2 + 1$

14. (a) Find the traces of the function $f(x, y) = x^2 + y^2$ in the planes $x = k$, $y = k$, and $z = k$. Use these traces to sketch the graph.
(b) Sketch the graph of $g(x, y) = -x^2 - y^2$. How is it related to the graph of f?
(c) Sketch the graph of $h(x, y) = 3 - x^2 - y^2$. How is it related to the graph of g?

15. Match the function with its graph (labeled I–VI). Give reasons for your choices.
(a) $f(x, y) = |x| + |y|$ (b) $f(x, y) = |xy|$
(c) $f(x, y) = \dfrac{1}{1 + x^2 + y^2}$ (d) $f(x, y) = (x^2 - y^2)^2$
(e) $f(x, y) = (x - y)^2$ (f) $f(x, y) = \sin(|x| + |y|)$

I

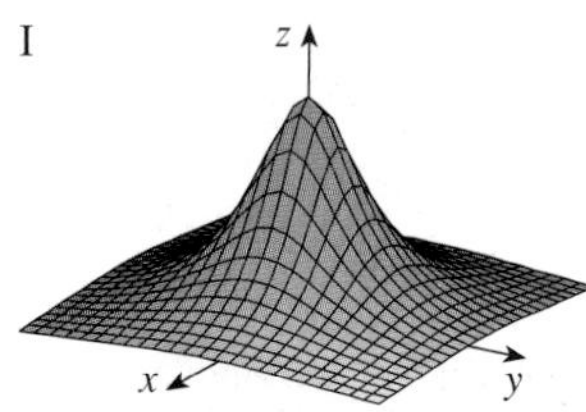

II

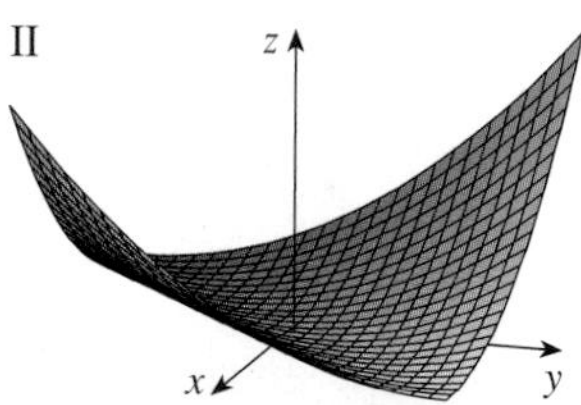

III

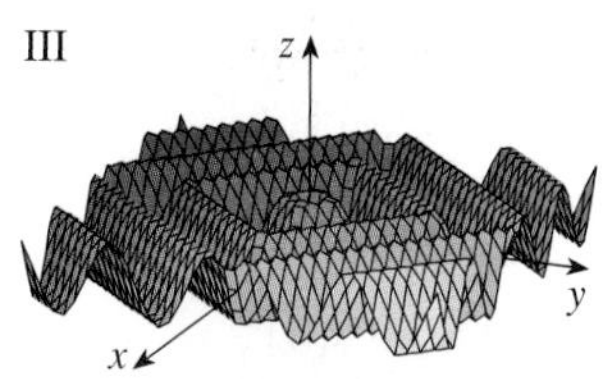

IV

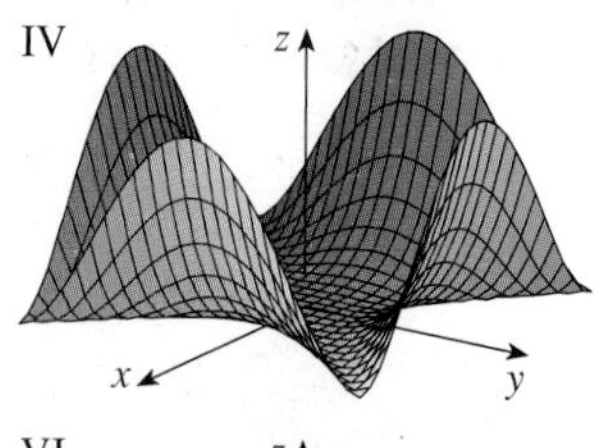

V

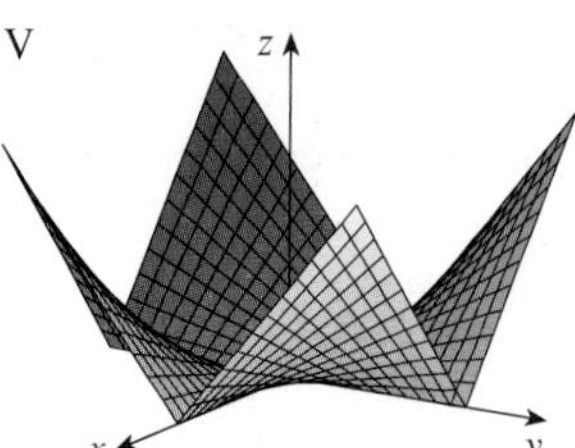

VI

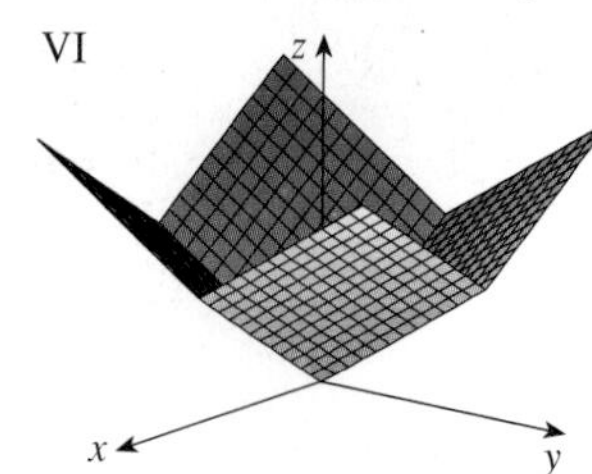

16–18 Use traces to sketch the graph of the function.

16. $f(x, y) = \sqrt{16 - x^2 - 16y^2}$

17. $f(x, y) = \sqrt{4x^2 + y^2}$

18. $f(x, y) = x^2 - y^2$

19–20 Use traces to sketch the surface.

19. $y = z^2 - x^2$ **20.** $x = y^2 + 4z^2$

21–22 Classify the surface by comparing with one of the standard forms in Table 2. Then sketch its graph.

21. $4x^2 + y^2 + 4z^2 - 4y - 24z + 36 = 0$

22. $4y^2 + z^2 - x - 16y - 4z + 20 = 0$

23. (a) What does the equation $x^2 + y^2 = 1$ represent as a curve in $\mathbb{R}^2$?
(b) What does it represent as a surface in $\mathbb{R}^3$?
(c) What does the equation $x^2 + z^2 = 1$ represent?

24. (a) Identify the traces of the surface $z^2 = x^2 + y^2$.
(b) Sketch the surface.
(c) Sketch the graphs of the functions $f(x, y) = \sqrt{x^2 + y^2}$ and $g(x, y) = -\sqrt{x^2 + y^2}$.

25. (a) Find and identify the traces of the quadric surface $x^2 + y^2 - z^2 = 1$ and explain why the graph looks like the graph of the hyperboloid of one sheet in Table 2.
(b) If we change the equation in part (a) to $x^2 - y^2 + z^2 = 1$, how is the graph affected?
(c) What if we change the equation in part (a) to $x^2 + y^2 + 2y - z^2 = 0$?

26. (a) Find and identify the traces of the quadric surface $-x^2 - y^2 + z^2 = 1$ and explain why the graph looks like the graph of the hyperboloid of two sheets in Table 2.
(b) If the equation in part (a) is changed to $x^2 - y^2 - z^2 = 1$, what happens to the graph? Sketch the new graph.

27. The figure shows vertical traces for a function $z = f(x, y)$. Which one of the graphs I–IV has these traces? Explain.

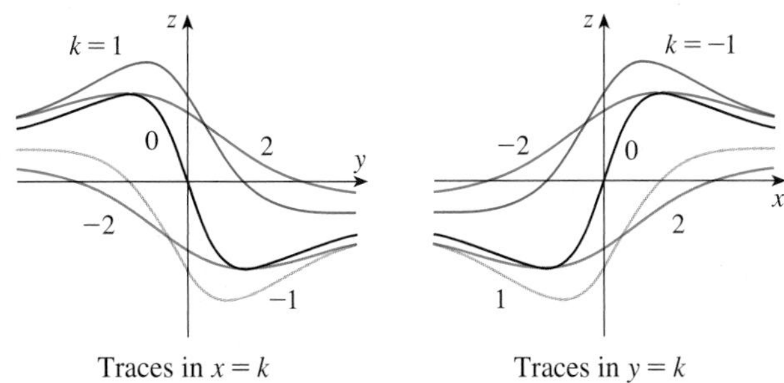

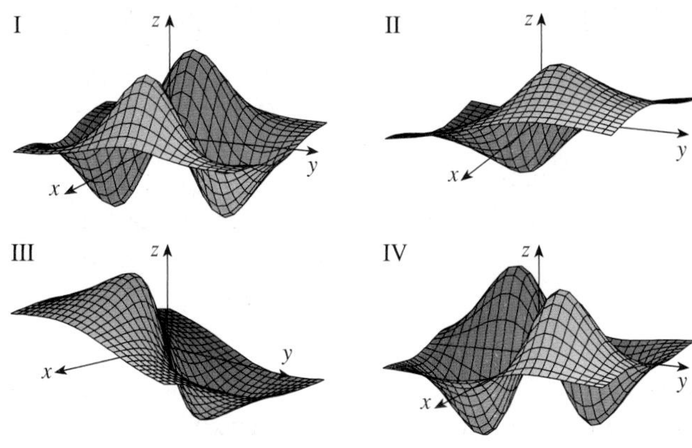

28–29 Use a computer to graph the function using various domains and viewpoints. Get a printout that gives a good view of the "peaks and valleys." Would you say that the function has a maximum value? Can you identify any points on the graph that you might consider to be "local maximum points"? What about "local minimum points"?

28. $f(x, y) = x^2y^2e^{x-4x^2-4y^2}$

29. $f(x, y) = xye^{x+2y-9x^2-9y^2}$

30. Use a computer to graph the function using various domains and viewpoints. Comment on the limiting behavior of the function. What happens as both x and y become large? What happens as (x, y) approaches the origin?

(a) $f(x, y) = \dfrac{x + y}{x^2 + y^2}$ (b) $f(x, y) = \dfrac{xy}{x^2 + y^2}$

31. Graph the surfaces $z = x^2 + y^2$ and $z = 1 - y^2$ on a common screen using the domain $|x| \leqslant 1.2$, $|y| \leqslant 1.2$ and observe the curve of intersection of these surfaces. Show that the projection of this curve onto the xy-plane is an ellipse.

32. Show that the curve of intersection of the surfaces $x^2 + 2y^2 - z^2 + 3x = 1$ and $2x^2 + 4y^2 - 2z^2 - 5y = 0$ lies in a plane.

33. Show that if the point (a, b, c) lies on the hyperbolic paraboloid $z = y^2 - x^2$, then the lines with parametric equations $x = a + t$, $y = b + t$, $z = c + 2(b - a)t$ and $x = a + t$, $y = b - t$, $z = c - 2(b + a)t$ both lie entirely on this paraboloid. (This shows that the hyperbolic paraboloid is what is called a **ruled surface**; that is, it can be generated by the motion of a straight line. In fact, this exercise shows that through each point on the hyperbolic paraboloid there are two generating lines. The only other quadric surfaces that are ruled surfaces are cylinders, cones, and hyperboloids of one sheet.)

34. Find an equation for the surface consisting of all points P for which the distance from P to the x-axis is twice the distance from P to the yz-plane. Identify the surface.

9.7 Cylindrical and Spherical Coordinates

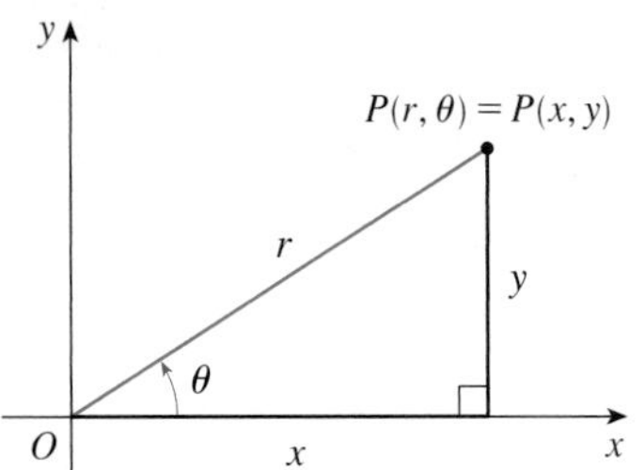

FIGURE 1

In plane geometry the polar coordinate system is used to give a convenient description of certain curves and regions. (See Appendix H.) Figure 1 enables us to recall the connection between polar and Cartesian coordinates. If the point P has Cartesian coordinates (x, y) and polar coordinates (r, θ), then, from the figure,

$$x = r\cos\theta \qquad y = r\sin\theta$$

$$r^2 = x^2 + y^2 \qquad \tan\theta = \frac{y}{x}$$

In three dimensions there are two coordinate systems that are similar to polar coordinates and give convenient descriptions of some commonly occurring surfaces and solids. They will be especially useful in Chapter 12 when we compute volumes and triple integrals.

Cylindrical Coordinates

In the **cylindrical coordinate system**, a point P in three-dimensional space is represented by the ordered triple (r, θ, z), where r and θ are polar coordinates of the projection of P onto the xy-plane and z is the directed distance from the xy-plane to P. (See Figure 2.)

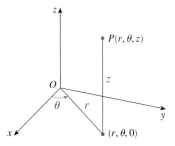

FIGURE 2
The cylindrical coordinates of a point

To convert from cylindrical to rectangular coordinates, we use the equations

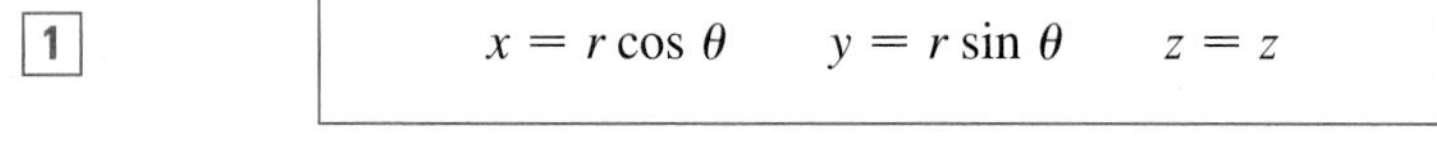

1 $$x = r\cos\theta \qquad y = r\sin\theta \qquad z = z$$

whereas to convert from rectangular to cylindrical coordinates, we use

2 $$r^2 = x^2 + y^2 \qquad \tan\theta = \frac{y}{x} \qquad z = z$$

EXAMPLE 1 Converting between cylindrical and rectangular coordinates
(a) Plot the point with cylindrical coordinates $(2, 2\pi/3, 1)$ and find its rectangular coordinates.
(b) Find cylindrical coordinates of the point with rectangular coordinates $(3, -3, -7)$.

SOLUTION
(a) The point with cylindrical coordinates $(2, 2\pi/3, 1)$ is plotted in Figure 3. From Equations 1, its rectangular coordinates are

$$x = 2\cos\frac{2\pi}{3} = 2\left(-\frac{1}{2}\right) = -1$$

$$y = 2\sin\frac{2\pi}{3} = 2\left(\frac{\sqrt{3}}{2}\right) = \sqrt{3}$$

$$z = 1$$

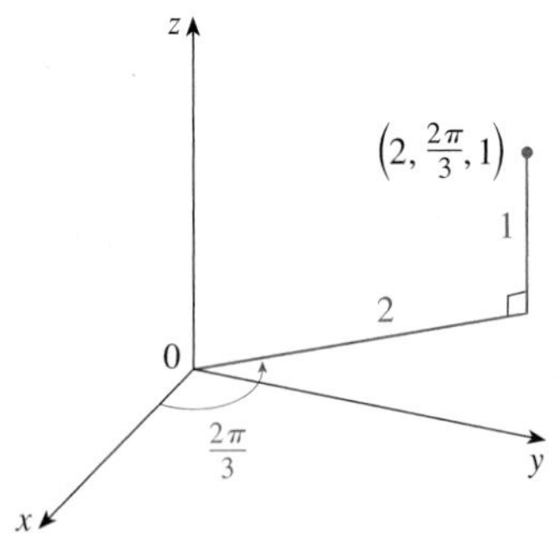

FIGURE 3

Thus the point is $(-1, \sqrt{3}, 1)$ in rectangular coordinates.

(b) From Equations 2 we have

$$r = \sqrt{3^2 + (-3)^2} = 3\sqrt{2}$$

$$\tan\theta = \frac{-3}{3} = -1 \qquad \text{so} \qquad \theta = \frac{7\pi}{4} + 2n\pi$$

$$z = -7$$

Therefore one set of cylindrical coordinates is $(3\sqrt{2}, 7\pi/4, -7)$. Another is $(3\sqrt{2}, -\pi/4, -7)$. As with polar coordinates, there are infinitely many choices.

Cylindrical coordinates are useful in problems that involve symmetry about an axis, and the z-axis is chosen to coincide with this axis of symmetry. For instance, the axis of the circular cylinder with Cartesian equation $x^2 + y^2 = c^2$ is the z-axis. In cylindrical coordinates this cylinder has the very simple equation $r = c$. (See Figure 4.) This is the reason for the name "cylindrical" coordinates.

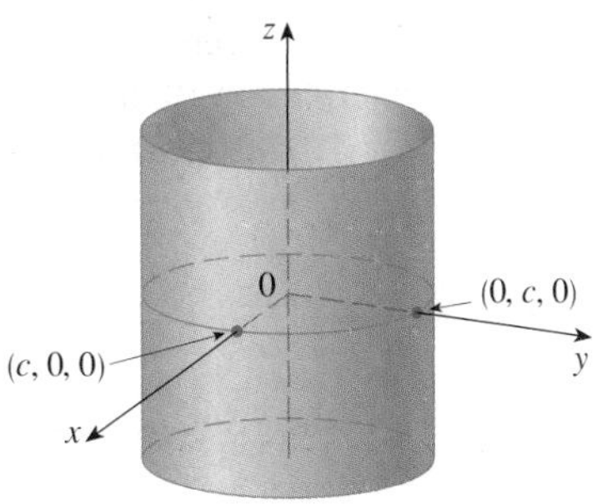

FIGURE 4
$r = c$, a cylinder

V EXAMPLE 2 Describe the surface whose equation in cylindrical coordinates is $z = r$.

SOLUTION The equation says that the z-value, or height, of each point on the surface is the same as r, the distance from the point to the z-axis. Because θ doesn't appear, it can vary. So any horizontal trace in the plane $z = k$ $(k > 0)$ is a circle of radius k. These traces suggest that the surface is a cone. This prediction can be confirmed by converting the equation into rectangular coordinates. From the first equation in (2) we have

$$z^2 = r^2 = x^2 + y^2$$

We recognize the equation $z^2 = x^2 + y^2$ (by comparison with Table 2 in Section 9.6) as being a circular cone whose axis is the z-axis (see Figure 5).

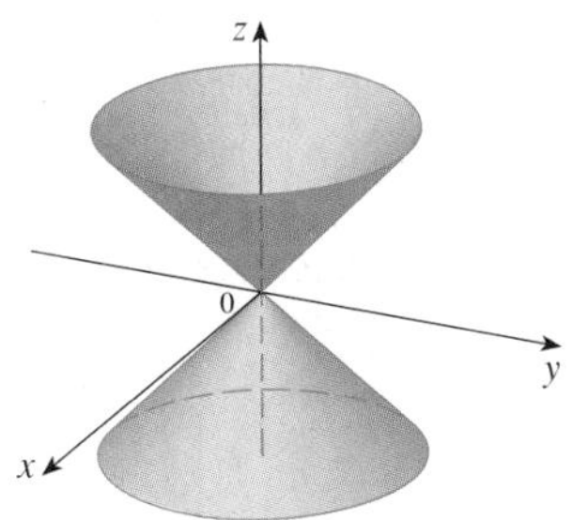

FIGURE 5
$z = r$, a cone

EXAMPLE 3 A cylindrical equation for an ellipsoid Find an equation in cylindrical coordinates for the ellipsoid $4x^2 + 4y^2 + z^2 = 1$.

SOLUTION Since $r^2 = x^2 + y^2$ from Equations 2, we have

$$z^2 = 1 - 4(x^2 + y^2) = 1 - 4r^2$$

So an equation of the ellipsoid in cylindrical coordinates is $z^2 = 1 - 4r^2$.

Spherical Coordinates

The **spherical coordinates** (ρ, θ, ϕ) of a point P in space are shown in Figure 6, where $\rho = |OP|$ is the distance from the origin to P, θ is the same angle as in cylindrical coordinates, and ϕ is the angle between the positive z-axis and the line segment OP. Note that

$$\rho \geqslant 0 \qquad 0 \leqslant \phi \leqslant \pi$$

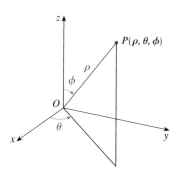

FIGURE 6
The spherical coordinates of a point

The spherical coordinate system is especially useful in problems where there is symmetry about a point, and the origin is placed at this point. For example, the sphere with center the origin and radius c has the simple equation $\rho = c$ (see Figure 7); this is the reason for the name "spherical" coordinates. The graph of the equation $\theta = c$ is a vertical half-plane (see Figure 8), and the equation $\phi = c$ represents a half-cone with the z-axis as its axis (see Figure 9).

FIGURE 7 $\rho = c$, a sphere

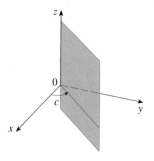

FIGURE 8 $\theta = c$, a half-plane

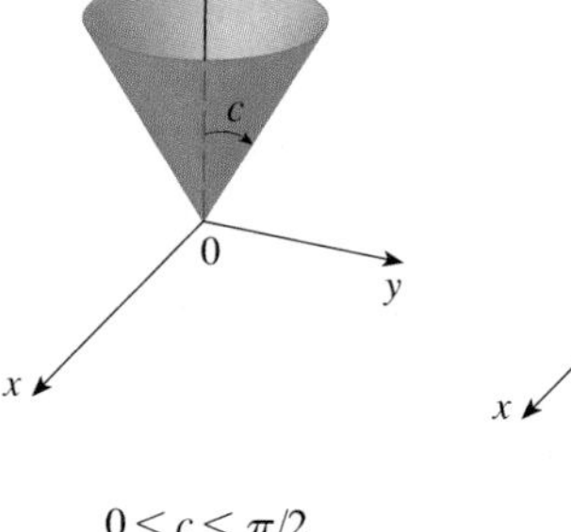

$0 < c < \pi/2$

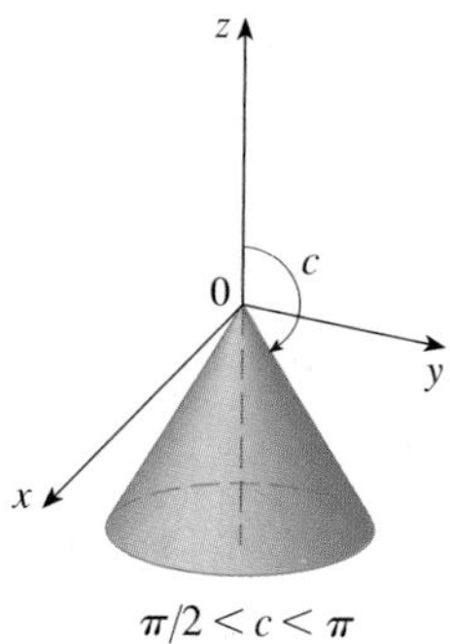

$\pi/2 < c < \pi$

FIGURE 9 $\phi = c$, a half-cone

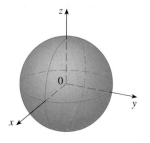

The relationship between rectangular and spherical coordinates can be seen from Figure 10. From triangles OPQ and OPP' we have

$$z = \rho \cos \phi \qquad r = \rho \sin \phi$$

But $x = r \cos \theta$ and $y = r \sin \theta$, so to convert from spherical to rectangular coordinates, we use the equations

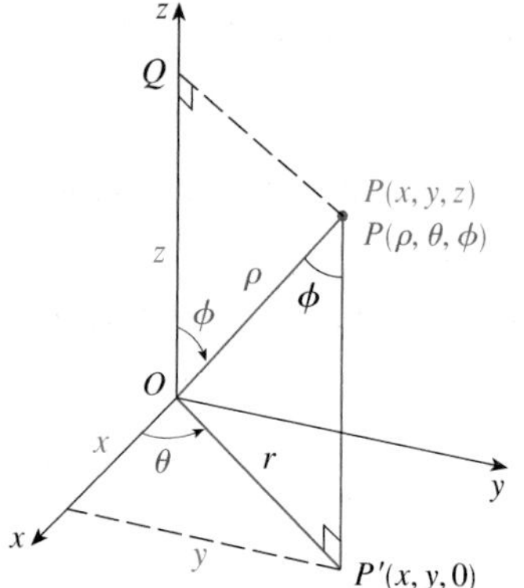

FIGURE 10

3 $$x = \rho \sin \phi \cos \theta \qquad y = \rho \sin \phi \sin \theta \qquad z = \rho \cos \phi$$

Also, the distance formula shows that

4 $$\rho^2 = x^2 + y^2 + z^2$$

We use this equation in converting from rectangular to spherical coordinates.

V EXAMPLE 4 Converting from spherical to rectangular coordinates
The point $(2, \pi/4, \pi/3)$ is given in spherical coordinates. Plot the point and find its rectangular coordinates.

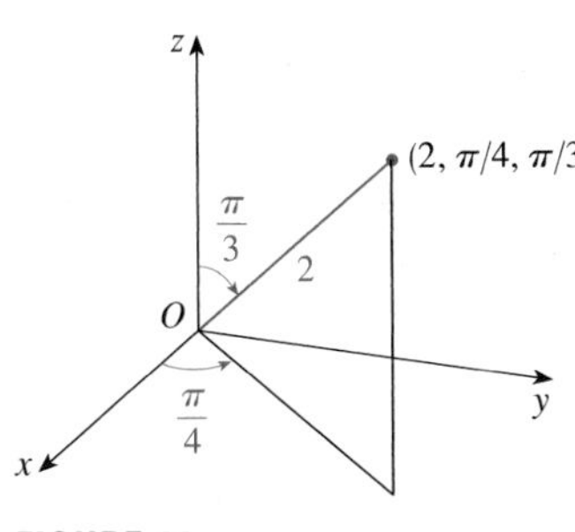

FIGURE 11

SOLUTION We plot the point in Figure 11. From Equations 3 we have

$$x = \rho \sin \phi \cos \theta = 2 \sin \frac{\pi}{3} \cos \frac{\pi}{4} = 2\left(\frac{\sqrt{3}}{2}\right)\left(\frac{1}{\sqrt{2}}\right) = \sqrt{\frac{3}{2}}$$

$$y = \rho \sin \phi \sin \theta = 2 \sin \frac{\pi}{3} \sin \frac{\pi}{4} = 2\left(\frac{\sqrt{3}}{2}\right)\left(\frac{1}{\sqrt{2}}\right) = \sqrt{\frac{3}{2}}$$

$$z = \rho \cos \phi = 2 \cos \frac{\pi}{3} = 2\left(\tfrac{1}{2}\right) = 1$$

Thus the point $(2, \pi/4, \pi/3)$ is $\left(\sqrt{3/2}, \sqrt{3/2}, 1\right)$ in rectangular coordinates.

V EXAMPLE 5 Converting from rectangular to spherical coordinates
The point $\left(0, 2\sqrt{3}, -2\right)$ is given in rectangular coordinates. Find spherical coordinates for this point.

SOLUTION From Equation 4 we have

$$\rho = \sqrt{x^2 + y^2 + z^2} = \sqrt{0 + 12 + 4} = 4$$

and so Equations 3 give

$$\cos \phi = \frac{z}{\rho} = \frac{-2}{4} = -\frac{1}{2} \qquad \phi = \frac{2\pi}{3}$$

$$\cos \theta = \frac{x}{\rho \sin \phi} = 0 \qquad \theta = \frac{\pi}{2}$$

(Note that $\theta \neq 3\pi/2$ because $y = 2\sqrt{3} > 0$.) Therefore spherical coordinates of the given point are $(4, \pi/2, 2\pi/3)$.

Warning: There is not universal agreement on the notation for spherical coordinates. Most books on physics reverse the meanings of θ and ϕ and use r in place of ρ.

EXAMPLE 6 A spherical equation for a hyperboloid Find an equation in spherical coordinates for the hyperboloid of two sheets with equation $x^2 - y^2 - z^2 = 1$.

SOLUTION Substituting the expressions in Equations 3 into the given equation, we have

$$\rho^2 \sin^2\phi \cos^2\theta - \rho^2 \sin^2\phi \sin^2\theta - \rho^2 \cos^2\phi = 1$$

$$\rho^2[\sin^2\phi (\cos^2\theta - \sin^2\theta) - \cos^2\phi] = 1$$

or

$$\rho^2(\sin^2\phi \cos 2\theta - \cos^2\phi) = 1$$

TEC In Module 9.7 you can investigate families of surfaces in cylindrical and spherical coordinates.

EXAMPLE 7 Find a rectangular equation for the surface whose spherical equation is $\rho = \sin \theta \sin \phi$.

SOLUTION From Equations 4 and 3 we have

$$x^2 + y^2 + z^2 = \rho^2 = \rho \sin \theta \sin \phi = y$$

or

$$x^2 + \left(y - \tfrac{1}{2}\right)^2 + z^2 = \tfrac{1}{4}$$

which is the equation of a sphere with center $\left(0, \tfrac{1}{2}, 0\right)$ and radius $\tfrac{1}{2}$.

EXAMPLE 8 Use a computer to draw a picture of the solid that remains when a hole of radius 3 is drilled through the center of a sphere of radius 4.

SOLUTION To keep the equations simple, let's choose the coordinate system so that the center of the sphere is at the origin and the axis of the cylinder that forms the hole is the z-axis. We could use either cylindrical or spherical coordinates to describe the solid, but the description is somewhat simpler if we use cylindrical coordinates. Then the equation of the cylinder is $r = 3$ and the equation of the sphere is $x^2 + y^2 + z^2 = 16$, or $r^2 + z^2 = 16$. The points in the solid lie outside the cylinder and inside the sphere, so they satisfy the inequalities

$$3 \leqslant r \leqslant \sqrt{16 - z^2}$$

Most three-dimensional graphing programs can graph surfaces whose equations are given in cylindrical or spherical coordinates. As Example 8 demonstrates, this is often the most convenient way of drawing a solid.

To ensure that the computer graphs only the appropriate parts of these surfaces, we find where they intersect by solving the equations $r = 3$ and $r = \sqrt{16 - z^2}$:

$$\sqrt{16 - z^2} = 3 \quad \Rightarrow \quad 16 - z^2 = 9 \quad \Rightarrow \quad z^2 = 7 \quad \Rightarrow \quad z = \pm\sqrt{7}$$

The solid lies between $z = -\sqrt{7}$ and $z = \sqrt{7}$, so we ask the computer to graph the surfaces with the following equations and domains:

$$r = 3 \qquad 0 \leqslant \theta \leqslant 2\pi \qquad -\sqrt{7} \leqslant z \leqslant \sqrt{7}$$

$$r = \sqrt{16 - z^2} \qquad 0 \leqslant \theta \leqslant 2\pi \qquad -\sqrt{7} \leqslant z \leqslant \sqrt{7}$$

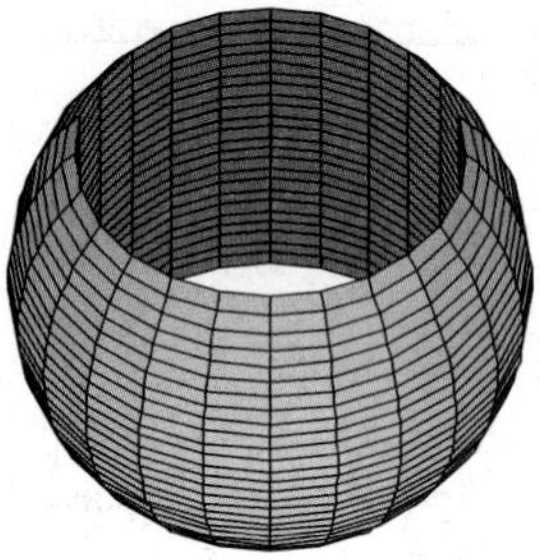

FIGURE 12

The resulting picture, shown in Figure 12, is exactly what we want.

9.7 Exercises

1. What are cylindrical coordinates? For what types of surfaces do they provide convenient descriptions?

2. What are spherical coordinates? For what types of surfaces do they provide convenient descriptions?

3–4 Plot the point whose cylindrical coordinates are given. Then find the rectangular coordinates of the point.

3. (a) $(2, \pi/4, 1)$ (b) $(4, -\pi/3, 5)$

4. (a) $(1, \pi, e)$ (b) $(1, 3\pi/2, 2)$

5–6 Change from rectangular to cylindrical coordinates.

5. (a) $(1, -1, 4)$ (b) $(-1, -\sqrt{3}, 2)$

6. (a) $(2\sqrt{3}, 2, -1)$ (b) $(4, -3, 2)$

7–8 Plot the point whose spherical coordinates are given. Then find the rectangular coordinates of the point.

7. (a) $(1, 0, 0)$ (b) $(2, \pi/3, \pi/4)$

8. (a) $(5, \pi, \pi/2)$ (b) $(4, 3\pi/4, \pi/3)$

9–10 Change from rectangular to spherical coordinates.

9. (a) $(1, \sqrt{3}, 2\sqrt{3})$ (b) $(0, -1, -1)$

10. (a) $(0, \sqrt{3}, 1)$ (b) $(-1, 1, \sqrt{6})$

11–14 Describe in words the surface whose equation is given.

11. $\theta = \pi/4$

12. $r = 5$

13. $\phi = \pi/3$

14. $\rho = 3$

15–20 Identify the surface whose equation is given.

15. $z = 4 - r^2$

16. $\rho \sin \phi = 2$

17. $r = 2 \cos \theta$

18. $2r^2 + z^2 = 1$

19. $\rho = \sin \theta \sin \phi$

20. $\rho^2(\sin^2\phi \sin^2\theta + \cos^2\phi) = 9$

Graphing calculator or computer with graphing software required 1. Homework Hints available in TEC

21–24 Write the equation (a) in cylindrical coordinates and (b) in spherical coordinates.

21. $x^2 + y^2 = 2y$

22. $x^2 + y^2 + z^2 = 2$

23. $3x + 2y + z = 6$

24. $x^2 - 2x + y^2 + z^2 = 0$

25–30 Sketch the solid described by the given inequalities.

25. $0 \leqslant r \leqslant 2, \quad -\pi/2 \leqslant \theta \leqslant \pi/2, \quad 0 \leqslant z \leqslant 1$

26. $0 \leqslant \theta \leqslant \pi/2, \quad r \leqslant z \leqslant 2$

27. $\rho \leqslant 2, \quad 0 \leqslant \phi \leqslant \pi/2, \quad 0 \leqslant \theta \leqslant \pi/2$

28. $2 \leqslant \rho \leqslant 3, \quad \pi/2 \leqslant \phi \leqslant \pi$

29. $\rho \leqslant 1, \quad 3\pi/4 \leqslant \phi \leqslant \pi$

30. $\rho \leqslant 2, \quad \rho \leqslant \csc \phi$

31. A cylindrical shell is 20 cm long, with inner radius 6 cm and outer radius 7 cm. Write inequalities that describe the shell in an appropriate coordinate system. Explain how you have positioned the coordinate system with respect to the shell.

32. (a) Find inequalities that describe a hollow ball with diameter 30 cm and thickness 0.5 cm. Explain how you have positioned the coordinate system that you have chosen.
(b) Suppose the ball is cut in half. Write inequalities that describe one of the halves.

33. A solid lies above the cone $z = \sqrt{x^2 + y^2}$ and below the sphere $x^2 + y^2 + z^2 = z$. Write a description of the solid in terms of inequalities involving spherical coordinates.

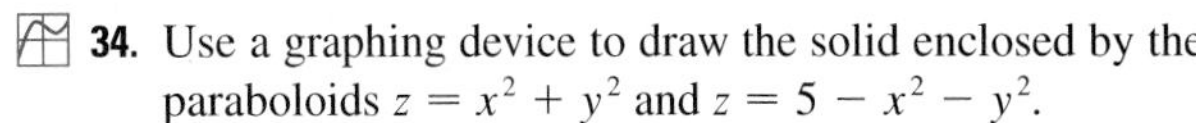

34. Use a graphing device to draw the solid enclosed by the paraboloids $z = x^2 + y^2$ and $z = 5 - x^2 - y^2$.

35. Use a graphing device to draw a silo consisting of a cylinder with radius 3 and height 10 surmounted by a hemisphere.

36. The latitude and longitude of a point P in the Northern Hemisphere are related to spherical coordinates ρ, θ, ϕ as follows. We take the origin to be the center of the earth and the positive z-axis to pass through the North Pole. The positive x-axis passes through the point where the prime meridian (the meridian through Greenwich, England) intersects the equator. Then the latitude of P is $\alpha = 90° - \phi°$ and the longitude is $\beta = 360° - \theta°$. Find the great-circle distance from Los Angeles (lat. 34.06° N, long. 118.25° W) to Montréal (lat. 45.50° N, long. 73.60° W). Take the radius of the earth to be 3960 mi. (A *great circle* is the circle of intersection of a sphere and a plane through the center of the sphere.)

LABORATORY PROJECT  Families of Surfaces

In this project you will discover the interesting shapes that members of families of surfaces can take. You will also see how the shape of the surface evolves as you vary the constants.

1. Use a computer to investigate the family of functions

$$f(x, y) = (ax^2 + by^2)e^{-x^2-y^2}$$

How does the shape of the graph depend on the numbers a and b?

2. Use a computer to investigate the family of surfaces $z = x^2 + y^2 + cxy$. In particular, you should determine the transitional values of c for which the surface changes from one type of quadric surface to another.

3. Members of the family of surfaces given in spherical coordinates by the equation

$$\rho = 1 + 0.2 \sin m\theta \sin n\phi$$

have been suggested as models for tumors and have been called *bumpy spheres* and *wrinkled spheres*. Use a computer to investigate this family of surfaces, assuming that m and n are positive integers. What roles do the values of m and n play in the shape of the surface?

Graphing calculator or computer with graphing software required

9 Review

Concept Check

1. What is the difference between a vector and a scalar?
2. How do you add two vectors geometrically? How do you add them algebraically?
3. If **a** is a vector and c is a scalar, how is $c\mathbf{a}$ related to **a** geometrically? How do you find $c\mathbf{a}$ algebraically?
4. How do you find the vector from one point to another?
5. How do you find the dot product $\mathbf{a} \cdot \mathbf{b}$ of two vectors if you know their lengths and the angle between them? What if you know their components?
6. How are dot products useful?
7. Write expressions for the scalar and vector projections of **b** onto **a**. Illustrate with diagrams.
8. How do you find the cross product $\mathbf{a} \times \mathbf{b}$ of two vectors if you know their lengths and the angle between them? What if you know their components?
9. How are cross products useful?
10. (a) How do you find the area of the parallelogram determined by **a** and **b**?
    (b) How do you find the volume of the parallelepiped determined by **a**, **b**, and **c**?
11. How do you find a vector perpendicular to a plane?
12. How do you find the angle between two intersecting planes?
13. Write a vector equation, parametric equations, and symmetric equations for a line.
14. Write a vector equation and a scalar equation for a plane.
15. (a) How do you tell if two vectors are parallel?
    (b) How do you tell if two vectors are perpendicular?
    (c) How do you tell if two planes are parallel?
16. (a) Describe a method for determining whether three points P, Q, and R lie on the same line.
    (b) Describe a method for determining whether four points P, Q, R, and S lie in the same plane.
17. (a) How do you find the distance from a point to a line?
    (b) How do you find the distance from a point to a plane?
    (c) How do you find the distance between two lines?
18. How do you sketch the graph of a function of two variables?
19. Write equations in standard form of the six types of quadric surfaces.
20. (a) Write the equations for converting from cylindrical to rectangular coordinates. In what situation would you use cylindrical coordinates?
    (b) Write the equations for converting from spherical to rectangular coordinates. In what situation would you use spherical coordinates?

True-False Quiz

Determine whether the statement is true or false. If it is true, explain why. If it is false, explain why or give an example that disproves the statement.

1. For any vectors **u** and **v** in V_3, $\mathbf{u} \cdot \mathbf{v} = \mathbf{v} \cdot \mathbf{u}$.
2. For any vectors **u** and **v** in V_3, $\mathbf{u} \times \mathbf{v} = \mathbf{v} \times \mathbf{u}$.
3. For any vectors **u** and **v** in V_3, $|\mathbf{u} \times \mathbf{v}| = |\mathbf{v} \times \mathbf{u}|$.
4. For any vectors **u** and **v** in V_3 and any scalar k, $k(\mathbf{u} \cdot \mathbf{v}) = (k\mathbf{u}) \cdot \mathbf{v}$.
5. For any vectors **u** and **v** in V_3 and any scalar k, $k(\mathbf{u} \times \mathbf{v}) = (k\mathbf{u}) \times \mathbf{v}$.
6. For any vectors **u**, **v**, and **w** in V_3, $(\mathbf{u} + \mathbf{v}) \times \mathbf{w} = \mathbf{u} \times \mathbf{w} + \mathbf{v} \times \mathbf{w}$.
7. For any vectors **u**, **v**, and **w** in V_3, $\mathbf{u} \cdot (\mathbf{v} \times \mathbf{w}) = (\mathbf{u} \times \mathbf{v}) \cdot \mathbf{w}$.
8. For any vectors **u**, **v**, and **w** in V_3, $\mathbf{u} \times (\mathbf{v} \times \mathbf{w}) = (\mathbf{u} \times \mathbf{v}) \times \mathbf{w}$.
9. For any vectors **u** and **v** in V_3, $(\mathbf{u} \times \mathbf{v}) \cdot \mathbf{u} = 0$.
10. For any vectors **u** and **v** in V_3, $(\mathbf{u} + \mathbf{v}) \times \mathbf{v} = \mathbf{u} \times \mathbf{v}$.
11. The cross product of two unit vectors is a unit vector.
12. A linear equation $Ax + By + Cz + D = 0$ represents a line in space.
13. The set of points $\{(x, y, z) \mid x^2 + y^2 = 1\}$ is a circle.
14. If $\mathbf{u} = \langle u_1, u_2 \rangle$ and $\mathbf{v} = \langle v_1, v_2 \rangle$, then $\mathbf{u} \cdot \mathbf{v} = \langle u_1 v_1, u_2 v_2 \rangle$.
15. If $\mathbf{u} \cdot \mathbf{v} = 0$, then $\mathbf{u} = \mathbf{0}$ or $\mathbf{v} = \mathbf{0}$.
16. If $\mathbf{u} \times \mathbf{v} = \mathbf{0}$, then $\mathbf{u} = \mathbf{0}$ or $\mathbf{v} = \mathbf{0}$.
17. If $\mathbf{u} \cdot \mathbf{v} = 0$ and $\mathbf{u} \times \mathbf{v} = \mathbf{0}$, then $\mathbf{u} = \mathbf{0}$ or $\mathbf{v} = \mathbf{0}$.
18. If **u** and **v** are in V_3, then $|\mathbf{u} \cdot \mathbf{v}| \leqslant |\mathbf{u}||\mathbf{v}|$.

Exercises

1. (a) Find an equation of the sphere that passes through the point $(6, -2, 3)$ and has center $(-1, 2, 1)$.
   (b) Find the curve in which this sphere intersects the yz-plane.
   (c) Find the center and radius of the sphere

$$x^2 + y^2 + z^2 - 8x + 2y + 6z + 1 = 0$$

2. Copy the vectors in the figure and use them to draw each of the following vectors.
   (a) $\mathbf{a} + \mathbf{b}$ (b) $\mathbf{a} - \mathbf{b}$ (c) $-\frac{1}{2}\mathbf{a}$ (d) $2\mathbf{a} + \mathbf{b}$

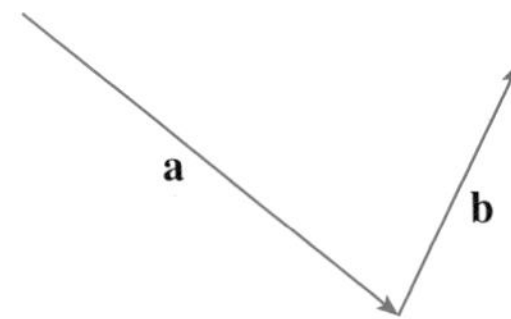

3. If $\mathbf{u}$ and $\mathbf{v}$ are the vectors shown in the figure, find $\mathbf{u} \cdot \mathbf{v}$ and $|\mathbf{u} \times \mathbf{v}|$. Is $\mathbf{u} \times \mathbf{v}$ directed into the page or out of it?

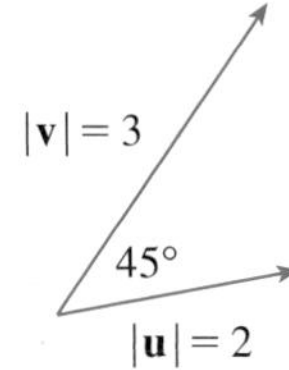

4. Calculate the given quantity if

$$\mathbf{a} = \mathbf{i} + \mathbf{j} - 2\mathbf{k}$$
$$\mathbf{b} = 3\mathbf{i} - 2\mathbf{j} + \mathbf{k}$$
$$\mathbf{c} = \mathbf{j} - 5\mathbf{k}$$

   (a) $2\mathbf{a} + 3\mathbf{b}$ (b) $|\mathbf{b}|$
   (c) $\mathbf{a} \cdot \mathbf{b}$ (d) $\mathbf{a} \times \mathbf{b}$
   (e) $|\mathbf{b} \times \mathbf{c}|$ (f) $\mathbf{a} \cdot (\mathbf{b} \times \mathbf{c})$
   (g) $\mathbf{c} \times \mathbf{c}$ (h) $\mathbf{a} \times (\mathbf{b} \times \mathbf{c})$
   (i) $\text{comp}_{\mathbf{a}}\, \mathbf{b}$ (j) $\text{proj}_{\mathbf{a}}\, \mathbf{b}$
   (k) The angle between $\mathbf{a}$ and $\mathbf{b}$ (correct to the nearest degree)

5. Find the values of x such that the vectors $\langle 3, 2, x \rangle$ and $\langle 2x, 4, x \rangle$ are orthogonal.

6. Find two unit vectors that are orthogonal to both $\mathbf{j} + 2\mathbf{k}$ and $\mathbf{i} - 2\mathbf{j} + 3\mathbf{k}$.

7. Suppose that $\mathbf{u} \cdot (\mathbf{v} \times \mathbf{w}) = 2$. Find
   (a) $(\mathbf{u} \times \mathbf{v}) \cdot \mathbf{w}$ (b) $\mathbf{u} \cdot (\mathbf{w} \times \mathbf{v})$
   (c) $\mathbf{v} \cdot (\mathbf{u} \times \mathbf{w})$ (d) $(\mathbf{u} \times \mathbf{v}) \cdot \mathbf{v}$

8. Show that if $\mathbf{a}$, $\mathbf{b}$, and $\mathbf{c}$ are in V_3, then

$$(\mathbf{a} \times \mathbf{b}) \cdot [(\mathbf{b} \times \mathbf{c}) \times (\mathbf{c} \times \mathbf{a})] = [\mathbf{a} \cdot (\mathbf{b} \times \mathbf{c})]^2$$

9. Find the acute angle between two diagonals of a cube.

10. Given the points $A(1, 0, 1)$, $B(2, 3, 0)$, $C(-1, 1, 4)$, and $D(0, 3, 2)$, find the volume of the parallelepiped with adjacent edges AB, AC, and AD.

11. (a) Find a vector perpendicular to the plane through the points $A(1, 0, 0)$, $B(2, 0, -1)$, and $C(1, 4, 3)$.
    (b) Find the area of triangle ABC.

12. A constant force $\mathbf{F} = 3\mathbf{i} + 5\mathbf{j} + 10\mathbf{k}$ moves an object along the line segment from $(1, 0, 2)$ to $(5, 3, 8)$. Find the work done if the distance is measured in meters and the force in newtons.

13. A boat is pulled onto shore using two ropes, as shown in the diagram. If a force of 255 N is needed, find the magnitude of the force in each rope.

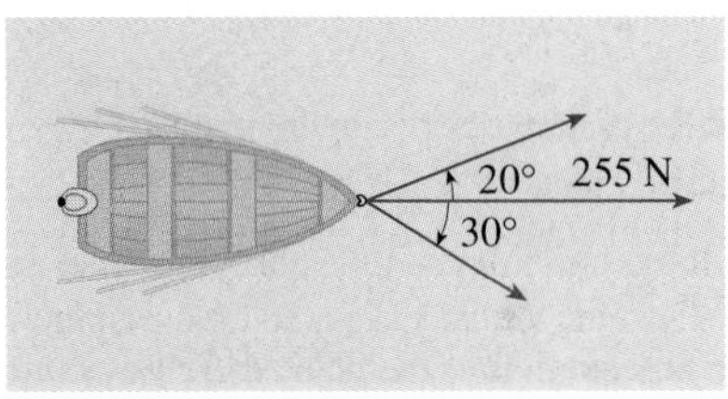

14. Find the magnitude of the torque about P if a 50-N force is applied as shown.

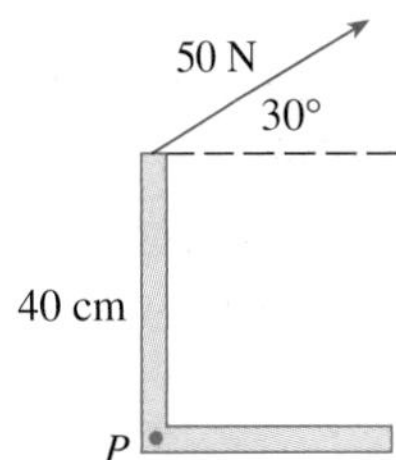

15–17 Find parametric equations for the line.

15. The line through $(4, -1, 2)$ and $(1, 1, 5)$

16. The line through $(1, 0, -1)$ and parallel to the line $\frac{1}{3}(x - 4) = \frac{1}{2}y = z + 2$

17. The line through $(-2, 2, 4)$ and perpendicular to the plane $2x - y + 5z = 12$

18–21 Find an equation of the plane.

18. The plane through $(2, 1, 0)$ and parallel to $x + 4y - 3z = 1$

19. The plane through $(3, -1, 1)$, $(4, 0, 2)$, and $(6, 3, 1)$

20. The plane through $(1, 2, -2)$ that contains the line $x = 2t$, $y = 3 - t$, $z = 1 + 3t$

21. The plane through the line of intersection of the planes $x - z = 1$ and $y + 2z = 3$ and perpendicular to the plane $x + y - 2z = 1$

22. Find the point in which the line with parametric equations $x = 2 - t$, $y = 1 + 3t$, $z = 4t$ intersects the plane $2x - y + z = 2$.

23. Determine whether the lines given by the symmetric equations

$$\frac{x-1}{2} = \frac{y-2}{3} = \frac{z-3}{4}$$

and
$$\frac{x+1}{6} = \frac{y-3}{-1} = \frac{z+5}{2}$$

are parallel, skew, or intersecting.

24. (a) Show that the planes $x + y - z = 1$ and $2x - 3y + 4z = 5$ are neither parallel nor perpendicular.
(b) Find, correct to the nearest degree, the angle between these planes.

25. (a) Find the distance between the planes $3x + y - 4z = 2$ and $3x + y - 4z = 24$.
(b) Find the distance from the origin to the line $x = 1 + t$, $y = 2 - t$, $z = -1 + 2t$.

26. (a) Find an equation of the plane that passes through the points $A(2, 1, 1)$, $B(-1, -1, 10)$, and $C(1, 3, -4)$.
(b) Find symmetric equations for the line through B that is perpendicular to the plane in part (a).
(c) A second plane passes through $(2, 0, 4)$ and has normal vector $\langle 2, -4, -3 \rangle$. Show that the acute angle between the planes is approximately 43°.
(d) Find parametric equations for the line of intersection of the two planes.

27–28 Find and sketch the domain of the function.

27. $f(x, y) = x \ln(x - y^2)$

28. $f(x, y) = \sqrt{\sin \pi(x^2 + y^2)}$

29–32 Sketch the graph of the function.

29. $f(x, y) = 6 - 2x - 3y$

30. $f(x, y) = \cos y$

31. $f(x, y) = 4 - x^2 - 4y^2$

32. $f(x, y) = \sqrt{4 - x^2 - 4y^2}$

33–36 Identify and sketch the graph of the surface. Include several traces in your sketch.

33. $y^2 + z^2 = 1 - 4x^2$

34. $y^2 + z^2 = x$

35. $y^2 + z^2 = 1$

36. $y^2 + z^2 = 1 + x^2$

---

37. The cylindrical coordinates of a point are $(2\sqrt{3}, \pi/3, 2)$. Find the rectangular and spherical coordinates of the point.

38. The rectangular coordinates of a point are $(2, 2, -1)$. Find the cylindrical and spherical coordinates of the point.

39. The spherical coordinates of a point are $(8, \pi/4, \pi/6)$. Find the rectangular and cylindrical coordinates of the point.

40. Identify the surfaces whose equations are given.
(a) $\theta = \pi/4$ (b) $\phi = \pi/4$

41–42 Write the equation in cylindrical coordinates and in spherical coordinates.

41. $x^2 + y^2 + z^2 = 4$

42. $x^2 + y^2 = 4$

---

43. The parabola $z = 4y^2$, $x = 0$ is rotated about the z-axis. Write an equation of the resulting surface in cylindrical coordinates.

44. Sketch the solid consisting of all points with spherical coordinates (ρ, θ, ϕ) such that $0 \leqslant \theta \leqslant \pi/2$, $0 \leqslant \phi \leqslant \pi/6$, and $0 \leqslant \rho \leqslant 2 \cos \phi$.

Focus on Problem Solving

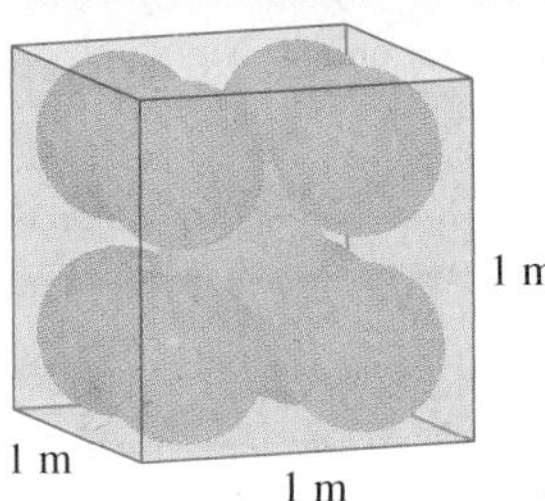

FIGURE FOR PROBLEM 1

1. Each edge of a cubical box has length 1 m. The box contains nine spherical balls with the same radius r. The center of one ball is at the center of the cube and it touches the other eight balls. Each of the other eight balls touches three sides of the box. Thus the balls are tightly packed in the box. (See the figure.) Find r. (If you have trouble with this problem, read about the problem-solving strategy entitled *Use Analogy* on page 83.)

2. Let B be a solid box with length L, width W, and height H. Let S be the set of all points that are a distance at most 1 from some point of B. Express the volume of S in terms of L, W, and H.

3. Let L be the line of intersection of the planes $cx + y + z = c$ and $x - cy + cz = -1$, where c is a real number.
   (a) Find symmetric equations for L.
   (b) As the number c varies, the line L sweeps out a surface S. Find an equation for the curve of intersection of S with the horizontal plane $z = t$ (the trace of S in the plane $z = t$).
   (c) Find the volume of the solid bounded by S and the planes $z = 0$ and $z = 1$.

4. A plane is capable of flying at a speed of 180 km/h in still air. The pilot takes off from an airfield and heads due north according to the plane's compass. After 30 minutes of flight time, the pilot notices that, due to the wind, the plane has actually traveled 80 km at an angle 5° east of north.
   (a) What is the wind velocity?
   (b) In what direction should the pilot have headed to reach the intended destination?

5. Suppose $\mathbf{v}_1$ and $\mathbf{v}_2$ are vectors with $|\mathbf{v}_1| = 2$, $|\mathbf{v}_2| = 3$, and $\mathbf{v}_1 \cdot \mathbf{v}_2 = 5$. Let $\mathbf{v}_3 = \text{proj}_{\mathbf{v}_1}\mathbf{v}_2$, $\mathbf{v}_4 = \text{proj}_{\mathbf{v}_2}\mathbf{v}_3$, $\mathbf{v}_5 = \text{proj}_{\mathbf{v}_3}\mathbf{v}_4$, and so on. Compute $\sum_{n=1}^{\infty} |\mathbf{v}_n|$.

6. Find an equation of the largest sphere that passes through the point $(-1, 1, 4)$ and is such that each of the points (x, y, z) inside the sphere satisfies the condition

$$x^2 + y^2 + z^2 < 136 + 2(x + 2y + 3z)$$

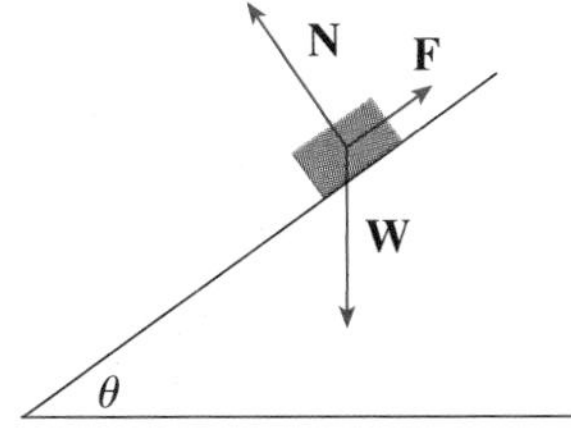

FIGURE FOR PROBLEM 7

7. Suppose a block of mass m is placed on an inclined plane, as shown in the figure. The block's descent down the plane is slowed by friction; if θ is not too large, friction will prevent the block from moving at all. The forces acting on the block are the weight $\mathbf{W}$, where $|\mathbf{W}| = mg$ (g is the acceleration due to gravity); the normal force $\mathbf{N}$ (the normal component of the reactionary force of the plane on the block), where $|\mathbf{N}| = n$; and the force $\mathbf{F}$ due to friction, which acts parallel to the inclined plane, opposing the direction of motion. If the block is at rest and θ is increased, $|\mathbf{F}|$ must also increase until ultimately $|\mathbf{F}|$ reaches its maximum, beyond which the block begins to slide. At this angle θ_s, it has been observed that $|\mathbf{F}|$ is proportional to n. Thus, when $|\mathbf{F}|$ is maximal, we can say that $|\mathbf{F}| = \mu_s n$, where μ_s is called the *coefficient of static friction* and depends on the materials that are in contact.
   (a) Observe that $\mathbf{N} + \mathbf{F} + \mathbf{W} = \mathbf{0}$ and deduce that $\mu_s = \tan(\theta_s)$.
   (b) Suppose that, for $\theta > \theta_s$, an additional outside force $\mathbf{H}$ is applied to the block, horizontally from the left, and let $|\mathbf{H}| = h$. If h is small, the block may still slide down the plane; if h is large enough, the block will move up the plane. Let $h_{\min}$ be the smallest value of h that allows the block to remain motionless (so that $|\mathbf{F}|$ is maximal).

   By choosing the coordinate axes so that $\mathbf{F}$ lies along the x-axis, resolve each force into components parallel and perpendicular to the inclined plane and show that

$$h_{\min} \sin\theta + mg\cos\theta = n \qquad \text{and} \qquad h_{\min}\cos\theta + \mu_s n = mg\sin\theta$$

   (c) Show that

$$h_{\min} = mg\tan(\theta - \theta_s)$$

   Does this equation seem reasonable? Does it make sense for $\theta = \theta_s$? As $\theta \to 90°$? Explain.

(d) Let h_{max} be the largest value of h that allows the block to remain motionless. (In which direction is **F** heading?) Show that

$$h_{max} = mg\tan(\theta + \theta_s)$$

Does this equation seem reasonable? Explain.

8. A solid has the following properties. When illuminated by rays parallel to the z-axis, its shadow is a circular disk. If the rays are parallel to the y-axis, its shadow is a square. If the rays are parallel to the x-axis, its shadow is an isosceles triangle. (In Exercise 42 in Section 9.1 you were asked to describe and sketch an example of such a solid, but there are many such solids.) Assume that the projection onto the xz-plane is a square whose sides have length 1.

(a) What is the volume of the largest such solid?

(b) Is there a smallest volume?

Courtesy of Frank O. Gehry

11 Partial Derivatives

Physical quantities often depend on two or more variables. In this chapter we extend the basic ideas of differential calculus to such functions.

11.1 Functions of Several Variables

In Section 9.6 we discussed functions of two variables and their graphs. Here we study functions of two or more variables from four points of view:

- verbally (by a description in words)
- numerically (by a table of values)
- algebraically (by an explicit formula)
- visually (by a graph or level curves)

Recall that a function f of two variables is a rule that assigns to each ordered pair (x, y) of real numbers in its domain a unique real number denoted by $f(x, y)$. In Example 3 in Section 9.6 we looked at the wave heights h in the open sea as a function of the wind speed v and the length of time t that the wind has been blowing at that speed. We presented a table of observed wave heights that represent the function $h = f(v, t)$ numerically. The function in the next example is also described verbally and numerically.

EXAMPLE 1 **Wind chill is a function of temperature and wind speed** In regions with severe winter weather, the *wind-chill index* is often used to describe the apparent severity of the cold. This index W is a subjective temperature that depends on the actual temperature T and the wind speed v. So W is a function of T and v, and we can write $W = f(T, v)$. Table 1 records values of W compiled by the National Weather Service of the US and the Meteorological Service of Canada.

TABLE 1
Wind-chill index as a function of air temperature and wind speed

THE NEW WIND-CHILL INDEX

A new wind-chill index was introduced in November of 2001 and is more accurate than the old index for measuring how cold it feels when it's windy. The new index is based on a model of how fast a human face loses heat. It was developed through clinical trials in which volunteers were exposed to a variety of temperatures and wind speeds in a refrigerated wind tunnel.

Wind speed (km/h); rows: Actual temperature (°C)

T \ v	5	10	15	20	25	30	40	50	60	70	80
5	4	3	2	1	1	0	−1	−1	−2	−2	−3
0	−2	−3	−4	−5	−6	−6	−7	−8	−9	−9	−10
−5	−7	−9	−11	−12	−12	−13	−14	−15	−16	−16	−17
−10	−13	−15	−17	−18	−19	−20	−21	−22	−23	−23	−24
−15	−19	−21	−23	−24	−25	−26	−27	−29	−30	−30	−31
−20	−24	−27	−29	−30	−32	−33	−34	−35	−36	−37	−38
−25	−30	−33	−35	−37	−38	−39	−41	−42	−43	−44	−45
−30	−36	−39	−41	−43	−44	−46	−48	−49	−50	−51	−52
−35	−41	−45	−48	−49	−51	−52	−54	−56	−57	−58	−60
−40	−47	−51	−54	−56	−57	−59	−61	−63	−64	−65	−67

For instance, the table shows that if the temperature is $-5°C$ and the wind speed is 50 km/h, then subjectively it would feel as cold as a temperature of about $-15°C$ with no wind. So

$$f(-5, 50) = -15$$

EXAMPLE 2 **The Cobb-Douglas production function** In 1928 Charles Cobb and Paul Douglas published a study in which they modeled the growth of the American economy during the period 1899–1922. They considered a simplified view of the economy in

TABLE 2

Year	P	L	K
1899	100	100	100
1900	101	105	107
1901	112	110	114
1902	122	117	122
1903	124	122	131
1904	122	121	138
1905	143	125	149
1906	152	134	163
1907	151	140	176
1908	126	123	185
1909	155	143	198
1910	159	147	208
1911	153	148	216
1912	177	155	226
1913	184	156	236
1914	169	152	244
1915	189	156	266
1916	225	183	298
1917	227	198	335
1918	223	201	366
1919	218	196	387
1920	231	194	407
1921	179	146	417
1922	240	161	431

which production output is determined by the amount of labor involved and the amount of capital invested. While there are many other factors affecting economic performance, their model proved to be remarkably accurate. The function they used to model production was of the form

1 $$P(L, K) = bL^{\alpha}K^{1-\alpha}$$

where P is the total production (the monetary value of all goods produced in a year), L is the amount of labor (the total number of person-hours worked in a year), and K is the amount of capital invested (the monetary worth of all machinery, equipment, and buildings). In Section 11.3 we will show how the form of Equation 1 follows from certain economic assumptions.

Cobb and Douglas used economic data published by the government to obtain Table 2. They took the year 1899 as a baseline and P, L, and K for 1899 were each assigned the value 100. The values for other years were expressed as percentages of the 1899 figures.

Cobb and Douglas used the method of least squares to fit the data of Table 2 to the function

2 $$P(L, K) = 1.01L^{0.75}K^{0.25}$$

(See Exercise 49 for the details.)

If we use the model given by the function in Equation 2 to compute the production in the years 1910 and 1920, we get the values

$$P(147, 208) = 1.01(147)^{0.75}(208)^{0.25} \approx 161.9$$

$$P(194, 407) = 1.01(194)^{0.75}(407)^{0.25} \approx 235.8$$

which are quite close to the actual values, 159 and 231.

The production function (1) has subsequently been used in many settings, ranging from individual firms to global economics. It has become known as the **Cobb-Douglas production function.**

The domain of the production function in Example 2 is $\{(L, K) \mid L \geqslant 0, K \geqslant 0\}$ because L and K represent labor and capital and are therefore never negative. For a function f given by an algebraic formula, recall that the domain consists of all pairs (x, y) for which the expression for $f(x, y)$ is a well-defined real number.

EXAMPLE 3 Find the domain and range of $g(x, y) = \sqrt{9 - x^2 - y^2}$.

SOLUTION The domain of g is

$$D = \{(x, y) \mid 9 - x^2 - y^2 \geqslant 0\} = \{(x, y) \mid x^2 + y^2 \leqslant 9\}$$

which is the disk with center (0, 0) and radius 3. (See Figure 1.) The range of g is

$$\{z \mid z = \sqrt{9 - x^2 - y^2}, (x, y) \in D\}$$

Since z is a positive square root, $z \geqslant 0$. Also, because $9 - x^2 - y^2 \leqslant 9$, we have

$$\sqrt{9 - x^2 - y^2} \leqslant 3$$

So the range is

$$\{z \mid 0 \leqslant z \leqslant 3\} = [0, 3]$$

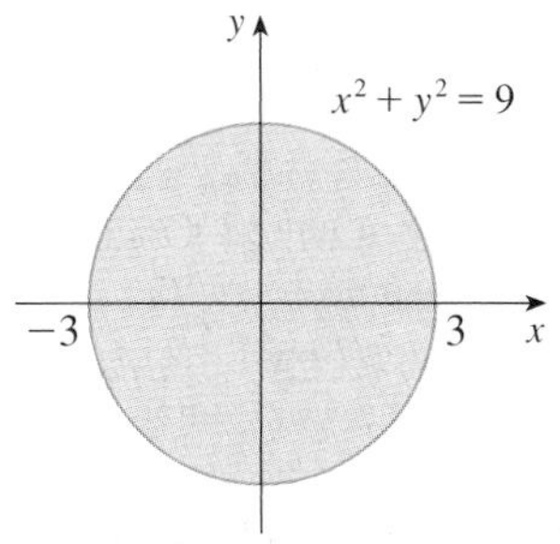

FIGURE 1
Domain of $g(x, y) = \sqrt{9 - x^2 - y^2}$

Visual Representations

One way to visualize a function of two variables is through its graph. Recall from Section 9.6 that the graph of f is the surface with equation $z = f(x, y)$.

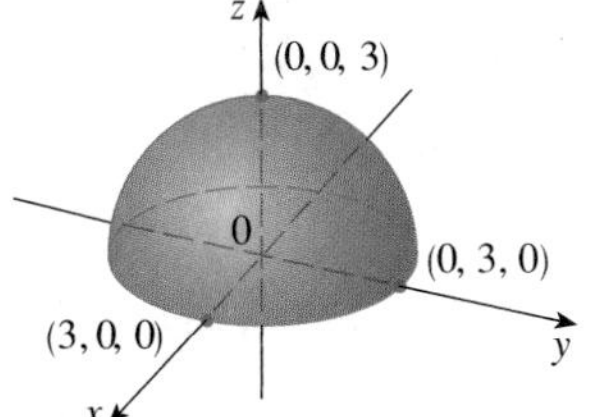

FIGURE 2
Graph of $g(x, y) = \sqrt{9 - x^2 - y^2}$

V EXAMPLE 4 Sketch the graph of $g(x, y) = \sqrt{9 - x^2 - y^2}$.

SOLUTION The graph has equation $z = \sqrt{9 - x^2 - y^2}$. We square both sides of this equation to obtain $z^2 = 9 - x^2 - y^2$, or $x^2 + y^2 + z^2 = 9$, which we recognize as an equation of the sphere with center the origin and radius 3. But, since $z \geqslant 0$, the graph of g is just the top half of this sphere (see Figure 2).

Note: An entire sphere can't be represented by a single function of x and y. As we saw in Example 4, the upper hemisphere of the sphere $x^2 + y^2 + z^2 = 9$ is represented by the function $g(x, y) = \sqrt{9 - x^2 - y^2}$. The lower hemisphere is represented by the function $h(x, y) = -\sqrt{9 - x^2 - y^2}$.

EXAMPLE 5 Use a computer to draw the graph of the Cobb-Douglas production function $P(L, K) = 1.01L^{0.75}K^{0.25}$.

SOLUTION Figure 3 shows the graph of P for values of the labor L and capital K that lie between 0 and 300. The computer has drawn the surface by plotting vertical traces. We see from these traces that the value of the production P increases as either L or K increases, as is to be expected.

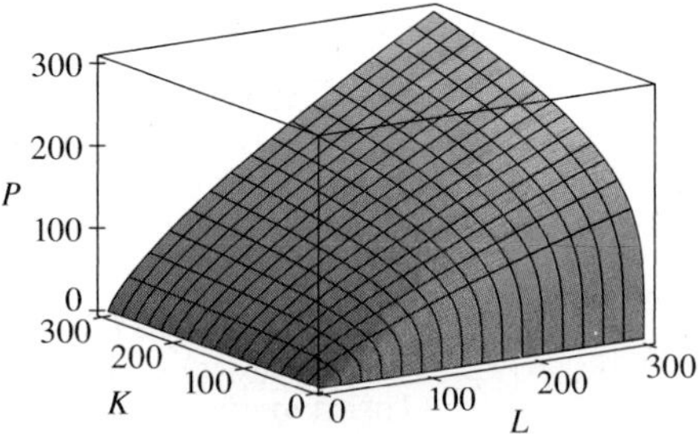

FIGURE 3

Another method for visualizing functions, borrowed from mapmakers, is a contour map on which points of constant elevation are joined to form *contour lines*, or *level curves*.

> **Definition** The **level curves** of a function f of two variables are the curves with equations $f(x, y) = k$, where k is a constant (in the range of f).

A level curve $f(x, y) = k$ is the set of all points in the domain of f at which f takes on a given value k. In other words, it shows where the graph of f has height k.

You can see from Figure 4 the relation between level curves and horizontal traces. The level curves $f(x, y) = k$ are just the traces of the graph of f in the horizontal plane $z = k$ projected down to the xy-plane. So if you draw the level curves of a function and visualize them being lifted up to the surface at the indicated height, then you can mentally piece together a picture of the graph. The surface is steep where the level curves are close together. It is somewhat flatter where they are farther apart.

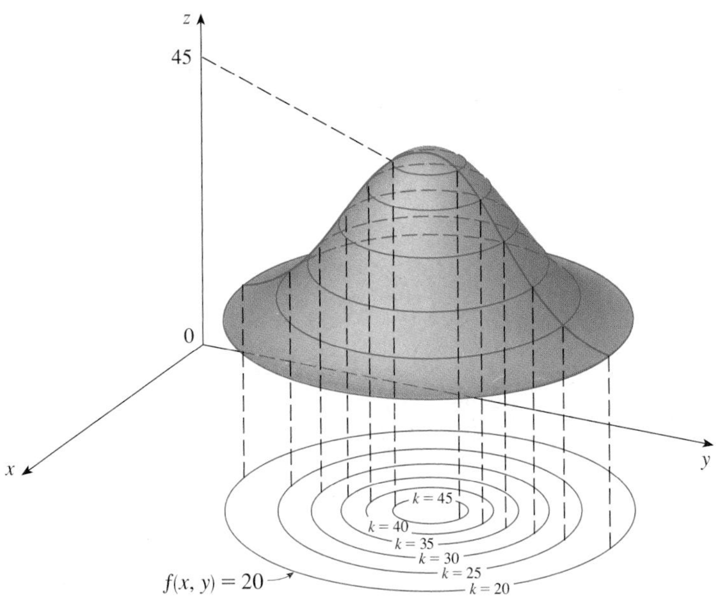

FIGURE 4

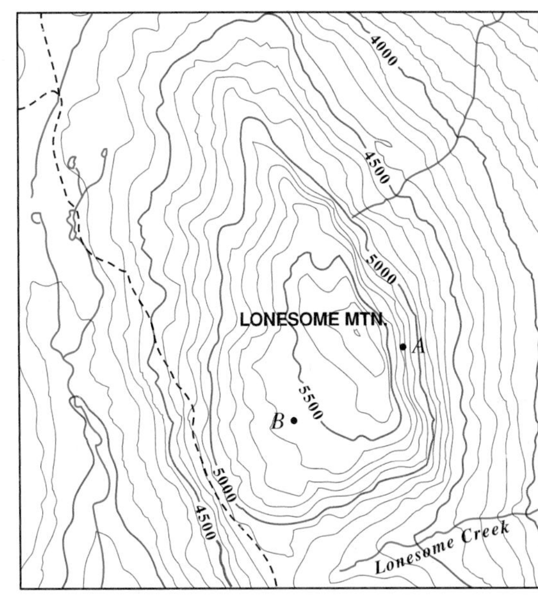

FIGURE 5

TEC Visual 11.1A animates Figure 4 by showing level curves being lifted up to graphs of functions.

One common example of level curves occurs in topographic maps of mountainous regions, such as the map in Figure 5. The level curves are curves of constant elevation above sea level. If you walk along one of these contour lines, you neither ascend nor descend. Another common example is the temperature at locations (x, y) with longitude x and latitude y. Here the level curves are called **isothermals** and join locations with the same temperature. Figure 6 shows a weather map of the world indicating the average January temperatures. The isothermals are the curves that separate the colored bands.

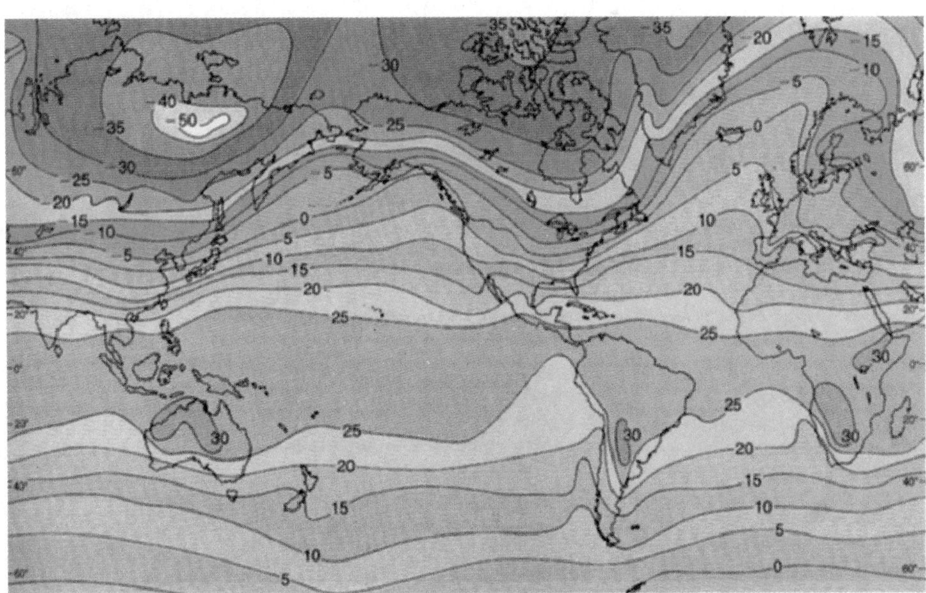

FIGURE 6

World mean sea-level temperatures in January in degrees Celsius

From *Atmosphere: Introduction to Meteorology*, 4th Edition, 1989. © 1989 Pearson Education, Inc.

In weather maps of atmospheric pressure at a given time as a function of longitude and latitude, the level curves are called **isobars**. They join locations with the same pressure (see

Exercise 10). Surface winds tend to flow from areas of high pressure across the isobars toward areas of low pressure, and are strongest where the isobars are tightly packed.

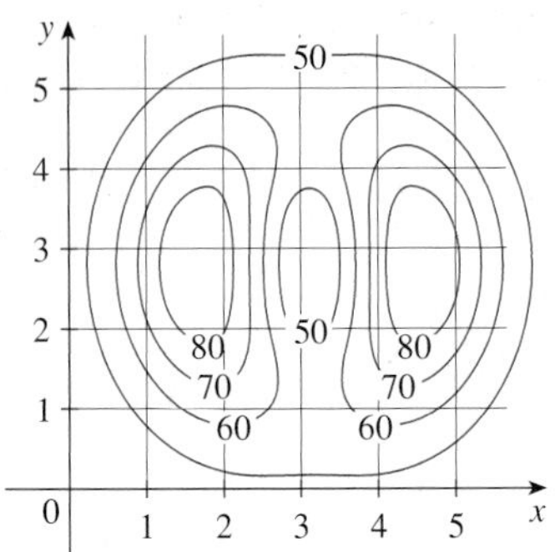

FIGURE 7

EXAMPLE 6 Using level curves to estimate function values A contour map for a function f is shown in Figure 7. Use it to estimate the values of $f(1, 3)$ and $f(4, 5)$.

SOLUTION The point (1, 3) lies partway between the level curves with z-values 70 and 80. We estimate that

$$f(1, 3) \approx 73$$

Similarly, we estimate that

$$f(4, 5) \approx 56$$

EXAMPLE 7 Drawing a contour map Sketch the level curves of the function $f(x, y) = 6 - 3x - 2y$ for the values $k = -6, 0, 6, 12$.

SOLUTION The level curves are

$$6 - 3x - 2y = k \qquad \text{or} \qquad 3x + 2y + (k - 6) = 0$$

This is a family of lines with slope $-\frac{3}{2}$. The four particular level curves with $k = -6, 0, 6$, and 12 are $3x + 2y - 12 = 0$, $3x + 2y - 6 = 0$, $3x + 2y = 0$, and $3x + 2y + 6 = 0$. They are sketched in Figure 8. The level curves are equally spaced parallel lines because the graph of f is a plane (see Figure 4 in Section 9.6).

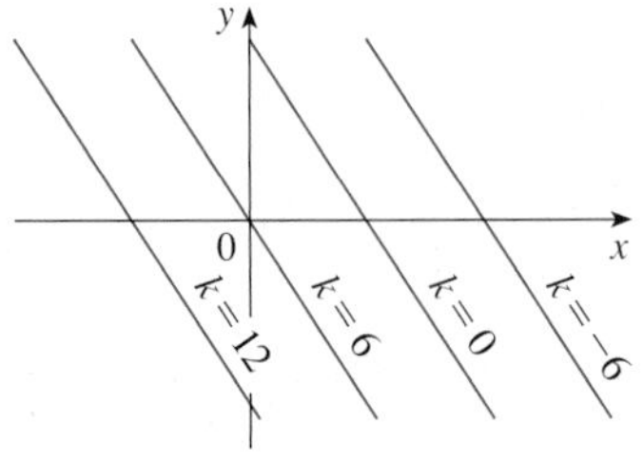

FIGURE 8
Contour map of $f(x, y) = 6 - 3x - 2y$

V EXAMPLE 8 Sketch the level curves of the function

$$g(x, y) = \sqrt{9 - x^2 - y^2} \qquad \text{for} \quad k = 0, 1, 2, 3$$

SOLUTION The level curves are

$$\sqrt{9 - x^2 - y^2} = k \qquad \text{or} \qquad x^2 + y^2 = 9 - k^2$$

This is a family of concentric circles with center (0, 0) and radius $\sqrt{9 - k^2}$. The cases $k = 0, 1, 2, 3$ are shown in Figure 9. Try to visualize these level curves lifted up to form a surface and compare with the graph of g (a hemisphere) in Figure 2. (See TEC Visual 11.1A.)

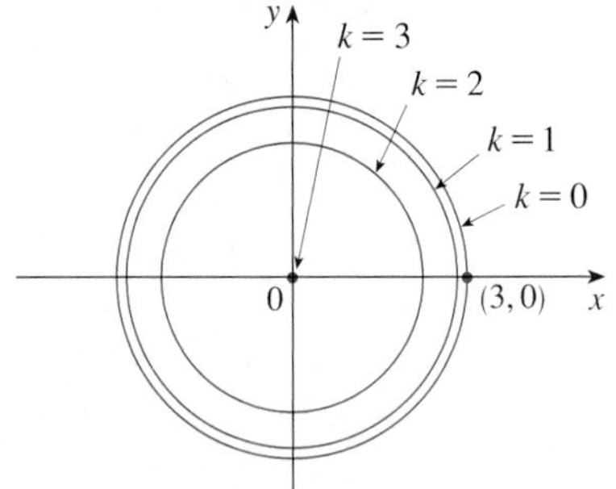

FIGURE 9
Contour map of $g(x, y) = \sqrt{9 - x^2 - y^2}$

EXAMPLE 9 Sketch some level curves of the function $h(x, y) = 4x^2 + y^2 + 1$.

SOLUTION The level curves are

$$4x^2 + y^2 + 1 = k \qquad \text{or} \qquad \frac{x^2}{\frac{1}{4}(k - 1)} + \frac{y^2}{k - 1} = 1$$

which, for $k > 1$, describes a family of ellipses with semiaxes $\frac{1}{2}\sqrt{k-1}$ and $\sqrt{k-1}$. Figure 10(a) shows a contour map of h drawn by a computer. Figure 10(b) shows these level curves lifted up to the graph of h (an elliptic paraboloid) where they become horizontal traces. We see from Figure 10 how the graph of h is put together from the level curves.

TEC Visual 11.1B demonstrates the connection between surfaces and their contour maps.

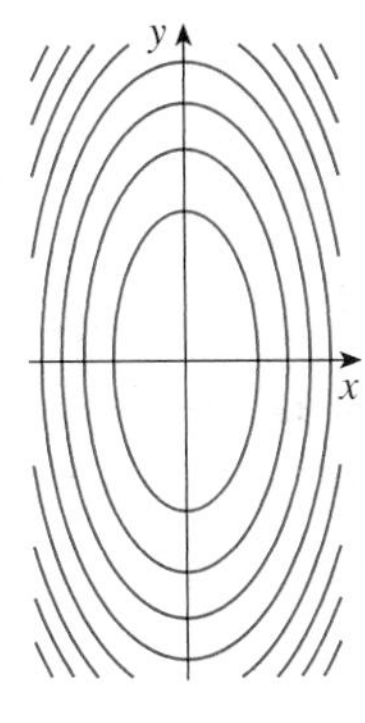

(a) Contour map

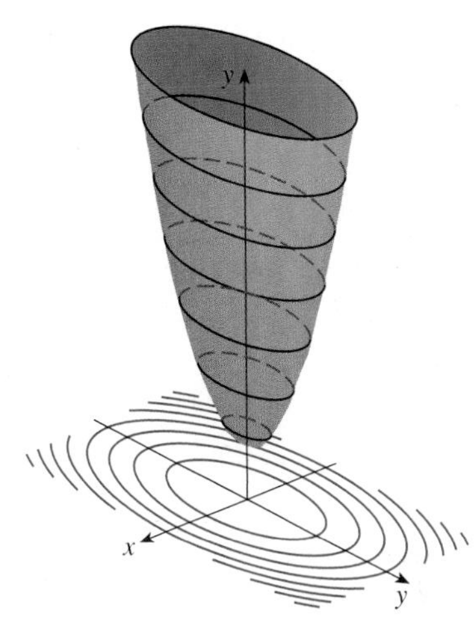

(b) Horizontal traces are raised level curves

FIGURE 10
The graph of $h(x, y) = 4x^2 + y^2 + 1$ is formed by lifting the level curves.

EXAMPLE 10 Plot level curves for the Cobb-Douglas production function of Example 2.

SOLUTION In Figure 11 we use a computer to draw a contour plot for the Cobb-Douglas production function

$$P(L, K) = 1.01L^{0.75}K^{0.25}$$

Level curves are labeled with the value of the production P. For instance, the level curve labeled 140 shows all values of the labor L and capital investment K that result in a production of $P = 140$. We see that, for a fixed value of P, as L increases K decreases, and vice versa.

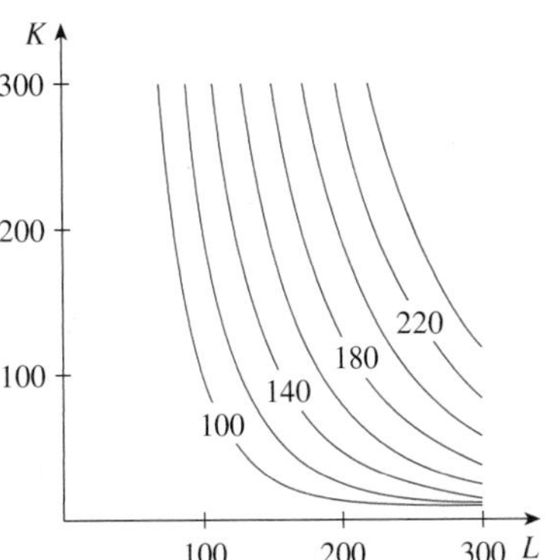

FIGURE 11

For some purposes, a contour map is more useful than a graph. That is certainly true in Example 10. (Compare Figure 11 with Figure 3.) It is also true in estimating function values, as in Example 6.

Figure 12 shows some computer-generated level curves together with the corresponding computer-generated graphs. Notice that the level curves in part (c) crowd together near the origin. That corresponds to the fact that the graph in part (d) is very steep near the origin.

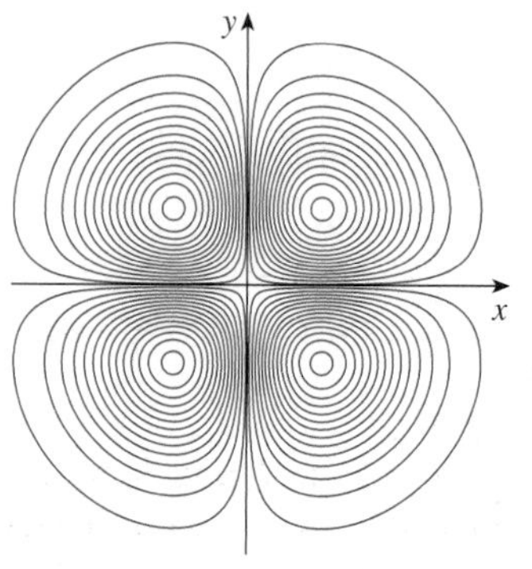

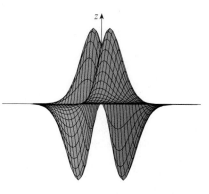

(a) Level curves of $f(x, y) = -xye^{-x^2-y^2}$

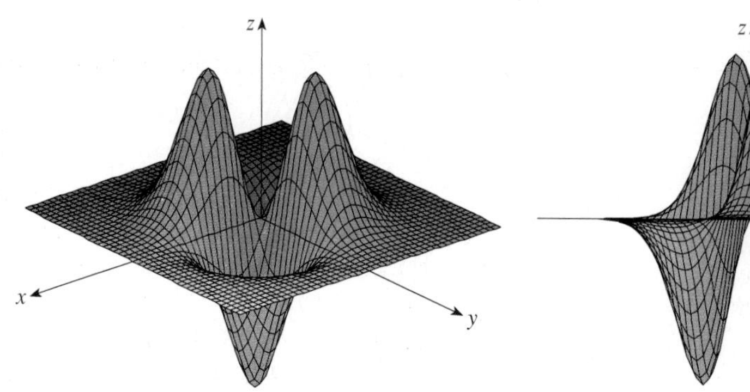

(b) Two views of $f(x, y) = -xye^{-x^2-y^2}$

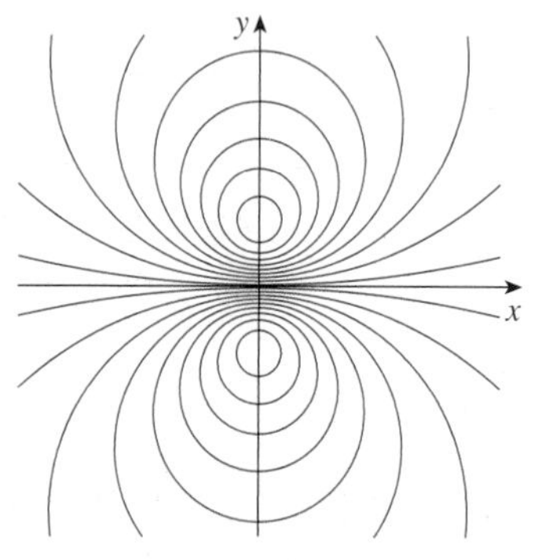

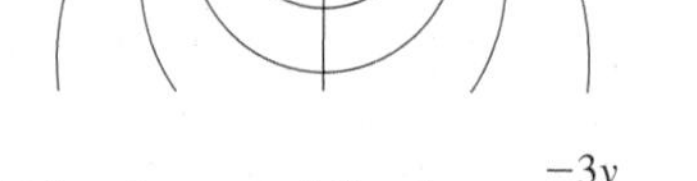

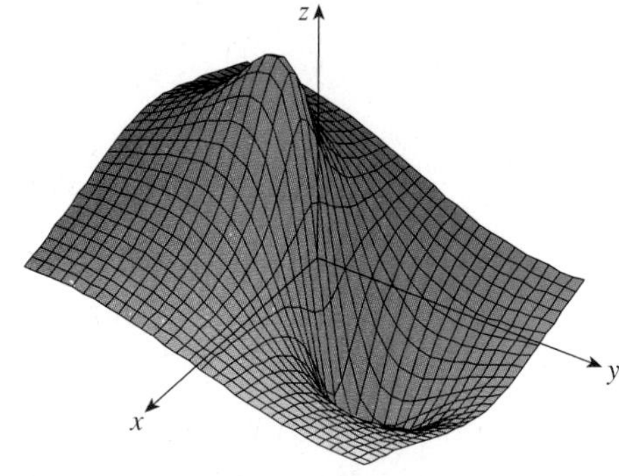

FIGURE 12 (c) Level curves of $f(x, y) = \dfrac{-3y}{x^2 + y^2 + 1}$ (d) $f(x, y) = \dfrac{-3y}{x^2 + y^2 + 1}$

Functions of Three or More Variables

A **function of three variables**, f, is a rule that assigns to each ordered triple (x, y, z) in a domain $D \subset \mathbb{R}^3$ a unique real number denoted by $f(x, y, z)$. For instance, the temperature T at a point on the surface of the earth depends on the longitude x and latitude y of the point and on the time t, so we could write $T = f(x, y, t)$.

EXAMPLE 11 Find the domain of f if

$$f(x, y, z) = \ln(z - y) + xy \sin z$$

SOLUTION The expression for $f(x, y, z)$ is defined as long as $z - y > 0$, so the domain of f is

$$D = \{(x, y, z) \in \mathbb{R}^3 \mid z > y\}$$

This is a **half-space** consisting of all points that lie above the plane $z = y$.

It's very difficult to visualize a function f of three variables by its graph, since that would lie in a four-dimensional space. However, we do gain some insight into f by examining its **level surfaces**, which are the surfaces with equations $f(x, y, z) = k$, where k is a constant. If the point (x, y, z) moves along a level surface, the value of $f(x, y, z)$ remains fixed.

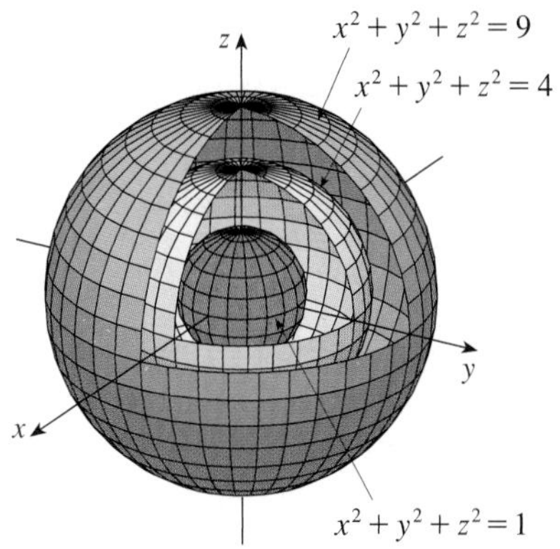

FIGURE 13

EXAMPLE 12 Find the level surfaces of the function

$$f(x, y, z) = x^2 + y^2 + z^2$$

SOLUTION The level surfaces are $x^2 + y^2 + z^2 = k$, where $k \geqslant 0$. These form a family of concentric spheres with radius $\sqrt{k}$. (See Figure 13.) Thus, as (x, y, z) varies over any sphere with center O, the value of $f(x, y, z)$ remains fixed.

Functions of any number of variables can be considered. A **function of n variables** is a rule that assigns a number $z = f(x_1, x_2, \dots, x_n)$ to an n-tuple $(x_1, x_2, \dots, x_n)$ of real numbers. We denote by $\mathbb{R}^n$ the set of all such n-tuples. For example, if a company uses n different ingredients in making a food product, c_i is the cost per unit of the ith ingredient, and x_i units of the ith ingredient are used, then the total cost C of the ingredients is a function of the n variables $x_1, x_2, \dots, x_n$:

$$\boxed{3} \qquad C = f(x_1, x_2, \dots, x_n) = c_1x_1 + c_2x_2 + \cdots + c_nx_n$$

The function f is a real-valued function whose domain is a subset of $\mathbb{R}^n$. Sometimes we will use vector notation to write such functions more compactly: If $\mathbf{x} = \langle x_1, x_2, \dots, x_n \rangle$, we often write $f(\mathbf{x})$ in place of $f(x_1, x_2, \dots, x_n)$. With this notation we can rewrite the function defined in Equation 3 as

$$f(\mathbf{x}) = \mathbf{c} \cdot \mathbf{x}$$

where $\mathbf{c} = \langle c_1, c_2, \dots, c_n \rangle$ and $\mathbf{c} \cdot \mathbf{x}$ denotes the dot product of the vectors $\mathbf{c}$ and $\mathbf{x}$ in V_n.

In view of the one-to-one correspondence between points $(x_1, x_2, \dots, x_n)$ in $\mathbb{R}^n$ and their position vectors $\mathbf{x} = \langle x_1, x_2, \dots, x_n \rangle$ in V_n, we have three ways of looking at a function f defined on a subset of $\mathbb{R}^n$:

1. As a function of n real variables $x_1, x_2, \dots, x_n$
2. As a function of a single point variable $(x_1, x_2, \dots, x_n)$
3. As a function of a single vector variable $\mathbf{x} = \langle x_1, x_2, \dots, x_n \rangle$

We will see that all three points of view are useful.

11.1 Exercises

1. In Example 1 we considered the function $W = f(T, v)$, where W is the wind-chill index, T is the actual temperature, and v is the wind speed. A numerical representation is given in Table 1.
   (a) What is the value of $f(-15, 40)$? What is its meaning?
   (b) Describe in words the meaning of the question "For what value of v is $f(-20, v) = -30$?" Then answer the question.
   (c) Describe in words the meaning of the question "For what value of T is $f(T, 20) = -49$?" Then answer the question.
   (d) What is the meaning of the function $W = f(-5, v)$? Describe the behavior of this function.
   (e) What is the meaning of the function $W = f(T, 50)$? Describe the behavior of this function.

2. The *temperature-humidity index I* (or humidex, for short) is the perceived air temperature when the actual temperature is T and the relative humidity is h, so we can write $I = f(T, h)$. The following table of values of I is an excerpt from a table compiled by the National Oceanic & Atmospheric Administration.

TABLE 3 Apparent temperature as a function of temperature and humidity

Relative humidity (%)

Actual temperature (°F)

T \ h	20	30	40	50	60	70
80	77	78	79	81	82	83
85	82	84	86	88	90	93
90	87	90	93	96	100	106
95	93	96	101	107	114	124
100	99	104	110	120	132	144

(a) What is the value of $f(95, 70)$? What is its meaning?
(b) For what value of h is $f(90, h) = 100$?
(c) For what value of T is $f(T, 50) = 88$?
(d) What are the meanings of the functions $I = f(80, h)$ and $I = f(100, h)$? Compare the behavior of these two functions of h.

3. Verify for the Cobb-Douglas production function

$$P(L, K) = 1.01L^{0.75}K^{0.25}$$

discussed in Example 2 that the production will be doubled if both the amount of labor and the amount of capital are doubled. Determine whether this is also true for the general production function

$$P(L, K) = bL^{\alpha}K^{1-\alpha}$$

4. The wind-chill index W discussed in Example 1 has been modeled by the following function:

$$W(T, v) = 13.12 + 0.6215T - 11.37v^{0.16} + 0.3965Tv^{0.16}$$

Check to see how closely this model agrees with the values in Table 1 for a few values of T and v.

5. Find and sketch the domain of the function $f(x, y) = \ln(9 - x^2 - 9y^2)$. What is the range of f?

6. Find and sketch the domain of the function $f(x, y) = \sqrt{y} + \sqrt{25 - x^2 - y^2}$.

7. Let $f(x, y, z) = \sqrt{x} + \sqrt{y} + \sqrt{z} + \ln(4 - x^2 - y^2 - z^2)$.
(a) Evaluate $f(1, 1, 1)$.
(b) Find and describe the domain of f.

8. Let $g(x, y, z) = x^3y^2z\sqrt{10 - x - y - z}$.
(a) Evaluate $g(1, 2, 3)$.
(b) Find and describe the domain of g.

9. A contour map for a function f is shown. Use it to estimate the values of $f(-3, 3)$ and $f(3, -2)$. What can you say about the shape of the graph?

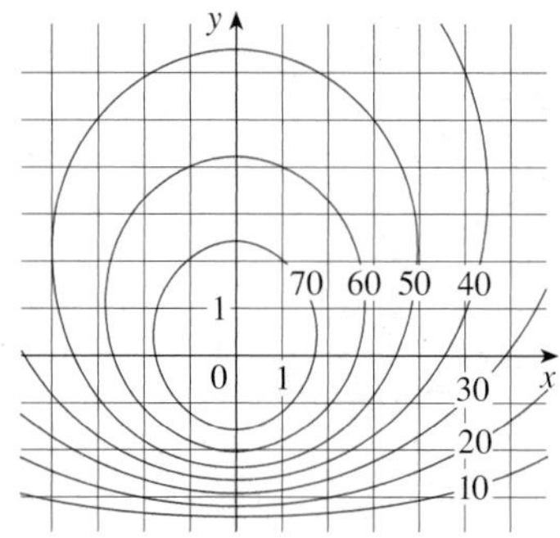

10. Shown is a contour map of atmospheric pressure in North America on August 12, 2008. On the level curves (called isobars) the pressure is indicated in millibars (mb).
(a) Estimate the pressure at C (Chicago), N (Nashville), S (San Francisco), and V (Vancouver).
(b) At which of these locations were the winds strongest?

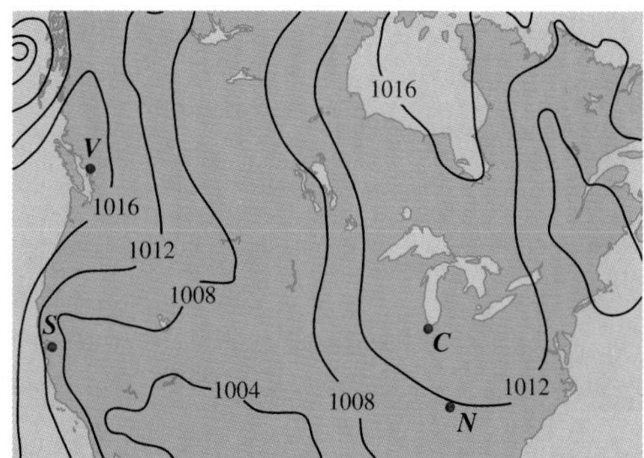

11. Level curves (isothermals) are shown for the water temperature (in °C) in Long Lake (Minnesota) in 1998 as a function of depth and time of year. Estimate the temperature in the lake on June 9 (day 160) at a depth of 10 m and on June 29 (day 180) at a depth of 5 m.

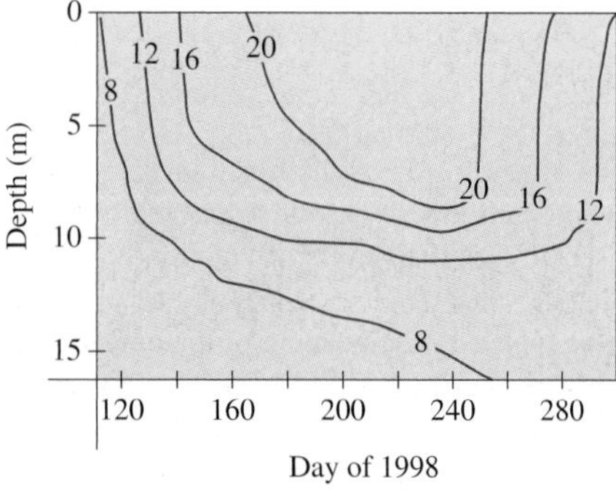

12. Two contour maps are shown. One is for a function f whose graph is a cone. The other is for a function g whose graph is a paraboloid. Which is which, and why?

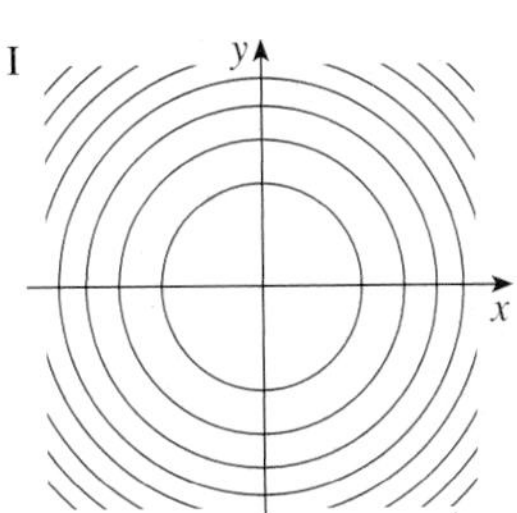

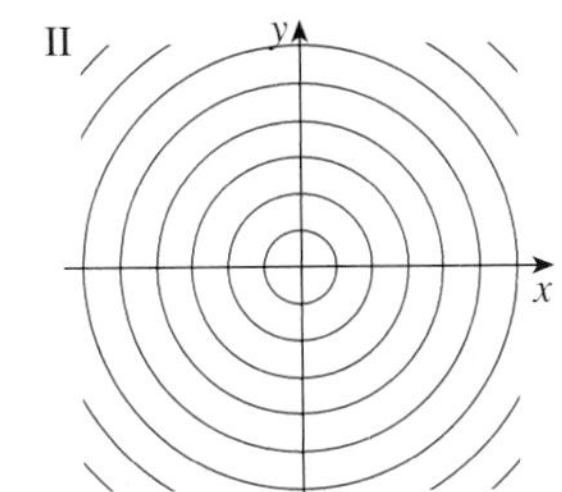

13. Locate the points A and B on the map of Lonesome Mountain (Figure 5). How would you describe the terrain near A? Near B?

14. Make a rough sketch of a contour map for the function whose graph is shown.

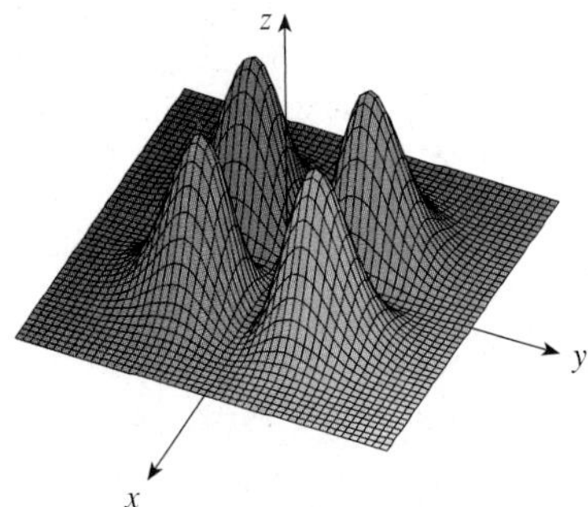

15–18 A contour map of a function is shown. Use it to make a rough sketch of the graph of f.

15.

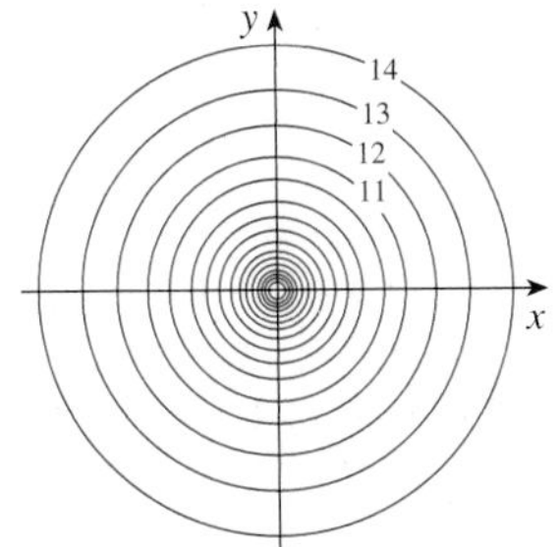

16.

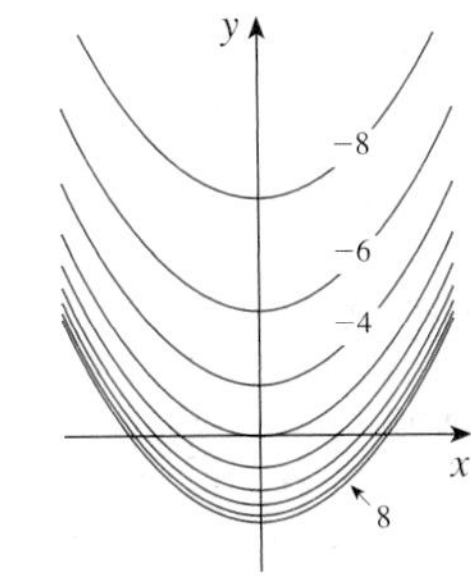

17.

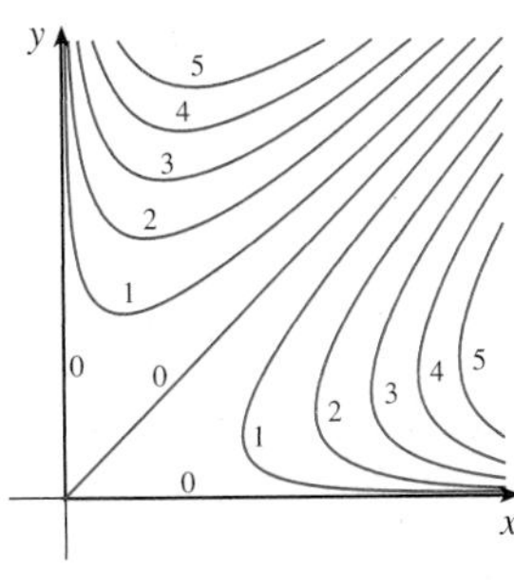

18.

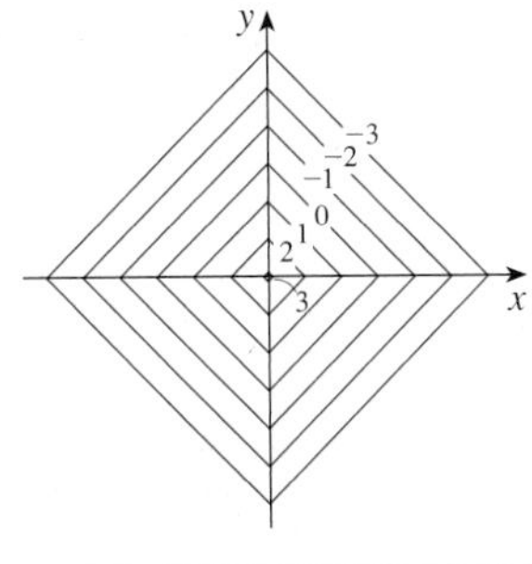

19–26 Draw a contour map of the function showing several level curves.

19. $f(x, y) = (y - 2x)^2$

20. $f(x, y) = x^3 - y$

21. $f(x, y) = \sqrt{x} + y$

22. $f(x, y) = \ln(x^2 + 4y^2)$

23. $f(x, y) = ye^x$

24. $f(x, y) = y \sec x$

25. $f(x, y) = \sqrt{y^2 - x^2}$

26. $f(x, y) = y/(x^2 + y^2)$

27–28 Sketch both a contour map and a graph of the function and compare them.

27. $f(x, y) = x^2 + 9y^2$

28. $f(x, y) = \sqrt{36 - 9x^2 - 4y^2}$

29. A thin metal plate, located in the xy-plane, has temperature $T(x, y)$ at the point (x, y). The level curves of T are called *isothermals* because at all points on such a curve the temperature is the same. Sketch some isothermals if the temperature function is given by

$$T(x, y) = \frac{100}{1 + x^2 + 2y^2}$$

30. If $V(x, y)$ is the electric potential at a point (x, y) in the xy-plane, then the level curves of V are called *equipotential curves* because at all points on such a curve the electric potential is the same. Sketch some equipotential curves if $V(x, y) = c/\sqrt{r^2 - x^2 - y^2}$, where c is a positive constant.

31–34 Use a computer to graph the function using various domains and viewpoints. Get a printout of one that, in your opinion, gives a good view. If your software also produces level curves, then plot some contour lines of the same function and compare with the graph.

31. $f(x, y) = xy^2 - x^3$ (monkey saddle)

32. $f(x, y) = xy^3 - yx^3$ (dog saddle)

33. $f(x, y) = e^{-(x^2+y^2)/3}(\sin(x^2) + \cos(y^2))$

34. $f(x, y) = \cos x \cos y$

Graphs and Contour Maps for Exercises 35–40

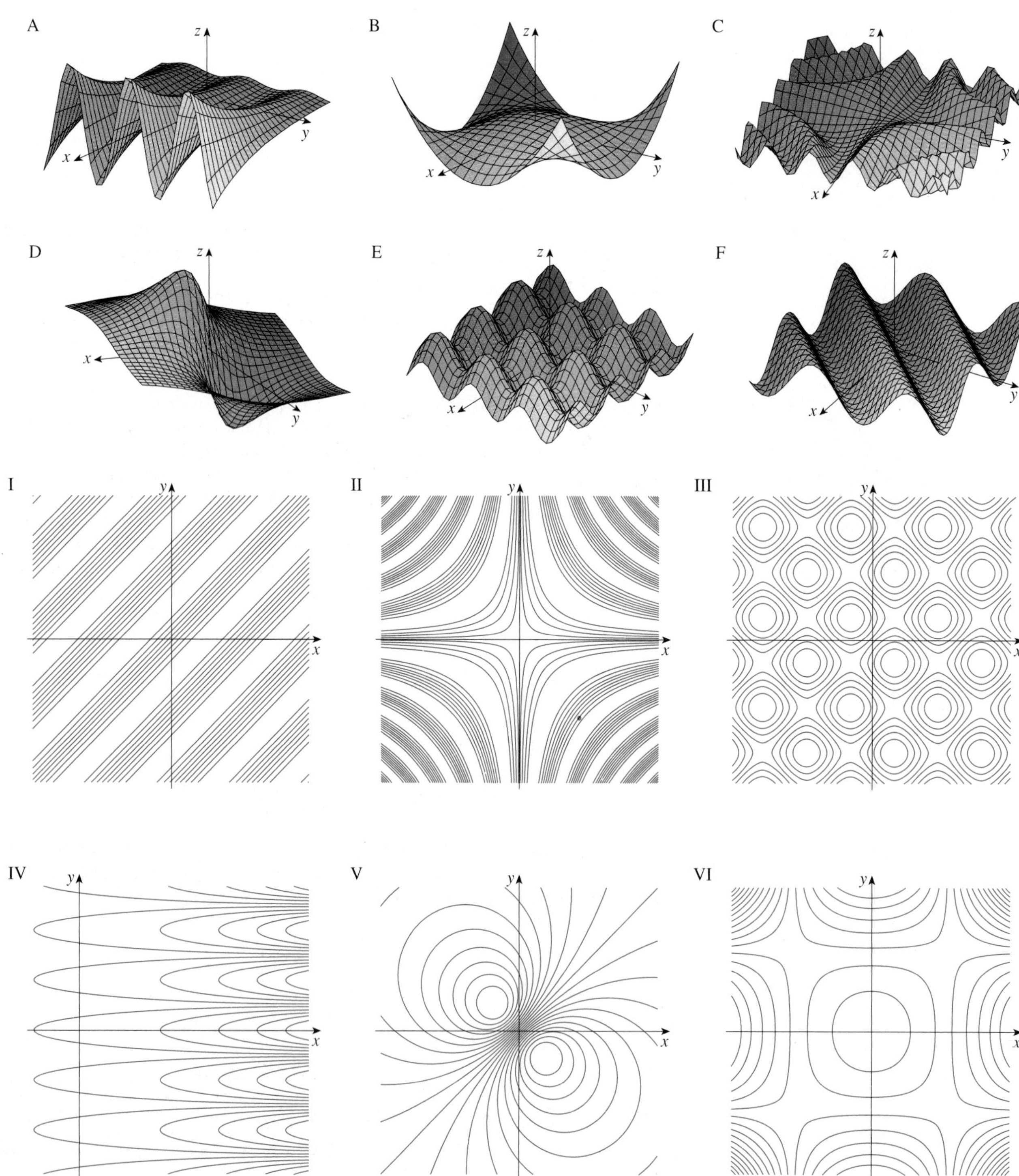

35–40 Match the function (a) with its graph (labeled A–F at the left) and (b) with its contour map (labeled I–VI). Give reasons for your choices.

35. $z = \sin(xy)$

36. $z = e^x \cos y$

37. $z = \sin(x - y)$

38. $z = \sin x - \sin y$

39. $z = (1 - x^2)(1 - y^2)$

40. $z = \dfrac{x - y}{1 + x^2 + y^2}$

41–44 Describe the level surfaces of the function.

41. $f(x, y, z) = x + 3y + 5z$

42. $f(x, y, z) = x^2 + 3y^2 + 5z^2$

43. $f(x, y, z) = y^2 + z^2$

44. $f(x, y, z) = x^2 - y^2 - z^2$

45–46 Describe how the graph of g is obtained from the graph of f.

45. (a) $g(x, y) = f(x, y) + 2$ (b) $g(x, y) = 2f(x, y)$
(c) $g(x, y) = -f(x, y)$ (d) $g(x, y) = 2 - f(x, y)$

46. (a) $g(x, y) = f(x - 2, y)$
(b) $g(x, y) = f(x, y + 2)$
(c) $g(x, y) = f(x + 3, y - 4)$

47. Use a computer to investigate the family of functions $f(x, y) = e^{cx^2+y^2}$. How does the shape of the graph depend on c?

48. Graph the functions

$$f(x, y) = \sqrt{x^2 + y^2} \qquad f(x, y) = e^{\sqrt{x^2+y^2}}$$

$$f(x, y) = \ln\sqrt{x^2 + y^2} \qquad f(x, y) = \sin\left(\sqrt{x^2 + y^2}\right)$$

and $$f(x, y) = \frac{1}{\sqrt{x^2 + y^2}}$$

In general, if g is a function of one variable, how is the graph of $f(x, y) = g\left(\sqrt{x^2 + y^2}\right)$ obtained from the graph of g?

49. (a) Show that, by taking logarithms, the general Cobb-Douglas function $P = bL^\alpha K^{1-\alpha}$ can be expressed as

$$\ln\frac{P}{K} = \ln b + \alpha \ln\frac{L}{K}$$

(b) If we let $x = \ln(L/K)$ and $y = \ln(P/K)$, the equation in part (a) becomes the linear equation $y = \alpha x + \ln b$. Use Table 2 (in Example 2) to make a table of values of $\ln(L/K)$ and $\ln(P/K)$ for the years 1899–1922. Then use a graphing calculator or computer to find the least squares regression line through the points $(\ln(L/K), \ln(P/K))$.

(c) Deduce that the Cobb-Douglas production function is $P = 1.01L^{0.75}K^{0.25}$.

11.2 Limits and Continuity

Let's compare the behavior of the functions

$$f(x, y) = \frac{\sin(x^2 + y^2)}{x^2 + y^2} \qquad \text{and} \qquad g(x, y) = \frac{x^2 - y^2}{x^2 + y^2}$$

as x and y both approach 0 [and therefore the point (x, y) approaches the origin].

Tables 1 and 2 show values of $f(x, y)$ and $g(x, y)$, correct to three decimal places, for points (x, y) near the origin. (Notice that neither function is defined at the origin.)

TABLE 1 Values of $f(x, y)$

x \ y	−1.0	−0.5	−0.2	0	0.2	0.5	1.0
−1.0	0.455	0.759	0.829	0.841	0.829	0.759	0.455
−0.5	0.759	0.959	0.986	0.990	0.986	0.959	0.759
−0.2	0.829	0.986	0.999	1.000	0.999	0.986	0.829
0	0.841	0.990	1.000		1.000	0.990	0.841
0.2	0.829	0.986	0.999	1.000	0.999	0.986	0.829
0.5	0.759	0.959	0.986	0.990	0.986	0.959	0.759
1.0	0.455	0.759	0.829	0.841	0.829	0.759	0.455

TABLE 2 Values of $g(x, y)$

x \ y	−1.0	−0.5	−0.2	0	0.2	0.5	1.0
−1.0	0.000	0.600	0.923	1.000	0.923	0.600	0.000
−0.5	−0.600	0.000	0.724	1.000	0.724	0.000	−0.600
−0.2	−0.923	−0.724	0.000	1.000	0.000	−0.724	−0.923
0	−1.000	−1.000	−1.000		−1.000	−1.000	−1.000
0.2	−0.923	−0.724	0.000	1.000	0.000	−0.724	−0.923
0.5	−0.600	0.000	0.724	1.000	0.724	0.000	−0.600
1.0	0.000	0.600	0.923	1.000	0.923	0.600	0.000

It appears that as (x, y) approaches $(0, 0)$, the values of $f(x, y)$ are approaching 1 whereas the values of $g(x, y)$ aren't approaching any number. It turns out that these guesses based on numerical evidence are correct, and we write

$$\lim_{(x, y) \to (0, 0)} \frac{\sin(x^2 + y^2)}{x^2 + y^2} = 1 \qquad \text{and} \qquad \lim_{(x, y) \to (0, 0)} \frac{x^2 - y^2}{x^2 + y^2} \quad \text{does not exist}$$

In general, we use the notation

$$\lim_{(x, y) \to (a, b)} f(x, y) = L$$

to indicate that the values of $f(x, y)$ approach the number L as the point (x, y) approaches the point (a, b) along any path that stays within the domain of f.

1 Definition We write

$$\lim_{(x, y) \to (a, b)} f(x, y) = L$$

and we say that the **limit of $f(x, y)$ as (x, y) approaches (a, b)** is L if we can make the values of $f(x, y)$ as close to L as we like by taking the point (x, y) sufficiently close to the point (a, b), but not equal to (a, b).

A more precise definition of the limit of a function of two variables is given in Appendix D.

Other notations for the limit in Definition 1 are

$$\lim_{\substack{x \to a \\ y \to b}} f(x, y) = L \qquad \text{and} \qquad f(x, y) \to L \text{ as } (x, y) \to (a, b)$$

For functions of a single variable, when we let x approach a, there are only two possible directions of approach, from the left or from the right. We recall from Chapter 2 that if $\lim_{x \to a^-} f(x) \neq \lim_{x \to a^+} f(x)$, then $\lim_{x \to a} f(x)$ does not exist.

For functions of two variables the situation is not as simple because we can let (x, y) approach (a, b) from an infinite number of directions in any manner whatsoever (see Figure 1) as long as (x, y) stays within the domain of f.

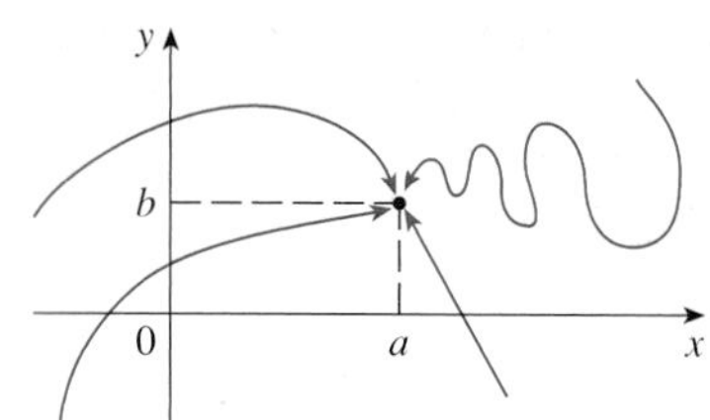

FIGURE 1

Definition 1 says that the distance between $f(x, y)$ and L can be made arbitrarily small by making the distance from (x, y) to (a, b) sufficiently small (but not 0). The definition refers only to the *distance* between (x, y) and (a, b). It does not refer to the direction of approach. Therefore, if the limit exists, then $f(x, y)$ must approach the same limit no matter how (x, y) approaches (a, b). Thus, if we can find two different paths of approach along which the function $f(x, y)$ has different limits, then it follows that $\lim_{(x, y) \to (a, b)} f(x, y)$ does not exist.

If $f(x, y) \to L_1$ as $(x, y) \to (a, b)$ along a path C_1 and $f(x, y) \to L_2$ as $(x, y) \to (a, b)$ along a path C_2, where $L_1 \neq L_2$, then $\lim_{(x, y) \to (a, b)} f(x, y)$ does not exist.

V EXAMPLE 1 Show that $\displaystyle\lim_{(x, y) \to (0, 0)} \frac{x^2 - y^2}{x^2 + y^2}$ does not exist.

SOLUTION Let $f(x, y) = (x^2 - y^2)/(x^2 + y^2)$. First let's approach $(0, 0)$ along the x-axis. Then $y = 0$ gives $f(x, 0) = x^2/x^2 = 1$ for all $x \neq 0$, so

$$f(x, y) \to 1 \qquad \text{as} \qquad (x, y) \to (0, 0) \text{ along the } x\text{-axis}$$

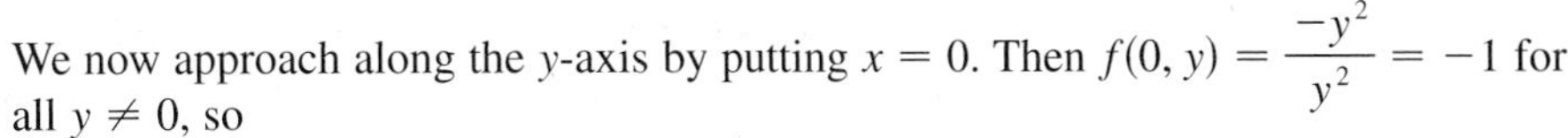

We now approach along the y-axis by putting $x = 0$. Then $f(0, y) = \dfrac{-y^2}{y^2} = -1$ for all $y \neq 0$, so

$$f(x, y) \to -1 \qquad \text{as} \qquad (x, y) \to (0, 0) \text{ along the } y\text{-axis}$$

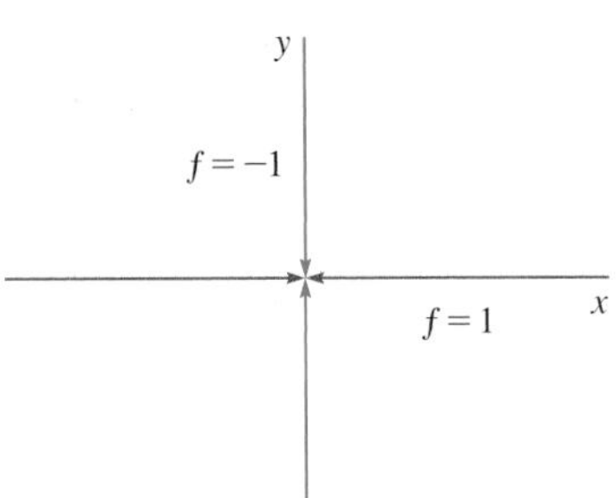

FIGURE 2

(See Figure 2.) Since f has two different limits along two different lines, the given limit does not exist. (This confirms the conjecture we made on the basis of numerical evidence at the beginning of this section.)

EXAMPLE 2 Deciding whether a limit exists

If $f(x, y) = xy/(x^2 + y^2)$, does $\displaystyle\lim_{(x, y) \to (0, 0)} f(x, y)$ exist?

SOLUTION If $y = 0$, then $f(x, 0) = 0/x^2 = 0$. Therefore

$$f(x, y) \to 0 \qquad \text{as} \qquad (x, y) \to (0, 0) \text{ along the } x\text{-axis}$$

If $x = 0$, then $f(0, y) = 0/y^2 = 0$, so

$$f(x, y) \to 0 \qquad \text{as} \qquad (x, y) \to (0, 0) \text{ along the } y\text{-axis}$$

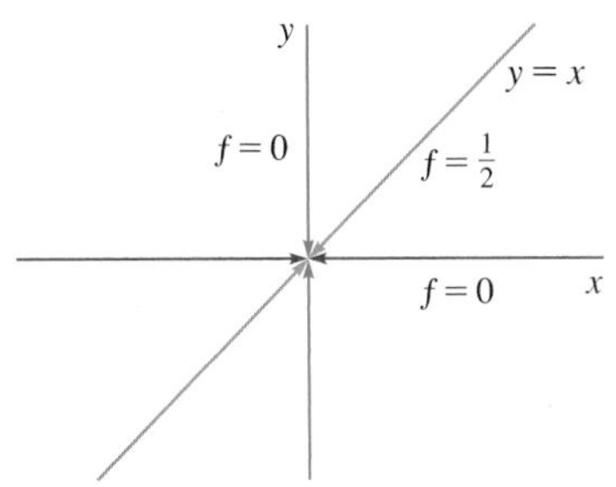

FIGURE 3

Although we have obtained identical limits along the axes, that does not show that the given limit is 0. Let's now approach $(0, 0)$ along another line, say $y = x$. For all $x \neq 0$,

$$f(x, x) = \frac{x^2}{x^2 + x^2} = \frac{1}{2}$$

Therefore $\qquad f(x, y) \to \frac{1}{2} \qquad$ as $\qquad (x, y) \to (0, 0)$ along $y = x$

(See Figure 3.) Since we have obtained different limits along different paths, the given limit does not exist.

Figure 4 sheds some light on Example 2. The ridge that occurs above the line $y = x$ corresponds to the fact that $f(x, y) = \frac{1}{2}$ for all points (x, y) on that line except the origin.

TEC In Visual 11.2 a rotating line on the surface in Figure 4 shows different limits at the origin from different directions.

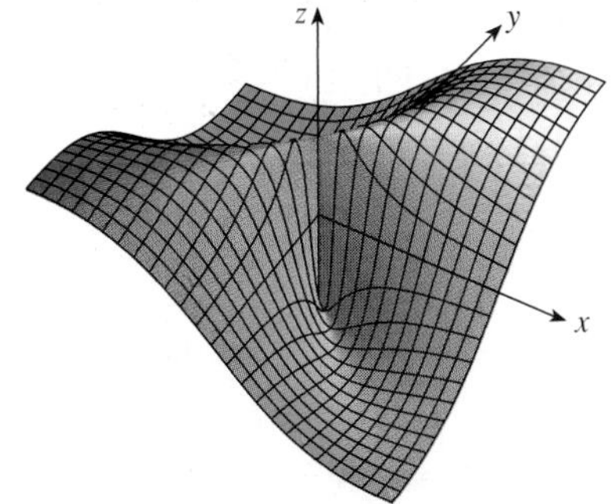

FIGURE 4

$$f(x, y) = \frac{xy}{x^2 + y^2}$$

V EXAMPLE 3 If $f(x, y) = \dfrac{xy^2}{x^2 + y^4}$, does $\displaystyle\lim_{(x, y) \to (0, 0)} f(x, y)$ exist?

SOLUTION With the solution of Example 2 in mind, let's try to save time by letting $(x, y) \to (0, 0)$ along any nonvertical line through the origin. Then $y = mx$, where m is the slope, and

$$f(x, y) = f(x, mx) = \frac{x(mx)^2}{x^2 + (mx)^4} = \frac{m^2x^3}{x^2 + m^4x^4} = \frac{m^2x}{1 + m^4x^2}$$

So $\qquad f(x, y) \to 0 \qquad$ as $\qquad (x, y) \to (0, 0)$ along $y = mx$

Figure 5 shows the graph of the function in Example 3. Notice the ridge above the parabola $x = y^2$.

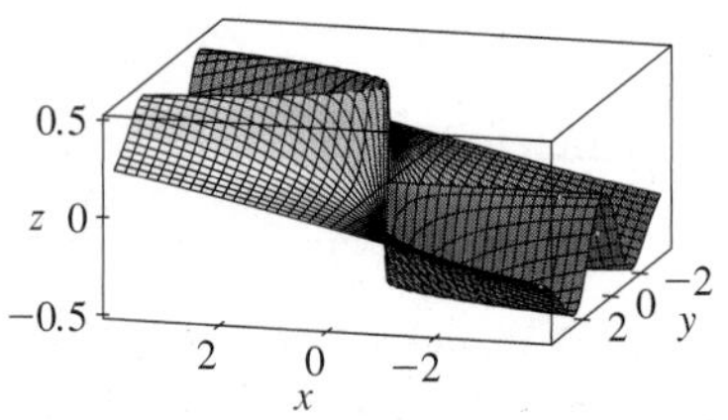

FIGURE 5

Thus f has the same limiting value along every nonvertical line through the origin. But that does not show that the given limit is 0, for if we now let $(x, y) \to (0, 0)$ along the parabola $x = y^2$, we have

$$f(x, y) = f(y^2, y) = \frac{y^2 \cdot y^2}{(y^2)^2 + y^4} = \frac{y^4}{2y^4} = \frac{1}{2}$$

so $$f(x, y) \to \tfrac{1}{2} \quad \text{as} \quad (x, y) \to (0, 0) \text{ along } x = y^2$$

Since different paths lead to different limiting values, the given limit does not exist. ∎

Now let's look at limits that *do* exist. Just as for functions of one variable, the calculation of limits for functions of two variables can be greatly simplified by the use of properties of limits. The Limit Laws listed in Section 2.3 can be extended to functions of two variables: The limit of a sum is the sum of the limits, the limit of a product is the product of the limits, and so on. In particular, the following equations are true.

2 $$\lim_{(x, y) \to (a, b)} x = a \qquad \lim_{(x, y) \to (a, b)} y = b \qquad \lim_{(x, y) \to (a, b)} c = c$$

The Squeeze Theorem also holds.

EXAMPLE 4 Guessing and proving a limit Find $\displaystyle\lim_{(x, y) \to (0, 0)} \frac{3x^2y}{x^2 + y^2}$ if it exists.

SOLUTION As in Example 3, we could show that the limit along any line through the origin is 0. This doesn't prove that the given limit is 0, but the limits along the parabolas $y = x^2$ and $x = y^2$ also turn out to be 0, so we begin to suspect that the limit does exist and is equal to 0. To prove it we look at the distance from $f(x, y)$ to 0:

$$\left| \frac{3x^2y}{x^2 + y^2} - 0 \right| = \left| \frac{3x^2y}{x^2 + y^2} \right| = \frac{3x^2|y|}{x^2 + y^2}$$

Notice that $x^2 \leqslant x^2 + y^2$ because $y^2 \geqslant 0$. So

$$\frac{x^2}{x^2 + y^2} \leqslant 1$$

Thus $$0 \leqslant \frac{3x^2|y|}{x^2 + y^2} \leqslant 3|y|$$

Now we use the Squeeze Theorem. Since

$$\lim_{(x, y) \to (0, 0)} 0 = 0 \quad \text{and} \quad \lim_{(x, y) \to (0, 0)} 3|y| = 0 \quad \text{[by (2)]}$$

we conclude that $$\lim_{(x, y) \to (0, 0)} \frac{3x^2y}{x^2 + y^2} = 0$$ ∎

Continuity

Recall that evaluating limits of *continuous* functions of a single variable is easy. It can be accomplished by direct substitution because the defining property of a continuous function is $\lim_{x \to a} f(x) = f(a)$. Continuous functions of two variables are also defined by the direct substitution property.

3 Definition A function f of two variables is called **continuous at** (a, b) if

$$\lim_{(x, y)\to(a, b)} f(x, y) = f(a, b)$$

We say f is **continuous on** D if f is continuous at every point (a, b) in D.

The intuitive meaning of continuity is that if the point (x, y) changes by a small amount, then the value of $f(x, y)$ changes by a small amount. This means that a surface that is the graph of a continuous function has no hole or break.

Using the properties of limits, you can see that sums, differences, products, and quotients of continuous functions are continuous on their domains. Let's use this fact to give examples of continuous functions.

A **polynomial function of two variables** (or polynomial, for short) is a sum of terms of the form $cx^m y^n$, where c is a constant and m and n are nonnegative integers. A **rational function** is a ratio of polynomials. For instance,

$$f(x, y) = x^4 + 5x^3y^2 + 6xy^4 - 7y + 6$$

is a polynomial, whereas

$$g(x, y) = \frac{2xy + 1}{x^2 + y^2}$$

is a rational function.

The limits in (2) show that the functions $f(x, y) = x$, $g(x, y) = y$, and $h(x, y) = c$ are continuous. Since any polynomial can be built up out of the simple functions f, g, and h by multiplication and addition, it follows that *all polynomials are continuous on* $\mathbb{R}^2$. Likewise, any rational function is continuous on its domain because it is a quotient of continuous functions.

V EXAMPLE 5 Using continuity to find a limit

Evaluate $\lim_{(x, y)\to(1, 2)} (x^2y^3 - x^3y^2 + 3x + 2y)$.

SOLUTION Since $f(x, y) = x^2y^3 - x^3y^2 + 3x + 2y$ is a polynomial, it is continuous everywhere, so we can find the limit by direct substitution:

$$\lim_{(x, y)\to(1, 2)} (x^2y^3 - x^3y^2 + 3x + 2y) = 1^2 \cdot 2^3 - 1^3 \cdot 2^2 + 3 \cdot 1 + 2 \cdot 2 = 11$$

EXAMPLE 6 Where is the function $f(x, y) = \dfrac{x^2 - y^2}{x^2 + y^2}$ continuous?

SOLUTION The function f is discontinuous at $(0, 0)$ because it is not defined there. Since f is a rational function, it is continuous on its domain, which is the set $D = \{(x, y) \mid (x, y) \neq (0, 0)\}$.

EXAMPLE 7 A function that is discontinuous at the origin

Let

$$g(x, y) = \begin{cases} \dfrac{x^2 - y^2}{x^2 + y^2} & \text{if } (x, y) \neq (0, 0) \\ 0 & \text{if } (x, y) = (0, 0) \end{cases}$$

Here g is defined at $(0, 0)$ but g is still discontinuous there because $\lim_{(x, y)\to(0, 0)} g(x, y)$ does not exist (see Example 1).

Figure 6 shows the graph of the continuous function in Example 8.

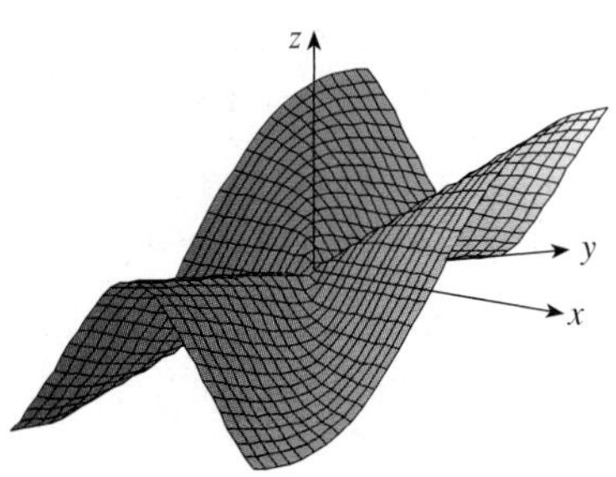

FIGURE 6

EXAMPLE 8 **A function that is continuous everywhere**
Let

$$f(x, y) = \begin{cases} \dfrac{3x^2y}{x^2 + y^2} & \text{if } (x, y) \neq (0, 0) \\ 0 & \text{if } (x, y) = (0, 0) \end{cases}$$

We know f is continuous for $(x, y) \neq (0, 0)$ since it is equal to a rational function there. Also, from Example 4, we have

$$\lim_{(x, y) \to (0, 0)} f(x, y) = \lim_{(x, y) \to (0, 0)} \frac{3x^2y}{x^2 + y^2} = 0 = f(0, 0)$$

Therefore f is continuous at $(0, 0)$, and so it is continuous on $\mathbb{R}^2$.

Just as for functions of one variable, composition is another way of combining two continuous functions to get a third. In fact, it can be shown that if f is a continuous function of two variables and g is a continuous function of a single variable that is defined on the range of f, then the composite function $h = g \circ f$ defined by $h(x, y) = g(f(x, y))$ is also a continuous function.

EXAMPLE 9 Where is the function $h(x, y) = \arctan(y/x)$ continuous?

SOLUTION The function $f(x, y) = y/x$ is a rational function and therefore continuous except on the line $x = 0$. The function $g(t) = \arctan t$ is continuous everywhere. So the composite function

$$g(f(x, y)) = \arctan(y/x) = h(x, y)$$

is continuous except where $x = 0$. The graph in Figure 7 shows the break in the graph of h above the y-axis.

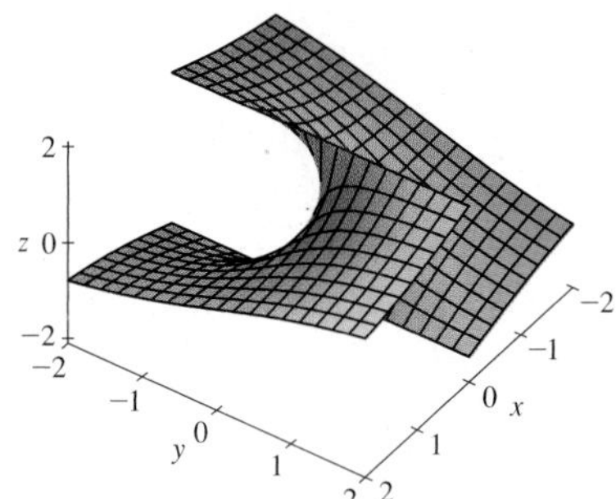

FIGURE 7
The function $h(x, y) = \arctan(y/x)$ is discontinuous where $x = 0$.

Everything that we have done in this section can be extended to functions of three or more variables. The notation

$$\lim_{(x, y, z) \to (a, b, c)} f(x, y, z) = L$$

means that the values of $f(x, y, z)$ approach the number L as the point (x, y, z) approaches the point (a, b, c) along any path in the domain of f. The function f is **continuous** at (a, b, c) if

$$\lim_{(x, y, z) \to (a, b, c)} f(x, y, z) = f(a, b, c)$$

For instance, the function

$$f(x, y, z) = \frac{1}{x^2 + y^2 + z^2 - 1}$$

is a rational function of three variables and so is continuous at every point in $\mathbb{R}^3$ except where $x^2 + y^2 + z^2 = 1$. In other words, it is discontinuous on the sphere with center the origin and radius 1.

11.2 Exercises

1. Suppose that $\lim_{(x, y)\to(3, 1)} f(x, y) = 6$. What can you say about the value of $f(3, 1)$? What if f is continuous?

2. Explain why each function is continuous or discontinuous.
   (a) The outdoor temperature as a function of longitude, latitude, and time
   (b) Elevation (height above sea level) as a function of longitude, latitude, and time
   (c) The cost of a taxi ride as a function of distance traveled and time

3–4 Use a table of numerical values of $f(x, y)$ for (x, y) near the origin to make a conjecture about the value of the limit of $f(x, y)$ as $(x, y) \to (0, 0)$. Then explain why your guess is correct.

3. $f(x, y) = \dfrac{x^2y^3 + x^3y^2 - 5}{2 - xy}$

4. $f(x, y) = \dfrac{2xy}{x^2 + 2y^2}$

5–20 Find the limit, if it exists, or show that the limit does not exist.

5. $\displaystyle\lim_{(x, y)\to(1, 2)} (5x^3 - x^2y^2)$

6. $\displaystyle\lim_{(x, y)\to(1, -1)} e^{-xy}\cos(x + y)$

7. $\displaystyle\lim_{(x, y)\to(0, 0)} \frac{y^4}{x^4 + 3y^4}$

8. $\displaystyle\lim_{(x, y)\to(0, 0)} \frac{x^2 + \sin^2 y}{2x^2 + y^2}$

9. $\displaystyle\lim_{(x, y)\to(0, 0)} \frac{xy\cos y}{3x^2 + y^2}$

10. $\displaystyle\lim_{(x, y)\to(0, 0)} \frac{6x^3y}{2x^4 + y^4}$

11. $\displaystyle\lim_{(x, y)\to(0, 0)} \frac{xy}{\sqrt{x^2 + y^2}}$

12. $\displaystyle\lim_{(x, y)\to(0, 0)} \frac{x^2\sin^2 y}{x^2 + 2y^2}$

13. $\displaystyle\lim_{(x, y)\to(0, 0)} \frac{x^2ye^y}{x^4 + 4y^2}$

14. $\displaystyle\lim_{(x, y)\to(0, 0)} \frac{xy^4}{x^2 + y^8}$

15. $\displaystyle\lim_{(x, y)\to(0, 0)} \frac{x^2 + y^2}{\sqrt{x^2 + y^2 + 1} - 1}$

16. $\displaystyle\lim_{(x, y)\to(0, 0)} \frac{x^4 - y^4}{x^2 + y^2}$

17. $\displaystyle\lim_{(x, y, z)\to(3, 0, 1)} e^{-xy}\sin(\pi z/2)$

18. $\displaystyle\lim_{(x, y, z)\to(0, 0, 0)} \frac{x^2 + 2y^2 + 3z^2}{x^2 + y^2 + z^2}$

19. $\displaystyle\lim_{(x, y, z)\to(0, 0, 0)} \frac{xy + yz^2 + xz^2}{x^2 + y^2 + z^4}$

20. $\displaystyle\lim_{(x, y, z)\to(0, 0, 0)} \frac{yz}{x^2 + 4y^2 + 9z^2}$

21–22 Use a computer graph of the function to explain why the limit does not exist.

21. $\displaystyle\lim_{(x, y)\to(0, 0)} \frac{2x^2 + 3xy + 4y^2}{3x^2 + 5y^2}$

22. $\displaystyle\lim_{(x, y)\to(0, 0)} \frac{xy^3}{x^2 + y^6}$

23–24 Find $h(x, y) = g(f(x, y))$ and the set on which h is continuous.

23. $g(t) = t^2 + \sqrt{t}, \quad f(x, y) = 2x + 3y - 6$

24. $g(t) = t + \ln t, \quad f(x, y) = \dfrac{1 - xy}{1 + x^2y^2}$

25–26 Graph the function and observe where it is discontinuous. Then use the formula to explain what you have observed.

25. $f(x, y) = e^{1/(x-y)}$

26. $f(x, y) = \dfrac{1}{1 - x^2 - y^2}$

27–34 Determine the set of points at which the function is continuous.

27. $F(x, y) = \arctan(x + \sqrt{y})$

28. $F(x, y) = \cos\sqrt{1 + x - y}$

29. $G(x, y) = \ln(x^2 + y^2 - 4)$

30. $H(x, y) = \dfrac{e^x + e^y}{e^{xy} - 1}$

31. $f(x, y, z) = \dfrac{\sqrt{y}}{x^2 - y^2 + z^2}$

32. $f(x, y, z) = \sqrt{x + y + z}$

33. $f(x, y) = \begin{cases} \dfrac{x^2y^3}{2x^2 + y^2} & \text{if } (x, y) \neq (0, 0) \\ 1 & \text{if } (x, y) = (0, 0) \end{cases}$

34. $f(x, y) = \begin{cases} \dfrac{xy}{x^2 + xy + y^2} & \text{if } (x, y) \neq (0, 0) \\ 0 & \text{if } (x, y) = (0, 0) \end{cases}$

35–36 Use polar coordinates to find the limit. [If (r, θ) are polar coordinates of the point (x, y) with $r \geq 0$, note that $r \to 0^+$ as $(x, y) \to (0, 0)$.]

35. $\displaystyle\lim_{(x, y)\to(0, 0)} \frac{x^3 + y^3}{x^2 + y^2}$

36. $\lim_{(x, y) \to (0, 0)} (x^2 + y^2) \ln(x^2 + y^2)$

37. Use spherical coordinates to find

$$\lim_{(x, y, z) \to (0, 0, 0)} \frac{xyz}{x^2 + y^2 + z^2}$$

38. At the beginning of this section we considered the function

$$f(x, y) = \frac{\sin(x^2 + y^2)}{x^2 + y^2}$$

and guessed that $f(x, y) \to 1$ as $(x, y) \to (0, 0)$ on the basis of numerical evidence. Use polar coordinates to confirm the value of the limit. Then graph the function.

39. Graph and discuss the continuity of the function

$$f(x, y) = \begin{cases} \dfrac{\sin xy}{xy} & \text{if } xy \neq 0 \\ 1 & \text{if } xy = 0 \end{cases}$$

40. Let

$$f(x, y) = \begin{cases} 0 & \text{if } y \leqslant 0 \quad \text{or} \quad y \geqslant x^4 \\ 1 & \text{if } 0 < y < x^4 \end{cases}$$

(a) Show that $f(x, y) \to 0$ as $(x, y) \to (0, 0)$ along any path through $(0, 0)$ of the form $y = mx^a$ with $a < 4$.
(b) Despite part (a), show that f is discontinuous at $(0, 0)$.
(c) Show that f is discontinuous on two entire curves.

11.3 Partial Derivatives

On a hot day, extreme humidity makes us think the temperature is higher than it really is, whereas in very dry air we perceive the temperature to be lower than the thermometer indicates. The National Weather Service has devised the *heat index* (also called the temperature-humidity index, or humidex, in some countries) to describe the combined effects of temperature and humidity. The heat index I is the perceived air temperature when the actual temperature is T and the relative humidity is H. So I is a function of T and H and we can write $I = f(T, H)$. The following table of values of I is an excerpt from a table compiled by the National Weather Service.

TABLE 1
Heat index I as a function of temperature and humidity

Relative humidity (%)

Actual temperature (°F) T \ H	50	55	60	65	70	75	80	85	90
90	96	98	100	103	106	109	112	115	119
92	100	103	105	108	112	115	119	123	128
94	104	107	111	114	118	122	127	132	137
96	109	113	116	121	125	130	135	141	146
98	114	118	123	127	133	138	144	150	157
100	119	124	129	135	141	147	154	161	168

If we concentrate on the highlighted column of the table, which corresponds to a relative humidity of $H = 70\%$, we are considering the heat index as a function of the single variable T for a fixed value of H. Let's write $g(T) = f(T, 70)$. Then $g(T)$ describes how the heat index I increases as the actual temperature T increases when the relative humidity is 70%. The derivative of g when $T = 96°\text{F}$ is the rate of change of I with respect to T when $T = 96°\text{F}$:

$$g'(96) = \lim_{h \to 0} \frac{g(96 + h) - g(96)}{h} = \lim_{h \to 0} \frac{f(96 + h, 70) - f(96, 70)}{h}$$

We can approximate $g'(96)$ using the values in Table 1 by taking $h = 2$ and -2:

$$g'(96) \approx \frac{g(98) - g(96)}{2} = \frac{f(98, 70) - f(96, 70)}{2} = \frac{133 - 125}{2} = 4$$

$$g'(96) \approx \frac{g(94) - g(96)}{-2} = \frac{f(94, 70) - f(96, 70)}{-2} = \frac{118 - 125}{-2} = 3.5$$

Averaging these values, we can say that the derivative $g'(96)$ is approximately 3.75. This means that, when the actual temperature is 96°F and the relative humidity is 70%, the apparent temperature (heat index) rises by about 3.75°F for every degree that the actual temperature rises!

Now let's look at the highlighted row in Table 1, which corresponds to a fixed temperature of $T = 96°\text{F}$. The numbers in this row are values of the function $G(H) = f(96, H)$, which describes how the heat index increases as the relative humidity H increases when the actual temperature is $T = 96°\text{F}$. The derivative of this function when $H = 70\%$ is the rate of change of I with respect to H when $H = 70\%$:

$$G'(70) = \lim_{h \to 0} \frac{G(70 + h) - G(70)}{h} = \lim_{h \to 0} \frac{f(96, 70 + h) - f(96, 70)}{h}$$

By taking $h = 5$ and -5, we approximate $G'(70)$ using the tabular values:

$$G'(70) \approx \frac{G(75) - G(70)}{5} = \frac{f(96, 75) - f(96, 70)}{5} = \frac{130 - 125}{5} = 1$$

$$G'(70) \approx \frac{G(65) - G(70)}{-5} = \frac{f(96, 65) - f(96, 70)}{-5} = \frac{121 - 125}{-5} = 0.8$$

By averaging these values we get the estimate $G'(70) \approx 0.9$. This says that, when the temperature is 96°F and the relative humidity is 70%, the heat index rises about 0.9°F for every percent that the relative humidity rises.

In general, suppose f is a function of two variables x and y and we let only x vary while keeping y fixed, say $y = b$, where b is a constant. Then we are really considering a function of a single variable x, namely, $g(x) = f(x, b)$. If g has a derivative at a, then we call it the **partial derivative of f with respect to x at (a, b)** and denote it by $f_x(a, b)$. Thus

1

$$f_x(a, b) = g'(a) \quad \text{where} \quad g(x) = f(x, b)$$

By the definition of a derivative, we have

$$g'(a) = \lim_{h \to 0} \frac{g(a + h) - g(a)}{h}$$

and so Equation 1 becomes

2

$$f_x(a, b) = \lim_{h \to 0} \frac{f(a + h, b) - f(a, b)}{h}$$

Similarly, the **partial derivative of f with respect to y at (a, b)**, denoted by $f_y(a, b)$, is obtained by keeping x fixed ($x = a$) and finding the ordinary derivative at b of the function $G(y) = f(a, y)$:

3
$$f_y(a, b) = \lim_{h \to 0} \frac{f(a, b + h) - f(a, b)}{h}$$

With this notation for partial derivatives, we can write the rates of change of the heat index I with respect to the actual temperature T and relative humidity H when $T = 96°\text{F}$ and $H = 70\%$ as follows:

$$f_T(96, 70) \approx 3.75 \qquad f_H(96, 70) \approx 0.9$$

If we now let the point (a, b) vary in Equations 2 and 3, f_x and f_y become functions of two variables.

4 If f is a function of two variables, its **partial derivatives** are the functions f_x and f_y defined by

$$f_x(x, y) = \lim_{h \to 0} \frac{f(x + h, y) - f(x, y)}{h}$$

$$f_y(x, y) = \lim_{h \to 0} \frac{f(x, y + h) - f(x, y)}{h}$$

There are many alternative notations for partial derivatives. For instance, instead of f_x we can write f_1 or $D_1 f$ (to indicate differentiation with respect to the *first* variable) or $\partial f/\partial x$. But here $\partial f/\partial x$ can't be interpreted as a ratio of differentials.

Notations for Partial Derivatives If $z = f(x, y)$, we write

$$f_x(x, y) = f_x = \frac{\partial f}{\partial x} = \frac{\partial}{\partial x} f(x, y) = \frac{\partial z}{\partial x} = f_1 = D_1 f = D_x f$$

$$f_y(x, y) = f_y = \frac{\partial f}{\partial y} = \frac{\partial}{\partial y} f(x, y) = \frac{\partial z}{\partial y} = f_2 = D_2 f = D_y f$$

To compute partial derivatives, all we have to do is remember from Equation 1 that the partial derivative with respect to x is just the *ordinary* derivative of the function g of a single variable that we get by keeping y fixed. Thus we have the following rule.

Rule for Finding Partial Derivatives of $z = f(x, y)$

1. To find f_x, regard y as a constant and differentiate $f(x, y)$ with respect to x.
2. To find f_y, regard x as a constant and differentiate $f(x, y)$ with respect to y.

EXAMPLE 1 Evaluating partial derivatives If $f(x, y) = x^3 + x^2y^3 - 2y^2$, find $f_x(2, 1)$ and $f_y(2, 1)$.

SOLUTION Holding y constant and differentiating with respect to x, we get

$$f_x(x, y) = 3x^2 + 2xy^3$$

and so $$f_x(2, 1) = 3 \cdot 2^2 + 2 \cdot 2 \cdot 1^3 = 16$$

Holding x constant and differentiating with respect to y, we get

$$f_y(x, y) = 3x^2y^2 - 4y$$

$$f_y(2, 1) = 3 \cdot 2^2 \cdot 1^2 - 4 \cdot 1 = 8$$

Interpretations of Partial Derivatives

To give a geometric interpretation of partial derivatives, we recall that the equation $z = f(x, y)$ represents a surface S (the graph of f). If $f(a, b) = c$, then the point $P(a, b, c)$ lies on S. By fixing $y = b$, we are restricting our attention to the curve C_1 in which the vertical plane $y = b$ intersects S. (In other words, C_1 is the trace of S in the plane $y = b$.) Likewise, the vertical plane $x = a$ intersects S in a curve C_2. Both of the curves C_1 and C_2 pass through the point P. (See Figure 1.)

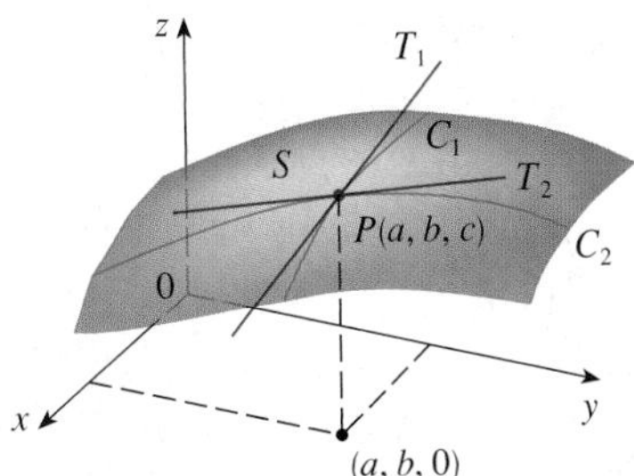

FIGURE 1
The partial derivatives of f at (a, b) are the slopes of the tangents to C_1 and C_2.

Notice that the curve C_1 is the graph of the function $g(x) = f(x, b)$, so the slope of its tangent T_1 at P is $g'(a) = f_x(a, b)$. The curve C_2 is the graph of the function $G(y) = f(a, y)$, so the slope of its tangent T_2 at P is $G'(b) = f_y(a, b)$.

Thus the partial derivatives $f_x(a, b)$ and $f_y(a, b)$ can be interpreted geometrically as the slopes of the tangent lines at $P(a, b, c)$ to the traces C_1 and C_2 of S in the planes $y = b$ and $x = a$.

As we have seen in the case of the heat index function, partial derivatives can also be interpreted as *rates of change*. If $z = f(x, y)$, then $\partial z/\partial x$ represents the rate of change of z with respect to x when y is fixed. Similarly, $\partial z/\partial y$ represents the rate of change of z with respect to y when x is fixed.

EXAMPLE 2 Partial derivatives as slopes of tangents If $f(x, y) = 4 - x^2 - 2y^2$, find $f_x(1, 1)$ and $f_y(1, 1)$ and interpret these numbers as slopes.

SOLUTION We have

$$f_x(x, y) = -2x \qquad f_y(x, y) = -4y$$

$$f_x(1, 1) = -2 \qquad f_y(1, 1) = -4$$

The graph of f is the paraboloid $z = 4 - x^2 - 2y^2$ and the vertical plane $y = 1$ intersects it in the parabola $z = 2 - x^2$, $y = 1$. (As in the preceding discussion, we label it C_1 in Figure 2.) The slope of the tangent line to this parabola at the point $(1, 1, 1)$ is $f_x(1, 1) = -2$. Similarly, the curve C_2 in which the plane $x = 1$ intersects the paraboloid is the parabola $z = 3 - 2y^2$, $x = 1$, and the slope of the tangent line at $(1, 1, 1)$ is $f_y(1, 1) = -4$. (See Figure 3.)

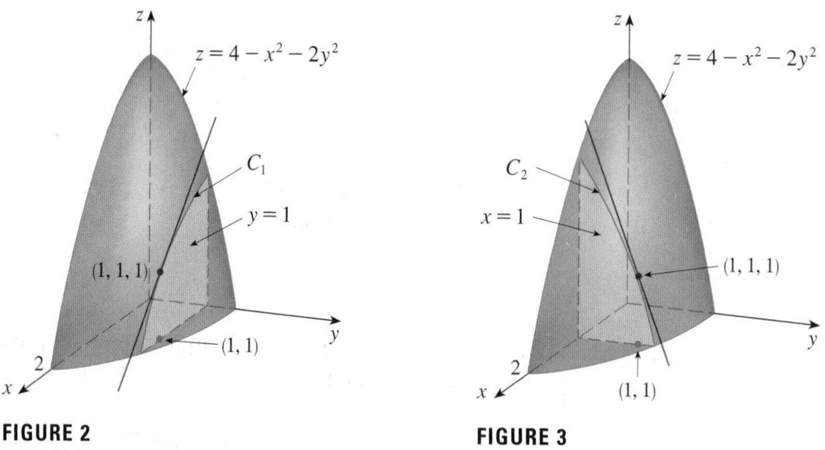

FIGURE 2

FIGURE 3

Figure 4 is a computer-drawn counterpart to Figure 2. Part (a) shows the plane $y = 1$ intersecting the surface to form the curve C_1 and part (b) shows C_1 and T_1. [We have used the vector equations $\mathbf{r}(t) = \langle t, 1, 2 - t^2 \rangle$ for C_1 and $\mathbf{r}(t) = \langle 1 + t, 1, 1 - 2t \rangle$ for T_1.] Similarly, Figure 5 corresponds to Figure 3.

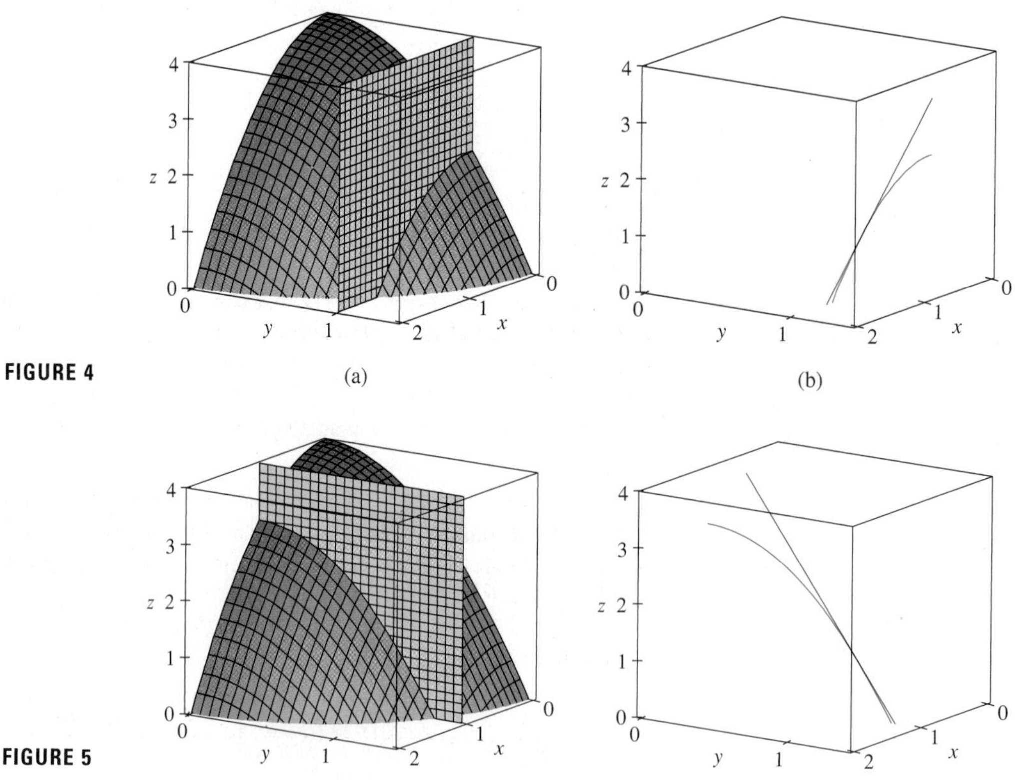

FIGURE 4

FIGURE 5

V EXAMPLE 3 If $f(x, y) = \sin\left(\dfrac{x}{1 + y}\right)$, calculate $\dfrac{\partial f}{\partial x}$ and $\dfrac{\partial f}{\partial y}$.

SOLUTION Using the Chain Rule for functions of one variable, we have

$$\frac{\partial f}{\partial x} = \cos\left(\frac{x}{1+y}\right) \cdot \frac{\partial}{\partial x}\left(\frac{x}{1+y}\right) = \cos\left(\frac{x}{1+y}\right) \cdot \frac{1}{1+y}$$

$$\frac{\partial f}{\partial y} = \cos\left(\frac{x}{1+y}\right) \cdot \frac{\partial}{\partial y}\left(\frac{x}{1+y}\right) = -\cos\left(\frac{x}{1+y}\right) \cdot \frac{x}{(1+y)^2}$$

Some computer algebra systems can plot surfaces defined by implicit equations in three variables. Figure 6 shows such a plot of the surface defined by the equation in Example 4.

FIGURE 6

V EXAMPLE 4 Implicit partial differentiation Find $\partial z/\partial x$ and $\partial z/\partial y$ if z is defined implicitly as a function of x and y by the equation

$$x^3 + y^3 + z^3 + 6xyz = 1$$

SOLUTION To find $\partial z/\partial x$, we differentiate implicitly with respect to x, being careful to treat y as a constant:

$$3x^2 + 3z^2 \frac{\partial z}{\partial x} + 6yz + 6xy \frac{\partial z}{\partial x} = 0$$

Solving this equation for $\partial z/\partial x$, we obtain

$$\frac{\partial z}{\partial x} = -\frac{x^2 + 2yz}{z^2 + 2xy}$$

Similarly, implicit differentiation with respect to y gives

$$\frac{\partial z}{\partial y} = -\frac{y^2 + 2xz}{z^2 + 2xy}$$

Functions of More Than Two Variables

Partial derivatives can also be defined for functions of three or more variables. For example, if f is a function of three variables x, y, and z, then its partial derivative with respect to x is defined as

$$f_x(x, y, z) = \lim_{h \to 0} \frac{f(x + h, y, z) - f(x, y, z)}{h}$$

and it is found by regarding y and z as constants and differentiating $f(x, y, z)$ with respect to x. If $w = f(x, y, z)$, then $f_x = \partial w/\partial x$ can be interpreted as the rate of change of w with respect to x when y and z are held fixed. But we can't interpret it geometrically because the graph of f lies in four-dimensional space.

In general, if u is a function of n variables, $u = f(x_1, x_2, \ldots, x_n)$, its partial derivative with respect to the ith variable x_i is

$$\frac{\partial u}{\partial x_i} = \lim_{h \to 0} \frac{f(x_1, \ldots, x_{i-1}, x_i + h, x_{i+1}, \ldots, x_n) - f(x_1, \ldots, x_i, \ldots, x_n)}{h}$$

and we also write

$$\frac{\partial u}{\partial x_i} = \frac{\partial f}{\partial x_i} = f_{x_i} = f_i = D_i f$$

EXAMPLE 5 Partial derivatives of a function of three variables
Find f_x, f_y, and f_z if $f(x, y, z) = e^{xy} \ln z$.

SOLUTION Holding y and z constant and differentiating with respect to x, we have

$$f_x = ye^{xy} \ln z$$

Similarly,

$$f_y = xe^{xy} \ln z \qquad \text{and} \qquad f_z = \frac{e^{xy}}{z}$$

Higher Derivatives

If f is a function of two variables, then its partial derivatives f_x and f_y are also functions of two variables, so we can consider their partial derivatives $(f_x)_x$, $(f_x)_y$, $(f_y)_x$, and $(f_y)_y$, which are called the **second partial derivatives** of f. If $z = f(x, y)$, we use the following notation:

$$(f_x)_x = f_{xx} = f_{11} = \frac{\partial}{\partial x}\left(\frac{\partial f}{\partial x}\right) = \frac{\partial^2 f}{\partial x^2} = \frac{\partial^2 z}{\partial x^2}$$

$$(f_x)_y = f_{xy} = f_{12} = \frac{\partial}{\partial y}\left(\frac{\partial f}{\partial x}\right) = \frac{\partial^2 f}{\partial y\, \partial x} = \frac{\partial^2 z}{\partial y\, \partial x}$$

$$(f_y)_x = f_{yx} = f_{21} = \frac{\partial}{\partial x}\left(\frac{\partial f}{\partial y}\right) = \frac{\partial^2 f}{\partial x\, \partial y} = \frac{\partial^2 z}{\partial x\, \partial y}$$

$$(f_y)_y = f_{yy} = f_{22} = \frac{\partial}{\partial y}\left(\frac{\partial f}{\partial y}\right) = \frac{\partial^2 f}{\partial y^2} = \frac{\partial^2 z}{\partial y^2}$$

Thus the notation f_{xy} (or $\partial^2 f/\partial y\, \partial x$) means that we first differentiate with respect to x and then with respect to y, whereas in computing f_{yx} the order is reversed.

EXAMPLE 6 Find the second partial derivatives of

$$f(x, y) = x^3 + x^2y^3 - 2y^2$$

SOLUTION In Example 1 we found that

$$f_x(x, y) = 3x^2 + 2xy^3 \qquad f_y(x, y) = 3x^2y^2 - 4y$$

Therefore

$$f_{xx} = \frac{\partial}{\partial x}(3x^2 + 2xy^3) = 6x + 2y^3 \qquad f_{xy} = \frac{\partial}{\partial y}(3x^2 + 2xy^3) = 6xy^2$$

$$f_{yx} = \frac{\partial}{\partial x}(3x^2y^2 - 4y) = 6xy^2 \qquad f_{yy} = \frac{\partial}{\partial y}(3x^2y^2 - 4y) = 6x^2y - 4$$

Figure 7 shows the graph of the function f in Example 6 and the graphs of its first- and second-order partial derivatives for $-2 \leqslant x \leqslant 2$, $-2 \leqslant y \leqslant 2$. Notice that these graphs are consistent with our interpretations of f_x and f_y as slopes of tangent lines to traces of the graph of f. For instance, the graph of f decreases if we start at $(0, -2)$ and move in the positive x-direction. This is reflected in the negative values of f_x. You should compare the graphs of f_{yx} and f_{yy} with the graph of f_y to see the relationships.

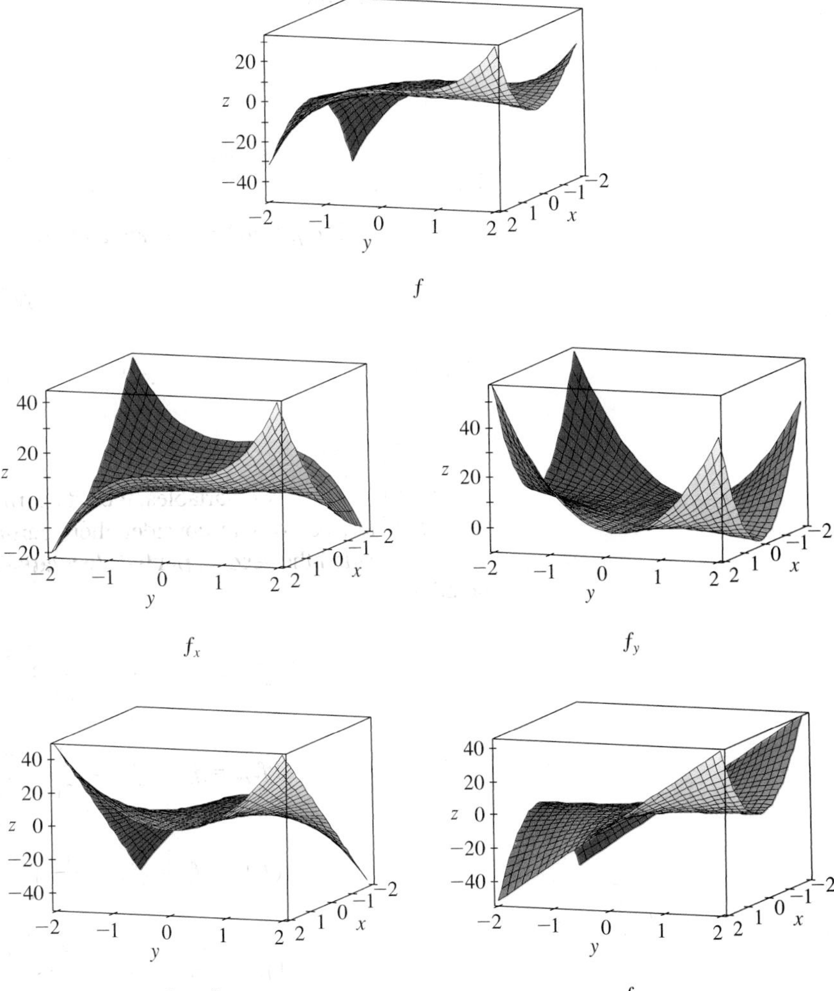

f

f_x f_y

f_{xx} $f_{xy} = f_{yx}$ f_{yy}

FIGURE 7

Notice that $f_{xy} = f_{yx}$ in Example 6. This is not just a coincidence. It turns out that the mixed partial derivatives f_{xy} and f_{yx} are equal for most functions that one meets in practice. The following theorem, which was discovered by the French mathematician Alexis Clairaut (1713–1765), gives conditions under which we can assert that $f_{xy} = f_{yx}$. The proof is given in Appendix E.

Clairaut's Theorem Suppose f is defined on a disk D that contains the point (a, b). If the functions f_{xy} and f_{yx} are both continuous on D, then

$$f_{xy}(a, b) = f_{yx}(a, b)$$

Clairaut

Alexis Clairaut was a child prodigy in mathematics: he read l'Hospital's textbook on calculus when he was ten and presented a paper on geometry to the French Academy of Sciences when he was 13. At the age of 18, Clairaut published *Recherches sur les courbes à double courbure,* which was the first systematic treatise on three-dimensional analytic geometry and included the calculus of space curves.

Partial derivatives of order 3 or higher can also be defined. For instance,

$$f_{xyy} = (f_{xy})_y = \frac{\partial}{\partial y}\left(\frac{\partial^2 f}{\partial y\, \partial x}\right) = \frac{\partial^3 f}{\partial y^2\, \partial x}$$

and using Clairaut's Theorem it can be shown that $f_{xyy} = f_{yxy} = f_{yyx}$ if these functions are continuous.

V EXAMPLE 7 **A higher-order derivative** Calculate f_{xxyz} if $f(x, y, z) = \sin(3x + yz)$.

SOLUTION

$$f_x = 3\cos(3x + yz)$$

$$f_{xx} = -9\sin(3x + yz)$$

$$f_{xxy} = -9z\cos(3x + yz)$$

$$f_{xxyz} = -9\cos(3x + yz) + 9yz\sin(3x + yz)$$

Partial Differential Equations

Partial derivatives occur in *partial differential equations* that express certain physical laws. For instance, the partial differential equation

$$\frac{\partial^2 u}{\partial x^2} + \frac{\partial^2 u}{\partial y^2} = 0$$

is called **Laplace's equation** after Pierre Laplace (1749–1827). Solutions of this equation are called **harmonic functions**; they play a role in problems of heat conduction, fluid flow, and electric potential.

EXAMPLE 8 Show that the function $u(x, y) = e^x \sin y$ is a solution of Laplace's equation.

SOLUTION We first compute the needed second-order partial derivatives:

$$u_x = e^x \sin y \qquad u_y = e^x \cos y$$

$$u_{xx} = e^x \sin y \qquad u_{yy} = -e^x \sin y$$

So

$$u_{xx} + u_{yy} = e^x \sin y - e^x \sin y = 0$$

Therefore u satisfies Laplace's equation.

The **wave equation**

$$\frac{\partial^2 u}{\partial t^2} = a^2 \frac{\partial^2 u}{\partial x^2}$$

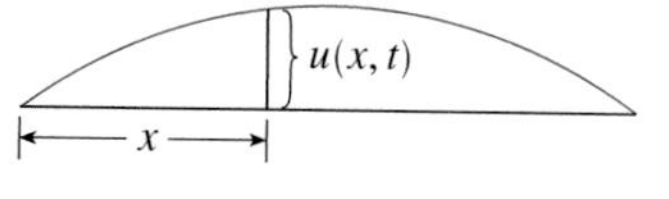

FIGURE 8

describes the motion of a waveform, which could be an ocean wave, a sound wave, a light wave, or a wave traveling along a vibrating string. For instance, if $u(x, t)$ represents the displacement of a vibrating violin string at time t and at a distance x from one end of the string (as in Figure 8), then $u(x, t)$ satisfies the wave equation. Here the constant a depends on the density of the string and on the tension in the string.

EXAMPLE 9 Verify that the function $u(x, t) = \sin(x - at)$ satisfies the wave equation.

SOLUTION

$$u_x = \cos(x - at) \qquad u_t = -a\cos(x - at)$$

$$u_{xx} = -\sin(x - at) \qquad u_{tt} = -a^2\sin(x - at) = a^2 u_{xx}$$

So u satisfies the wave equation.

The Cobb-Douglas Production Function

In Example 2 in Section 11.1 we described the work of Cobb and Douglas in modeling the total production P of an economic system as a function of the amount of labor L and the capital investment K. Here we use partial derivatives to show how the particular form of their model follows from certain assumptions they made about the economy.

If the production function is denoted by $P = P(L, K)$, then the partial derivative $\partial P/\partial L$ is the rate at which production changes with respect to the amount of labor. Economists call it the marginal production with respect to labor or the *marginal productivity of labor.* Likewise, the partial derivative $\partial P/\partial K$ is the rate of change of production with respect to capital and is called the *marginal productivity of capital.* In these terms, the assumptions made by Cobb and Douglas can be stated as follows.

(i) If either labor or capital vanishes, then so will production.

(ii) The marginal productivity of labor is proportional to the amount of production per unit of labor.

(iii) The marginal productivity of capital is proportional to the amount of production per unit of capital.

Because the production per unit of labor is P/L, assumption (ii) says that

$$\frac{\partial P}{\partial L} = \alpha \frac{P}{L}$$

for some constant α. If we keep K constant ($K = K_0$), then this partial differential equation becomes an ordinary differential equation:

5 $$\frac{dP}{dL} = \alpha \frac{P}{L}$$

If we solve this separable differential equation by the methods of Section 7.3 (see also Exercise 77), we get

6 $$P(L, K_0) = C_1(K_0)L^{\alpha}$$

Notice that we have written the constant C_1 as a function of K_0 because it could depend on the value of K_0.

Similarly, assumption (iii) says that

$$\frac{\partial P}{\partial K} = \beta \frac{P}{K}$$

and we can solve this differential equation to get

7 $$P(L_0, K) = C_2(L_0)K^{\beta}$$

Comparing Equations 6 and 7, we have

8 $$P(L, K) = bL^{\alpha}K^{\beta}$$

where b is a constant that is independent of both L and K. Assumption (i) shows that $\alpha > 0$ and $\beta > 0$.

Notice from Equation 8 that if labor and capital are both increased by a factor m, then

$$P(mL, mK) = b(mL)^{\alpha}(mK)^{\beta} = m^{\alpha+\beta}bL^{\alpha}K^{\beta} = m^{\alpha+\beta}P(L, K)$$

If $\alpha + \beta = 1$, then $P(mL, mK) = mP(L, K)$, which means that production is also increased by a factor of m. That is why Cobb and Douglas assumed that $\alpha + \beta = 1$ and therefore

$$P(L, K) = bL^{\alpha}K^{1-\alpha}$$

This is the Cobb-Douglas production function that we discussed in Section 11.1.

11.3 Exercises

1. The temperature T at a location in the Northern Hemisphere depends on the longitude x, latitude y, and time t, so we can write $T = f(x, y, t)$. Let's measure time in hours from the beginning of January.
   (a) What are the meanings of the partial derivatives $\partial T/\partial x$, $\partial T/\partial y$, and $\partial T/\partial t$?
   (b) Honolulu has longitude 158° W and latitude 21° N. Suppose that at 9:00 AM on January 1 the wind is blowing hot air to the northeast, so the air to the west and south is warm and the air to the north and east is cooler. Would you expect $f_x(158, 21, 9)$, $f_y(158, 21, 9)$, and $f_t(158, 21, 9)$ to be positive or negative? Explain.

2. At the beginning of this section we discussed the function $I = f(T, H)$, where I is the heat index, T is the temperature, and H is the relative humidity. Use Table 1 to estimate $f_T(92, 60)$ and $f_H(92, 60)$. What are the practical interpretations of these values?

3. The wind-chill index W is the perceived temperature when the actual temperature is T and the wind speed is v, so we can write $W = f(T, v)$. The following table of values is an excerpt from Table 1 in Section 11.1.

Wind speed (km/h); Actual temperature (°C)

T \ v	20	30	40	50	60	70
−10	−18	−20	−21	−22	−23	−23
−15	−24	−26	−27	−29	−30	−30
−20	−30	−33	−34	−35	−36	−37
−25	−37	−39	−41	−42	−43	−44

   (a) Estimate the values of $f_T(-15, 30)$ and $f_v(-15, 30)$. What are the practical interpretations of these values?
   (b) In general, what can you say about the signs of $\partial W/\partial T$ and $\partial W/\partial v$?
   (c) What appears to be the value of the following limit?

$$\lim_{v \to \infty} \frac{\partial W}{\partial v}$$

4. The wave heights h in the open sea depend on the speed v of the wind and the length of time t that the wind has been blowing at that speed. Values of the function $h = f(v, t)$ are recorded in feet in the following table.

Duration (hours); Wind speed (knots)

v \ t	5	10	15	20	30	40	50
10	2	2	2	2	2	2	2
15	4	4	5	5	5	5	5
20	5	7	8	8	9	9	9
30	9	13	16	17	18	19	19
40	14	21	25	28	31	33	33
50	19	29	36	40	45	48	50
60	24	37	47	54	62	67	69

   (a) What are the meanings of the partial derivatives $\partial h/\partial v$ and $\partial h/\partial t$?
   (b) Estimate the values of $f_v(40, 15)$ and $f_t(40, 15)$. What are the practical interpretations of these values?
   (c) What appears to be the value of the following limit?

$$\lim_{t \to \infty} \frac{\partial h}{\partial t}$$

5–8 Determine the signs of the partial derivatives for the function f whose graph is shown.

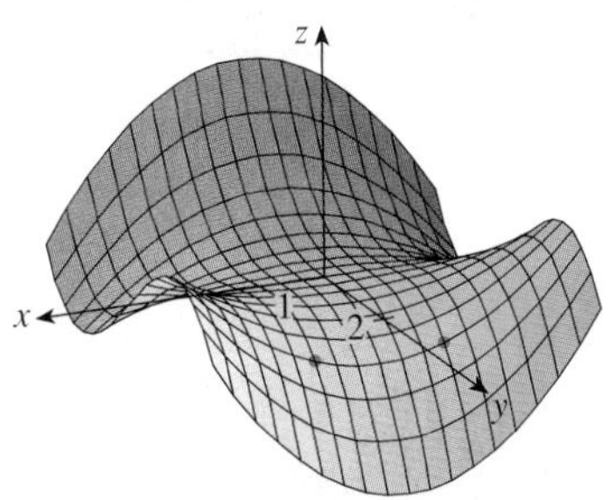

5. (a) $f_x(1, 2)$ (b) $f_y(1, 2)$

6. (a) $f_x(-1, 2)$ (b) $f_y(-1, 2)$

7. (a) $f_{xx}(-1, 2)$ (b) $f_{yy}(-1, 2)$

8. (a) $f_{xy}(1, 2)$ (b) $f_{xy}(-1, 2)$

9. The following surfaces, labeled a, b, and c, are graphs of a function f and its partial derivatives f_x and f_y. Identify each surface and give reasons for your choices.

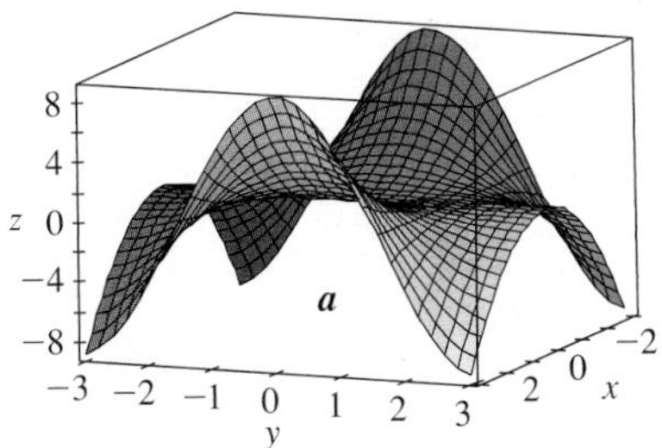

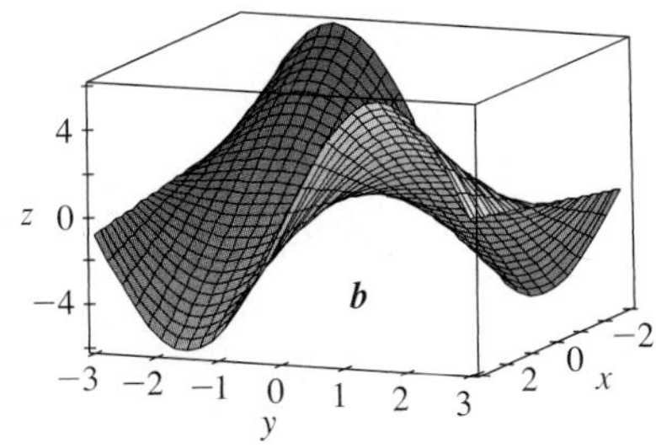

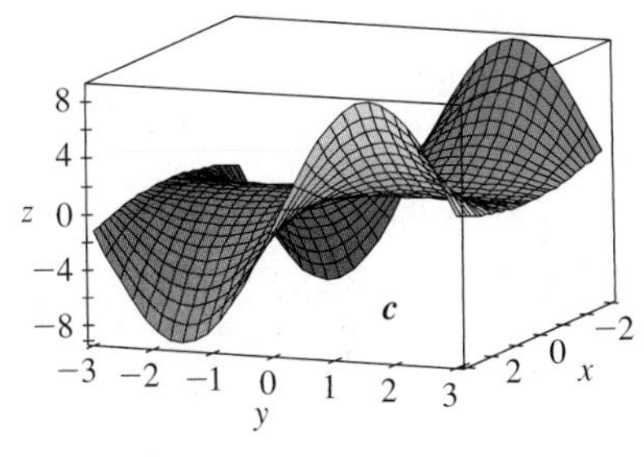

10. A contour map is given for a function f. Use it to estimate $f_x(2, 1)$ and $f_y(2, 1)$.

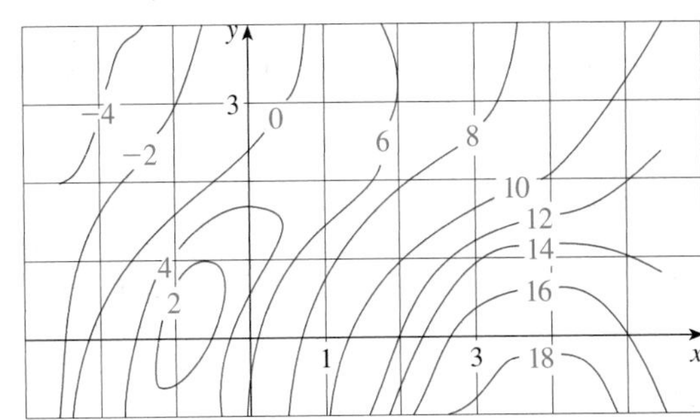

11. If $f(x, y) = 16 - 4x^2 - y^2$, find $f_x(1, 2)$ and $f_y(1, 2)$ and interpret these numbers as slopes. Illustrate with either hand-drawn sketches or computer plots.

12. If $f(x, y) = \sqrt{4 - x^2 - 4y^2}$, find $f_x(1, 0)$ and $f_y(1, 0)$ and interpret these numbers as slopes. Illustrate with either hand-drawn sketches or computer plots.

13–14 Find f_x and f_y and graph f, f_x, and f_y with domains and viewpoints that enable you to see the relationships between them.

13. $f(x, y) = x^2 + y^2 + x^2y$

14. $f(x, y) = xe^{-x^2-y^2}$

15–38 Find the first partial derivatives of the function.

15. $f(x, y) = y^5 - 3xy$

16. $f(x, y) = x^4y^3 + 8x^2y$

17. $f(x, t) = e^{-t}\cos \pi x$

18. $f(x, t) = \sqrt{x}\ \ln t$

19. $z = (2x + 3y)^{10}$

20. $z = \tan xy$

21. $f(x, y) = \dfrac{x - y}{x + y}$

22. $f(x, y) = x^y$

23. $w = \sin \alpha \cos \beta$

24. $w = e^v/(u + v^2)$

25. $f(r, s) = r \ln(r^2 + s^2)$

26. $f(x, t) = \arctan\left(x\sqrt{t}\right)$

27. $u = te^{w/t}$

28. $f(x, y) = \displaystyle\int_y^x \cos(t^2)\, dt$

29. $f(x, y, z) = xz - 5x^2y^3z^4$

30. $f(x, y, z) = x \sin(y - z)$

31. $w = \ln(x + 2y + 3z)$

32. $w = ze^{xyz}$

33. $u = xy \sin^{-1}(yz)$

34. $u = x^{y/z}$

35. $f(x, y, z, t) = xyz^2 \tan(yt)$

36. $f(x, y, z, t) = \dfrac{xy^2}{t + 2z}$

37. $u = \sqrt{x_1^2 + x_2^2 + \cdots + x_n^2}$

38. $u = \sin(x_1 + 2x_2 + \cdots + nx_n)$

39–42 Find the indicated partial derivatives.

39. $f(x, y) = \ln\left(x + \sqrt{x^2 + y^2}\right)$; $f_x(3, 4)$

40. $f(x, y) = \arctan(y/x)$; $f_x(2, 3)$

41. $f(x, y, z) = \dfrac{y}{x + y + z}$; $f_y(2, 1, -1)$

42. $f(x, y, z) = \sqrt{\sin^2 x + \sin^2 y + \sin^2 z}$; $f_z(0, 0, \pi/4)$

43–44 Use the definition of partial derivatives as limits (4) to find $f_x(x, y)$ and $f_y(x, y)$.

43. $f(x, y) = xy^2 - x^3y$

44. $f(x, y) = \dfrac{x}{x + y^2}$

45–48 Use implicit differentiation to find $\partial z/\partial x$ and $\partial z/\partial y$.

45. $x^2 + y^2 + z^2 = 3xyz$

46. $yz = \ln(x + z)$

47. $x - z = \arctan(yz)$

48. $\sin(xyz) = x + 2y + 3z$

49–50 Find $\partial z/\partial x$ and $\partial z/\partial y$.

49. (a) $z = f(x) + g(y)$ (b) $z = f(x + y)$

50. (a) $z = f(x)g(y)$ (b) $z = f(xy)$
(c) $z = f(x/y)$

51–56 Find all the second partial derivatives.

51. $f(x, y) = x^3y^5 + 2x^4y$

52. $f(x, y) = \sin^2(mx + ny)$

53. $w = \sqrt{u^2 + v^2}$

54. $v = \dfrac{xy}{x - y}$

55. $z = \arctan \dfrac{x + y}{1 - xy}$

56. $v = e^{xe^y}$

57–58 Verify that the conclusion of Clairaut's Theorem holds, that is, $u_{xy} = u_{yx}$.

57. $u = xe^{xy}$

58. $u = \tan(2x + 3y)$

59–64 Find the indicated partial derivative(s).

59. $f(x, y) = 3xy^4 + x^3y^2$; f_{xxy}, f_{yyy}

60. $f(x, t) = x^2e^{-ct}$; f_{ttt}, f_{txx}

61. $f(x, y, z) = \cos(4x + 3y + 2z)$; f_{xyz}, f_{yzz}

62. $f(r, s, t) = r\ln(rs^2t^3)$; f_{rss}, f_{rst}

63. $u = e^{r\theta}\sin\theta$; $\dfrac{\partial^3 u}{\partial r^2\,\partial\theta}$

64. $u = x^ay^bz^c$; $\dfrac{\partial^6 u}{\partial x\,\partial y^2\,\partial z^3}$

65. If $f(x, y, z) = xy^2z^3 + \arcsin(x\sqrt{z})$, find f_{xzy}. [*Hint:* Which order of differentiation is easiest?]

66. If $g(x, y, z) = \sqrt{1 + xz} + \sqrt{1 - xy}$, find g_{xyz}. [*Hint:* Use a different order of differentiation for each term.]

67. Use the table of values of $f(x, y)$ to estimate the values of $f_x(3, 2)$, $f_x(3, 2.2)$, and $f_{xy}(3, 2)$.

x \ y	1.8	2.0	2.2
2.5	12.5	10.2	9.3
3.0	18.1	17.5	15.9
3.5	20.0	22.4	26.1

68. Level curves are shown for a function f. Determine whether the following partial derivatives are positive or negative at the point P.
(a) f_x (b) f_y (c) f_{xx}
(d) f_{xy} (e) f_{yy}

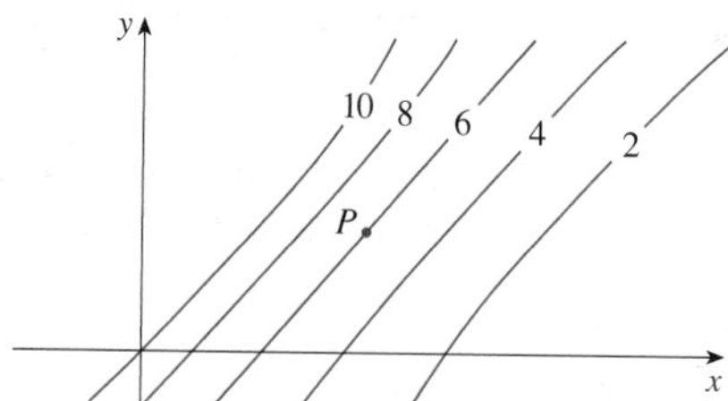

69. Verify that the function $u = e^{-\alpha^2k^2t}\sin kx$ is a solution of the *heat conduction equation* $u_t = \alpha^2u_{xx}$.

70. Determine whether each of the following functions is a solution of Laplace's equation $u_{xx} + u_{yy} = 0$.
(a) $u = x^2 + y^2$ (b) $u = x^2 - y^2$
(c) $u = x^3 + 3xy^2$ (d) $u = \ln\sqrt{x^2 + y^2}$
(e) $u = e^{-x}\cos y - e^{-y}\cos x$

71. Verify that the function $u = 1/\sqrt{x^2 + y^2 + z^2}$ is a solution of the three-dimensional Laplace equation $u_{xx} + u_{yy} + u_{zz} = 0$.

72. Show that each of the following functions is a solution of the wave equation $u_{tt} = a^2u_{xx}$.
(a) $u = \sin(kx)\sin(akt)$ (b) $u = t/(a^2t^2 - x^2)$
(c) $u = (x - at)^6 + (x + at)^6$
(d) $u = \sin(x - at) + \ln(x + at)$

73. If f and g are twice differentiable functions of a single variable, show that the function

$$u(x, t) = f(x + at) + g(x - at)$$

is a solution of the wave equation given in Exercise 72.

74. If $u = e^{a_1x_1 + a_2x_2 + \cdots + a_nx_n}$, where $a_1^2 + a_2^2 + \cdots + a_n^2 = 1$, show that

$$\frac{\partial^2 u}{\partial x_1^2} + \frac{\partial^2 u}{\partial x_2^2} + \cdots + \frac{\partial^2 u}{\partial x_n^2} = u$$

75. If $u = xe^y + ye^x$, show that

$$\frac{\partial^3 u}{\partial x^3} + \frac{\partial^3 u}{\partial y^3} = x\frac{\partial^3 u}{\partial x\,\partial y^2} + y\frac{\partial^3 u}{\partial x^2\,\partial y}$$

76. Show that the Cobb-Douglas production function $P = bL^\alpha K^\beta$ satisfies the equation

$$L\frac{\partial P}{\partial L} + K\frac{\partial P}{\partial K} = (\alpha + \beta)P$$

77. Show that the Cobb-Douglas production function satisfies $P(L, K_0) = C_1(K_0)L^\alpha$ by solving the differential equation

$$\frac{dP}{dL} = \alpha\frac{P}{L}$$

(See Equation 5.)

78. The temperature at a point (x, y) on a flat metal plate is given by $T(x, y) = 60/(1 + x^2 + y^2)$, where T is measured in °C and x, y in meters. Find the rate of change of temperature with respect to distance at the point $(2, 1)$ in (a) the x-direction and (b) the y-direction.

79. The total resistance R produced by three conductors with resistances R_1, R_2, R_3 connected in a parallel electrical circuit is given by the formula

$$\frac{1}{R} = \frac{1}{R_1} + \frac{1}{R_2} + \frac{1}{R_3}$$

Find $\partial R/\partial R_1$.

80. The *van der Waals equation* for n moles of a gas is

$$\left(P + \frac{n^2a}{V^2}\right)(V - nb) = nRT$$

where P is the pressure, V is the volume, and T is the temperature of the gas. The constant R is the universal gas constant and a and b are positive constants that are characteristic of a particular gas. Calculate $\partial T/\partial P$ and $\partial P/\partial V$.

81. (a) The gas law for a fixed mass m of an ideal gas at absolute temperature T, pressure P, and volume V is $PV = mRT$, where R is the gas constant. Show that

$$\frac{\partial P}{\partial V}\frac{\partial V}{\partial T}\frac{\partial T}{\partial P} = -1$$

(b) Show that, for an ideal gas,

$$T\frac{\partial P}{\partial T}\frac{\partial V}{\partial T} = mR$$

82. The wind-chill index is modeled by the function

$$W = 13.12 + 0.6215T - 11.37v^{0.16} + 0.3965Tv^{0.16}$$

where T is the temperature (°C) and v is the wind speed (km/h). When $T = -15$°C and $v = 30$ km/h, by how much would you expect the apparent temperature W to drop if the actual temperature decreases by 1°C? What if the wind speed increases by 1 km/h?

83. The kinetic energy of a body with mass m and velocity v is $K = \frac{1}{2}mv^2$. Show that

$$\frac{\partial K}{\partial m}\frac{\partial^2 K}{\partial v^2} = K$$

84. If a, b, c are the sides of a triangle and A, B, C are the opposite angles, find $\partial A/\partial a$, $\partial A/\partial b$, $\partial A/\partial c$ by implicit differentiation of the Law of Cosines.

85. You are told that there is a function f whose partial derivatives are $f_x(x, y) = x + 4y$ and $f_y(x, y) = 3x - y$. Should you believe it?

86. The paraboloid $z = 6 - x - x^2 - 2y^2$ intersects the plane $x = 1$ in a parabola. Find parametric equations for the tangent line to this parabola at the point $(1, 2, -4)$. Use a computer to graph the paraboloid, the parabola, and the tangent line on the same screen.

87. The ellipsoid $4x^2 + 2y^2 + z^2 = 16$ intersects the plane $y = 2$ in an ellipse. Find parametric equations for the tangent line to this ellipse at the point $(1, 2, 2)$.

88. In a study of frost penetration it was found that the temperature T at time t (measured in days) at a depth x (measured in feet) can be modeled by the function

$$T(x, t) = T_0 + T_1e^{-\lambda x}\sin(\omega t - \lambda x)$$

where $\omega = 2\pi/365$ and λ is a positive constant.
(a) Find $\partial T/\partial x$. What is its physical significance?
(b) Find $\partial T/\partial t$. What is its physical significance?
(c) Show that T satisfies the heat equation $T_t = kT_{xx}$ for a certain constant k.
(d) If $\lambda = 0.2$, $T_0 = 0$, and $T_1 = 10$, use a computer to graph $T(x, t)$.
(e) What is the physical significance of the term $-\lambda x$ in the expression $\sin(\omega t - \lambda x)$?

89. If $f(x, y) = x(x^2 + y^2)^{-3/2}e^{\sin(x^2y)}$, find $f_x(1, 0)$. [*Hint:* Instead of finding $f_x(x, y)$ first, note that it's easier to use Equation 1 or Equation 2.]

90. If $f(x, y) = \sqrt[3]{x^3 + y^3}$, find $f_x(0, 0)$.

91. Let

$$f(x, y) = \begin{cases} \dfrac{x^3y - xy^3}{x^2 + y^2} & \text{if } (x, y) \neq (0, 0) \\ 0 & \text{if } (x, y) = (0, 0) \end{cases}$$

(a) Use a computer to graph f.
(b) Find $f_x(x, y)$ and $f_y(x, y)$ when $(x, y) \neq (0, 0)$.
(c) Find $f_x(0, 0)$ and $f_y(0, 0)$ using Equations 2 and 3.
(d) Show that $f_{xy}(0, 0) = -1$ and $f_{yx}(0, 0) = 1$.
CAS (e) Does the result of part (d) contradict Clairaut's Theorem? Use graphs of f_{xy} and f_{yx} to illustrate your answer.

11.4 Tangent Planes and Linear Approximations

One of the most important ideas in single-variable calculus is that as we zoom in toward a point on the graph of a differentiable function, the graph becomes indistinguishable from its tangent line and we can approximate the function by a linear function. (See Section 3.9.) Here we develop similar ideas in three dimensions. As we zoom in toward a point on a surface that is the graph of a differentiable function of two variables, the surface looks more and more like a plane (its tangent plane) and we can approximate the function by a linear function of two variables. We also extend the idea of a differential to functions of two or more variables.

Tangent Planes

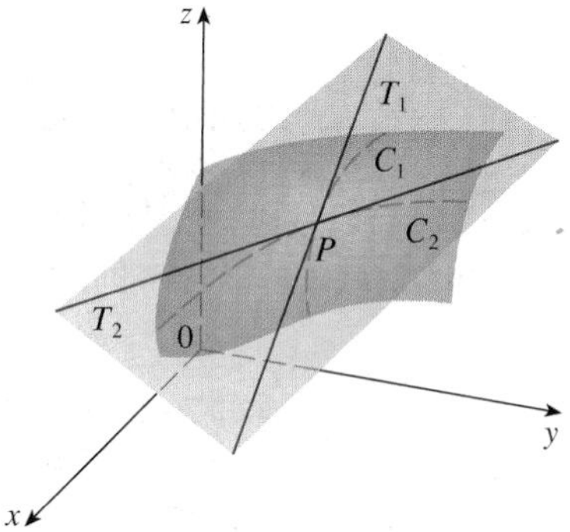

Suppose a surface S has equation $z = f(x, y)$, where f has continuous first partial derivatives, and let $P(x_0, y_0, z_0)$ be a point on S. As in the preceding section, let C_1 and C_2 be the curves obtained by intersecting the vertical planes $y = y_0$ and $x = x_0$ with the surface S. Then the point P lies on both C_1 and C_2. Let T_1 and T_2 be the tangent lines to the curves C_1 and C_2 at the point P. Then the **tangent plane** to the surface S at the point P is defined to be the plane that contains both tangent lines T_1 and T_2. (See Figure 1.)

FIGURE 1
The tangent plane contains the tangent lines T_1 and T_2.

We will see in Section 11.6 that if C is any other curve that lies on the surface S and passes through P, then its tangent line at P also lies in the tangent plane. Therefore you can think of the tangent plane to S at P as consisting of all possible tangent lines at P to curves that lie on S and pass through P. The tangent plane at P is the plane that most closely approximates the surface S near the point P.

We know from Equation 9.5.7 that any plane passing through the point $P(x_0, y_0, z_0)$ has an equation of the form

$$A(x - x_0) + B(y - y_0) + C(z - z_0) = 0$$

By dividing this equation by C and letting $a = -A/C$ and $b = -B/C$, we can write it in the form

$$\boxed{1} \qquad z - z_0 = a(x - x_0) + b(y - y_0)$$

If Equation 1 represents the tangent plane at P, then its intersection with the plane $y = y_0$ must be the tangent line T_1. Setting $y = y_0$ in Equation 1 gives

$$z - z_0 = a(x - x_0) \qquad \text{where } y = y_0$$

and we recognize this as the equation (in point-slope form) of a line with slope a lying in the plane $y = y_0$. But from Section 11.3 we know that the slope of the tangent T_1 is $f_x(x_0, y_0)$. Therefore $a = f_x(x_0, y_0)$.

Similarly, putting $x = x_0$ in Equation 1, we get $z - z_0 = b(y - y_0)$, which must represent the tangent line T_2, so $b = f_y(x_0, y_0)$.

Note the similarity between the equation of a tangent plane and the equation of a tangent line:
$$y - y_0 = f'(x_0)(x - x_0)$$

2 Suppose f has continuous partial derivatives. An equation of the tangent plane to the surface $z = f(x, y)$ at the point $P(x_0, y_0, z_0)$ is

$$z - z_0 = f_x(x_0, y_0)(x - x_0) + f_y(x_0, y_0)(y - y_0)$$

V EXAMPLE 1 Find the tangent plane to the elliptic paraboloid $z = 2x^2 + y^2$ at the point $(1, 1, 3)$.

SOLUTION Let $f(x, y) = 2x^2 + y^2$. Then

$$f_x(x, y) = 4x \qquad f_y(x, y) = 2y$$

$$f_x(1, 1) = 4 \qquad f_y(1, 1) = 2$$

Then (2) gives the equation of the tangent plane at $(1, 1, 3)$ as

$$z - 3 = 4(x - 1) + 2(y - 1)$$

or

$$z = 4x + 2y - 3$$

TEC Visual 11.4 shows an animation of Figures 2 and 3.

Figure 2(a) shows the elliptic paraboloid and its tangent plane at $(1, 1, 3)$ that we found in Example 1. In parts (b) and (c) we zoom in toward the point $(1, 1, 3)$ by restricting the domain of the function $f(x, y) = 2x^2 + y^2$. Notice that the more we zoom in, the flatter the graph appears and the more it resembles its tangent plane.

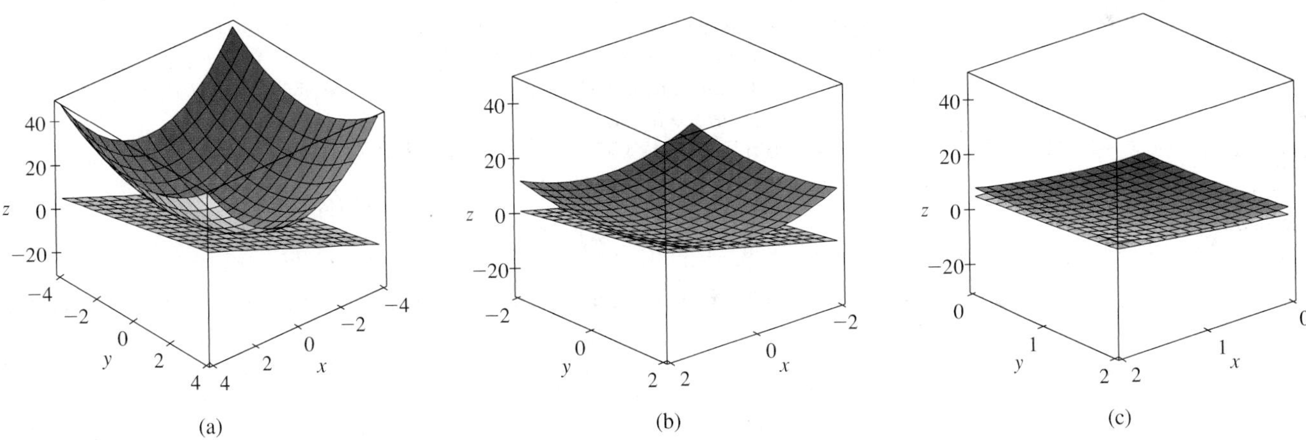

FIGURE 2 The elliptic paraboloid $z = 2x^2 + y^2$ appears to coincide with its tangent plane as we zoom in toward $(1, 1, 3)$.

In Figure 3 we corroborate this impression by zooming in toward the point $(1, 1)$ on a contour map of the function $f(x, y) = 2x^2 + y^2$. Notice that the more we zoom in, the more the level curves look like equally spaced parallel lines, which is characteristic of a plane.

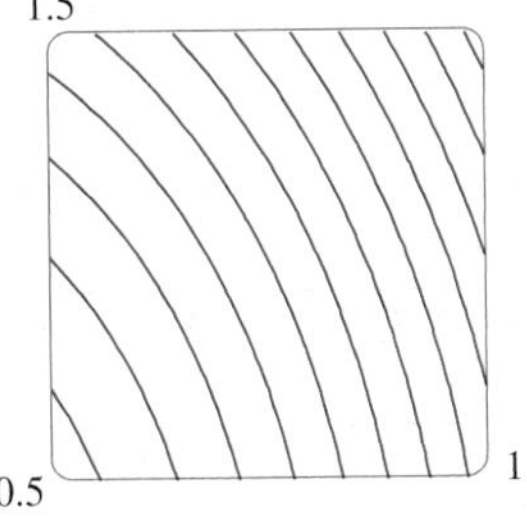

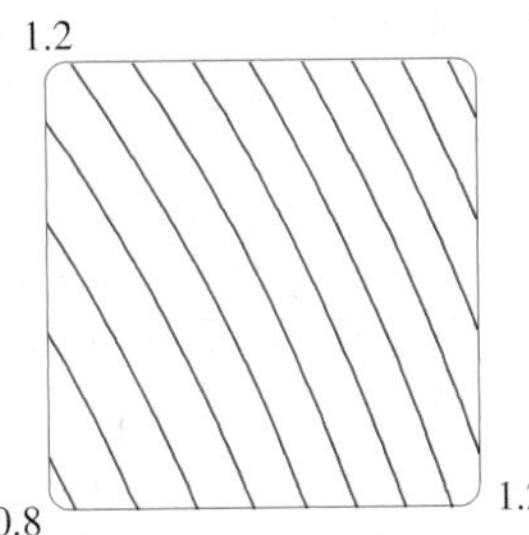

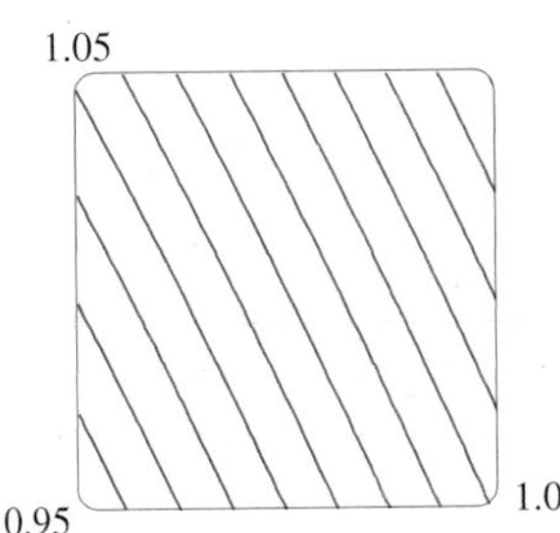

FIGURE 3 Zooming in toward $(1, 1)$ on a contour map of $f(x, y) = 2x^2 + y^2$

Linear Approximations

In Example 1 we found that an equation of the tangent plane to the graph of the function $f(x, y) = 2x^2 + y^2$ at the point $(1, 1, 3)$ is $z = 4x + 2y - 3$. Therefore, in view of the visual evidence in Figures 2 and 3, the linear function of two variables

$$L(x, y) = 4x + 2y - 3$$

is a good approximation to $f(x, y)$ when (x, y) is near $(1, 1)$. The function L is called the *linearization* of f at $(1, 1)$ and the approximation

$$f(x, y) \approx 4x + 2y - 3$$

is called the *linear approximation* or *tangent plane approximation* of f at $(1, 1)$.

For instance, at the point $(1.1, 0.95)$ the linear approximation gives

$$f(1.1, 0.95) \approx 4(1.1) + 2(0.95) - 3 = 3.3$$

which is quite close to the true value of $f(1.1, 0.95) = 2(1.1)^2 + (0.95)^2 = 3.3225$. But if we take a point farther away from $(1, 1)$, such as $(2, 3)$, we no longer get a good approximation. In fact, $L(2, 3) = 11$ whereas $f(2, 3) = 17$.

In general, we know from (2) that an equation of the tangent plane to the graph of a function f of two variables at the point $(a, b, f(a, b))$ is

$$z = f(a, b) + f_x(a, b)(x - a) + f_y(a, b)(y - b)$$

The linear function whose graph is this tangent plane, namely

$$\boxed{3} \qquad L(x, y) = f(a, b) + f_x(a, b)(x - a) + f_y(a, b)(y - b)$$

is called the **linearization** of f at (a, b) and the approximation

$$\boxed{4} \qquad f(x, y) \approx f(a, b) + f_x(a, b)(x - a) + f_y(a, b)(y - b)$$

is called the **linear approximation** or the **tangent plane approximation** of f at (a, b).

We have defined tangent planes for surfaces $z = f(x, y)$, where f has continuous first partial derivatives. What happens if f_x and f_y are not continuous? Figure 4 pictures such a function; its equation is

$$f(x, y) = \begin{cases} \dfrac{xy}{x^2 + y^2} & \text{if } (x, y) \neq (0, 0) \\ 0 & \text{if } (x, y) = (0, 0) \end{cases}$$

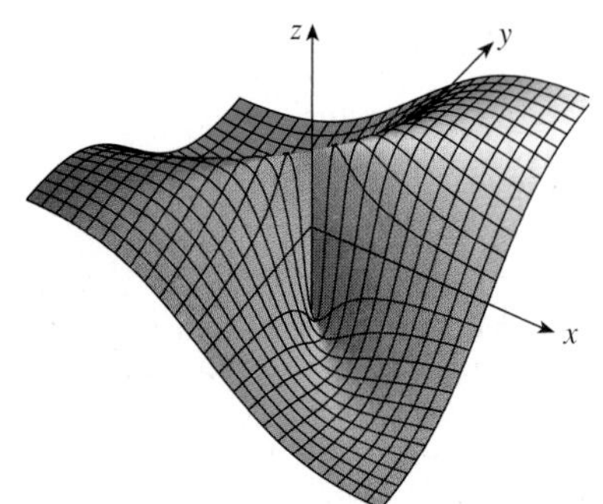

FIGURE 4

$f(x, y) = \dfrac{xy}{x^2 + y^2}$ if $(x, y) \neq (0, 0)$,
$f(0, 0) = 0$

You can verify (see Exercise 48) that its partial derivatives exist at the origin and, in fact, $f_x(0, 0) = 0$ and $f_y(0, 0) = 0$, but f_x and f_y are not continuous. The linear approximation would be $f(x, y) \approx 0$, but $f(x, y) = \frac{1}{2}$ at all points on the line $y = x$. So a function of two variables can behave badly even though both of its partial derivatives exist. To rule out such behavior, we formulate the idea of a differentiable function of two variables.

Recall that for a function of one variable, $y = f(x)$, if x changes from a to $a + \Delta x$, we defined the increment of y as

$$\Delta y = f(a + \Delta x) - f(a)$$

In Chapter 3 we showed that if f is differentiable at a, then

This is Equation 3.4.8.

$$\boxed{5} \qquad \Delta y = f'(a)\,\Delta x + \varepsilon\,\Delta x \qquad \text{where } \varepsilon \to 0 \text{ as } \Delta x \to 0$$

Now consider a function of two variables, $z = f(x, y)$, and suppose x changes from a to $a + \Delta x$ and y changes from b to $b + \Delta y$. Then the corresponding **increment** of z is

$$\boxed{6} \qquad \Delta z = f(a + \Delta x, b + \Delta y) - f(a, b)$$

Thus the increment Δz represents the change in the value of f when (x, y) changes from (a, b) to $(a + \Delta x, b + \Delta y)$. By analogy with (5) we define the differentiability of a function of two variables as follows.

7 Definition If $z = f(x, y)$, then f is **differentiable** at (a, b) if Δz can be expressed in the form

$$\Delta z = f_x(a, b)\,\Delta x + f_y(a, b)\,\Delta y + \varepsilon_1\,\Delta x + \varepsilon_2\,\Delta y$$

where ε_1 and $\varepsilon_2 \to 0$ as $(\Delta x,\ \Delta y) \to (0, 0)$.

Definition 7 says that a differentiable function is one for which the linear approximation (4) is a good approximation when (x, y) is near (a, b). In other words, the tangent plane approximates the graph of f well near the point of tangency.

It's sometimes hard to use Definition 7 directly to check the differentiability of a function, but the next theorem provides a convenient sufficient condition for differentiability.

Theorem 8 is proved in Appendix E.

8 Theorem If the partial derivatives f_x and f_y exist near (a, b) and are continuous at (a, b), then f is differentiable at (a, b).

V EXAMPLE 2 Using a linearization to estimate a function value

Show that $f(x, y) = xe^{xy}$ is differentiable at $(1, 0)$ and find its linearization there. Then use it to approximate $f(1.1, -0.1)$.

SOLUTION The partial derivatives are

$$f_x(x, y) = e^{xy} + xye^{xy} \qquad f_y(x, y) = x^2e^{xy}$$

$$f_x(1, 0) = 1 \qquad f_y(1, 0) = 1$$

Figure 5 shows the graphs of the function f and its linearization L in Example 2.

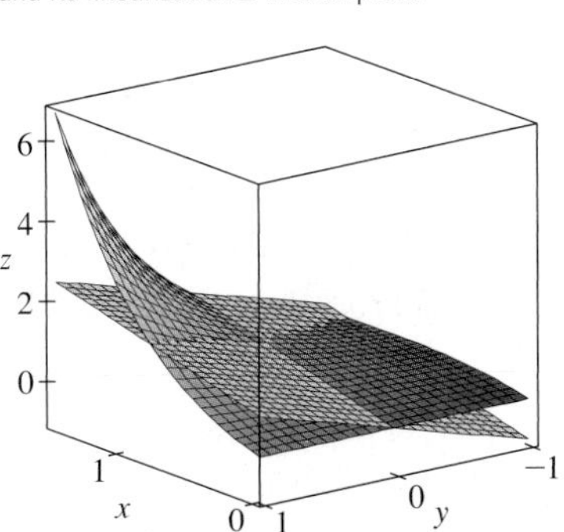

FIGURE 5

Both f_x and f_y are continuous functions, so f is differentiable by Theorem 8. The linearization is

$$L(x, y) = f(1, 0) + f_x(1, 0)(x - 1) + f_y(1, 0)(y - 0)$$

$$= 1 + 1(x - 1) + 1 \cdot y = x + y$$

The corresponding linear approximation is

$$xe^{xy} \approx x + y$$

so

$$f(1.1, -0.1) \approx 1.1 - 0.1 = 1$$

Compare this with the actual value of $f(1.1, -0.1) = 1.1e^{-0.11} \approx 0.98542$.

EXAMPLE 3 Estimating the heat index from tabular values At the beginning of Section 11.3 we discussed the heat index (perceived temperature) I as a function of the actual temperature T and the relative humidity H and gave the following table of values from the National Weather Service.

Relative humidity (%)

Actual temperature (°F)	T \ H	50	55	60	65	70	75	80	85	90
	90	96	98	100	103	106	109	112	115	119
	92	100	103	105	108	112	115	119	123	128
	94	104	107	111	114	118	122	127	132	137
	96	109	113	116	121	125	130	135	141	146
	98	114	118	123	127	133	138	144	150	157
	100	119	124	129	135	141	147	154	161	168

Find a linear approximation for the heat index $I = f(T, H)$ when T is near 96°F and H is near 70%. Use it to estimate the heat index when the temperature is 97°F and the relative humidity is 72%.

SOLUTION We read from the table that $f(96, 70) = 125$. In Section 11.3 we used the tabular values to estimate that $f_T(96, 70) \approx 3.75$ and $f_H(96, 70) \approx 0.9$. (See page 757–58.) So the linear approximation is

$$\begin{aligned} f(T, H) &\approx f(96, 70) + f_T(96, 70)(T - 96) + f_H(96, 70)(H - 70) \\ &\approx 125 + 3.75(T - 96) + 0.9(H - 70) \end{aligned}$$

In particular,

$$f(97, 72) \approx 125 + 3.75(1) + 0.9(2) = 130.55$$

Therefore, when $T = 97$°F and $H = 72$%, the heat index is

$$I \approx 131°\text{F}$$

Differentials

For a differentiable function of one variable, $y = f(x)$, we define the differential dx to be an independent variable; that is, dx can be given the value of any real number. The differential of y is then defined as

$$\boxed{9} \qquad dy = f'(x)\,dx$$

(See Section 3.9.) Figure 6 shows the relationship between the increment Δy and the differential dy: Δy represents the change in height of the curve $y = f(x)$ and dy represents the change in height of the tangent line when x changes by an amount $dx = \Delta x$.

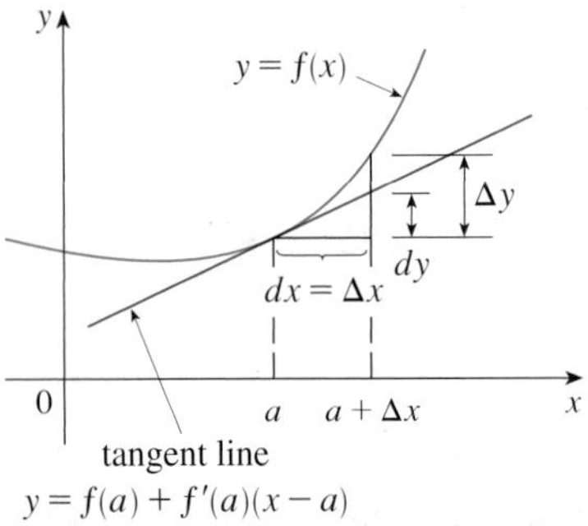

For a differentiable function of two variables, $z = f(x, y)$, we define the **differentials** dx and dy to be independent variables; that is, they can be given any values. Then the **differential** dz, also called the **total differential**, is defined by

$$\boxed{10} \qquad dz = f_x(x, y)\,dx + f_y(x, y)\,dy = \frac{\partial z}{\partial x}\,dx + \frac{\partial z}{\partial y}\,dy$$

FIGURE 6

(Compare with Equation 9.) Sometimes the notation df is used in place of dz.

If we take $dx = \Delta x = x - a$ and $dy = \Delta y = y - b$ in Equation 10, then the differential of z is

$$dz = f_x(a, b)(x - a) + f_y(a, b)(y - b)$$

So, in the notation of differentials, the linear approximation (4) can be written as

$$f(x, y) \approx f(a, b) + dz$$

Figure 7 is the three-dimensional counterpart of Figure 6 and shows the geometric interpretation of the differential dz and the increment Δz: dz represents the change in height of the tangent plane, whereas Δz represents the change in height of the surface $z = f(x, y)$ when (x, y) changes from (a, b) to $(a + \Delta x, b + \Delta y)$.

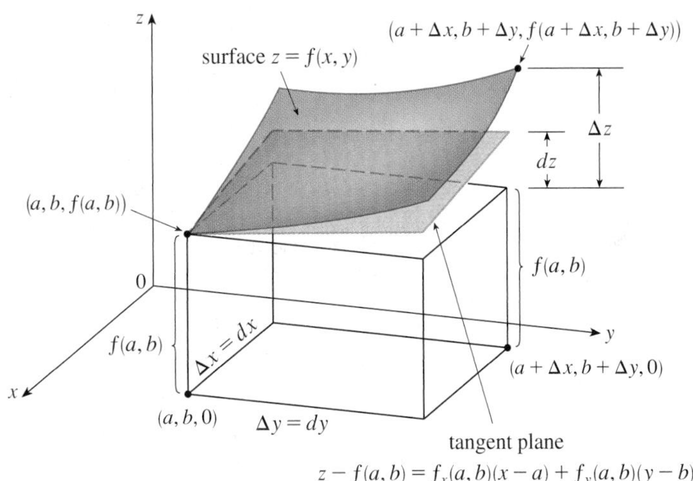

FIGURE 7

EXAMPLE 4 **Differentials versus increments**

(a) If $z = f(x, y) = x^2 + 3xy - y^2$, find the differential dz.

(b) If x changes from 2 to 2.05 and y changes from 3 to 2.96, compare the values of Δz and dz.

SOLUTION

(a) Definition 10 gives

$$dz = \frac{\partial z}{\partial x}\,dx + \frac{\partial z}{\partial y}\,dy = (2x + 3y)\,dx + (3x - 2y)\,dy$$

In Example 4, dz is close to Δz because the tangent plane is a good approximation to the surface $z = x^2 + 3xy - y^2$ near $(2, 3, 13)$. (See Figure 8.)

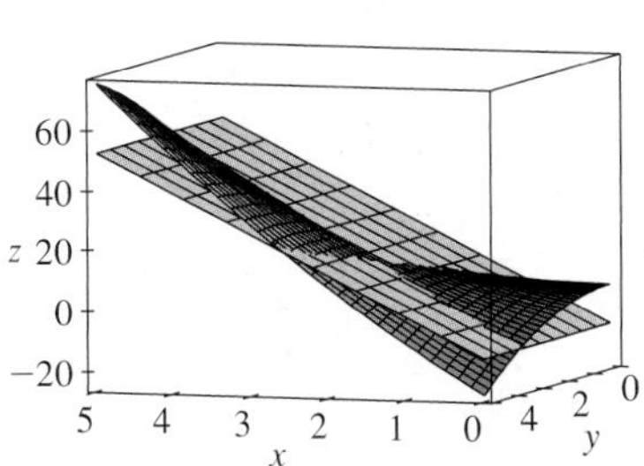

FIGURE 8

(b) Putting $x = 2$, $dx = \Delta x = 0.05$, $y = 3$, and $dy = \Delta y = -0.04$, we get

$$dz = [2(2) + 3(3)]0.05 + [3(2) - 2(3)](-0.04) = 0.65$$

The increment of z is

$$\begin{aligned}\Delta z &= f(2.05, 2.96) - f(2, 3) \\ &= [(2.05)^2 + 3(2.05)(2.96) - (2.96)^2] - [2^2 + 3(2)(3) - 3^2] \\ &= 0.6449\end{aligned}$$

Notice that $\Delta z \approx dz$ but dz is easier to compute.

EXAMPLE 5 **Using differentials to estimate an error** The base radius and height of a right circular cone are measured as 10 cm and 25 cm, respectively, with a possible error in measurement of as much as 0.1 cm in each. Use differentials to estimate the maximum error in the calculated volume of the cone.

SOLUTION The volume V of a cone with base radius r and height h is $V = \pi r^2 h/3$. So the differential of V is

$$dV = \frac{\partial V}{\partial r}\,dr + \frac{\partial V}{\partial h}\,dh = \frac{2\pi rh}{3}\,dr + \frac{\pi r^2}{3}\,dh$$

Since each error is at most 0.1 cm, we have $|\Delta r| \leqslant 0.1$, $|\Delta h| \leqslant 0.1$. To find the largest error in the volume we take the largest error in the measurement of r and of h. Therefore we take $dr = 0.1$ and $dh = 0.1$ along with $r = 10$, $h = 25$. This gives

$$dV = \frac{500\pi}{3}(0.1) + \frac{100\pi}{3}(0.1) = 20\pi$$

Thus the maximum error in the calculated volume is about $20\pi\ \text{cm}^3 \approx 63\ \text{cm}^3$.

Functions of Three or More Variables

Linear approximations, differentiability, and differentials can be defined in a similar manner for functions of more than two variables. A differentiable function is defined by an expression similar to the one in Definition 7. For such functions the **linear approximation** is

$$f(x, y, z) \approx f(a, b, c) + f_x(a, b, c)(x - a) + f_y(a, b, c)(y - b) + f_z(a, b, c)(z - c)$$

and the linearization $L(x, y, z)$ is the right side of this expression.

If $w = f(x, y, z)$, then the **increment** of w is

$$\Delta w = f(x + \Delta x, y + \Delta y, z + \Delta z) - f(x, y, z)$$

The **differential** dw is defined in terms of the differentials dx, dy, and dz of the independent variables by

$$dw = \frac{\partial w}{\partial x}\,dx + \frac{\partial w}{\partial y}\,dy + \frac{\partial w}{\partial z}\,dz$$

EXAMPLE 6 The dimensions of a rectangular box are measured to be 75 cm, 60 cm, and 40 cm, and each measurement is correct to within 0.2 cm. Use differentials to estimate the largest possible error when the volume of the box is calculated from these measurements.

SOLUTION If the dimensions of the box are x, y, and z, its volume is $V = xyz$ and so

$$dV = \frac{\partial V}{\partial x}\,dx + \frac{\partial V}{\partial y}\,dy + \frac{\partial V}{\partial z}\,dz = yz\,dx + xz\,dy + xy\,dz$$

We are given that $|\Delta x| \leqslant 0.2$, $|\Delta y| \leqslant 0.2$, and $|\Delta z| \leqslant 0.2$. To find the largest error in the volume, we therefore use $dx = 0.2$, $dy = 0.2$, and $dz = 0.2$ together with $x = 75$, $y = 60$, and $z = 40$:

$$\Delta V \approx dV = (60)(40)(0.2) + (75)(40)(0.2) + (75)(60)(0.2) = 1980$$

Thus an error of only 0.2 cm in measuring each dimension could lead to an error of as much as $1980\ \text{cm}^3$ in the calculated volume! This may seem like a large error, but it's only about 1% of the volume of the box.

Tangent Planes to Parametric Surfaces

Parametric surfaces were introduced in Section 10.5. We now find the tangent plane to a parametric surface S traced out by a vector function

$$\mathbf{r}(u, v) = x(u, v)\,\mathbf{i} + y(u, v)\,\mathbf{j} + z(u, v)\,\mathbf{k}$$

at a point P_0 with position vector $\mathbf{r}(u_0, v_0)$. If we keep u constant by putting $u = u_0$, then $\mathbf{r}(u_0, v)$ becomes a vector function of the single parameter v and defines a grid curve C_1 lying on S. (See Figure 9.) The tangent vector to C_1 at P_0 is obtained by taking the partial derivative of $\mathbf{r}$ with respect to v:

$$\mathbf{r}_v = \frac{\partial x}{\partial v}(u_0, v_0)\,\mathbf{i} + \frac{\partial y}{\partial v}(u_0, v_0)\,\mathbf{j} + \frac{\partial z}{\partial v}(u_0, v_0)\,\mathbf{k}$$

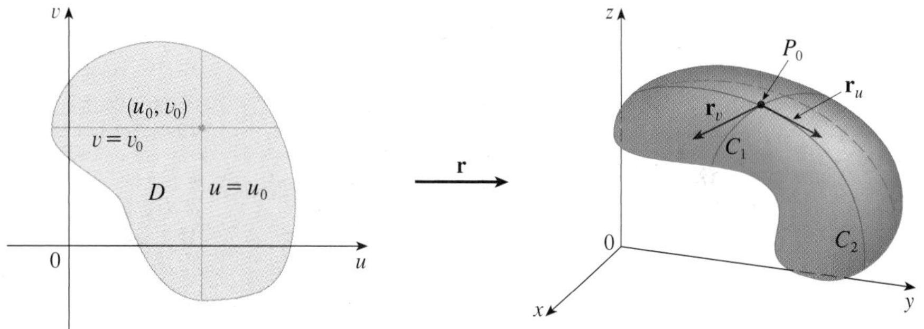

FIGURE 9

Similarly, if we keep v constant by putting $v = v_0$, we get a grid curve C_2 given by $\mathbf{r}(u, v_0)$ that lies on S, and its tangent vector at P_0 is

$$\mathbf{r}_u = \frac{\partial x}{\partial u}(u_0, v_0)\,\mathbf{i} + \frac{\partial y}{\partial u}(u_0, v_0)\,\mathbf{j} + \frac{\partial z}{\partial u}(u_0, v_0)\,\mathbf{k}$$

If $\mathbf{r}_u \times \mathbf{r}_v$ is not $\mathbf{0}$, then the surface S is called **smooth** (it has no "corners"). For a smooth surface, the **tangent plane** is the plane that contains the tangent vectors $\mathbf{r}_u$ and $\mathbf{r}_v$, and the vector $\mathbf{r}_u \times \mathbf{r}_v$ is a normal vector to the tangent plane.

V EXAMPLE 7 Find the tangent plane to the surface with parametric equations $x = u^2$, $y = v^2$, $z = u + 2v$ at the point $(1, 1, 3)$.

Figure 10 shows the self-intersecting surface in Example 7 and its tangent plane at (1, 1, 3).

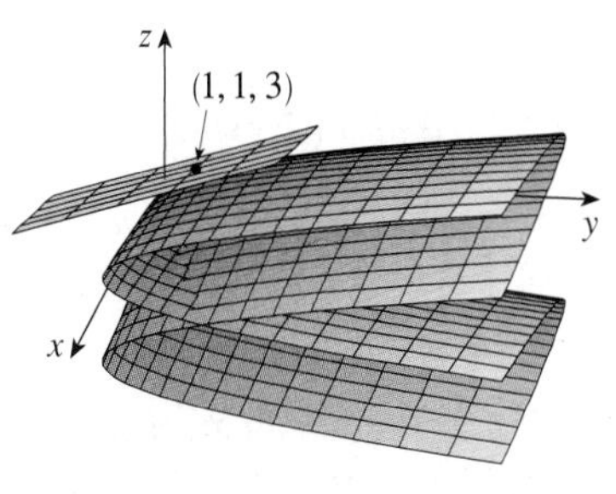

FIGURE 10

SOLUTION We first compute the tangent vectors:

$$\mathbf{r}_u = \frac{\partial x}{\partial u}\,\mathbf{i} + \frac{\partial y}{\partial u}\,\mathbf{j} + \frac{\partial z}{\partial u}\,\mathbf{k} = 2u\,\mathbf{i} + \mathbf{k}$$

$$\mathbf{r}_v = \frac{\partial x}{\partial v}\,\mathbf{i} + \frac{\partial y}{\partial v}\,\mathbf{j} + \frac{\partial z}{\partial v}\,\mathbf{k} = 2v\,\mathbf{j} + 2\,\mathbf{k}$$

Thus a normal vector to the tangent plane is

$$\mathbf{r}_u \times \mathbf{r}_v = \begin{vmatrix} \mathbf{i} & \mathbf{j} & \mathbf{k} \\ 2u & 0 & 1 \\ 0 & 2v & 2 \end{vmatrix} = -2v\,\mathbf{i} - 4u\,\mathbf{j} + 4uv\,\mathbf{k}$$

Notice that the point (1, 1, 3) corresponds to the parameter values $u = 1$ and $v = 1$, so the normal vector there is

$$-2\,\mathbf{i} - 4\,\mathbf{j} + 4\,\mathbf{k}$$

Therefore an equation of the tangent plane at (1, 1, 3) is

$$-2(x - 1) - 4(y - 1) + 4(z - 3) = 0$$

or

$$x + 2y - 2z + 3 = 0$$

11.4 Exercises

1–6 Find an equation of the tangent plane to the given surface at the specified point.

1. $z = 3y^2 - 2x^2 + x, \quad (2, -1, -3)$

2. $z = 3(x - 1)^2 + 2(y + 3)^2 + 7, \quad (2, -2, 12)$

3. $z = \sqrt{xy}, \quad (1, 1, 1)$

4. $z = xe^{xy}, \quad (2, 0, 2)$

5. $z = y\cos(x - y), \quad (2, 2, 2)$

6. $z = \ln(x - 2y), \quad (3, 1, 0)$

7–8 Graph the surface and the tangent plane at the given point. (Choose the domain and viewpoint so that you get a good view of both the surface and the tangent plane.) Then zoom in until the surface and the tangent plane become indistinguishable.

7. $z = x^2 + xy + 3y^2, \quad (1, 1, 5)$

8. $z = \arctan(xy^2), \quad (1, 1, \pi/4)$

CAS **9–10** Draw the graph of f and its tangent plane at the given point. (Use your computer algebra system both to compute the partial derivatives and to graph the surface and its tangent plane.) Then zoom in until the surface and the tangent plane become indistinguishable.

9. $f(x, y) = \dfrac{xy\sin(x - y)}{1 + x^2 + y^2}, \quad (1, 1, 0)$

10. $f(x, y) = e^{-xy/10}\left(\sqrt{x} + \sqrt{y} + \sqrt{xy}\right), \quad (1, 1, 3e^{-0.1})$

11–14 Explain why the function is differentiable at the given point. Then find the linearization $L(x, y)$ of the function at that point.

11. $f(x, y) = x\sqrt{y}, \quad (1, 4)$

12. $f(x, y) = x^3y^4, \quad (1, 1)$

13. $f(x, y) = \dfrac{x}{x + y}, \quad (2, 1)$

14. $f(x, y) = \sqrt{x + e^{4y}}, \quad (3, 0)$

15–16 Verify the linear approximation at (0, 0).

15. $\dfrac{2x + 3}{4y + 1} \approx 3 + 2x - 12y$

16. $\sqrt{y + \cos^2 x} \approx 1 + \frac{1}{2}y$

17. Given that f is a differentiable function with $f(2, 5) = 6$, $f_x(2, 5) = 1$, and $f_y(2, 5) = -1$, use a linear approximation to estimate $f(2.2, 4.9)$.

18. Find the linear approximation of the function $f(x, y) = \ln(x - 3y)$ at (7, 2) and use it to approximate $f(6.9, 2.06)$. Illustrate by graphing f and the tangent plane.

19. Find the linear approximation of the function $f(x, y, z) = \sqrt{x^2 + y^2 + z^2}$ at (3, 2, 6) and use it to approximate the number $\sqrt{(3.02)^2 + (1.97)^2 + (5.99)^2}$.

20. The wave heights h in the open sea depend on the speed v of the wind and the length of time t that the wind has been blowing at that speed. Values of the function $h = f(v, t)$ are recorded in feet in the following table. Use the table to find a linear approximation to the wave height function when v is near 40 knots and t is near 20 hours. Then estimate the wave heights when the wind has been blowing for 24 hours at 43 knots.

		Duration (hours)						
	v \ t	5	10	15	20	30	40	50
Wind speed (knots)	20	5	7	8	8	9	9	9
	30	9	13	16	17	18	19	19
	40	14	21	25	28	31	33	33
	50	19	29	36	40	45	48	50
	60	24	37	47	54	62	67	69

21. Use the table in Example 3 to find a linear approximation to the heat index function when the temperature is near 94°F and the relative humidity is near 80%. Then estimate the heat index when the temperature is 95°F and the relative humidity is 78%.

22. The wind-chill index W is the perceived temperature when the actual temperature is T and the wind speed is v, so we can write $W = f(T, v)$. The following table of values is an excerpt from Table 1 in Section 11.1. Use the table to find a linear approximation to the wind-chill index function when T is near -15°C and v is near 50 km/h. Then estimate the wind-chill index when the temperature is -17°C and the wind speed is 55 km/h.

Wind speed (km/h)

Actual temperature (°C) T \ v	20	30	40	50	60	70
−10	−18	−20	−21	−22	−23	−23
−15	−24	−26	−27	−29	−30	−30
−20	−30	−33	−34	−35	−36	−37
−25	−37	−39	−41	−42	−43	−44

23–28 Find the differential of the function.

23. $z = x^3 \ln(y^2)$

24. $u = e^{-t}\sin(s + 2t)$

25. $m = p^5 q^3$

26. $T = \dfrac{v}{1 + uvw}$

27. $R = \alpha\beta^2 \cos\gamma$

28. $w = xye^{xz}$

29. If $z = 5x^2 + y^2$ and (x, y) changes from $(1, 2)$ to $(1.05, 2.1)$, compare the values of Δz and dz.

30. If $z = x^2 - xy + 3y^2$ and (x, y) changes from $(3, -1)$ to $(2.96, -0.95)$, compare the values of Δz and dz.

31. The length and width of a rectangle are measured as 30 cm and 24 cm, respectively, with an error in measurement of at most 0.1 cm in each. Use differentials to estimate the maximum error in the calculated area of the rectangle.

32. The dimensions of a closed rectangular box are measured as 80 cm, 60 cm, and 50 cm, respectively, with a possible error of 0.2 cm in each dimension. Use differentials to estimate the maximum error in calculating the surface area of the box.

33. Use differentials to estimate the amount of tin in a closed tin can with diameter 8 cm and height 12 cm if the tin is 0.04 cm thick.

34. The wind-chill index is modeled by the function

$$W = 13.12 + 0.6215T - 11.37v^{0.16} + 0.3965Tv^{0.16}$$

where T is the temperature (in °C) and v is the wind speed (in km/h). The wind speed is measured as 26 km/h, with a possible error of ± 2 km/h, and the temperature is measured as -11°C, with a possible error of ± 1°C. Use differentials to estimate the maximum error in the calculated value of W due to the measurement errors in T and v.

35. A model for the surface area of a human body is given by $S = 0.1091w^{0.425}h^{0.725}$, where w is the weight (in pounds), h is the height (in inches), and S is measured in square feet. If the errors in measurement of w and h are at most 2%, use differentials to estimate the maximum percentage error in the calculated surface area.

36. The pressure, volume, and temperature of a mole of an ideal gas are related by the equation $PV = 8.31T$, where P is measured in kilopascals, V in liters, and T in kelvins. Use differentials to find the approximate change in the pressure if the volume increases from 12 L to 12.3 L and the temperature decreases from 310 K to 305 K.

37. If R is the total resistance of three resistors, connected in parallel, with resistances R_1, R_2, R_3, then

$$\frac{1}{R} = \frac{1}{R_1} + \frac{1}{R_2} + \frac{1}{R_3}$$

If the resistances are measured in ohms as $R_1 = 25\ \Omega$, $R_2 = 40\ \Omega$, and $R_3 = 50\ \Omega$, with a possible error of 0.5% in each case, estimate the maximum error in the calculated value of R.

38. Four positive numbers, each less than 50, are rounded to the first decimal place and then multiplied together. Use differentials to estimate the maximum possible error in the computed product that might result from the rounding.

39–43 Find an equation of the tangent plane to the parametric surface at the given point. If you have software that graphs parametric surfaces, use a computer to graph the surface and the tangent plane.

39. $x = u + v, \quad y = 3u^2, \quad z = u - v; \qquad (2, 3, 0)$

40. $x = u^2, \quad y = v^2, \quad z = uv; \quad u = 1, v = 1$

41. $\mathbf{r}(u, v) = u^2\,\mathbf{i} + 2u \sin v\,\mathbf{j} + u \cos v\,\mathbf{k}; \quad u = 1, v = 0$

42. $\mathbf{r}(u, v) = uv\,\mathbf{i} + u \sin v\,\mathbf{j} + v \cos u\,\mathbf{k}; \quad u = 0, v = \pi$

43. $\mathbf{r}(u, v) = u\,\mathbf{i} + \ln(uv)\,\mathbf{j} + v\,\mathbf{k}; \quad u = 1, v = 1$

44. Suppose you need to know an equation of the tangent plane to a surface S at the point $P(2, 1, 3)$. You don't have an equation for S but you know that the curves

$$\mathbf{r}_1(t) = \langle 2 + 3t, 1 - t^2, 3 - 4t + t^2 \rangle$$

$$\mathbf{r}_2(u) = \langle 1 + u^2, 2u^3 - 1, 2u + 1 \rangle$$

both lie on S. Find an equation of the tangent plane at P.

45–46 Show that the function is differentiable by finding values of ε_1 and ε_2 that satisfy Definition 7.

45. $f(x, y) = x^2 + y^2$

46. $f(x, y) = xy - 5y^2$

47. Prove that if f is a function of two variables that is differentiable at (a, b), then f is continuous at (a, b).
Hint: Show that

$$\lim_{(\Delta x, \Delta y) \to (0, 0)} f(a + \Delta x, b + \Delta y) = f(a, b)$$

48. (a) The function

$$f(x, y) = \begin{cases} \dfrac{xy}{x^2 + y^2} & \text{if } (x, y) \neq (0, 0) \\ 0 & \text{if } (x, y) = (0, 0) \end{cases}$$

was graphed in Figure 4. Show that $f_x(0, 0)$ and $f_y(0, 0)$ both exist but f is not differentiable at $(0, 0)$. [*Hint:* Use the result of Exercise 47.]

(b) Explain why f_x and f_y are not continuous at $(0, 0)$.

11.5 The Chain Rule

Recall that the Chain Rule for functions of a single variable gives the rule for differentiating a composite function: If $y = f(x)$ and $x = g(t)$, where f and g are differentiable functions, then y is indirectly a differentiable function of t and

1
$$\frac{dy}{dt} = \frac{dy}{dx}\frac{dx}{dt}$$

For functions of more than one variable, the Chain Rule has several versions, each of them giving a rule for differentiating a composite function. The first version (Theorem 2) deals with the case where $z = f(x, y)$ and each of the variables x and y is, in turn, a function of a variable t. This means that z is indirectly a function of t, $z = f(g(t), h(t))$, and the Chain Rule gives a formula for differentiating z as a function of t. We assume that f is differentiable (Definition 11.4.7). Recall that this is the case when f_x and f_y are continuous (Theorem 11.4.8).

2 **The Chain Rule (Case 1)** Suppose that $z = f(x, y)$ is a differentiable function of x and y, where $x = g(t)$ and $y = h(t)$ are both differentiable functions of t. Then z is a differentiable function of t and

$$\frac{dz}{dt} = \frac{\partial f}{\partial x}\frac{dx}{dt} + \frac{\partial f}{\partial y}\frac{dy}{dt}$$

PROOF A change of Δt in t produces changes of Δx in x and Δy in y. These, in turn, produce a change of Δz in z, and from Definition 11.4.7 we have

$$\Delta z = \frac{\partial f}{\partial x}\Delta x + \frac{\partial f}{\partial y}\Delta y + \varepsilon_1 \Delta x + \varepsilon_2 \Delta y$$

where $\varepsilon_1 \to 0$ and $\varepsilon_2 \to 0$ as $(\Delta x, \Delta y) \to (0, 0)$. [If the functions ε_1 and ε_2 are not defined at $(0, 0)$, we can define them to be 0 there.] Dividing both sides of this equation by Δt, we have

$$\frac{\Delta z}{\Delta t} = \frac{\partial f}{\partial x}\frac{\Delta x}{\Delta t} + \frac{\partial f}{\partial y}\frac{\Delta y}{\Delta t} + \varepsilon_1 \frac{\Delta x}{\Delta t} + \varepsilon_2 \frac{\Delta y}{\Delta t}$$

If we now let $\Delta t \to 0$, then $\Delta x = g(t + \Delta t) - g(t) \to 0$ because g is differentiable and therefore continuous. Similarly, $\Delta y \to 0$. This, in turn, means that $\varepsilon_1 \to 0$ and $\varepsilon_2 \to 0$, so

$$\begin{aligned}\frac{dz}{dt} &= \lim_{\Delta t \to 0} \frac{\Delta z}{\Delta t} \\ &= \frac{\partial f}{\partial x} \lim_{\Delta t \to 0} \frac{\Delta x}{\Delta t} + \frac{\partial f}{\partial y} \lim_{\Delta t \to 0} \frac{\Delta y}{\Delta t} + \left(\lim_{\Delta t \to 0} \varepsilon_1\right) \lim_{\Delta t \to 0} \frac{\Delta x}{\Delta t} + \left(\lim_{\Delta t \to 0} \varepsilon_2\right) \lim_{\Delta t \to 0} \frac{\Delta y}{\Delta t} \\ &= \frac{\partial f}{\partial x}\frac{dx}{dt} + \frac{\partial f}{\partial y}\frac{dy}{dt} + 0 \cdot \frac{dx}{dt} + 0 \cdot \frac{dy}{dt} \\ &= \frac{\partial f}{\partial x}\frac{dx}{dt} + \frac{\partial f}{\partial y}\frac{dy}{dt}\end{aligned}$$

□

Since we often write $\partial z/\partial x$ in place of $\partial f/\partial x$, we can rewrite the Chain Rule in the form

Notice the similarity to the definition of the differential:

$$dz = \frac{\partial z}{\partial x}dx + \frac{\partial z}{\partial y}dy$$

$$\boxed{\frac{dz}{dt} = \frac{\partial z}{\partial x}\frac{dx}{dt} + \frac{\partial z}{\partial y}\frac{dy}{dt}}$$

EXAMPLE 1 **Using the Chain Rule** If $z = x^2y + 3xy^4$, where $x = \sin 2t$ and $y = \cos t$, find dz/dt when $t = 0$.

SOLUTION The Chain Rule gives

$$\begin{aligned}\frac{dz}{dt} &= \frac{\partial z}{\partial x}\frac{dx}{dt} + \frac{\partial z}{\partial y}\frac{dy}{dt} \\ &= (2xy + 3y^4)(2\cos 2t) + (x^2 + 12xy^3)(-\sin t)\end{aligned}$$

It's not necessary to substitute the expressions for x and y in terms of t. We simply observe that when $t = 0$, we have $x = \sin 0 = 0$ and $y = \cos 0 = 1$. Therefore

$$\left.\frac{dz}{dt}\right|_{t=0} = (0 + 3)(2\cos 0) + (0 + 0)(-\sin 0) = 6$$

■

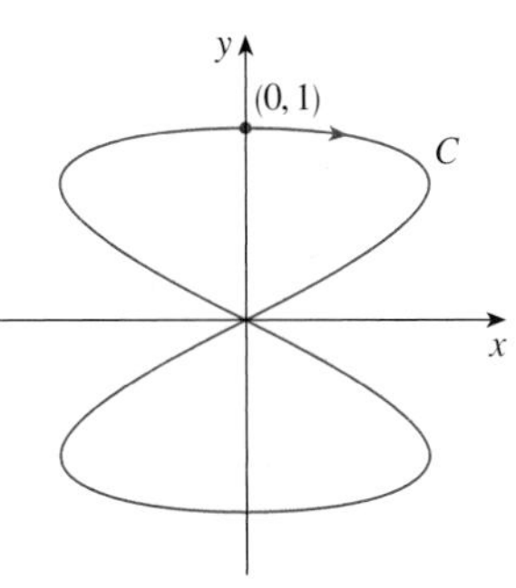

FIGURE 1
The curve $x = \sin 2t$, $y = \cos t$

The derivative in Example 1 can be interpreted as the rate of change of z with respect to t as the point (x, y) moves along the curve C with parametric equations $x = \sin 2t$, $y = \cos t$. (See Figure 1.) In particular, when $t = 0$, the point (x, y) is $(0, 1)$ and $dz/dt = 6$ is the rate of increase as we move along the curve C through $(0, 1)$. If, for instance, $z = T(x, y) = x^2y + 3xy^4$ represents the temperature at the point (x, y), then the composite function $z = T(\sin 2t, \cos t)$ represents the temperature at points on C and the derivative dz/dt represents the rate at which the temperature changes along C.

V **EXAMPLE 2** **The Chain Rule applied to chemistry** The pressure P (in kilopascals), volume V (in liters), and temperature T (in kelvins) of a mole of an ideal gas are related by the equation $PV = 8.31T$. Find the rate at which the pressure is changing when the temperature is 300 K and increasing at a rate of 0.1 K/s and the volume is 100 L and increasing at a rate of 0.2 L/s.

SOLUTION If t represents the time elapsed in seconds, then at the given instant we have $T = 300$, $dT/dt = 0.1$, $V = 100$, $dV/dt = 0.2$. Since

$$P = 8.31\frac{T}{V}$$

the Chain Rule gives

$$\frac{dP}{dt} = \frac{\partial P}{\partial T}\frac{dT}{dt} + \frac{\partial P}{\partial V}\frac{dV}{dt} = \frac{8.31}{V}\frac{dT}{dt} - \frac{8.31T}{V^2}\frac{dV}{dt}$$

$$= \frac{8.31}{100}(0.1) - \frac{8.31(300)}{100^2}(0.2) = -0.04155$$

The pressure is decreasing at a rate of about 0.042 kPa/s.

We now consider the situation where $z = f(x, y)$ but each of x and y is a function of two variables s and t: $x = g(s, t)$, $y = h(s, t)$. Then z is indirectly a function of s and t and we wish to find $\partial z/\partial s$ and $\partial z/\partial t$. Recall that in computing $\partial z/\partial t$ we hold s fixed and compute the ordinary derivative of z with respect to t. Therefore we can apply Theorem 2 to obtain

$$\frac{\partial z}{\partial t} = \frac{\partial z}{\partial x}\frac{\partial x}{\partial t} + \frac{\partial z}{\partial y}\frac{\partial y}{\partial t}$$

A similar argument holds for $\partial z/\partial s$ and so we have proved the following version of the Chain Rule.

3 The Chain Rule (Case 2) Suppose that $z = f(x, y)$ is a differentiable function of x and y, where $x = g(s, t)$ and $y = h(s, t)$ are differentiable functions of s and t. Then

$$\frac{\partial z}{\partial s} = \frac{\partial z}{\partial x}\frac{\partial x}{\partial s} + \frac{\partial z}{\partial y}\frac{\partial y}{\partial s} \qquad \frac{\partial z}{\partial t} = \frac{\partial z}{\partial x}\frac{\partial x}{\partial t} + \frac{\partial z}{\partial y}\frac{\partial y}{\partial t}$$

EXAMPLE 3 The Chain Rule with two independent variables If $z = e^x \sin y$, where $x = st^2$ and $y = s^2t$, find $\partial z/\partial s$ and $\partial z/\partial t$.

SOLUTION Applying Case 2 of the Chain Rule, we get

$$\frac{\partial z}{\partial s} = \frac{\partial z}{\partial x}\frac{\partial x}{\partial s} + \frac{\partial z}{\partial y}\frac{\partial y}{\partial s} = (e^x \sin y)(t^2) + (e^x \cos y)(2st)$$

$$= t^2 e^{st^2} \sin(s^2t) + 2ste^{st^2} \cos(s^2t)$$

$$\frac{\partial z}{\partial t} = \frac{\partial z}{\partial x}\frac{\partial x}{\partial t} + \frac{\partial z}{\partial y}\frac{\partial y}{\partial t} = (e^x \sin y)(2st) + (e^x \cos y)(s^2)$$

$$= 2ste^{st^2} \sin(s^2t) + s^2e^{st^2} \cos(s^2t)$$

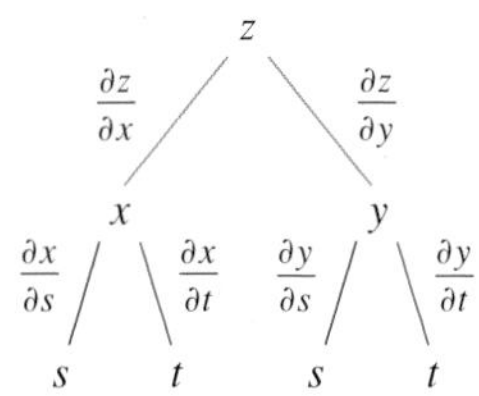

FIGURE 2

Case 2 of the Chain Rule contains three types of variables: s and t are **independent** variables, x and y are called **intermediate** variables, and z is the **dependent** variable. Notice that Theorem 3 has one term for each intermediate variable and each of these terms resembles the one-dimensional Chain Rule in Equation 1.

To remember the Chain Rule, it's helpful to draw the **tree diagram** in Figure 2. We draw branches from the dependent variable z to the intermediate variables x and y to indicate that z is a function of x and y. Then we draw branches from x and y to the independent variables s and t. On each branch we write the corresponding partial derivative. To find

$\partial z/\partial s$, we find the product of the partial derivatives along each path from z to s and then add these products:

$$\frac{\partial z}{\partial s} = \frac{\partial z}{\partial x}\frac{\partial x}{\partial s} + \frac{\partial z}{\partial y}\frac{\partial y}{\partial s}$$

Similarly, we find $\partial z/\partial t$ by using the paths from z to t.

Now we consider the general situation in which a dependent variable u is a function of n intermediate variables $x_1, \dots, x_n$, each of which is, in turn, a function of m independent variables $t_1, \dots, t_m$. Notice that there are n terms, one for each intermediate variable. The proof is similar to that of Case 1.

4 The Chain Rule (General Version) Suppose that u is a differentiable function of the n variables $x_1, x_2, \dots, x_n$ and each x_j is a differentiable function of the m variables $t_1, t_2, \dots, t_m$. Then u is a function of $t_1, t_2, \dots, t_m$ and

$$\frac{\partial u}{\partial t_i} = \frac{\partial u}{\partial x_1}\frac{\partial x_1}{\partial t_i} + \frac{\partial u}{\partial x_2}\frac{\partial x_2}{\partial t_i} + \cdots + \frac{\partial u}{\partial x_n}\frac{\partial x_n}{\partial t_i}$$

for each $i = 1, 2, \dots, m$.

V EXAMPLE 4 The Chain Rule with two independent variables and four intermediate variables Write out the Chain Rule for the case where $w = f(x, y, z, t)$ and $x = x(u, v)$, $y = y(u, v)$, $z = z(u, v)$, and $t = t(u, v)$.

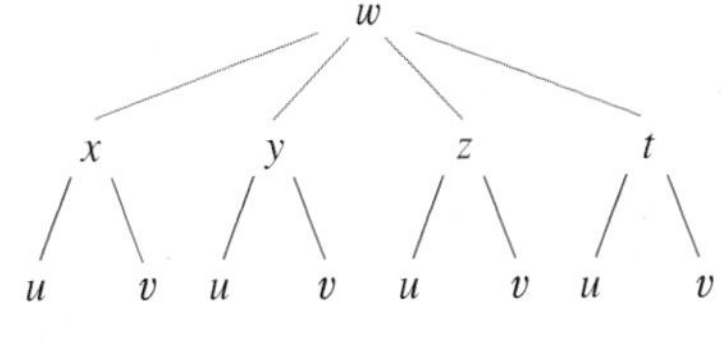

FIGURE 3

SOLUTION We apply Theorem 4 with $n = 4$ and $m = 2$. Figure 3 shows the tree diagram. Although we haven't written the derivatives on the branches, it's understood that if a branch leads from y to u, then the partial derivative for that branch is $\partial y/\partial u$. With the aid of the tree diagram, we can now write the required expressions:

$$\frac{\partial w}{\partial u} = \frac{\partial w}{\partial x}\frac{\partial x}{\partial u} + \frac{\partial w}{\partial y}\frac{\partial y}{\partial u} + \frac{\partial w}{\partial z}\frac{\partial z}{\partial u} + \frac{\partial w}{\partial t}\frac{\partial t}{\partial u}$$

$$\frac{\partial w}{\partial v} = \frac{\partial w}{\partial x}\frac{\partial x}{\partial v} + \frac{\partial w}{\partial y}\frac{\partial y}{\partial v} + \frac{\partial w}{\partial z}\frac{\partial z}{\partial v} + \frac{\partial w}{\partial t}\frac{\partial t}{\partial v}$$

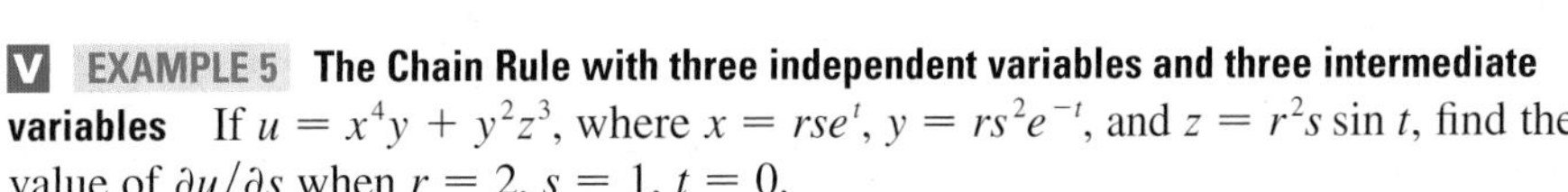

V EXAMPLE 5 The Chain Rule with three independent variables and three intermediate variables If $u = x^4y + y^2z^3$, where $x = rse^t$, $y = rs^2e^{-t}$, and $z = r^2s\sin t$, find the value of $\partial u/\partial s$ when $r = 2$, $s = 1$, $t = 0$.

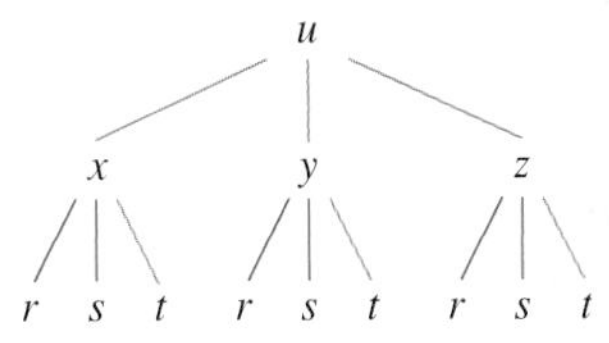

FIGURE 4

SOLUTION With the help of the tree diagram in Figure 4, we have

$$\frac{\partial u}{\partial s} = \frac{\partial u}{\partial x}\frac{\partial x}{\partial s} + \frac{\partial u}{\partial y}\frac{\partial y}{\partial s} + \frac{\partial u}{\partial z}\frac{\partial z}{\partial s}$$

$$= (4x^3y)(re^t) + (x^4 + 2yz^3)(2rse^{-t}) + (3y^2z^2)(r^2\sin t)$$

When $r = 2$, $s = 1$, and $t = 0$, we have $x = 2$, $y = 2$, and $z = 0$, so

$$\frac{\partial u}{\partial s} = (64)(2) + (16)(4) + (0)(0) = 192$$

EXAMPLE 6 If $g(s, t) = f(s^2 - t^2, t^2 - s^2)$ and f is differentiable, show that g satisfies the equation

$$t\frac{\partial g}{\partial s} + s\frac{\partial g}{\partial t} = 0$$

SOLUTION Let $x = s^2 - t^2$ and $y = t^2 - s^2$. Then $g(s, t) = f(x, y)$ and the Chain Rule gives

$$\frac{\partial g}{\partial s} = \frac{\partial f}{\partial x}\frac{\partial x}{\partial s} + \frac{\partial f}{\partial y}\frac{\partial y}{\partial s} = \frac{\partial f}{\partial x}(2s) + \frac{\partial f}{\partial y}(-2s)$$

$$\frac{\partial g}{\partial t} = \frac{\partial f}{\partial x}\frac{\partial x}{\partial t} + \frac{\partial f}{\partial y}\frac{\partial y}{\partial t} = \frac{\partial f}{\partial x}(-2t) + \frac{\partial f}{\partial y}(2t)$$

Therefore

$$t\frac{\partial g}{\partial s} + s\frac{\partial g}{\partial t} = \left(2st\frac{\partial f}{\partial x} - 2st\frac{\partial f}{\partial y}\right) + \left(-2st\frac{\partial f}{\partial x} + 2st\frac{\partial f}{\partial y}\right) = 0$$

EXAMPLE 7 If $z = f(x, y)$ has continuous second-order partial derivatives and $x = r^2 + s^2$ and $y = 2rs$, find (a) $\partial z/\partial r$ and (b) $\partial^2 z/\partial r^2$.

SOLUTION

(a) The Chain Rule gives

$$\frac{\partial z}{\partial r} = \frac{\partial z}{\partial x}\frac{\partial x}{\partial r} + \frac{\partial z}{\partial y}\frac{\partial y}{\partial r} = \frac{\partial z}{\partial x}(2r) + \frac{\partial z}{\partial y}(2s)$$

(b) Applying the Product Rule to the expression in part (a), we get

5
$$\begin{aligned}\frac{\partial^2 z}{\partial r^2} &= \frac{\partial}{\partial r}\left(2r\frac{\partial z}{\partial x} + 2s\frac{\partial z}{\partial y}\right)\\ &= 2\frac{\partial z}{\partial x} + 2r\frac{\partial}{\partial r}\left(\frac{\partial z}{\partial x}\right) + 2s\frac{\partial}{\partial r}\left(\frac{\partial z}{\partial y}\right)\end{aligned}$$

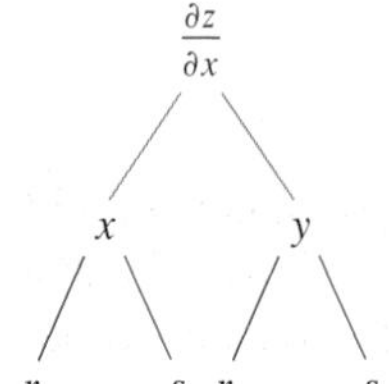

FIGURE 5

But, using the Chain Rule again (see Figure 5), we have

$$\frac{\partial}{\partial r}\left(\frac{\partial z}{\partial x}\right) = \frac{\partial}{\partial x}\left(\frac{\partial z}{\partial x}\right)\frac{\partial x}{\partial r} + \frac{\partial}{\partial y}\left(\frac{\partial z}{\partial x}\right)\frac{\partial y}{\partial r} = \frac{\partial^2 z}{\partial x^2}(2r) + \frac{\partial^2 z}{\partial y\,\partial x}(2s)$$

$$\frac{\partial}{\partial r}\left(\frac{\partial z}{\partial y}\right) = \frac{\partial}{\partial x}\left(\frac{\partial z}{\partial y}\right)\frac{\partial x}{\partial r} + \frac{\partial}{\partial y}\left(\frac{\partial z}{\partial y}\right)\frac{\partial y}{\partial r} = \frac{\partial^2 z}{\partial x\,\partial y}(2r) + \frac{\partial^2 z}{\partial y^2}(2s)$$

Putting these expressions into Equation 5 and using the equality of the mixed second-order derivatives, we obtain

$$\begin{aligned}\frac{\partial^2 z}{\partial r^2} &= 2\frac{\partial z}{\partial x} + 2r\left(2r\frac{\partial^2 z}{\partial x^2} + 2s\frac{\partial^2 z}{\partial y\,\partial x}\right) + 2s\left(2r\frac{\partial^2 z}{\partial x\,\partial y} + 2s\frac{\partial^2 z}{\partial y^2}\right)\\ &= 2\frac{\partial z}{\partial x} + 4r^2\frac{\partial^2 z}{\partial x^2} + 8rs\frac{\partial^2 z}{\partial x\,\partial y} + 4s^2\frac{\partial^2 z}{\partial y^2}\end{aligned}$$

Implicit Differentiation

The Chain Rule can be used to give a more complete description of the process of implicit differentiation that was introduced in Sections 3.5 and 11.3. We suppose that an equation of the form $F(x, y) = 0$ defines y implicitly as a differentiable function of x, that is,

$y = f(x)$, where $F(x, f(x)) = 0$ for all x in the domain of f. If F is differentiable, we can apply Case 1 of the Chain Rule to differentiate both sides of the equation $F(x, y) = 0$ with respect to x. Since both x and y are functions of x, we obtain

$$\frac{\partial F}{\partial x}\frac{dx}{dx} + \frac{\partial F}{\partial y}\frac{dy}{dx} = 0$$

But $dx/dx = 1$, so if $\partial F/\partial y \neq 0$ we solve for dy/dx and obtain

6 $$\frac{dy}{dx} = -\frac{\dfrac{\partial F}{\partial x}}{\dfrac{\partial F}{\partial y}} = -\frac{F_x}{F_y}$$

To derive this equation we assumed that $F(x, y) = 0$ defines y implicitly as a function of x. The **Implicit Function Theorem**, proved in advanced calculus, gives conditions under which this assumption is valid: It states that if F is defined on a disk containing (a, b), where $F(a, b) = 0$, $F_y(a, b) \neq 0$, and F_x and F_y are continuous on the disk, then the equation $F(x, y) = 0$ defines y as a function of x near the point (a, b) and the derivative of this function is given by Equation 6.

EXAMPLE 8 Implicit differentiation Find y' if $x^3 + y^3 = 6xy$.

SOLUTION The given equation can be written as

$$F(x, y) = x^3 + y^3 - 6xy = 0$$

so Equation 6 gives

$$\frac{dy}{dx} = -\frac{F_x}{F_y} = -\frac{3x^2 - 6y}{3y^2 - 6x} = -\frac{x^2 - 2y}{y^2 - 2x}$$

The solution to Example 8 should be compared to the one in Example 2 in Section 3.5.

Now we suppose that z is given implicitly as a function $z = f(x, y)$ by an equation of the form $F(x, y, z) = 0$. This means that $F(x, y, f(x, y)) = 0$ for all (x, y) in the domain of f. If F and f are differentiable, then we can use the Chain Rule to differentiate the equation $F(x, y, z) = 0$ as follows:

$$\frac{\partial F}{\partial x}\frac{\partial x}{\partial x} + \frac{\partial F}{\partial y}\frac{\partial y}{\partial x} + \frac{\partial F}{\partial z}\frac{\partial z}{\partial x} = 0$$

But $$\frac{\partial}{\partial x}(x) = 1 \quad \text{and} \quad \frac{\partial}{\partial x}(y) = 0$$

so this equation becomes

$$\frac{\partial F}{\partial x} + \frac{\partial F}{\partial z}\frac{\partial z}{\partial x} = 0$$

If $\partial F/\partial z \neq 0$, we solve for $\partial z/\partial x$ and obtain the first formula in Equations 7. The formula for $\partial z/\partial y$ is obtained in a similar manner.

7
$$\frac{\partial z}{\partial x} = -\frac{\dfrac{\partial F}{\partial x}}{\dfrac{\partial F}{\partial z}} \qquad \frac{\partial z}{\partial y} = -\frac{\dfrac{\partial F}{\partial y}}{\dfrac{\partial F}{\partial z}}$$

Again, a version of the **Implicit Function Theorem** gives conditions under which our assumption is valid: If F is defined within a sphere containing (a, b, c), where $F(a, b, c) = 0$, $F_z(a, b, c) \neq 0$, and F_x, F_y, and F_z are continuous inside the sphere, then the equation $F(x, y, z) = 0$ defines z as a function of x and y near the point (a, b, c) and this function is differentiable, with partial derivatives given by (7).

EXAMPLE 9 Find $\dfrac{\partial z}{\partial x}$ and $\dfrac{\partial z}{\partial y}$ if $x^3 + y^3 + z^3 + 6xyz = 1$.

The solution to Example 9 should be compared to the one in Example 4 in Section 11.3.

SOLUTION Let $F(x, y, z) = x^3 + y^3 + z^3 + 6xyz - 1$. Then, from Equations 7, we have

$$\frac{\partial z}{\partial x} = -\frac{F_x}{F_z} = -\frac{3x^2 + 6yz}{3z^2 + 6xy} = -\frac{x^2 + 2yz}{z^2 + 2xy}$$

$$\frac{\partial z}{\partial y} = -\frac{F_y}{F_z} = -\frac{3y^2 + 6xz}{3z^2 + 6xy} = -\frac{y^2 + 2xz}{z^2 + 2xy}$$

11.5 Exercises

1–6 Use the Chain Rule to find dz/dt or dw/dt.

1. $z = x^2 + y^2 + xy$, $x = \sin t$, $y = e^t$

2. $z = \cos(x + 4y)$, $x = 5t^4$, $y = 1/t$

3. $z = \sqrt{1 + x^2 + y^2}$, $x = \ln t$, $y = \cos t$

4. $z = \tan^{-1}(y/x)$, $x = e^t$, $y = 1 - e^{-t}$

5. $w = xe^{y/z}$, $x = t^2$, $y = 1 - t$, $z = 1 + 2t$

6. $w = \ln\sqrt{x^2 + y^2 + z^2}$, $x = \sin t$, $y = \cos t$, $z = \tan t$

7–12 Use the Chain Rule to find $\partial z/\partial s$ and $\partial z/\partial t$.

7. $z = x^2y^3$, $x = s\cos t$, $y = s\sin t$

8. $z = \arcsin(x - y)$, $x = s^2 + t^2$, $y = 1 - 2st$

9. $z = \sin\theta\cos\phi$, $\theta = st^2$, $\phi = s^2t$

10. $z = e^{x+2y}$, $x = s/t$, $y = t/s$

11. $z = e^r\cos\theta$, $r = st$, $\theta = \sqrt{s^2 + t^2}$

12. $z = \tan(u/v)$, $u = 2s + 3t$, $v = 3s - 2t$

13. If $z = f(x, y)$, where f is differentiable, and

$$\begin{array}{ll} x = g(t) & y = h(t) \\ g(3) = 2 & h(3) = 7 \\ g'(3) = 5 & h'(3) = -4 \\ f_x(2, 7) = 6 & f_y(2, 7) = -8 \end{array}$$

find dz/dt when $t = 3$.

14. Let $W(s, t) = F(u(s, t), v(s, t))$, where F, u, and v are differentiable, and

$$\begin{array}{ll} u(1, 0) = 2 & v(1, 0) = 3 \\ u_s(1, 0) = -2 & v_s(1, 0) = 5 \\ u_t(1, 0) = 6 & v_t(1, 0) = 4 \\ F_u(2, 3) = -1 & F_v(2, 3) = 10 \end{array}$$

Find $W_s(1, 0)$ and $W_t(1, 0)$.

1. Homework Hints available in TEC

15. Suppose f is a differentiable function of x and y, and $g(u, v) = f(e^u + \sin v, e^u + \cos v)$. Use the table of values to calculate $g_u(0, 0)$ and $g_v(0, 0)$.

	f	g	f_x	f_y
(0, 0)	3	6	4	8
(1, 2)	6	3	2	5

16. Suppose f is a differentiable function of x and y, and $g(r, s) = f(2r - s, s^2 - 4r)$. Use the table of values in Exercise 15 to calculate $g_r(1, 2)$ and $g_s(1, 2)$.

17–20 Use a tree diagram to write out the Chain Rule for the given case. Assume all functions are differentiable.

17. $u = f(x, y)$, where $x = x(r, s, t)$, $y = y(r, s, t)$

18. $R = f(x, y, z, t)$, where $x = x(u, v, w)$, $y = y(u, v, w)$, $z = z(u, v, w)$, $t = t(u, v, w)$

19. $w = f(r, s, t)$, where $r = r(x, y)$, $s = s(x, y)$, $t = t(x, y)$

20. $t = f(u, v, w)$, where $u = u(p, q, r, s)$, $v = v(p, q, r, s)$, $w = w(p, q, r, s)$

21–25 Use the Chain Rule to find the indicated partial derivatives.

21. $z = x^2 + xy^3$, $x = uv^2 + w^3$, $y = u + ve^w$;
$\dfrac{\partial z}{\partial u}, \dfrac{\partial z}{\partial v}, \dfrac{\partial z}{\partial w}$ when $u = 2$, $v = 1$, $w = 0$

22. $u = \sqrt{r^2 + s^2}$, $r = y + x\cos t$, $s = x + y\sin t$;
$\dfrac{\partial u}{\partial x}, \dfrac{\partial u}{\partial y}, \dfrac{\partial u}{\partial t}$ when $x = 1$, $y = 2$, $t = 0$

23. $R = \ln(u^2 + v^2 + w^2)$,
$u = x + 2y$, $v = 2x - y$, $w = 2xy$;
$\dfrac{\partial R}{\partial x}, \dfrac{\partial R}{\partial y}$ when $x = y = 1$

24. $M = xe^{y - z^2}$, $x = 2uv$, $y = u - v$, $z = u + v$;
$\dfrac{\partial M}{\partial u}, \dfrac{\partial M}{\partial v}$ when $u = 3$, $v = -1$

25. $u = x^2 + yz$, $x = pr\cos\theta$, $y = pr\sin\theta$, $z = p + r$;
$\dfrac{\partial u}{\partial p}, \dfrac{\partial u}{\partial r}, \dfrac{\partial u}{\partial \theta}$ when $p = 2$, $r = 3$, $\theta = 0$

26–28 Use Equation 6 to find dy/dx.

26. $y^5 + x^2y^3 = 1 + ye^{x^2}$

27. $\cos(x - y) = xe^y$

28. $\sin x + \cos y = \sin x \cos y$

29–32 Use Equations 7 to find $\partial z/\partial x$ and $\partial z/\partial y$.

29. $x^2 + y^2 + z^2 = 3xyz$

30. $xyz = \cos(x + y + z)$

31. $x - z = \arctan(yz)$

32. $yz = \ln(x + z)$

33. The temperature at a point (x, y) is $T(x, y)$, measured in degrees Celsius. A bug crawls so that its position after t seconds is given by $x = \sqrt{1 + t}$, $y = 2 + \frac{1}{3}t$, where x and y are measured in centimeters. The temperature function satisfies $T_x(2, 3) = 4$ and $T_y(2, 3) = 3$. How fast is the temperature rising on the bug's path after 3 seconds?

34. Wheat production W in a given year depends on the average temperature T and the annual rainfall R. Scientists estimate that the average temperature is rising at a rate of 0.15°C/year and rainfall is decreasing at a rate of 0.1 cm/year. They also estimate that, at current production levels, $\partial W/\partial T = -2$ and $\partial W/\partial R = 8$.

(a) What is the significance of the signs of these partial derivatives?

(b) Estimate the current rate of change of wheat production, dW/dt.

35. The speed of sound traveling through ocean water with salinity 35 parts per thousand has been modeled by the equation

$$C = 1449.2 + 4.6T - 0.055T^2 + 0.00029T^3 + 0.016D$$

where C is the speed of sound (in meters per second), T is the temperature (in degrees Celsius), and D is the depth below the ocean surface (in meters). A scuba diver began a leisurely dive into the ocean water; the diver's depth and the surrounding water temperature over time are recorded in the following graphs. Estimate the rate of change (with respect to time) of the speed of sound through the ocean water experienced by the diver 20 minutes into the dive. What are the units?

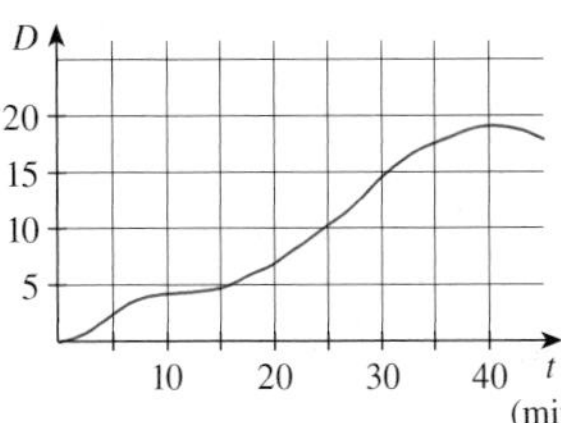

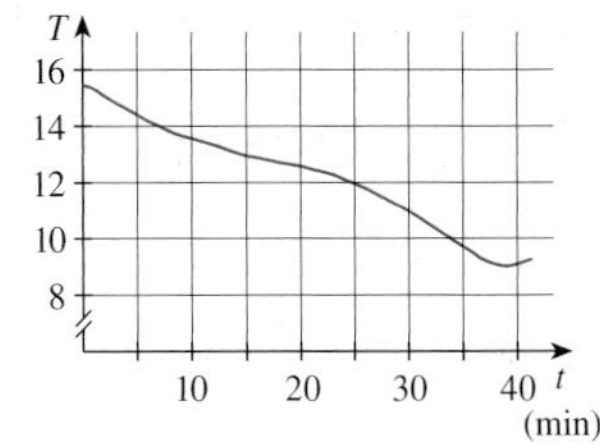

36. The radius of a right circular cone is increasing at a rate of 1.8 in/s while its height is decreasing at a rate of 2.5 in/s. At what rate is the volume of the cone changing when the radius is 120 in. and the height is 140 in.?

37. The length ℓ, width w, and height h of a box change with time. At a certain instant the dimensions are $\ell = 1$ m and $w = h = 2$ m, and ℓ and w are increasing at a rate of 2 m/s while h is decreasing at a rate of 3 m/s. At that instant find the rates at which the following quantities are changing.

(a) The volume

(b) The surface area

(c) The length of a diagonal

38. The voltage V in a simple electrical circuit is slowly decreasing as the battery wears out. The resistance R is slowly increasing as the resistor heats up. Use Ohm's Law, $V = IR$, to find how the current I is changing at the moment when $R = 400\ \Omega$, $I = 0.08$ A, $dV/dt = -0.01$ V/s, and $dR/dt = 0.03\ \Omega$/s.

39. The pressure of 1 mole of an ideal gas is increasing at a rate of 0.05 kPa/s and the temperature is increasing at a rate of 0.15 K/s. Use the equation in Example 2 to find the rate of change of the volume when the pressure is 20 kPa and the temperature is 320 K.

40. A manufacturer has modeled its yearly production function P (the value of its entire production in millions of dollars) as a Cobb-Douglas function

$$P(L, K) = 1.47L^{0.65}K^{0.35}$$

where L is the number of labor hours (in thousands) and K is the invested capital (in millions of dollars). Suppose that when $L = 30$ and $K = 8$, the labor force is decreasing at a rate of 2000 labor hours per year and capital is increasing at a rate of \$500,000 per year. Find the rate of change of production.

41. One side of a triangle is increasing at a rate of 3 cm/s and a second side is decreasing at a rate of 2 cm/s. If the area of the triangle remains constant, at what rate does the angle between the sides change when the first side is 20 cm long, the second side is 30 cm, and the angle is $\pi/6$?

42. If a sound with frequency f_s is produced by a source traveling along a line with speed v_s and an observer is traveling with speed v_o along the same line from the opposite direction toward the source, then the frequency of the sound heard by the observer is

$$f_o = \left(\frac{c + v_o}{c - v_s}\right) f_s$$

where c is the speed of sound, about 332 m/s. (This is the **Doppler effect**.) Suppose that, at a particular moment, you are in a train traveling at 34 m/s and accelerating at 1.2 m/s^2. A train is approaching you from the opposite direction on the other track at 40 m/s, accelerating at 1.4 m/s^2, and sounds its whistle, which has a frequency of 460 Hz. At that instant, what is the perceived frequency that you hear and how fast is it changing?

43–46 Assume that all the given functions are differentiable.

43. If $z = f(x, y)$, where $x = r\cos\theta$ and $y = r\sin\theta$, (a) find $\partial z/\partial r$ and $\partial z/\partial\theta$ and (b) show that

$$\left(\frac{\partial z}{\partial x}\right)^2 + \left(\frac{\partial z}{\partial y}\right)^2 = \left(\frac{\partial z}{\partial r}\right)^2 + \frac{1}{r^2}\left(\frac{\partial z}{\partial \theta}\right)^2$$

44. If $u = f(x, y)$, where $x = e^s\cos t$ and $y = e^s\sin t$, show that

$$\left(\frac{\partial u}{\partial x}\right)^2 + \left(\frac{\partial u}{\partial y}\right)^2 = e^{-2s}\left[\left(\frac{\partial u}{\partial s}\right)^2 + \left(\frac{\partial u}{\partial t}\right)^2\right]$$

45. If $z = f(x - y)$, show that $\dfrac{\partial z}{\partial x} + \dfrac{\partial z}{\partial y} = 0$.

46. If $z = f(x, y)$, where $x = s + t$ and $y = s - t$, show that

$$\left(\frac{\partial z}{\partial x}\right)^2 - \left(\frac{\partial z}{\partial y}\right)^2 = \frac{\partial z}{\partial s}\frac{\partial z}{\partial t}$$

47–52 Assume that all the given functions have continuous second-order partial derivatives.

47. Show that any function of the form

$$z = f(x + at) + g(x - at)$$

is a solution of the wave equation

$$\frac{\partial^2 z}{\partial t^2} = a^2\frac{\partial^2 z}{\partial x^2}$$

[*Hint:* Let $u = x + at$, $v = x - at$.]

48. If $u = f(x, y)$, where $x = e^s\cos t$ and $y = e^s\sin t$, show that

$$\frac{\partial^2 u}{\partial x^2} + \frac{\partial^2 u}{\partial y^2} = e^{-2s}\left[\frac{\partial^2 u}{\partial s^2} + \frac{\partial^2 u}{\partial t^2}\right]$$

49. If $z = f(x, y)$, where $x = r^2 + s^2$ and $y = 2rs$, find $\partial^2 z/\partial r\,\partial s$. (Compare with Example 7.)

50. If $z = f(x, y)$, where $x = r\cos\theta$ and $y = r\sin\theta$, find (a) $\partial z/\partial r$, (b) $\partial z/\partial\theta$, and (c) $\partial^2 z/\partial r\,\partial\theta$.

51. If $z = f(x, y)$, where $x = r\cos\theta$ and $y = r\sin\theta$, show that

$$\frac{\partial^2 z}{\partial x^2} + \frac{\partial^2 z}{\partial y^2} = \frac{\partial^2 z}{\partial r^2} + \frac{1}{r^2}\frac{\partial^2 z}{\partial\theta^2} + \frac{1}{r}\frac{\partial z}{\partial r}$$

52. Suppose $z = f(x, y)$, where $x = g(s, t)$ and $y = h(s, t)$.
(a) Show that

$$\frac{\partial^2 z}{\partial t^2} = \frac{\partial^2 z}{\partial x^2}\left(\frac{\partial x}{\partial t}\right)^2 + 2\frac{\partial^2 z}{\partial x\,\partial y}\frac{\partial x}{\partial t}\frac{\partial y}{\partial t} + \frac{\partial^2 z}{\partial y^2}\left(\frac{\partial y}{\partial t}\right)^2 + \frac{\partial z}{\partial x}\frac{\partial^2 x}{\partial t^2} + \frac{\partial z}{\partial y}\frac{\partial^2 y}{\partial t^2}$$

(b) Find a similar formula for $\partial^2 z/\partial s\,\partial t$.

53. Suppose that the equation $F(x, y, z) = 0$ implicitly defines each of the three variables x, y, and z as functions of the other two: $z = f(x, y)$, $y = g(x, z)$, $x = h(y, z)$. If F is differentiable and F_x, F_y, and F_z are all nonzero, show that

$$\frac{\partial z}{\partial x}\frac{\partial x}{\partial y}\frac{\partial y}{\partial z} = -1$$

54. Equation 6 is a formula for the derivative dy/dx of a function defined implicitly by an equation $F(x, y) = 0$, provided that F is differentiable and $F_y \neq 0$. Prove that if F has continuous second derivatives, then a formula for the second derivative of y is

$$\frac{d^2y}{dx^2} = -\frac{F_{xx}F_y^2 - 2F_{xy}F_xF_y + F_{yy}F_x^2}{F_y^3}$$

11.6 Directional Derivatives and the Gradient Vector

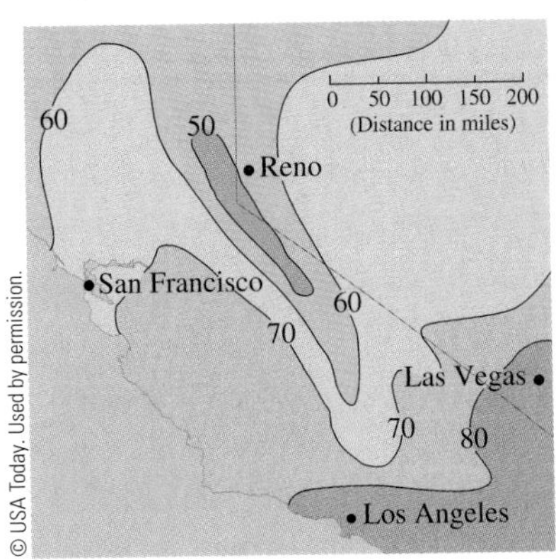

FIGURE 1

The weather map in Figure 1 shows a contour map of the temperature function $T(x, y)$ for the states of California and Nevada at 3:00 PM on a day in October. The level curves, or isothermals, join locations with the same temperature. The partial derivative T_x at a location such as Reno is the rate of change of temperature with respect to distance if we travel east from Reno; T_y is the rate of change of temperature if we travel north. But what if we want to know the rate of change of temperature when we travel southeast (toward Las Vegas), or in some other direction? In this section we introduce a type of derivative, called a *directional derivative,* that enables us to find the rate of change of a function of two or more variables in any direction.

Directional Derivatives

Recall that if $z = f(x, y)$, then the partial derivatives f_x and f_y are defined as

1
$$f_x(x_0, y_0) = \lim_{h \to 0} \frac{f(x_0 + h, y_0) - f(x_0, y_0)}{h}$$
$$f_y(x_0, y_0) = \lim_{h \to 0} \frac{f(x_0, y_0 + h) - f(x_0, y_0)}{h}$$

and represent the rates of change of z in the x- and y-directions, that is, in the directions of the unit vectors **i** and **j**.

Suppose that we now wish to find the rate of change of z at (x_0, y_0) in the direction of an arbitrary unit vector $\mathbf{u} = \langle a, b \rangle$. (See Figure 2.) To do this we consider the surface S with the equation $z = f(x, y)$ (the graph of f) and we let $z_0 = f(x_0, y_0)$. Then the point $P(x_0, y_0, z_0)$ lies on S. The vertical plane that passes through P in the direction of **u** intersects S in a curve C. (See Figure 3.) The slope of the tangent line T to C at the point P is the rate of change of z in the direction of **u**.

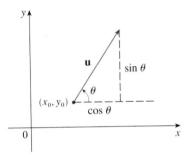

FIGURE 2
A unit vector $\mathbf{u} = \langle a, b \rangle = \langle \cos\theta, \sin\theta \rangle$

TEC Visual 11.6A animates Figure 3 by rotating **u** and therefore T.

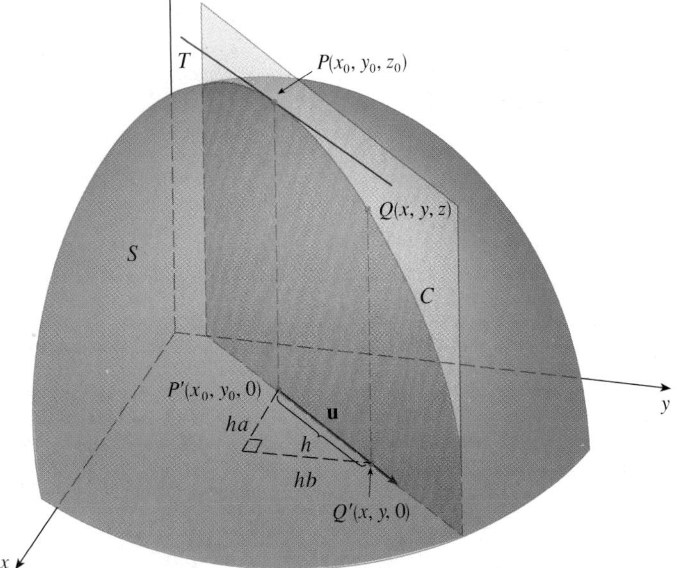

FIGURE 3

If $Q(x, y, z)$ is another point on C and P', Q' are the projections of P, Q onto the xy-plane, then the vector $\overrightarrow{P'Q'}$ is parallel to $\mathbf{u}$ and so

$$\overrightarrow{P'Q'} = h\mathbf{u} = \langle ha, hb \rangle$$

for some scalar h. Therefore $x - x_0 = ha$, $y - y_0 = hb$, so $x = x_0 + ha$, $y = y_0 + hb$, and

$$\frac{\Delta z}{h} = \frac{z - z_0}{h} = \frac{f(x_0 + ha, y_0 + hb) - f(x_0, y_0)}{h}$$

If we take the limit as $h \to 0$, we obtain the rate of change of z (with respect to distance) in the direction of $\mathbf{u}$, which is called the directional derivative of f in the direction of $\mathbf{u}$.

2 Definition The **directional derivative** of f at (x_0, y_0) in the direction of a unit vector $\mathbf{u} = \langle a, b \rangle$ is

$$D_{\mathbf{u}} f(x_0, y_0) = \lim_{h \to 0} \frac{f(x_0 + ha, y_0 + hb) - f(x_0, y_0)}{h}$$

if this limit exists.

By comparing Definition 2 with Equations (1), we see that if $\mathbf{u} = \mathbf{i} = \langle 1, 0 \rangle$, then $D_{\mathbf{i}} f = f_x$ and if $\mathbf{u} = \mathbf{j} = \langle 0, 1 \rangle$, then $D_{\mathbf{j}} f = f_y$. In other words, the partial derivatives of f with respect to x and y are just special cases of the directional derivative.

EXAMPLE 1 Estimating a directional derivative Use the weather map in Figure 1 to estimate the value of the directional derivative of the temperature function at Reno in the southeasterly direction.

SOLUTION The unit vector directed toward the southeast is $\mathbf{u} = (\mathbf{i} - \mathbf{j})/\sqrt{2}$, but we won't need to use this expression. We start by drawing a line through Reno toward the southeast (see Figure 4).

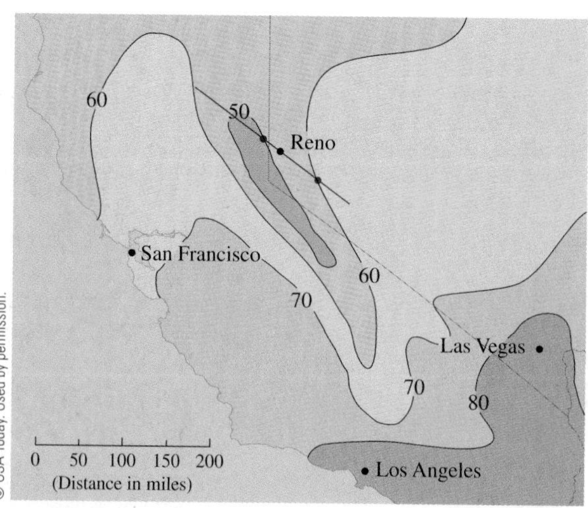

FIGURE 4

We approximate the directional derivative $D_{\mathbf{u}} T$ by the average rate of change of the temperature between the points where this line intersects the isothermals $T = 50$ and

$T = 60$. The temperature at the point southeast of Reno is $T = 60°\text{F}$ and the temperature at the point northwest of Reno is $T = 50°\text{F}$. The distance between these points looks to be about 75 miles. So the rate of change of the temperature in the southeasterly direction is

$$D_{\mathbf{u}}T \approx \frac{60 - 50}{75} = \frac{10}{75} \approx 0.13°\text{F/mi}$$

When we compute the directional derivative of a function defined by a formula, we generally use the following theorem.

3 Theorem If f is a differentiable function of x and y, then f has a directional derivative in the direction of any unit vector $\mathbf{u} = \langle a, b \rangle$ and

$$D_{\mathbf{u}} f(x, y) = f_x(x, y)\, a + f_y(x, y)\, b$$

PROOF If we define a function g of the single variable h by

$$g(h) = f(x_0 + ha, y_0 + hb)$$

then, by the definition of a derivative, we have

4
$$g'(0) = \lim_{h \to 0} \frac{g(h) - g(0)}{h} = \lim_{h \to 0} \frac{f(x_0 + ha, y_0 + hb) - f(x_0, y_0)}{h}$$
$$= D_{\mathbf{u}} f(x_0, y_0)$$

On the other hand, we can write $g(h) = f(x, y)$, where $x = x_0 + ha$, $y = y_0 + hb$, so the Chain Rule (Theorem 11.5.2) gives

$$g'(h) = \frac{\partial f}{\partial x}\frac{dx}{dh} + \frac{\partial f}{\partial y}\frac{dy}{dh} = f_x(x, y)\, a + f_y(x, y)\, b$$

If we now put $h = 0$, then $x = x_0$, $y = y_0$, and

5
$$g'(0) = f_x(x_0, y_0)\, a + f_y(x_0, y_0)\, b$$

Comparing Equations 4 and 5, we see that

$$D_{\mathbf{u}} f(x_0, y_0) = f_x(x_0, y_0)\, a + f_y(x_0, y_0)\, b$$

If the unit vector $\mathbf{u}$ makes an angle θ with the positive x-axis (as in Figure 2), then we can write $\mathbf{u} = \langle \cos\theta, \sin\theta \rangle$ and the formula in Theorem 3 becomes

6
$$D_{\mathbf{u}} f(x, y) = f_x(x, y) \cos\theta + f_y(x, y) \sin\theta$$

EXAMPLE 2 Find the directional derivative $D_{\mathbf{u}} f(x, y)$ if

$$f(x, y) = x^3 - 3xy + 4y^2$$

and $\mathbf{u}$ is the unit vector given by angle $\theta = \pi/6$. What is $D_{\mathbf{u}} f(1, 2)$?

The directional derivative $D_{\mathbf{u}} f(1, 2)$ in Example 2 represents the rate of change of z in the direction of $\mathbf{u}$. This is the slope of the tangent line to the curve of intersection of the surface $z = x^3 - 3xy + 4y^2$ and the vertical plane through $(1, 2, 0)$ in the direction of $\mathbf{u}$ shown in Figure 5.

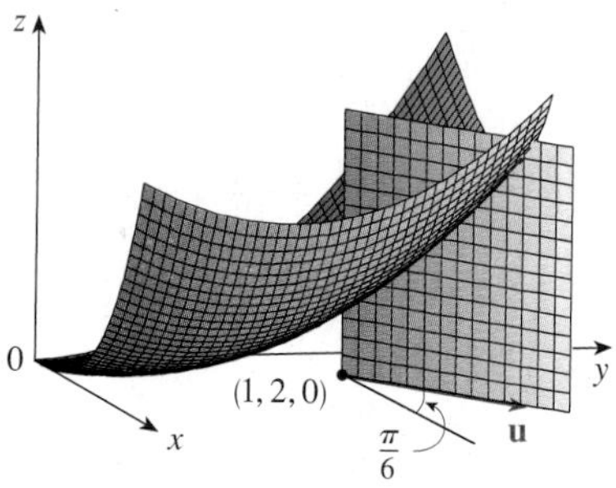

FIGURE 5

SOLUTION Formula 6 gives

$$\begin{aligned} D_{\mathbf{u}} f(x, y) &= f_x(x, y) \cos \frac{\pi}{6} + f_y(x, y) \sin \frac{\pi}{6} \\ &= (3x^2 - 3y) \frac{\sqrt{3}}{2} + (-3x + 8y) \tfrac{1}{2} \\ &= \tfrac{1}{2}\left[3\sqrt{3}\, x^2 - 3x + \left(8 - 3\sqrt{3}\right) y\right] \end{aligned}$$

Therefore

$$D_{\mathbf{u}} f(1, 2) = \tfrac{1}{2}\left[3\sqrt{3}(1)^2 - 3(1) + \left(8 - 3\sqrt{3}\right)(2)\right] = \frac{13 - 3\sqrt{3}}{2}$$

The Gradient Vector

Notice from Theorem 3 that the directional derivative of a differentiable function can be written as the dot product of two vectors:

7

$$\begin{aligned} D_{\mathbf{u}} f(x, y) &= f_x(x, y)\, a + f_y(x, y)\, b \\ &= \langle f_x(x, y), f_y(x, y) \rangle \cdot \langle a, b \rangle \\ &= \langle f_x(x, y), f_y(x, y) \rangle \cdot \mathbf{u} \end{aligned}$$

The first vector in this dot product occurs not only in computing directional derivatives but in many other contexts as well. So we give it a special name (the *gradient* of f) and a special notation (**grad** f or ∇f, which is read "del f").

8 Definition If f is a function of two variables x and y, then the **gradient** of f is the vector function ∇f defined by

$$\nabla f(x, y) = \langle f_x(x, y), f_y(x, y) \rangle = \frac{\partial f}{\partial x}\mathbf{i} + \frac{\partial f}{\partial y}\mathbf{j}$$

EXAMPLE 3 Evaluating a gradient vector If $f(x, y) = \sin x + e^{xy}$, then

$$\nabla f(x, y) = \langle f_x, f_y \rangle = \langle \cos x + ye^{xy}, xe^{xy} \rangle$$

and

$$\nabla f(0, 1) = \langle 2, 0 \rangle$$

With this notation for the gradient vector, we can rewrite the expression (7) for the directional derivative of a differentiable function as

9

$$D_{\mathbf{u}} f(x, y) = \nabla f(x, y) \cdot \mathbf{u}$$

This expresses the directional derivative in the direction of $\mathbf{u}$ as the scalar projection of the gradient vector onto $\mathbf{u}$.

The gradient vector $\nabla f(2, -1)$ in Example 4 is shown in Figure 6 with initial point $(2, -1)$. Also shown is the vector $\mathbf{v}$ that gives the direction of the directional derivative. Both of these vectors are superimposed on a contour plot of the graph of f.

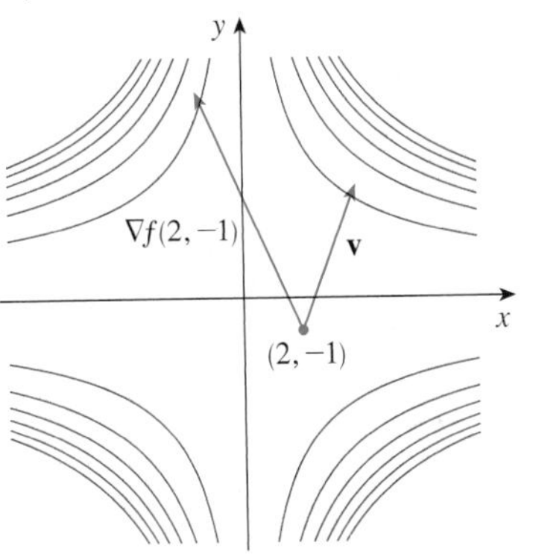

FIGURE 6

V EXAMPLE 4 Using a gradient vector to find a directional derivative Find the directional derivative of the function $f(x, y) = x^2y^3 - 4y$ at the point $(2, -1)$ in the direction of the vector $\mathbf{v} = 2\mathbf{i} + 5\mathbf{j}$.

SOLUTION We first compute the gradient vector at $(2, -1)$:

$$\nabla f(x, y) = 2xy^3\mathbf{i} + (3x^2y^2 - 4)\mathbf{j}$$

$$\nabla f(2, -1) = -4\mathbf{i} + 8\mathbf{j}$$

Note that $\mathbf{v}$ is not a unit vector, but since $|\mathbf{v}| = \sqrt{29}$, the unit vector in the direction of $\mathbf{v}$ is

$$\mathbf{u} = \frac{\mathbf{v}}{|\mathbf{v}|} = \frac{2}{\sqrt{29}}\mathbf{i} + \frac{5}{\sqrt{29}}\mathbf{j}$$

Therefore, by Equation 9, we have

$$D_{\mathbf{u}}f(2, -1) = \nabla f(2, -1) \cdot \mathbf{u} = (-4\mathbf{i} + 8\mathbf{j}) \cdot \left(\frac{2}{\sqrt{29}}\mathbf{i} + \frac{5}{\sqrt{29}}\mathbf{j}\right)$$

$$= \frac{-4 \cdot 2 + 8 \cdot 5}{\sqrt{29}} = \frac{32}{\sqrt{29}}$$

Functions of Three Variables

For functions of three variables we can define directional derivatives in a similar manner. Again $D_{\mathbf{u}}f(x, y, z)$ can be interpreted as the rate of change of the function in the direction of a unit vector $\mathbf{u}$.

> **10 Definition** The **directional derivative** of f at (x_0, y_0, z_0) in the direction of a unit vector $\mathbf{u} = \langle a, b, c \rangle$ is
>
> $$D_{\mathbf{u}}f(x_0, y_0, z_0) = \lim_{h \to 0} \frac{f(x_0 + ha, y_0 + hb, z_0 + hc) - f(x_0, y_0, z_0)}{h}$$
>
> if this limit exists.

If we use vector notation, then we can write both definitions (2 and 10) of the directional derivative in the compact form

$$D_{\mathbf{u}}f(\mathbf{x}_0) = \lim_{h \to 0} \frac{f(\mathbf{x}_0 + h\mathbf{u}) - f(\mathbf{x}_0)}{h} \tag{11}$$

where $\mathbf{x}_0 = \langle x_0, y_0 \rangle$ if $n = 2$ and $\mathbf{x}_0 = \langle x_0, y_0, z_0 \rangle$ if $n = 3$. This is reasonable because the vector equation of the line through $\mathbf{x}_0$ in the direction of the vector $\mathbf{u}$ is given by $\mathbf{x} = \mathbf{x}_0 + t\mathbf{u}$ (Equation 9.5.1) and so $f(\mathbf{x}_0 + h\mathbf{u})$ represents the value of f at a point on this line.

If $f(x, y, z)$ is differentiable and $\mathbf{u} = \langle a, b, c \rangle$, then the same method that was used to prove Theorem 3 can be used to show that

12
$$D_{\mathbf{u}} f(x, y, z) = f_x(x, y, z)\, a + f_y(x, y, z)\, b + f_z(x, y, z)\, c$$

For a function f of three variables, the **gradient vector**, denoted by ∇f or **grad** f, is

$$\nabla f(x, y, z) = \langle f_x(x, y, z), f_y(x, y, z), f_z(x, y, z) \rangle$$

or, for short,

13
$$\nabla f = \langle f_x, f_y, f_z \rangle = \frac{\partial f}{\partial x}\mathbf{i} + \frac{\partial f}{\partial y}\mathbf{j} + \frac{\partial f}{\partial z}\mathbf{k}$$

Then, just as with functions of two variables, Formula 12 for the directional derivative can be rewritten as

14
$$D_{\mathbf{u}} f(x, y, z) = \nabla f(x, y, z) \cdot \mathbf{u}$$

V EXAMPLE 5 If $f(x, y, z) = x \sin yz$, (a) find the gradient of f and (b) find the directional derivative of f at $(1, 3, 0)$ in the direction of $\mathbf{v} = \mathbf{i} + 2\mathbf{j} - \mathbf{k}$.

SOLUTION

(a) The gradient of f is

$$\begin{aligned} \nabla f(x, y, z) &= \langle f_x(x, y, z), f_y(x, y, z), f_z(x, y, z) \rangle \\ &= \langle \sin yz, xz \cos yz, xy \cos yz \rangle \end{aligned}$$

(b) At $(1, 3, 0)$ we have $\nabla f(1, 3, 0) = \langle 0, 0, 3 \rangle$. The unit vector in the direction of $\mathbf{v} = \mathbf{i} + 2\mathbf{j} - \mathbf{k}$ is

$$\mathbf{u} = \frac{1}{\sqrt{6}}\mathbf{i} + \frac{2}{\sqrt{6}}\mathbf{j} - \frac{1}{\sqrt{6}}\mathbf{k}$$

Therefore Equation 14 gives

$$\begin{aligned} D_{\mathbf{u}} f(1, 3, 0) &= \nabla f(1, 3, 0) \cdot \mathbf{u} \\ &= 3\mathbf{k} \cdot \left(\frac{1}{\sqrt{6}}\mathbf{i} + \frac{2}{\sqrt{6}}\mathbf{j} - \frac{1}{\sqrt{6}}\mathbf{k} \right) \\ &= 3\left(-\frac{1}{\sqrt{6}} \right) = -\sqrt{\frac{3}{2}} \end{aligned}$$

Maximizing the Directional Derivative

Suppose we have a function f of two or three variables and we consider all possible directional derivatives of f at a given point. These give the rates of change of f in all possible directions. We can then ask the questions: In which of these directions does f change fastest and what is the maximum rate of change? The answers are provided by the following theorem.

TEC Visual 11.6B provides visual confirmation of Theorem 15.

15 Theorem Suppose f is a differentiable function of two or three variables. The maximum value of the directional derivative $D_{\mathbf{u}}f(\mathbf{x})$ is $|\nabla f(\mathbf{x})|$ and it occurs when $\mathbf{u}$ has the same direction as the gradient vector $\nabla f(\mathbf{x})$.

PROOF From Equation 9 or 14 we have

$$D_{\mathbf{u}}f = \nabla f \cdot \mathbf{u} = |\nabla f||\mathbf{u}|\cos\theta = |\nabla f|\cos\theta$$

where θ is the angle between ∇f and $\mathbf{u}$. The maximum value of $\cos\theta$ is 1 and this occurs when $\theta = 0$. Therefore the maximum value of $D_{\mathbf{u}}f$ is $|\nabla f|$ and it occurs when $\theta = 0$, that is, when $\mathbf{u}$ has the same direction as ∇f. ☐

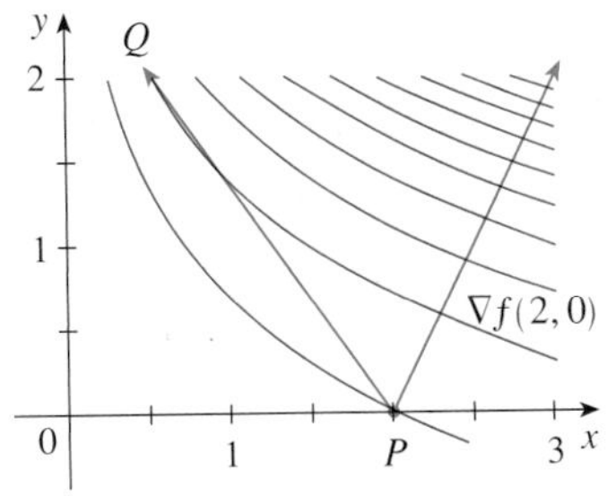

FIGURE 7

At (2, 0) the function in Example 6 increases fastest in the direction of the gradient vector $\nabla f(2, 0) = \langle 1, 2\rangle$. Notice from Figure 7 that this vector appears to be perpendicular to the level curve through (2, 0). Figure 8 shows the graph of f and the gradient vector.

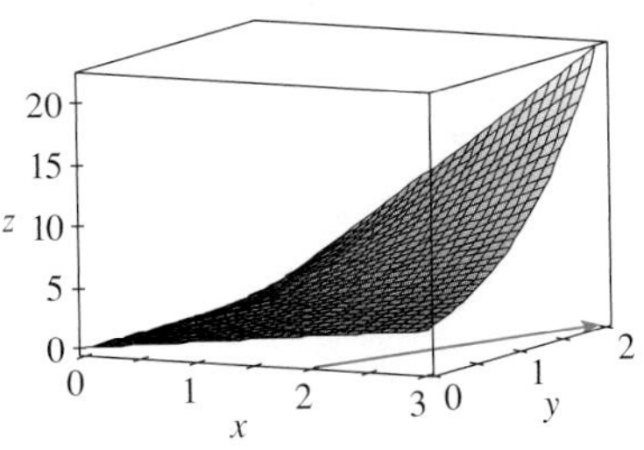

FIGURE 8

EXAMPLE 6 Determining a maximum rate of change

(a) If $f(x, y) = xe^y$, find the rate of change of f at the point $P(2, 0)$ in the direction from P to $Q(\frac{1}{2}, 2)$.

(b) In what direction does f have the maximum rate of change? What is this maximum rate of change?

SOLUTION

(a) We first compute the gradient vector:

$$\nabla f(x, y) = \langle f_x, f_y\rangle = \langle e^y, xe^y\rangle$$

$$\nabla f(2, 0) = \langle 1, 2\rangle$$

The unit vector in the direction of $\overrightarrow{PQ} = \langle -1.5, 2\rangle$ is $\mathbf{u} = \langle -\frac{3}{5}, \frac{4}{5}\rangle$, so the rate of change of f in the direction from P to Q is

$$D_{\mathbf{u}}f(2, 0) = \nabla f(2, 0) \cdot \mathbf{u} = \langle 1, 2\rangle \cdot \langle -\tfrac{3}{5}, \tfrac{4}{5}\rangle$$

$$= 1\left(-\tfrac{3}{5}\right) + 2\left(\tfrac{4}{5}\right) = 1$$

(b) According to Theorem 15, f increases fastest in the direction of the gradient vector $\nabla f(2, 0) = \langle 1, 2\rangle$. The maximum rate of change is

$$|\nabla f(2, 0)| = |\langle 1, 2\rangle| = \sqrt{5}$$

EXAMPLE 7 Suppose that the temperature at a point (x, y, z) in space is given by $T(x, y, z) = 80/(1 + x^2 + 2y^2 + 3z^2)$, where T is measured in degrees Celsius and x, y, z in meters. In which direction does the temperature increase fastest at the point $(1, 1, -2)$? What is the maximum rate of increase?

SOLUTION The gradient of T is

$$\nabla T = \frac{\partial T}{\partial x}\mathbf{i} + \frac{\partial T}{\partial y}\mathbf{j} + \frac{\partial T}{\partial z}\mathbf{k}$$

$$= -\frac{160x}{(1 + x^2 + 2y^2 + 3z^2)^2}\mathbf{i} - \frac{320y}{(1 + x^2 + 2y^2 + 3z^2)^2}\mathbf{j} - \frac{480z}{(1 + x^2 + 2y^2 + 3z^2)^2}\mathbf{k}$$

$$= \frac{160}{(1 + x^2 + 2y^2 + 3z^2)^2}(-x\,\mathbf{i} - 2y\,\mathbf{j} - 3z\,\mathbf{k})$$

At the point $(1, 1, -2)$ the gradient vector is

$$\nabla T(1, 1, -2) = \tfrac{160}{256}(-\mathbf{i} - 2\mathbf{j} + 6\mathbf{k}) = \tfrac{5}{8}(-\mathbf{i} - 2\mathbf{j} + 6\mathbf{k})$$

By Theorem 15 the temperature increases fastest in the direction of the gradient vector $\nabla T(1, 1, -2) = \frac{5}{8}(-\mathbf{i} - 2\mathbf{j} + 6\mathbf{k})$ or, equivalently, in the direction of $-\mathbf{i} - 2\mathbf{j} + 6\mathbf{k}$ or the unit vector $(-\mathbf{i} - 2\mathbf{j} + 6\mathbf{k})/\sqrt{41}$. The maximum rate of increase is the length of the gradient vector:

$$|\nabla T(1, 1, -2)| = \tfrac{5}{8}|-\mathbf{i} - 2\mathbf{j} + 6\mathbf{k}| = \tfrac{5}{8}\sqrt{41}$$

Therefore the maximum rate of increase of temperature is $\frac{5}{8}\sqrt{41} \approx 4°\text{C/m}$.

Tangent Planes to Level Surfaces

Suppose S is a surface with equation $F(x, y, z) = k$, that is, it is a level surface of a function F of three variables, and let $P(x_0, y_0, z_0)$ be a point on S. Let C be any curve that lies on the surface S and passes through the point P. Recall from Section 10.1 that the curve C is described by a continuous vector function $\mathbf{r}(t) = \langle x(t), y(t), z(t) \rangle$. Let t_0 be the parameter value corresponding to P; that is, $\mathbf{r}(t_0) = \langle x_0, y_0, z_0 \rangle$. Since C lies on S, any point $(x(t), y(t), z(t))$ must satisfy the equation of S, that is,

$$F(x(t), y(t), z(t)) = k \tag{16}$$

If x, y, and z are differentiable functions of t and F is also differentiable, then we can use the Chain Rule to differentiate both sides of Equation 16 as follows:

$$\frac{\partial F}{\partial x}\frac{dx}{dt} + \frac{\partial F}{\partial y}\frac{dy}{dt} + \frac{\partial F}{\partial z}\frac{dz}{dt} = 0 \tag{17}$$

But, since $\nabla F = \langle F_x, F_y, F_z \rangle$ and $\mathbf{r}'(t) = \langle x'(t), y'(t), z'(t) \rangle$, Equation 17 can be written in terms of a dot product as

$$\nabla F \cdot \mathbf{r}'(t) = 0$$

In particular, when $t = t_0$ we have $\mathbf{r}(t_0) = \langle x_0, y_0, z_0 \rangle$, so

$$\nabla F(x_0, y_0, z_0) \cdot \mathbf{r}'(t_0) = 0 \tag{18}$$

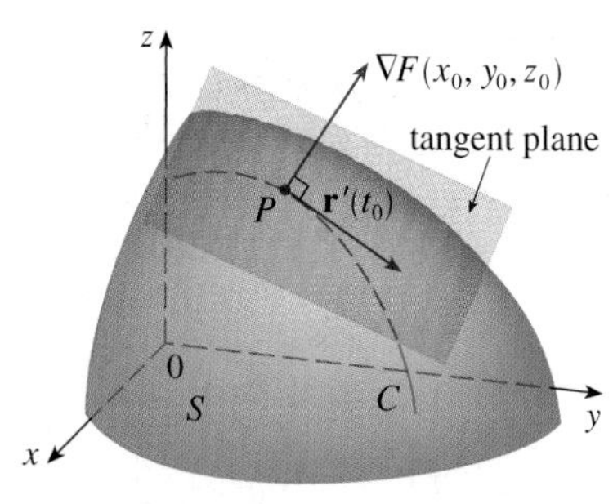

FIGURE 9

Equation 18 says that *the gradient vector at P, $\nabla F(x_0, y_0, z_0)$, is perpendicular to the tangent vector $\mathbf{r}'(t_0)$ to any curve C on S that passes through P.* (See Figure 9.) If $\nabla F(x_0, y_0, z_0) \neq \mathbf{0}$, it is therefore natural to define the **tangent plane to the level surface $F(x, y, z) = k$ at $P(x_0, y_0, z_0)$** as the plane that passes through P and has normal vector $\nabla F(x_0, y_0, z_0)$. Using the standard equation of a plane (Equation 9.5.7), we can write the equation of this tangent plane as

$$F_x(x_0, y_0, z_0)(x - x_0) + F_y(x_0, y_0, z_0)(y - y_0) + F_z(x_0, y_0, z_0)(z - z_0) = 0 \tag{19}$$

The **normal line** to S at P is the line passing through P and perpendicular to the tangent plane. The direction of the normal line is therefore given by the gradient vector $\nabla F(x_0, y_0, z_0)$ and so, by Equation 9.5.3, its symmetric equations are

20
$$\frac{x - x_0}{F_x(x_0, y_0, z_0)} = \frac{y - y_0}{F_y(x_0, y_0, z_0)} = \frac{z - z_0}{F_z(x_0, y_0, z_0)}$$

In the special case in which the equation of a surface S is of the form $z = f(x, y)$ (that is, S is the graph of a function f of two variables), we can rewrite the equation as

$$F(x, y, z) = f(x, y) - z = 0$$

and regard S as a level surface (with $k = 0$) of F. Then

$$F_x(x_0, y_0, z_0) = f_x(x_0, y_0)$$

$$F_y(x_0, y_0, z_0) = f_y(x_0, y_0)$$

$$F_z(x_0, y_0, z_0) = -1$$

so Equation 19 becomes

$$f_x(x_0, y_0)(x - x_0) + f_y(x_0, y_0)(y - y_0) - (z - z_0) = 0$$

which is equivalent to Equation 11.4.2. Thus our new, more general, definition of a tangent plane is consistent with the definition that was given for the special case of Section 11.4.

V EXAMPLE 8 Find the equations of the tangent plane and normal line at the point $(-2, 1, -3)$ to the ellipsoid

$$\frac{x^2}{4} + y^2 + \frac{z^2}{9} = 3$$

SOLUTION The ellipsoid is the level surface (with $k = 3$) of the function

$$F(x, y, z) = \frac{x^2}{4} + y^2 + \frac{z^2}{9}$$

Figure 10 shows the ellipsoid, tangent plane, and normal line in Example 8.

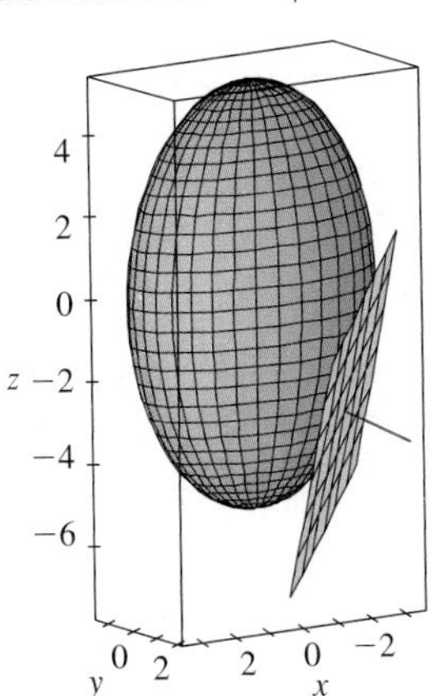

FIGURE 10

Therefore we have

$$F_x(x, y, z) = \frac{x}{2} \qquad F_y(x, y, z) = 2y \qquad F_z(x, y, z) = \frac{2z}{9}$$

$$F_x(-2, 1, -3) = -1 \qquad F_y(-2, 1, -3) = 2 \qquad F_z(-2, 1, -3) = -\tfrac{2}{3}$$

Then Equation 19 gives the equation of the tangent plane at $(-2, 1, -3)$ as

$$-1(x + 2) + 2(y - 1) - \tfrac{2}{3}(z + 3) = 0$$

which simplifies to $3x - 6y + 2z + 18 = 0$.

By Equation 20, symmetric equations of the normal line are

$$\frac{x + 2}{-1} = \frac{y - 1}{2} = \frac{z + 3}{-\frac{2}{3}}$$

Significance of the Gradient Vector

We now summarize the ways in which the gradient vector is significant. We first consider a function f of three variables and a point $P(x_0, y_0, z_0)$ in its domain. On the one hand, we know from Theorem 15 that the gradient vector $\nabla f(x_0, y_0, z_0)$ gives the direction of fastest increase of f. On the other hand, we know that $\nabla f(x_0, y_0, z_0)$ is orthogonal to the level surface S of f through P. (Refer to Figure 9.) These two properties are quite compatible intuitively because as we move away from P on the level surface S, the value of f does not change at all. So it seems reasonable that if we move in the perpendicular direction, we get the maximum increase.

In like manner we consider a function f of two variables and a point $P(x_0, y_0)$ in its domain. Again the gradient vector $\nabla f(x_0, y_0)$ gives the direction of fastest increase of f. Also, by considerations similar to our discussion of tangent planes, it can be shown that $\nabla f(x_0, y_0)$ is perpendicular to the level curve $f(x, y) = k$ that passes through P. Again this is intuitively plausible because the values of f remain constant as we move along the curve. (See Figure 11.)

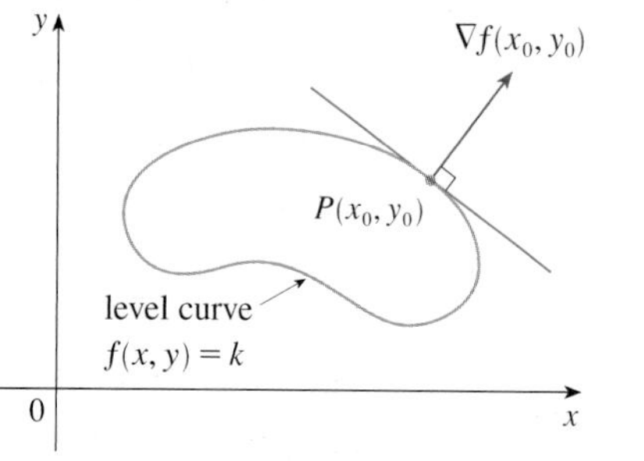

FIGURE 11

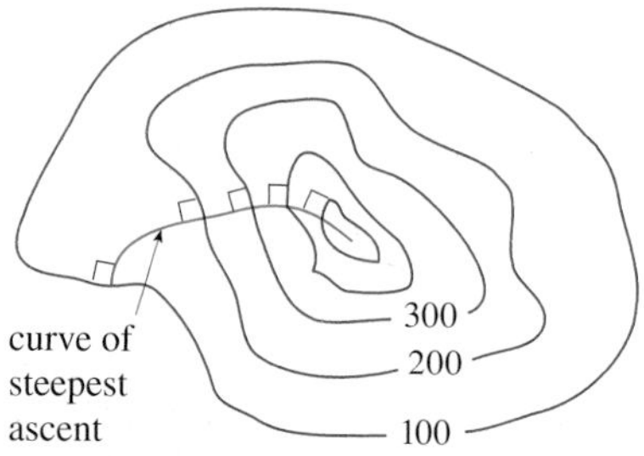

FIGURE 12

If we consider a topographical map of a hill and let $f(x, y)$ represent the height above sea level at a point with coordinates (x, y), then a curve of steepest ascent can be drawn as in Figure 12 by making it perpendicular to all of the contour lines. This phenomenon can also be noticed in Figure 5 in Section 11.1, where Lonesome Creek follows a curve of steepest descent.

Computer algebra systems have commands that plot sample gradient vectors. Each gradient vector $\nabla f(a, b)$ is plotted starting at the point (a, b). Figure 13 shows such a plot (called a *gradient vector field*) for the function $f(x, y) = x^2 - y^2$ superimposed on a contour map of f. As expected, the gradient vectors point "uphill" and are perpendicular to the level curves.

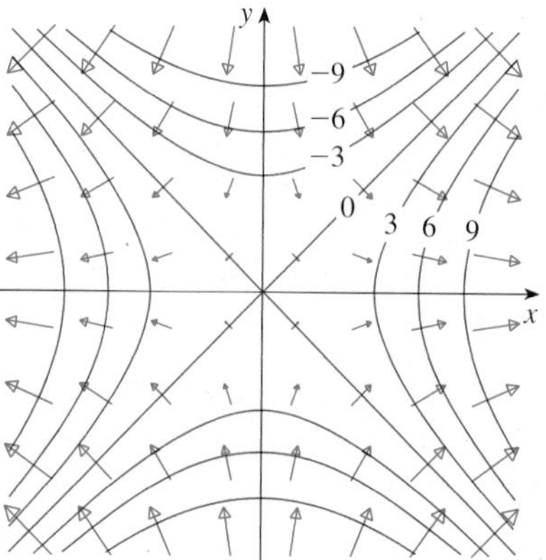

FIGURE 13

11.6 Exercises

1. Level curves for barometric pressure (in millibars) are shown for 6:00 AM on November 10, 1998. A deep low with pressure 972 mb is moving over northeast Iowa. The distance along the red line from K (Kearney, Nebraska) to S (Sioux City, Iowa) is 300 km. Estimate the value of the directional derivative of the pressure function at Kearney in the direction of Sioux City. What are the units of the directional derivative?

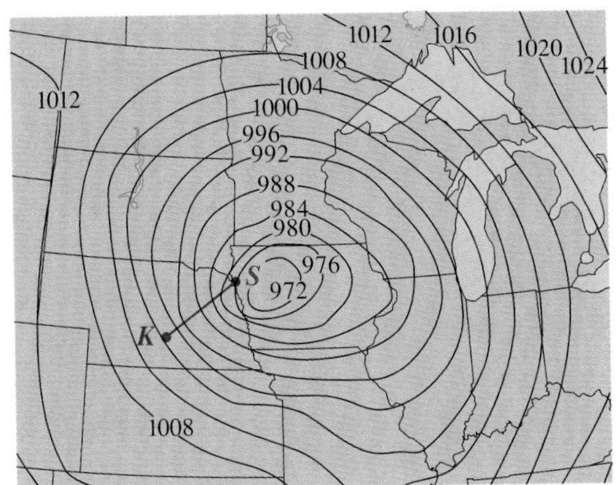

2. The contour map shows the average maximum temperature for November 2004 (in °C). Estimate the value of the directional derivative of this temperature function at Dubbo, New South Wales, in the direction of Sydney. What are the units?

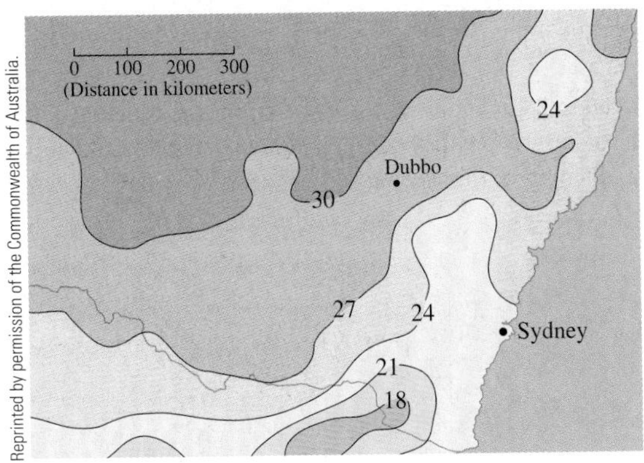

3. A table of values for the wind-chill index $W = f(T, v)$ is given in Exercise 3 on page 766. Use the table to estimate the value of $D_{\mathbf{u}} f(-20, 30)$, where $\mathbf{u} = (\mathbf{i} + \mathbf{j})/\sqrt{2}$.

4–6 Find the directional derivative of f at the given point in the direction indicated by the angle θ.

4. $f(x, y) = x^2y^3 - y^4$, $(2, 1)$, $\theta = \pi/4$

5. $f(x, y) = ye^{-x}$, $(0, 4)$, $\theta = 2\pi/3$

6. $f(x, y) = x \sin(xy)$, $(2, 0)$, $\theta = \pi/3$

7–10

(a) Find the gradient of f.
(b) Evaluate the gradient at the point P.
(c) Find the rate of change of f at P in the direction of the vector $\mathbf{u}$.

7. $f(x, y) = \sin(2x + 3y)$, $P(-6, 4)$, $\mathbf{u} = \frac{1}{2}\left(\sqrt{3}\,\mathbf{i} - \mathbf{j}\right)$

8. $f(x, y) = y^2/x$, $P(1, 2)$, $\mathbf{u} = \frac{1}{3}\left(2\mathbf{i} + \sqrt{5}\,\mathbf{j}\right)$

9. $f(x, y, z) = xe^{2yz}$, $P(3, 0, 2)$, $\mathbf{u} = \langle \frac{2}{3}, -\frac{2}{3}, \frac{1}{3} \rangle$

10. $f(x, y, z) = \sqrt{x + yz}$, $P(1, 3, 1)$, $\mathbf{u} = \langle \frac{2}{7}, \frac{3}{7}, \frac{6}{7} \rangle$

11–17 Find the directional derivative of the function at the given point in the direction of the vector $\mathbf{v}$.

11. $f(x, y) = 1 + 2x\sqrt{y}$, $(3, 4)$, $\mathbf{v} = \langle 4, -3 \rangle$

12. $f(x, y) = \ln(x^2 + y^2)$, $(2, 1)$, $\mathbf{v} = \langle -1, 2 \rangle$

13. $g(p, q) = p^4 - p^2q^3$, $(2, 1)$, $\mathbf{v} = \mathbf{i} + 3\mathbf{j}$

14. $g(r, s) = \tan^{-1}(rs)$, $(1, 2)$, $\mathbf{v} = 5\mathbf{i} + 10\mathbf{j}$

15. $f(x, y, z) = xe^y + ye^z + ze^x$, $(0, 0, 0)$, $\mathbf{v} = \langle 5, 1, -2 \rangle$

16. $f(x, y, z) = \sqrt{xyz}$, $(3, 2, 6)$, $\mathbf{v} = \langle -1, -2, 2 \rangle$

17. $g(x, y, z) = (x + 2y + 3z)^{3/2}$, $(1, 1, 2)$, $\mathbf{v} = 2\mathbf{j} - \mathbf{k}$

18. Use the figure to estimate $D_{\mathbf{u}} f(2, 2)$.

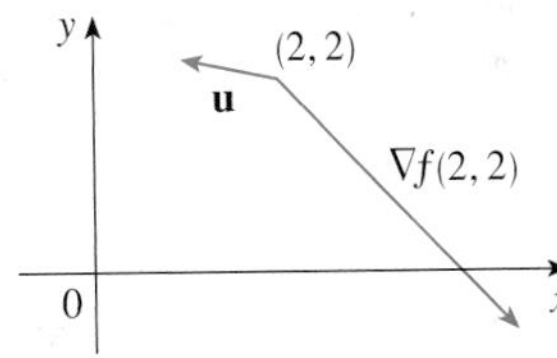

19. Find the directional derivative of $f(x, y) = \sqrt{xy}$ at $P(2, 8)$ in the direction of $Q(5, 4)$.

20. Find the directional derivative of $f(x, y, z) = xy + yz + zx$ at $P(1, -1, 3)$ in the direction of $Q(2, 4, 5)$.

21–24 Find the maximum rate of change of f at the given point and the direction in which it occurs.

21. $f(x, y) = \sin(xy)$, $(1, 0)$

22. $f(p, q) = qe^{-p} + pe^{-q}$, $(0, 0)$

23. $f(x, y, z) = \sqrt{x^2 + y^2 + z^2}$, $(3, 6, -2)$

24. $f(x, y, z) = (x + y)/z$, $(1, 1, -1)$

Graphing calculator or computer with graphing software required

1. Homework Hints available in TEC

25. (a) Show that a differentiable function f decreases most rapidly at $\mathbf{x}$ in the direction opposite to the gradient vector, that is, in the direction of $-\nabla f(\mathbf{x})$.
(b) Use the result of part (a) to find the direction in which the function $f(x, y) = x^4 y - x^2 y^3$ decreases fastest at the point $(2, -3)$.

26. Find the directions in which the directional derivative of $f(x, y) = ye^{-xy}$ at the point $(0, 2)$ has the value 1.

27. Find all points at which the direction of fastest change of the function $f(x, y) = x^2 + y^2 - 2x - 4y$ is $\mathbf{i} + \mathbf{j}$.

28. Near a buoy, the depth of a lake at the point with coordinates (x, y) is $z = 200 + 0.02x^2 - 0.001y^3$, where x, y, and z are measured in meters. A fisherman in a small boat starts at the point $(80, 60)$ and moves toward the buoy, which is located at $(0, 0)$. Is the water under the boat getting deeper or shallower when he departs? Explain.

29. The temperature T in a metal ball is inversely proportional to the distance from the center of the ball, which we take to be the origin. The temperature at the point $(1, 2, 2)$ is $120°$.
(a) Find the rate of change of T at $(1, 2, 2)$ in the direction toward the point $(2, 1, 3)$.
(b) Show that at any point in the ball the direction of greatest increase in temperature is given by a vector that points toward the origin.

30. The temperature at a point (x, y, z) is given by

$$T(x, y, z) = 200e^{-x^2-3y^2-9z^2}$$

where T is measured in °C and x, y, z in meters.
(a) Find the rate of change of temperature at the point $P(2, -1, 2)$ in the direction toward the point $(3, -3, 3)$.
(b) In which direction does the temperature increase fastest at P?
(c) Find the maximum rate of increase at P.

31. Suppose that over a certain region of space the electrical potential V is given by $V(x, y, z) = 5x^2 - 3xy + xyz$.
(a) Find the rate of change of the potential at $P(3, 4, 5)$ in the direction of the vector $\mathbf{v} = \mathbf{i} + \mathbf{j} - \mathbf{k}$.
(b) In which direction does V change most rapidly at P?
(c) What is the maximum rate of change at P?

32. Suppose you are climbing a hill whose shape is given by the equation $z = 1000 - 0.005x^2 - 0.01y^2$, where x, y, and z are measured in meters, and you are standing at a point with coordinates $(60, 40, 966)$. The positive x-axis points east and the positive y-axis points north.
(a) If you walk due south, will you start to ascend or descend? At what rate?
(b) If you walk northwest, will you start to ascend or descend? At what rate?
(c) In which direction is the slope largest? What is the rate of ascent in that direction? At what angle above the horizontal does the path in that direction begin?

33. Let f be a function of two variables that has continuous partial derivatives and consider the points $A(1, 3)$, $B(3, 3)$, $C(1, 7)$, and $D(6, 15)$. The directional derivative of f at A in the direction of the vector $\overrightarrow{AB}$ is 3 and the directional derivative at A in the direction of $\overrightarrow{AC}$ is 26. Find the directional derivative of f at A in the direction of the vector $\overrightarrow{AD}$.

34. Shown is a topographic map of Blue River Pine Provincial Park in British Columbia. Draw curves of steepest descent from Point A (descending to Mud Lake) and from point B.

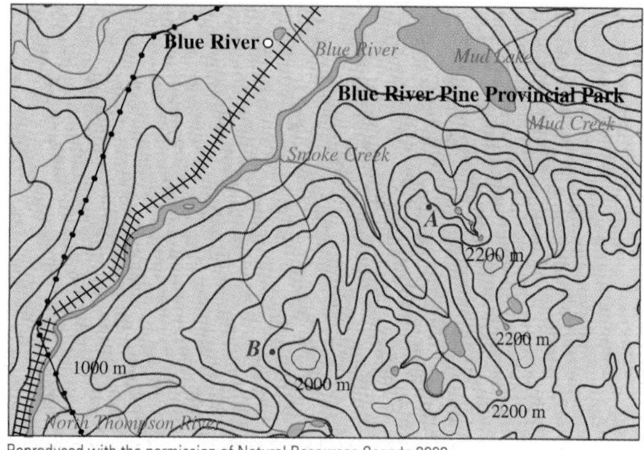

Reproduced with the permission of Natural Resources Canada 2009, courtesy of the Centre of Topographic Information.

35. Show that the operation of taking the gradient of a function has the given property. Assume that u and v are differentiable functions of x and y and that a, b are constants.
(a) $\nabla(au + bv) = a\,\nabla u + b\,\nabla v$ (b) $\nabla(uv) = u\,\nabla v + v\,\nabla u$
(c) $\nabla\left(\dfrac{u}{v}\right) = \dfrac{v\,\nabla u - u\,\nabla v}{v^2}$ (d) $\nabla u^n = nu^{n-1}\,\nabla u$

36. Sketch the gradient vector $\nabla f(4, 6)$ for the function f whose level curves are shown. Explain how you chose the direction and length of this vector.

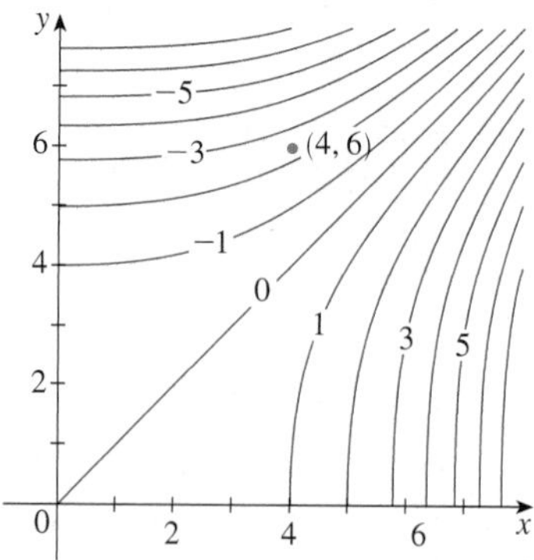

37. The **second directional derivative** of $f(x, y)$ is

$$D_{\mathbf{u}}^2 f(x, y) = D_{\mathbf{u}}[D_{\mathbf{u}} f(x, y)]$$

If $f(x, y) = x^3 + 5x^2y + y^3$ and $\mathbf{u} = \left\langle \frac{3}{5}, \frac{4}{5} \right\rangle$, calculate $D_{\mathbf{u}}^2 f(2, 1)$.

38. (a) If $\mathbf{u} = \langle a, b\rangle$ is a unit vector and f has continuous second partial derivatives, show that

$$D_{\mathbf{u}}^2 f = f_{xx}a^2 + 2f_{xy}ab + f_{yy}b^2$$

(b) Find the second directional derivative of $f(x, y) = xe^{2y}$ in the direction of $\mathbf{v} = \langle 4, 6\rangle$.

39–44 Find equations of (a) the tangent plane and (b) the normal line to the given surface at the specified point.

39. $2(x-2)^2 + (y-1)^2 + (z-3)^2 = 10$, $(3, 3, 5)$

40. $y = x^2 - z^2$, $(4, 7, 3)$

41. $x^2 - 2y^2 + z^2 + yz = 2$, $(2, 1, -1)$

42. $x - z = 4\arctan(yz)$, $(1+\pi, 1, 1)$

43. $z + 1 = xe^y\cos z$, $(1, 0, 0)$

44. $yz = \ln(x+z)$, $(0, 0, 1)$

45–46 Use a computer to graph the surface, the tangent plane, and the normal line on the same screen. Choose the domain carefully so that you avoid extraneous vertical planes. Choose the viewpoint so that you get a good view of all three objects.

45. $xy + yz + zx = 3$, $(1, 1, 1)$

46. $xyz = 6$, $(1, 2, 3)$

47. If $f(x, y) = xy$, find the gradient vector $\nabla f(3, 2)$ and use it to find the tangent line to the level curve $f(x, y) = 6$ at the point $(3, 2)$. Sketch the level curve, the tangent line, and the gradient vector.

48. If $g(x, y) = x^2 + y^2 - 4x$, find the gradient vector $\nabla g(1, 2)$ and use it to find the tangent line to the level curve $g(x, y) = 1$ at the point $(1, 2)$. Sketch the level curve, the tangent line, and the gradient vector.

49. Show that the equation of the tangent plane to the ellipsoid $x^2/a^2 + y^2/b^2 + z^2/c^2 = 1$ at the point (x_0, y_0, z_0) can be written as

$$\frac{xx_0}{a^2} + \frac{yy_0}{b^2} + \frac{zz_0}{c^2} = 1$$

50. At what point on the paraboloid $y = x^2 + z^2$ is the tangent plane parallel to the plane $x + 2y + 3z = 1$?

51. Are there any points on the hyperboloid $x^2 - y^2 - z^2 = 1$ where the tangent plane is parallel to the plane $z = x + y$?

52. Show that the ellipsoid $3x^2 + 2y^2 + z^2 = 9$ and the sphere $x^2 + y^2 + z^2 - 8x - 6y - 8z + 24 = 0$ are tangent to each other at the point $(1, 1, 2)$. (This means that they have a common tangent plane at the point.)

53. Show that every plane that is tangent to the cone $x^2 + y^2 = z^2$ passes through the origin.

54. Show that every normal line to the sphere $x^2 + y^2 + z^2 = r^2$ passes through the center of the sphere.

55. Show that the sum of the x-, y-, and z-intercepts of any tangent plane to the surface $\sqrt{x} + \sqrt{y} + \sqrt{z} = \sqrt{c}$ is a constant.

56. Show that the pyramids cut off from the first octant by any tangent planes to the surface $xyz = 1$ at points in the first octant must all have the same volume.

57. Find parametric equations for the tangent line to the curve of intersection of the paraboloid $z = x^2 + y^2$ and the ellipsoid $4x^2 + y^2 + z^2 = 9$ at the point $(-1, 1, 2)$.

58. (a) The plane $y + z = 3$ intersects the cylinder $x^2 + y^2 = 5$ in an ellipse. Find parametric equations for the tangent line to this ellipse at the point $(1, 2, 1)$.

(b) Graph the cylinder, the plane, and the tangent line on the same screen.

59. (a) Two surfaces are called **orthogonal** at a point of intersection if their normal lines are perpendicular at that point. Show that surfaces with equations $F(x, y, z) = 0$ and $G(x, y, z) = 0$ are orthogonal at a point P where $\nabla F \neq \mathbf{0}$ and $\nabla G \neq \mathbf{0}$ if and only if

$$F_xG_x + F_yG_y + F_zG_z = 0 \quad \text{at } P$$

(b) Use part (a) to show that the surfaces $z^2 = x^2 + y^2$ and $x^2 + y^2 + z^2 = r^2$ are orthogonal at every point of intersection. Can you see why this is true without using calculus?

60. (a) Show that the function $f(x, y) = \sqrt[3]{xy}$ is continuous and the partial derivatives f_x and f_y exist at the origin but the directional derivatives in all other directions do not exist.

(b) Graph f near the origin and comment on how the graph confirms part (a).

61. Suppose that the directional derivatives of $f(x, y)$ are known at a given point in two nonparallel directions given by unit vectors $\mathbf{u}$ and $\mathbf{v}$. Is it possible to find ∇f at this point? If so, how would you do it?

62. Show that if $z = f(x, y)$ is differentiable at $\mathbf{x}_0 = \langle x_0, y_0\rangle$, then

$$\lim_{\mathbf{x}\to\mathbf{x}_0} \frac{f(\mathbf{x}) - f(\mathbf{x}_0) - \nabla f(\mathbf{x}_0)\cdot(\mathbf{x}-\mathbf{x}_0)}{|\mathbf{x}-\mathbf{x}_0|} = 0$$

[*Hint:* Use Definition 11.4.7 directly.]

11.7 Maximum and Minimum Values

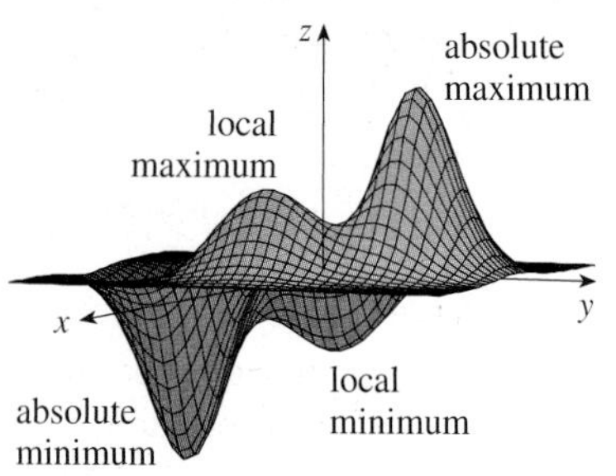

FIGURE 1

As we saw in Chapter 4, one of the main uses of ordinary derivatives is in finding maximum and minimum values (extreme values). In this section we see how to use partial derivatives to locate maxima and minima of functions of two variables. In particular, in Example 6 we will see how to maximize the volume of a box without a lid if we have a fixed amount of cardboard to work with.

Look at the hills and valleys in the graph of f shown in Figure 1. There are two points (a, b) where f has a *local maximum*, that is, where $f(a, b)$ is larger than nearby values of $f(x, y)$. The larger of these two values is the *absolute maximum*. Likewise, f has two *local minima*, where $f(a, b)$ is smaller than nearby values. The smaller of these two values is the *absolute minimum*.

1 Definition A function of two variables has a **local maximum** at (a, b) if $f(x, y) \leqslant f(a, b)$ when (x, y) is near (a, b). [This means that $f(x, y) \leqslant f(a, b)$ for all points (x, y) in some disk with center (a, b).] The number $f(a, b)$ is called a **local maximum value**. If $f(x, y) \geqslant f(a, b)$ when (x, y) is near (a, b), then f has a **local minimum** at (a, b) and $f(a, b)$ is a **local minimum value**.

If the inequalities in Definition 1 hold for *all* points (x, y) in the domain of f, then f has an **absolute maximum** (or **absolute minimum**) at (a, b).

Notice that the conclusion of Theorem 2 can be stated in the notation of gradient vectors as $\nabla f(a, b) = \mathbf{0}$.

2 Fermat's Theorem for Functions of Two Variables If f has a local maximum or minimum at (a, b) and the first-order partial derivatives of f exist there, then $f_x(a, b) = 0$ and $f_y(a, b) = 0$.

PROOF Let $g(x) = f(x, b)$. If f has a local maximum (or minimum) at (a, b), then g has a local maximum (or minimum) at a, so $g'(a) = 0$ by Fermat's Theorem for functions of one variable (see Theorem 4.2.4). But $g'(a) = f_x(a, b)$ (see Equation 11.3.1) and so $f_x(a, b) = 0$. Similarly, by applying Fermat's Theorem to the function $G(y) = f(a, y)$, we obtain $f_y(a, b) = 0$. □

If we put $f_x(a, b) = 0$ and $f_y(a, b) = 0$ in the equation of a tangent plane (Equation 11.4.2), we get $z = z_0$. Thus the geometric interpretation of Theorem 2 is that if the graph of f has a tangent plane at a local maximum or minimum, then the tangent plane must be horizontal.

A point (a, b) is called a **critical point** (or *stationary point*) of f if $f_x(a, b) = 0$ and $f_y(a, b) = 0$, or if one of these partial derivatives does not exist. Theorem 2 says that if f has a local maximum or minimum at (a, b), then (a, b) is a critical point of f. However, as in single-variable calculus, not all critical points give rise to maxima or minima. At a critical point, a function could have a local maximum or a local minimum or neither.

EXAMPLE 1 A function with an absolute minimum
Let $f(x, y) = x^2 + y^2 - 2x - 6y + 14$. Then

$$f_x(x, y) = 2x - 2 \qquad f_y(x, y) = 2y - 6$$

These partial derivatives are equal to 0 when $x = 1$ and $y = 3$, so the only critical point is $(1, 3)$. By completing the square, we find that

$$f(x, y) = 4 + (x - 1)^2 + (y - 3)^2$$

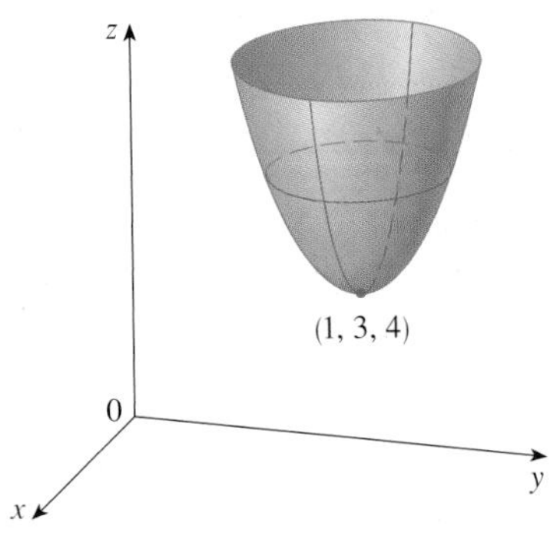

FIGURE 2
$z = x^2 + y^2 - 2x - 6y + 14$

Since $(x - 1)^2 \geq 0$ and $(y - 3)^2 \geq 0$, we have $f(x, y) \geq 4$ for all values of x and y. Therefore $f(1, 3) = 4$ is a local minimum, and in fact it is the absolute minimum of f. This can be confirmed geometrically from the graph of f, which is the elliptic paraboloid with vertex $(1, 3, 4)$ shown in Figure 2.

EXAMPLE 2 **A function with no extreme values**
Find the extreme values of $f(x, y) = y^2 - x^2$.

SOLUTION Since $f_x = -2x$ and $f_y = 2y$, the only critical point is $(0, 0)$. Notice that for points on the x-axis we have $y = 0$, so $f(x, y) = -x^2 < 0$ (if $x \neq 0$). However, for points on the y-axis we have $x = 0$, so $f(x, y) = y^2 > 0$ (if $y \neq 0$). Thus every disk with center $(0, 0)$ contains points where f takes positive values as well as points where f takes negative values. Therefore $f(0, 0) = 0$ can't be an extreme value for f, so f has no extreme value.

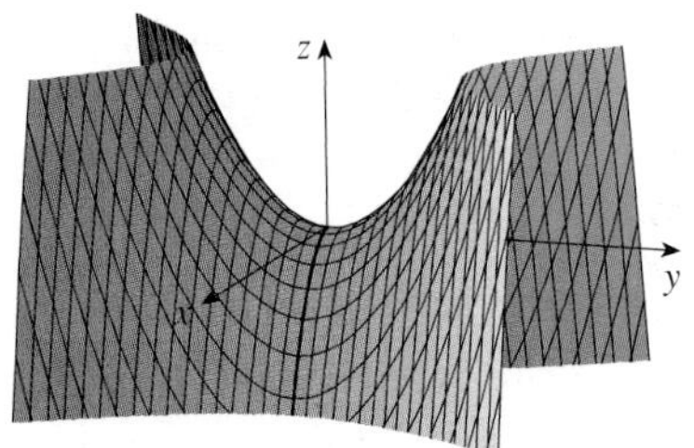

FIGURE 3
$z = y^2 - x^2$

Example 2 illustrates the fact that a function need not have a maximum or minimum value at a critical point. Figure 3 shows how this is possible. The graph of f is the hyperbolic paraboloid $z = y^2 - x^2$, which has a horizontal tangent plane ($z = 0$) at the origin. You can see that $f(0, 0) = 0$ is a maximum in the direction of the x-axis but a minimum in the direction of the y-axis. Near the origin the graph has the shape of a saddle and so $(0, 0)$ is called a *saddle point* of f.

We need to be able to determine whether or not a function has an extreme value at a critical point. The following test, which is proved in Appendix E, is analogous to the Second Derivative Test for functions of one variable.

3 **Second Derivatives Test** Suppose the second partial derivatives of f are continuous on a disk with center (a, b), and suppose that $f_x(a, b) = 0$ and $f_y(a, b) = 0$ [that is, (a, b) is a critical point of f]. Let

$$D = D(a, b) = f_{xx}(a, b) f_{yy}(a, b) - [f_{xy}(a, b)]^2$$

(a) If $D > 0$ and $f_{xx}(a, b) > 0$, then $f(a, b)$ is a local minimum.

(b) If $D > 0$ and $f_{xx}(a, b) < 0$, then $f(a, b)$ is a local maximum.

(c) If $D < 0$, then $f(a, b)$ is not a local maximum or minimum.

Note 1: In case (c) the point (a, b) is called a **saddle point** of f and the graph of f crosses its tangent plane at (a, b).

Note 2: If $D = 0$, the test gives no information: f could have a local maximum or local minimum at (a, b), or (a, b) could be a saddle point of f.

Note 3: To remember the formula for D, it's helpful to write it as a determinant:

$$D = \begin{vmatrix} f_{xx} & f_{xy} \\ f_{yx} & f_{yy} \end{vmatrix} = f_{xx} f_{yy} - (f_{xy})^2$$

V **EXAMPLE 3** **Classifying critical points** Find the local maximum and minimum values and saddle points of $f(x, y) = x^4 + y^4 - 4xy + 1$.

SOLUTION We first locate the critical points:

$$f_x = 4x^3 - 4y \qquad f_y = 4y^3 - 4x$$

Setting these partial derivatives equal to 0, we obtain the equations

$$x^3 - y = 0 \qquad \text{and} \qquad y^3 - x = 0$$

To solve these equations we substitute $y = x^3$ from the first equation into the second one. This gives

$$0 = x^9 - x = x(x^8 - 1) = x(x^4 - 1)(x^4 + 1) = x(x^2 - 1)(x^2 + 1)(x^4 + 1)$$

so there are three real roots: $x = 0, 1, -1$. The three critical points are $(0, 0)$, $(1, 1)$, and $(-1, -1)$.

Next we calculate the second partial derivatives and $D(x, y)$:

$$f_{xx} = 12x^2 \qquad f_{xy} = -4 \qquad f_{yy} = 12y^2$$

$$D(x, y) = f_{xx}f_{yy} - (f_{xy})^2 = 144x^2y^2 - 16$$

Since $D(0, 0) = -16 < 0$, it follows from case (c) of the Second Derivatives Test that the origin is a saddle point; that is, f has no local maximum or minimum at $(0, 0)$. Since $D(1, 1) = 128 > 0$ and $f_{xx}(1, 1) = 12 > 0$, we see from case (a) of the test that $f(1, 1) = -1$ is a local minimum. Similarly, we have $D(-1, -1) = 128 > 0$ and $f_{xx}(-1, -1) = 12 > 0$, so $f(-1, -1) = -1$ is also a local minimum.

The graph of f is shown in Figure 4.

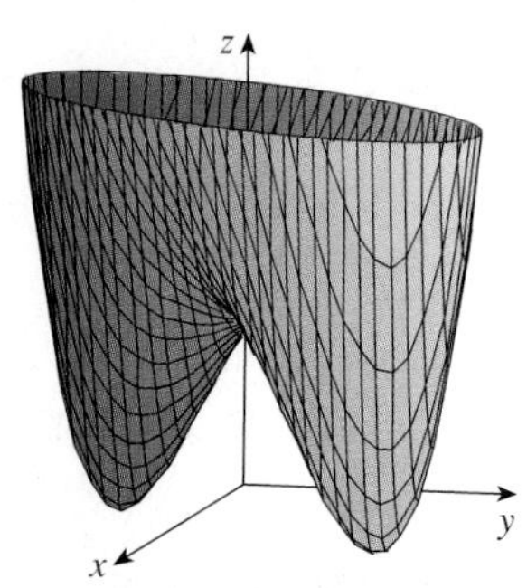

FIGURE 4
$z = x^4 + y^4 - 4xy + 1$

A contour map of the function f in Example 3 is shown in Figure 5. The level curves near $(1, 1)$ and $(-1, -1)$ are oval in shape and indicate that as we move away from $(1, 1)$ or $(-1, -1)$ in any direction the values of f are increasing. The level curves near $(0, 0)$, on the other hand, resemble hyperbolas. They reveal that as we move away from the origin (where the value of f is 1), the values of f decrease in some directions but increase in other directions. Thus the contour map suggests the presence of the minima and saddle point that we found in Example 3.

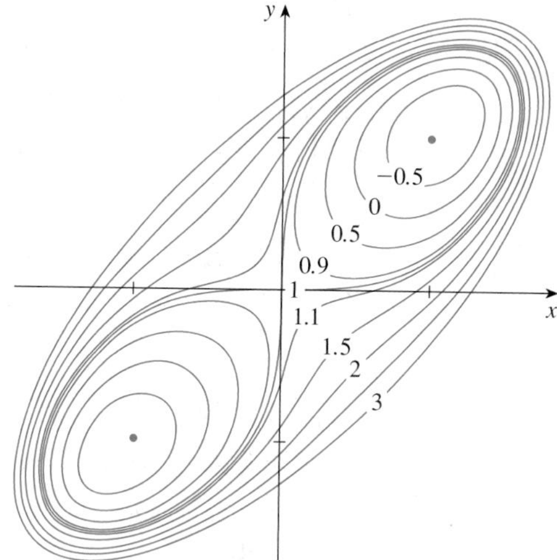

FIGURE 5

TEC In Module 11.7 you can use contour maps to estimate the locations of critical points.

EXAMPLE 4 **Estimating critical points numerically** Find and classify the critical points of the function

$$f(x, y) = 10x^2y - 5x^2 - 4y^2 - x^4 - 2y^4$$

Also find the highest point on the graph of f.

SOLUTION The first-order partial derivatives are

$$f_x = 20xy - 10x - 4x^3 \qquad f_y = 10x^2 - 8y - 8y^3$$

So to find the critical points we need to solve the equations

$$\boxed{4} \qquad 2x(10y - 5 - 2x^2) = 0$$

$$\boxed{5} \qquad 5x^2 - 4y - 4y^3 = 0$$

From Equation 4 we see that either

$$x = 0 \qquad \text{or} \qquad 10y - 5 - 2x^2 = 0$$

In the first case ($x = 0$), Equation 5 becomes $-4y(1 + y^2) = 0$, so $y = 0$ and we have the critical point $(0, 0)$.

In the second case ($10y - 5 - 2x^2 = 0$), we get

$$\boxed{6} \qquad x^2 = 5y - 2.5$$

and, putting this in Equation 5, we have $25y - 12.5 - 4y - 4y^3 = 0$. So we have to solve the cubic equation

$$\boxed{7} \qquad 4y^3 - 21y + 12.5 = 0$$

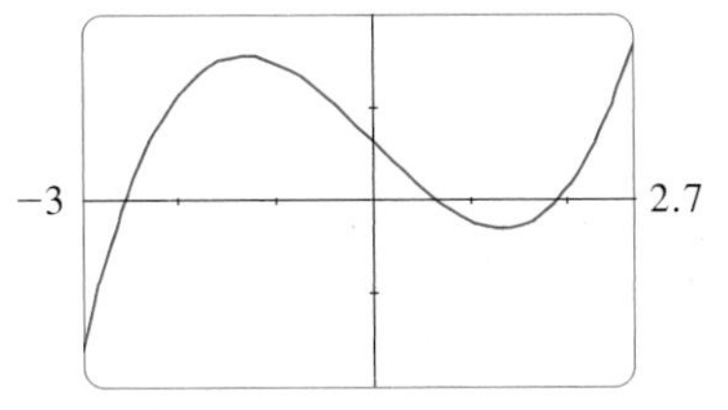

FIGURE 6

Using a graphing calculator or computer to graph the function

$$g(y) = 4y^3 - 21y + 12.5$$

as in Figure 6, we see that Equation 7 has three real roots. By zooming in, we can find the roots to four decimal places:

$$y \approx -2.5452 \qquad y \approx 0.6468 \qquad y \approx 1.8984$$

(Alternatively, we could have used Newton's method or a rootfinder to locate these roots.) From Equation 6, the corresponding x-values are given by

$$x = \pm\sqrt{5y - 2.5}$$

If $y \approx -2.5452$, then x has no corresponding real values. If $y \approx 0.6468$, then $x \approx \pm 0.8567$. If $y \approx 1.8984$, then $x \approx \pm 2.6442$. So we have a total of five critical points, which are analyzed in the following chart. All quantities are rounded to two decimal places.

Critical point	Value of f	f_{xx}	D	Conclusion
$(0, 0)$	0.00	-10.00	80.00	local maximum
$(\pm 2.64, 1.90)$	8.50	-55.93	2488.72	local maximum
$(\pm 0.86, 0.65)$	-1.48	-5.87	-187.64	saddle point

Figures 7 and 8 give two views of the graph of f and we see that the surface opens downward. [This can also be seen from the expression for $f(x, y)$: The dominant terms are $-x^4 - 2y^4$ when $|x|$ and $|y|$ are large.] Comparing the values of f at its local maximum points, we see that the absolute maximum value of f is $f(\pm 2.64, 1.90) \approx 8.50$. In other words, the highest points on the graph of f are $(\pm 2.64, 1.90, 8.50)$.

TEC Visual 11.7 shows several families of surfaces. The surface in Figures 7 and 8 is a member of one of these families.

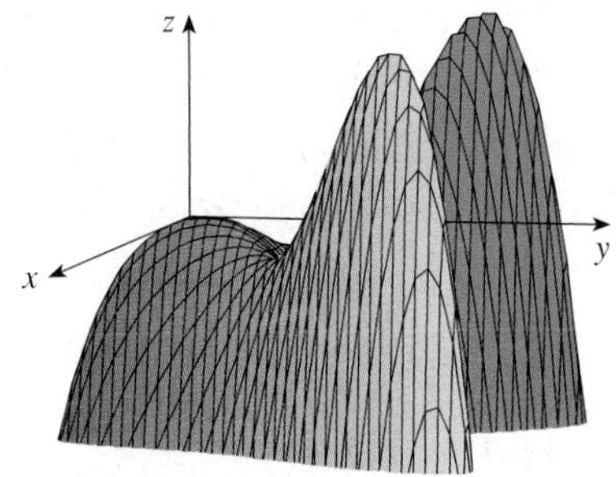

FIGURE 7

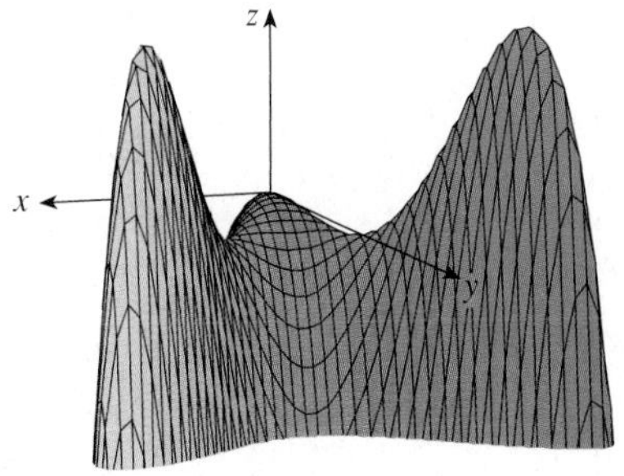

FIGURE 8

The five critical points of the function f in Example 4 are shown in red in the contour map of f in Figure 9.

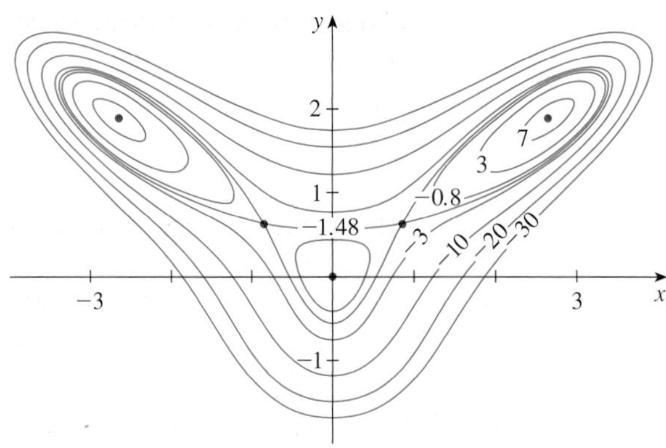

FIGURE 9

V EXAMPLE 5 Find the shortest distance from the point $(1, 0, -2)$ to the plane $x + 2y + z = 4$.

SOLUTION The distance from any point (x, y, z) to the point $(1, 0, -2)$ is

$$d = \sqrt{(x - 1)^2 + y^2 + (z + 2)^2}$$

but if (x, y, z) lies on the plane $x + 2y + z = 4$, then $z = 4 - x - 2y$ and so we have $d = \sqrt{(x - 1)^2 + y^2 + (6 - x - 2y)^2}$. We can minimize d by minimizing the simpler expression

$$d^2 = f(x, y) = (x - 1)^2 + y^2 + (6 - x - 2y)^2$$

By solving the equations

$$f_x = 2(x - 1) - 2(6 - x - 2y) = 4x + 4y - 14 = 0$$

$$f_y = 2y - 4(6 - x - 2y) = 4x + 10y - 24 = 0$$

we find that the only critical point is $\left(\frac{11}{6}, \frac{5}{3}\right)$. Since $f_{xx} = 4$, $f_{xy} = 4$, and $f_{yy} = 10$, we have $D(x, y) = f_{xx}f_{yy} - (f_{xy})^2 = 24 > 0$ and $f_{xx} > 0$, so by the Second Derivatives Test f has a local minimum at $\left(\frac{11}{6}, \frac{5}{3}\right)$. Intuitively, we can see that this local minimum is actually an absolute minimum because there must be a point on the given plane that is closest to $(1, 0, -2)$. If $x = \frac{11}{6}$ and $y = \frac{5}{3}$, then

Example 5 could also be solved using vectors. Compare with the methods of Section 9.5.

$$d = \sqrt{(x - 1)^2 + y^2 + (6 - x - 2y)^2} = \sqrt{\left(\tfrac{5}{6}\right)^2 + \left(\tfrac{5}{3}\right)^2 + \left(\tfrac{5}{6}\right)^2} = \tfrac{5}{6}\sqrt{6}$$

The shortest distance from $(1, 0, -2)$ to the plane $x + 2y + z = 4$ is $\frac{5}{6}\sqrt{6}$.

V EXAMPLE 6 A rectangular box without a lid is to be made from 12 m^2 of cardboard. Find the maximum volume of such a box.

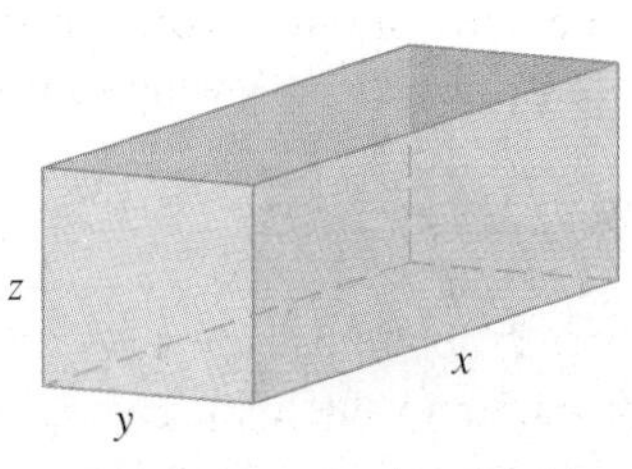

FIGURE 10

SOLUTION Let the length, width, and height of the box (in meters) be x, y, and z, as shown in Figure 10. Then the volume of the box is

$$V = xyz$$

We can express V as a function of just two variables x and y by using the fact that the area of the four sides and the bottom of the box is

$$2xz + 2yz + xy = 12$$

Solving this equation for z, we get $z = (12 - xy)/[2(x + y)]$, so the expression for V becomes

$$V = xy\frac{12 - xy}{2(x + y)} = \frac{12xy - x^2y^2}{2(x + y)}$$

We compute the partial derivatives:

$$\frac{\partial V}{\partial x} = \frac{y^2(12 - 2xy - x^2)}{2(x + y)^2} \qquad \frac{\partial V}{\partial y} = \frac{x^2(12 - 2xy - y^2)}{2(x + y)^2}$$

If V is a maximum, then $\partial V/\partial x = \partial V/\partial y = 0$, but $x = 0$ or $y = 0$ gives $V = 0$, so we must solve the equations

$$12 - 2xy - x^2 = 0 \qquad 12 - 2xy - y^2 = 0$$

These imply that $x^2 = y^2$ and so $x = y$. (Note that x and y must both be positive in this problem.) If we put $x = y$ in either equation we get $12 - 3x^2 = 0$, which gives $x = 2$, $y = 2$, and $z = (12 - 2 \cdot 2)/[2(2 + 2)] = 1$.

We could use the Second Derivatives Test to show that this gives a local maximum of V, or we could simply argue from the physical nature of this problem that there must be an absolute maximum volume, which has to occur at a critical point of V, so it must occur when $x = 2$, $y = 2$, $z = 1$. Then $V = 2 \cdot 2 \cdot 1 = 4$, so the maximum volume of the box is 4 m^3.

Absolute Maximum and Minimum Values

For a function f of one variable, the Extreme Value Theorem says that if f is continuous on a closed interval $[a, b]$, then f has an absolute minimum value and an absolute maximum value. According to the Closed Interval Method in Section 4.2, we found these by evaluating f not only at the critical numbers but also at the endpoints a and b.

There is a similar situation for functions of two variables. Just as a closed interval contains its endpoints, a **closed set** in $\mathbb{R}^2$ is one that contains all its boundary points. [A boundary point of D is a point (a, b) such that every disk with center (a, b) contains points in D and also points not in D.] For instance, the disk

$$D = \{(x, y) \mid x^2 + y^2 \leqslant 1\}$$

which consists of all points on and inside the circle $x^2 + y^2 = 1$, is a closed set because it contains all of its boundary points (which are the points on the circle $x^2 + y^2 = 1$). But if even one point on the boundary curve were omitted, the set would not be closed. (See Figure 11.)

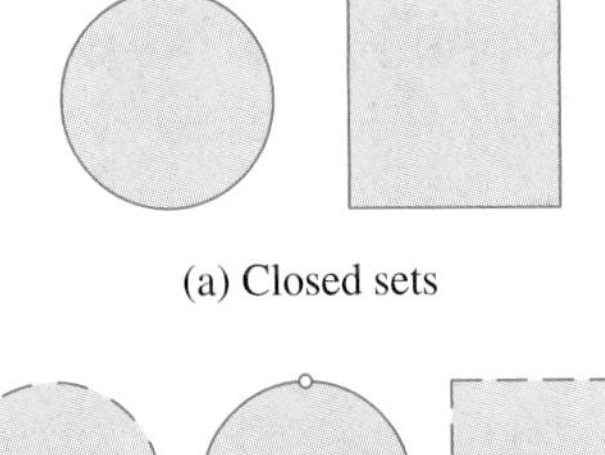

(a) Closed sets

(b) Sets that are not closed

FIGURE 11

A **bounded set** in $\mathbb{R}^2$ is one that is contained within some disk. In other words, it is finite in extent. Then, in terms of closed and bounded sets, we can state the following counterpart of the Extreme Value Theorem in two dimensions.

> **8 Extreme Value Theorem for Functions of Two Variables** If f is continuous on a closed, bounded set D in $\mathbb{R}^2$, then f attains an absolute maximum value $f(x_1, y_1)$ and an absolute minimum value $f(x_2, y_2)$ at some points (x_1, y_1) and (x_2, y_2) in D.

To find the extreme values guaranteed by Theorem 8, we note that, by Theorem 2, if f has an extreme value at (x_1, y_1), then (x_1, y_1) is either a critical point of f or a boundary point of D. Thus we have the following extension of the Closed Interval Method.

9 To find the absolute maximum and minimum values of a continuous function f on a closed, bounded set D:

1. Find the values of f at the critical points of f in D.
2. Find the extreme values of f on the boundary of D.
3. The largest of the values from steps 1 and 2 is the absolute maximum value; the smallest of these values is the absolute minimum value.

EXAMPLE 7 Testing for absolute extreme values on the boundary Find the absolute maximum and minimum values of the function $f(x, y) = x^2 - 2xy + 2y$ on the rectangle $D = \{(x, y) \mid 0 \leqslant x \leqslant 3, 0 \leqslant y \leqslant 2\}$.

SOLUTION Since f is a polynomial, it is continuous on the closed, bounded rectangle D, so Theorem 8 tells us there is both an absolute maximum and an absolute minimum. According to step 1 in (9), we first find the critical points. These occur when

$$f_x = 2x - 2y = 0 \qquad f_y = -2x + 2 = 0$$

so the only critical point is $(1, 1)$, and the value of f there is $f(1, 1) = 1$.

In step 2 we look at the values of f on the boundary of D, which consists of the four line segments L_1, L_2, L_3, L_4 shown in Figure 12. On L_1 we have $y = 0$ and

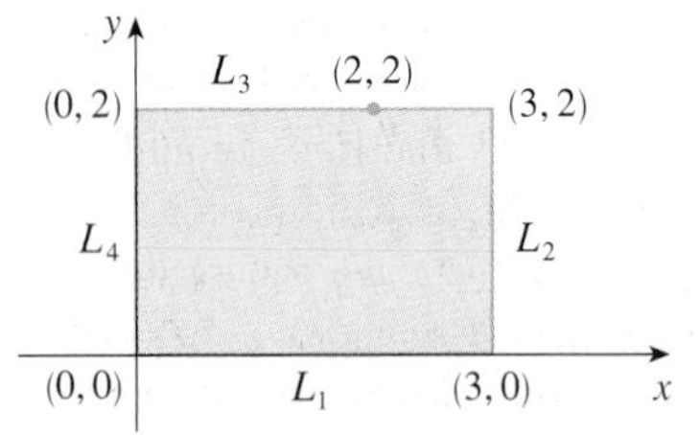

FIGURE 12

$$f(x, 0) = x^2 \qquad 0 \leqslant x \leqslant 3$$

This is an increasing function of x, so its minimum value is $f(0, 0) = 0$ and its maximum value is $f(3, 0) = 9$. On L_2 we have $x = 3$ and

$$f(3, y) = 9 - 4y \qquad 0 \leqslant y \leqslant 2$$

This is a decreasing function of y, so its maximum value is $f(3, 0) = 9$ and its minimum value is $f(3, 2) = 1$. On L_3 we have $y = 2$ and

$$f(x, 2) = x^2 - 4x + 4 \qquad 0 \leqslant x \leqslant 3$$

By the methods of Chapter 4, or simply by observing that $f(x, 2) = (x - 2)^2$, we see that the minimum value of this function is $f(2, 2) = 0$ and the maximum value is $f(0, 2) = 4$. Finally, on L_4 we have $x = 0$ and

$$f(0, y) = 2y \qquad 0 \leqslant y \leqslant 2$$

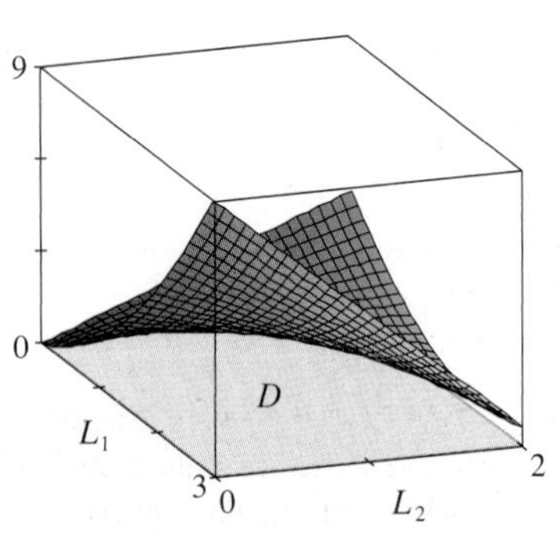

FIGURE 13
$f(x, y) = x^2 - 2xy + 2y$

with maximum value $f(0, 2) = 4$ and minimum value $f(0, 0) = 0$. Thus, on the boundary, the minimum value of f is 0 and the maximum is 9.

In step 3 we compare these values with the value $f(1, 1) = 1$ at the critical point and conclude that the absolute maximum value of f on D is $f(3, 0) = 9$ and the absolute minimum value is $f(0, 0) = f(2, 2) = 0$. Figure 13 shows the graph of f.

11.7 Exercises

1. Suppose $(1, 1)$ is a critical point of a function f with continuous second derivatives. In each case, what can you say about f?

   (a) $f_{xx}(1, 1) = 4, \quad f_{xy}(1, 1) = 1, \quad f_{yy}(1, 1) = 2$

   (b) $f_{xx}(1, 1) = 4, \quad f_{xy}(1, 1) = 3, \quad f_{yy}(1, 1) = 2$

2. Suppose $(0, 2)$ is a critical point of a function g with continuous second derivatives. In each case, what can you say about g?

   (a) $g_{xx}(0, 2) = -1, \quad g_{xy}(0, 2) = 6, \quad g_{yy}(0, 2) = 1$

   (b) $g_{xx}(0, 2) = -1, \quad g_{xy}(0, 2) = 2, \quad g_{yy}(0, 2) = -8$

   (c) $g_{xx}(0, 2) = 4, \quad g_{xy}(0, 2) = 6, \quad g_{yy}(0, 2) = 9$

3–4 Use the level curves in the figure to predict the location of the critical points of f and whether f has a saddle point or a local maximum or minimum at each critical point. Explain your reasoning. Then use the Second Derivatives Test to confirm your predictions.

3. $f(x, y) = 4 + x^3 + y^3 - 3xy$

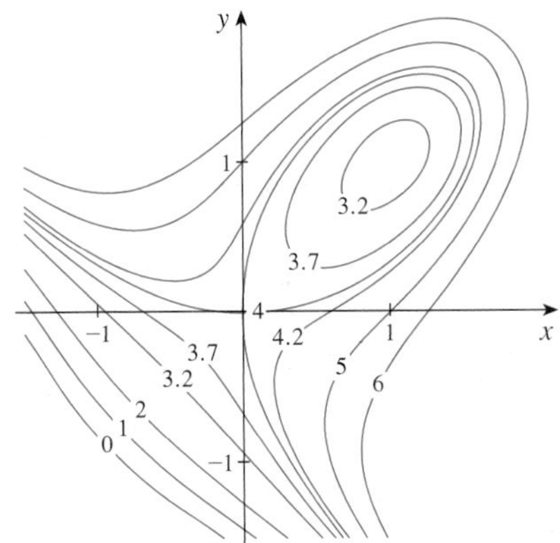

4. $f(x, y) = 3x - x^3 - 2y^2 + y^4$

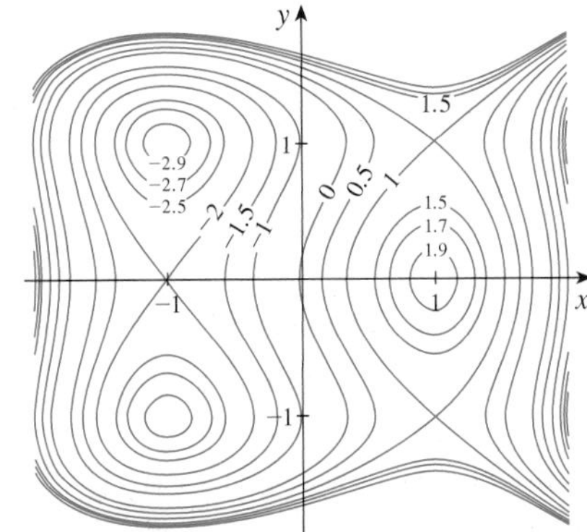

5–16 Find the local maximum and minimum values and saddle point(s) of the function. If you have three-dimensional graphing software, graph the function with a domain and viewpoint that reveal all the important aspects of the function.

5. $f(x, y) = x^2 + xy + y^2 + y$

6. $f(x, y) = x^3y + 12x^2 - 8y$

7. $f(x, y) = x^4 + y^4 - 4xy + 2$

8. $f(x, y) = xe^{-2x^2-2y^2}$

9. $f(x, y) = x^3 - 12xy + 8y^3$

10. $f(x, y) = xy + \dfrac{1}{x} + \dfrac{1}{y}$

11. $f(x, y) = e^x \cos y$

12. $f(x, y) = y \cos x$

13. $f(x, y) = (x^2 + y^2)e^{y^2-x^2}$

14. $f(x, y) = e^y(y^2 - x^2)$

15. $f(x, y) = y^2 - 2y \cos x, \quad -1 \leqslant x \leqslant 7$

16. $f(x, y) = \sin x \sin y, \quad -\pi < x < \pi, \quad -\pi < y < \pi$

17. Show that $f(x, y) = x^2 + 4y^2 - 4xy + 2$ has an infinite number of critical points and that $D = 0$ at each one. Then show that f has a local (and absolute) minimum at each critical point.

18. Show that $f(x, y) = x^2ye^{-x^2-y^2}$ has maximum values at $(\pm 1, 1/\sqrt{2})$ and minimum values at $(\pm 1, -1/\sqrt{2})$. Show also that f has infinitely many other critical points and $D = 0$ at each of them. Which of them give rise to maximum values? Minimum values? Saddle points?

19–22 Use a graph or level curves or both to estimate the local maximum and minimum values and saddle point(s) of the function. Then use calculus to find these values precisely.

19. $f(x, y) = x^2 + y^2 + x^{-2}y^{-2}$

20. $f(x, y) = xye^{-x^2-y^2}$

21. $f(x, y) = \sin x + \sin y + \sin(x + y)$, $0 \leqslant x \leqslant 2\pi, \ 0 \leqslant y \leqslant 2\pi$

22. $f(x, y) = \sin x + \sin y + \cos(x + y)$, $0 \leqslant x \leqslant \pi/4, \ 0 \leqslant y \leqslant \pi/4$

23–26 Use a graphing device as in Example 4 (or Newton's method or a rootfinder) to find the critical points of f correct to three decimal places. Then classify the critical points and find the highest or lowest points on the graph.

23. $f(x, y) = x^4 - 5x^2 + y^2 + 3x + 2$

Graphing calculator or computer with graphing software required

1. Homework Hints available in TEC

24. $f(x, y) = 5 - 10xy - 4x^2 + 3y - y^4$

25. $f(x, y) = 2x + 4x^2 - y^2 + 2xy^2 - x^4 - y^4$

26. $f(x, y) = e^x + y^4 - x^3 + 4 \cos y$

27–32 Find the absolute maximum and minimum values of f on the set D.

27. $f(x, y) = 1 + 4x - 5y$, D is the closed triangular region with vertices $(0, 0)$, $(2, 0)$, and $(0, 3)$

28. $f(x, y) = 3 + xy - x - 2y$, D is the closed triangular region with vertices $(1, 0)$, $(5, 0)$, and $(1, 4)$

29. $f(x, y) = x^2 + y^2 + x^2y + 4$, $D = \{(x, y) \mid |x| \leqslant 1, |y| \leqslant 1\}$

30. $f(x, y) = 4x + 6y - x^2 - y^2$, $D = \{(x, y) \mid 0 \leqslant x \leqslant 4, 0 \leqslant y \leqslant 5\}$

31. $f(x, y) = 2x^3 + y^4$, $D = \{(x, y) \mid x^2 + y^2 \leqslant 1\}$

32. $f(x, y) = x^3 - 3x - y^3 + 12y$, D is the quadrilateral whose vertices are $(-2, 3)$, $(2, 3)$, $(2, 2)$, and $(-2, -2)$.

---

33. For functions of one variable it is impossible for a continuous function to have two local maxima and no local minimum. But for functions of two variables such functions exist. Show that the function

$$f(x, y) = -(x^2 - 1)^2 - (x^2y - x - 1)^2$$

has only two critical points, but has local maxima at both of them. Then use a computer to produce a graph with a carefully chosen domain and viewpoint to see how this is possible.

34. If a function of one variable is continuous on an interval and has only one critical number, then a local maximum has to be an absolute maximum. But this is not true for functions of two variables. Show that the function

$$f(x, y) = 3xe^y - x^3 - e^{3y}$$

has exactly one critical point, and that f has a local maximum there that is not an absolute maximum. Then use a computer to produce a graph with a carefully chosen domain and viewpoint to see how this is possible.

35. Find the shortest distance from the point $(2, 1, -1)$ to the plane $x + y - z = 1$.

36. Find the point on the plane $x - y + z = 4$ that is closest to the point $(1, 2, 3)$.

37. Find the points on the cone $z^2 = x^2 + y^2$ that are closest to the point $(4, 2, 0)$.

38. Find the points on the surface $y^2 = 9 + xz$ that are closest to the origin.

39. Find three positive numbers whose sum is 100 and whose product is a maximum.

40. Find three positive numbers whose sum is 12 and the sum of whose squares is as small as possible.

41. Find the maximum volume of a rectangular box that is inscribed in a sphere of radius r.

42. Find the dimensions of the box with volume 1000 cm^3 that has minimal surface area.

43. Find the volume of the largest rectangular box in the first octant with three faces in the coordinate planes and one vertex in the plane $x + 2y + 3z = 6$.

44. Find the dimensions of the rectangular box with largest volume if the total surface area is given as 64 cm^2.

45. Find the dimensions of a rectangular box of maximum volume such that the sum of the lengths of its 12 edges is a constant c.

46. The base of an aquarium with given volume V is made of slate and the sides are made of glass. If slate costs five times as much (per unit area) as glass, find the dimensions of the aquarium that minimize the cost of the materials.

47. A cardboard box without a lid is to have a volume of $32{,}000 \text{ cm}^3$. Find the dimensions that minimize the amount of cardboard used.

48. A rectangular building is being designed to minimize heat loss. The east and west walls lose heat at a rate of 10 units/m^2 per day, the north and south walls at a rate of 8 units/m^2 per day, the floor at a rate of 1 unit/m^2 per day, and the roof at a rate of 5 units/m^2 per day. Each wall must be at least 30 m long, the height must be at least 4 m, and the volume must be exactly 4000 m^3.

(a) Find and sketch the domain of the heat loss as a function of the lengths of the sides.

(b) Find the dimensions that minimize heat loss. (Check both the critical points and the points on the boundary of the domain.)

(c) Could you design a building with even less heat loss if the restrictions on the lengths of the walls were removed?

49. If the length of the diagonal of a rectangular box must be L, what is the largest possible volume?

50. Three alleles (alternative versions of a gene) A, B, and O determine the four blood types A (AA or AO), B (BB or BO), O (OO), and AB. The Hardy-Weinberg Law states that the proportion of individuals in a population who carry two different alleles is

$$P = 2pq + 2pr + 2rq$$

where p, q, and r are the proportions of A, B, and O in the population. Use the fact that $p + q + r = 1$ to show that P is at most $\frac{2}{3}$.

51. Suppose that a scientist has reason to believe that two quantities x and y are related linearly, that is, $y = mx + b$, at least approximately, for some values of m and b. The scientist performs an experiment and collects data in the form of points $(x_1, y_1), (x_2, y_2), \ldots, (x_n, y_n)$, and then plots these points. The points don't lie exactly on a straight line, so the scientist wants to find constants m and b so that the line $y = mx + b$ "fits" the points as well as possible (see the figure).

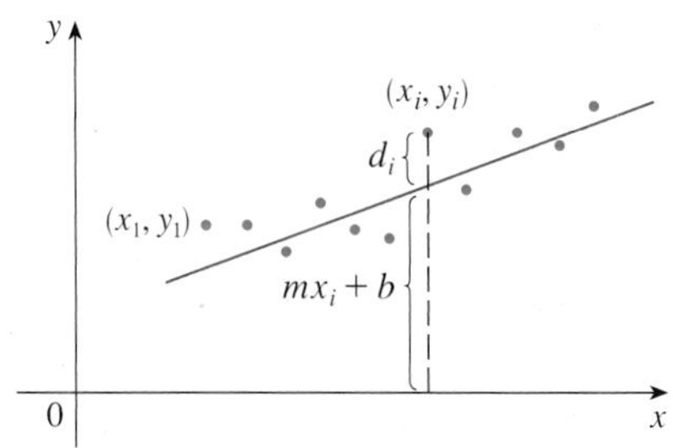

Let $d_i = y_i - (mx_i + b)$ be the vertical deviation of the point (x_i, y_i) from the line. The **method of least squares** determines m and b so as to minimize $\sum_{i=1}^{n} d_i^2$, the sum of the squares of these deviations. Show that, according to this method, the line of best fit is obtained when

$$m \sum_{i=1}^{n} x_i + bn = \sum_{i=1}^{n} y_i$$

$$m \sum_{i=1}^{n} x_i^2 + b \sum_{i=1}^{n} x_i = \sum_{i=1}^{n} x_i y_i$$

Thus the line is found by solving these two equations in the two unknowns m and b. (See Section 1.2 for a further discussion and applications of the method of least squares.)

52. Find an equation of the plane that passes through the point $(1, 2, 3)$ and cuts off the smallest volume in the first octant.

APPLIED PROJECT Designing a Dumpster

For this project we locate a rectangular trash Dumpster in order to study its shape and construction. We then attempt to determine the dimensions of a container of similar design that minimize construction cost.

1. First locate a trash Dumpster in your area. Carefully study and describe all details of its construction, and determine its volume. Include a sketch of the container.

2. While maintaining the general shape and method of construction, determine the dimensions such a container of the same volume should have in order to minimize the cost of construction. Use the following assumptions in your analysis:

- The sides, back, and front are to be made from 12-gauge (0.1046 inch thick) steel sheets, which cost \$0.70 per square foot (including any required cuts or bends).
- The base is to be made from a 10-gauge (0.1345 inch thick) steel sheet, which costs \$0.90 per square foot.
- Lids cost approximately \$50.00 each, regardless of dimensions.
- Welding costs approximately \$0.18 per foot for material and labor combined.

Give justification of any further assumptions or simplifications made of the details of construction.

3. Describe how any of your assumptions or simplifications may affect the final result.

4. If you were hired as a consultant on this investigation, what would your conclusions be? Would you recommend altering the design of the Dumpster? If so, describe the savings that would result.

DISCOVERY PROJECT Quadratic Approximations and Critical Points

The Taylor polynomial approximation to functions of one variable that we discussed in Chapter 8 can be extended to functions of two or more variables. Here we investigate quadratic approximations to functions of two variables and use them to give insight into the Second Derivatives Test for classifying critical points.

In Section 11.4 we discussed the linearization of a function f of two variables at a point (a, b):

$$L(x, y) = f(a, b) + f_x(a, b)(x - a) + f_y(a, b)(y - b)$$

Recall that the graph of L is the tangent plane to the surface $z = f(x, y)$ at $(a, b, f(a, b))$ and the corresponding linear approximation is $f(x, y) \approx L(x, y)$. The linearization L is also called the **first-degree Taylor polynomial** of f at (a, b).

1. If f has continuous second-order partial derivatives at (a, b), then the **second-degree Taylor polynomial** of f at (a, b) is

$$\begin{aligned} Q(x, y) &= f(a, b) + f_x(a, b)(x - a) + f_y(a, b)(y - b) \\ &\quad + \tfrac{1}{2} f_{xx}(a, b)(x - a)^2 + f_{xy}(a, b)(x - a)(y - b) + \tfrac{1}{2} f_{yy}(a, b)(y - b)^2 \end{aligned}$$

and the approximation $f(x, y) \approx Q(x, y)$ is called the **quadratic approximation** to f at (a, b). Verify that Q has the same first- and second-order partial derivatives as f at (a, b).

2. (a) Find the first- and second-degree Taylor polynomials L and Q of $f(x, y) = e^{-x^2-y^2}$ at $(0, 0)$.

(b) Graph f, L, and Q. Comment on how well L and Q approximate f.

3. (a) Find the first- and second-degree Taylor polynomials L and Q for $f(x, y) = xe^y$ at $(1, 0)$.

(b) Compare the values of L, Q, and f at $(0.9, 0.1)$.

(c) Graph f, L, and Q. Comment on how well L and Q approximate f.

4. In this problem we analyze the behavior of the polynomial $f(x, y) = ax^2 + bxy + cy^2$ (without using the Second Derivatives Test) by identifying the graph as a paraboloid.

(a) By completing the square, show that if $a \neq 0$, then

$$f(x, y) = ax^2 + bxy + cy^2 = a\left[\left(x + \frac{b}{2a}y\right)^2 + \left(\frac{4ac - b^2}{4a^2}\right)y^2\right]$$

(b) Let $D = 4ac - b^2$. Show that if $D > 0$ and $a > 0$, then f has a local minimum at $(0, 0)$.

(c) Show that if $D > 0$ and $a < 0$, then f has a local maximum at $(0, 0)$.

(d) Show that if $D < 0$, then $(0, 0)$ is a saddle point.

5. (a) Suppose f is any function with continuous second-order partial derivatives such that $f(0, 0) = 0$ and $(0, 0)$ is a critical point of f. Write an expression for the second-degree Taylor polynomial, Q, of f at $(0, 0)$.

(b) What can you conclude about Q from Problem 4?

(c) In view of the quadratic approximation $f(x, y) \approx Q(x, y)$, what does part (b) suggest about f?

Graphing calculator or computer with graphing software required

11.8 Lagrange Multipliers

In Example 6 in Section 11.7 we maximized a volume function $V = xyz$ subject to the constraint $2xz + 2yz + xy = 12$, which expressed the side condition that the surface area was 12 m^2. In this section we present Lagrange's method for maximizing or minimizing a general function $f(x, y, z)$ subject to a constraint (or side condition) of the form $g(x, y, z) = k$.

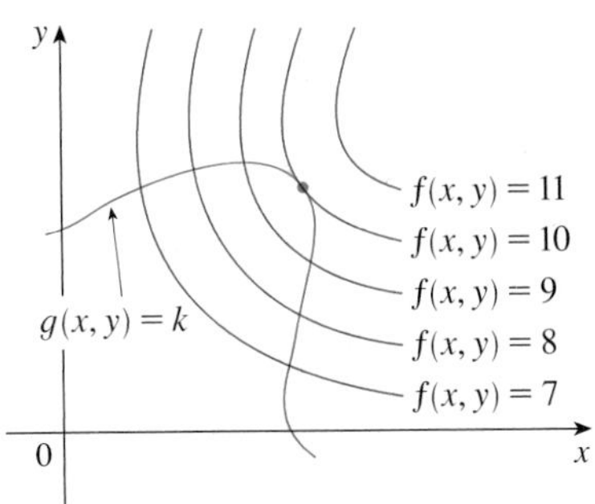

FIGURE 1

TEC Visual 11.8 animates Figure 1 for both level curves and level surfaces.

It's easier to explain the geometric basis of Lagrange's method for functions of two variables. So we start by trying to find the extreme values of $f(x, y)$ subject to a constraint of the form $g(x, y) = k$. In other words, we seek the extreme values of $f(x, y)$ when the point (x, y) is restricted to lie on the level curve $g(x, y) = k$. Figure 1 shows this curve together with several level curves of f. These have the equations $f(x, y) = c$, where $c = 7$, 8, 9, 10, 11. To maximize $f(x, y)$ subject to $g(x, y) = k$ is to find the largest value of c such that the level curve $f(x, y) = c$ intersects $g(x, y) = k$. It appears from Figure 1 that this happens when these curves just touch each other, that is, when they have a common tangent line. (Otherwise, the value of c could be increased further.) This means that the normal lines at the point (x_0, y_0) where they touch are identical. So the gradient vectors are parallel; that is, $\nabla f(x_0, y_0) = \lambda \nabla g(x_0, y_0)$ for some scalar λ.

This kind of argument also applies to the problem of finding the extreme values of $f(x, y, z)$ subject to the constraint $g(x, y, z) = k$. Thus the point (x, y, z) is restricted to lie on the level surface S with equation $g(x, y, z) = k$. Instead of the level curves in Figure 1, we consider the level surfaces $f(x, y, z) = c$ and argue that if the maximum value of f is $f(x_0, y_0, z_0) = c$, then the level surface $f(x, y, z) = c$ is tangent to the level surface $g(x, y, z) = k$ and so the corresponding gradient vectors are parallel.

This intuitive argument can be made precise as follows. Suppose that a function f has an extreme value at a point $P(x_0, y_0, z_0)$ on the surface S and let C be a curve with vector equation $\mathbf{r}(t) = \langle x(t), y(t), z(t) \rangle$ that lies on S and passes through P. If t_0 is the parameter value corresponding to the point P, then $\mathbf{r}(t_0) = \langle x_0, y_0, z_0 \rangle$. The composite function $h(t) = f(x(t), y(t), z(t))$ represents the values that f takes on the curve C. Since f has an extreme value at (x_0, y_0, z_0), it follows that h has an extreme value at t_0, so $h'(t_0) = 0$. But if f is differentiable, we can use the Chain Rule to write

$$\begin{aligned} 0 &= h'(t_0) \\ &= f_x(x_0, y_0, z_0)x'(t_0) + f_y(x_0, y_0, z_0)y'(t_0) + f_z(x_0, y_0, z_0)z'(t_0) \\ &= \nabla f(x_0, y_0, z_0) \cdot \mathbf{r}'(t_0) \end{aligned}$$

This shows that the gradient vector $\nabla f(x_0, y_0, z_0)$ is orthogonal to the tangent vector $\mathbf{r}'(t_0)$ to every such curve C. But we already know from Section 11.6 that the gradient vector of g, $\nabla g(x_0, y_0, z_0)$, is also orthogonal to $\mathbf{r}'(t_0)$ for every such curve. (See Equation 11.6.18.) This means that the gradient vectors $\nabla f(x_0, y_0, z_0)$ and $\nabla g(x_0, y_0, z_0)$ must be parallel. Therefore, if $\nabla g(x_0, y_0, z_0) \neq \mathbf{0}$, there is a number λ such that

Lagrange multipliers are named after the French-Italian mathematician Joseph-Louis Lagrange (1736–1813). See page 272 for a biographical sketch of Lagrange.

1 $$\nabla f(x_0, y_0, z_0) = \lambda \nabla g(x_0, y_0, z_0)$$

The number λ in Equation 1 is called a **Lagrange multiplier**. The procedure based on Equation 1 is as follows.

In deriving Lagrange's method we assumed that $\nabla g \neq \mathbf{0}$. In each of our examples you can check that $\nabla g \neq \mathbf{0}$ at all points where $g(x, y, z) = k$. See Exercise 21 for what can go wrong if $\nabla g = \mathbf{0}$.

Method of Lagrange Multipliers To find the maximum and minimum values of $f(x, y, z)$ subject to the constraint $g(x, y, z) = k$ [assuming that these extreme values exist and $\nabla g \neq \mathbf{0}$ on the surface $g(x, y, z) = k$]:

(a) Find all values of x, y, z, and λ such that

$$\nabla f(x, y, z) = \lambda \nabla g(x, y, z)$$

and

$$g(x, y, z) = k$$

(b) Evaluate f at all the points (x, y, z) that result from step (a). The largest of these values is the maximum value of f; the smallest is the minimum value of f.

If we write the vector equation $\nabla f = \lambda \nabla g$ in terms of components, then the equations in step (a) become

$$f_x = \lambda g_x \qquad f_y = \lambda g_y \qquad f_z = \lambda g_z \qquad g(x, y, z) = k$$

This is a system of four equations in the four unknowns x, y, z, and λ, but it is not necessary to find explicit values for λ.

For functions of two variables the method of Lagrange multipliers is similar to the method just described. To find the extreme values of $f(x, y)$ subject to the constraint $g(x, y) = k$, we look for values of x, y, and λ such that

$$\nabla f(x, y) = \lambda \nabla g(x, y) \qquad \text{and} \qquad g(x, y) = k$$

This amounts to solving three equations in three unknowns:

$$f_x = \lambda g_x \qquad f_y = \lambda g_y \qquad g(x, y) = k$$

Our first illustration of Lagrange's method is to reconsider the problem given in Example 6 in Section 11.7.

V EXAMPLE 1 Maximizing a volume using Lagrange multipliers A rectangular box without a lid is to be made from 12 m^2 of cardboard. Find the maximum volume of such a box.

SOLUTION As in Example 6 in Section 11.7, we let x, y, and z be the length, width, and height, respectively, of the box in meters. Then we wish to maximize

$$V = xyz$$

subject to the constraint

$$g(x, y, z) = 2xz + 2yz + xy = 12$$

Using the method of Lagrange multipliers, we look for values of x, y, z, and λ such that $\nabla V = \lambda \nabla g$ and $g(x, y, z) = 12$. This gives the equations

$$V_x = \lambda g_x$$

$$V_y = \lambda g_y$$

$$V_z = \lambda g_z$$

$$2xz + 2yz + xy = 12$$

which become

$$\boxed{2} \qquad yz = \lambda(2z + y)$$

$$\boxed{3} \qquad xz = \lambda(2z + x)$$

$$\boxed{4} \qquad xy = \lambda(2x + 2y)$$

$$\boxed{5} \qquad 2xz + 2yz + xy = 12$$

There are no general rules for solving systems of equations. Sometimes some ingenuity is required. In the present example you might notice that if we multiply (2) by x, (3) by y, and (4) by z, then the left sides of these equations will be identical. Doing this, we have

Another method for solving the system of equations (2–5) is to solve each of Equations 2, 3, and 4 for λ and then to equate the resulting expressions.

$$\boxed{6} \qquad xyz = \lambda(2xz + xy)$$

$$\boxed{7} \qquad xyz = \lambda(2yz + xy)$$

$$\boxed{8} \qquad xyz = \lambda(2xz + 2yz)$$

We observe that $\lambda \neq 0$ because $\lambda = 0$ would imply $yz = xz = xy = 0$ from (2), (3), and (4) and this would contradict (5). Therefore, from (6) and (7), we have

$$2xz + xy = 2yz + xy$$

which gives $xz = yz$. But $z \neq 0$ (since $z = 0$ would give $V = 0$), so $x = y$. From (7) and (8) we have

$$2yz + xy = 2xz + 2yz$$

which gives $2xz = xy$ and so (since $x \neq 0$) $y = 2z$. If we now put $x = y = 2z$ in (5), we get

$$4z^2 + 4z^2 + 4z^2 = 12$$

Since x, y, and z are all positive, we therefore have $z = 1$ and so $x = 2$ and $y = 2$. This agrees with our answer in Section 11.7.

In geometric terms, Example 2 asks for the highest and lowest points on the curve C in Figure 2 that lies on the paraboloid $z = x^2 + 2y^2$ and directly above the constraint circle $x^2 + y^2 = 1$.

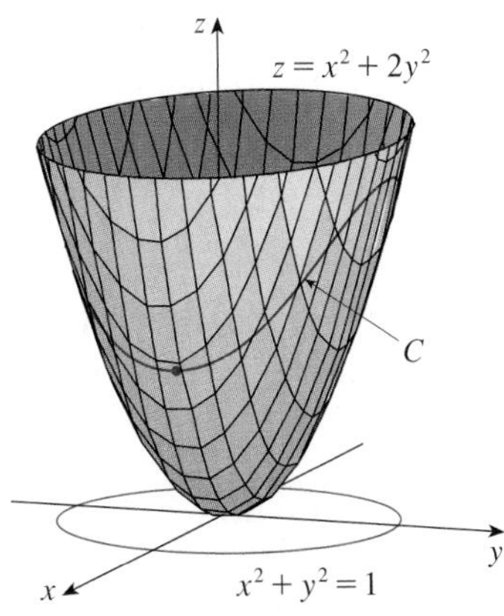

FIGURE 2

V EXAMPLE 2 Find the extreme values of the function $f(x, y) = x^2 + 2y^2$ on the circle $x^2 + y^2 = 1$.

SOLUTION We are asked for the extreme values of f subject to the constraint $g(x, y) = x^2 + y^2 = 1$. Using Lagrange multipliers, we solve the equations $\nabla f = \lambda \nabla g$ and $g(x, y) = 1$, which can be written as

$$f_x = \lambda g_x \qquad f_y = \lambda g_y \qquad g(x, y) = 1$$

or as

$$\boxed{9} \qquad 2x = 2x\lambda$$

$$\boxed{10} \qquad 4y = 2y\lambda$$

$$\boxed{11} \qquad x^2 + y^2 = 1$$

From (9) we have $x = 0$ or $\lambda = 1$. If $x = 0$, then (11) gives $y = \pm 1$. If $\lambda = 1$, then $y = 0$ from (10), so then (11) gives $x = \pm 1$. Therefore f has possible extreme values at the points $(0, 1)$, $(0, -1)$, $(1, 0)$, and $(-1, 0)$. Evaluating f at these four points,

The geometry behind the use of Lagrange multipliers in Example 2 is shown in Figure 3. The extreme values of $f(x, y) = x^2 + 2y^2$ correspond to the level curves that touch the circle $x^2 + y^2 = 1$.

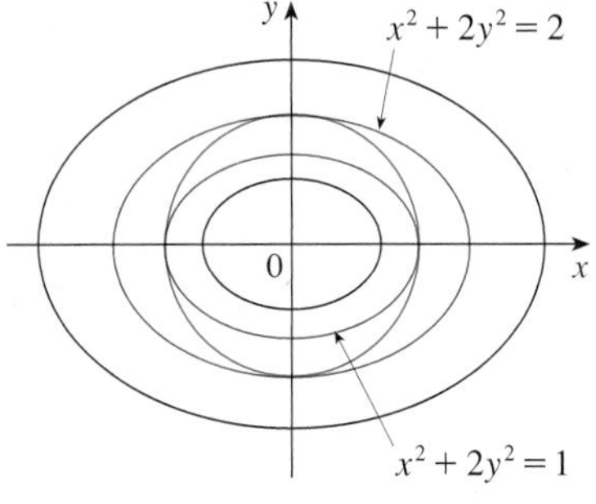

FIGURE 3

we find that

$$f(0, 1) = 2 \qquad f(0, -1) = 2 \qquad f(1, 0) = 1 \qquad f(-1, 0) = 1$$

Therefore the maximum value of f on the circle $x^2 + y^2 = 1$ is $f(0, \pm 1) = 2$ and the minimum value is $f(\pm 1, 0) = 1$. Checking with Figure 2, we see that these values look reasonable.

EXAMPLE 3 Find the extreme values of $f(x, y) = x^2 + 2y^2$ on the disk $x^2 + y^2 \leqslant 1$.

SOLUTION According to the procedure in (11.7.9), we compare the values of f at the critical points with values at the points on the boundary. Since $f_x = 2x$ and $f_y = 4y$, the only critical point is $(0, 0)$. We compare the value of f at that point with the extreme values on the boundary from Example 2:

$$f(0, 0) = 0 \qquad f(\pm 1, 0) = 1 \qquad f(0, \pm 1) = 2$$

Therefore the maximum value of f on the disk $x^2 + y^2 \leqslant 1$ is $f(0, \pm 1) = 2$ and the minimum value is $f(0, 0) = 0$.

EXAMPLE 4 Find the points on the sphere $x^2 + y^2 + z^2 = 4$ that are closest to and farthest from the point $(3, 1, -1)$.

SOLUTION The distance from a point (x, y, z) to the point $(3, 1, -1)$ is

$$d = \sqrt{(x - 3)^2 + (y - 1)^2 + (z + 1)^2}$$

but the algebra is simpler if we instead maximize and minimize the square of the distance:

$$d^2 = f(x, y, z) = (x - 3)^2 + (y - 1)^2 + (z + 1)^2$$

The constraint is that the point (x, y, z) lies on the sphere, that is,

$$g(x, y, z) = x^2 + y^2 + z^2 = 4$$

According to the method of Lagrange multipliers, we solve $\nabla f = \lambda \nabla g$, $g = 4$. This gives

$$2(x - 3) = 2x\lambda \tag{12}$$

$$2(y - 1) = 2y\lambda \tag{13}$$

$$2(z + 1) = 2z\lambda \tag{14}$$

$$x^2 + y^2 + z^2 = 4 \tag{15}$$

The simplest way to solve these equations is to solve for x, y, and z in terms of λ from (12), (13), and (14), and then substitute these values into (15). From (12) we have

$$x - 3 = x\lambda \qquad \text{or} \qquad x(1 - \lambda) = 3 \qquad \text{or} \qquad x = \frac{3}{1 - \lambda}$$

[Note that $1 - \lambda \neq 0$ because $\lambda = 1$ is impossible from (12).] Similarly, (13) and (14)

give

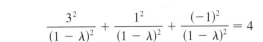

$$y = \frac{1}{1-\lambda} \qquad z = -\frac{1}{1-\lambda}$$

Therefore, from (15), we have

$$\frac{3^2}{(1-\lambda)^2} + \frac{1^2}{(1-\lambda)^2} + \frac{(-1)^2}{(1-\lambda)^2} = 4$$

which gives $(1-\lambda)^2 = \frac{11}{4}$, $1-\lambda = \pm\sqrt{11}/2$, so

$$\lambda = 1 \pm \frac{\sqrt{11}}{2}$$

These values of λ then give the corresponding points (x, y, z):

$$\left(\frac{6}{\sqrt{11}}, \frac{2}{\sqrt{11}}, -\frac{2}{\sqrt{11}}\right) \qquad \text{and} \qquad \left(-\frac{6}{\sqrt{11}}, -\frac{2}{\sqrt{11}}, \frac{2}{\sqrt{11}}\right)$$

It's easy to see that f has a smaller value at the first of these points, so the closest point is $(6/\sqrt{11}, 2/\sqrt{11}, -2/\sqrt{11})$ and the farthest is $(-6/\sqrt{11}, -2/\sqrt{11}, 2/\sqrt{11})$. ■

Figure 4 shows the sphere and the nearest point P in Example 4. Can you see how to find the coordinates of P without using calculus?

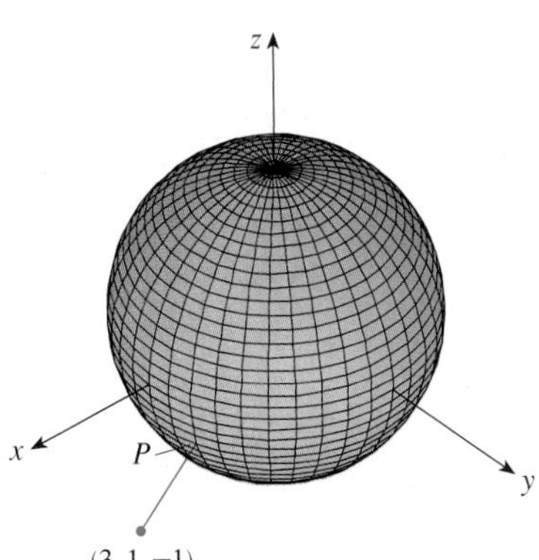

FIGURE 4

Two Constraints

Suppose now that we want to find the maximum and minimum values of a function $f(x, y, z)$ subject to two constraints (side conditions) of the form $g(x, y, z) = k$ and $h(x, y, z) = c$. Geometrically, this means that we are looking for the extreme values of f when (x, y, z) is restricted to lie on the curve of intersection C of the level surfaces $g(x, y, z) = k$ and $h(x, y, z) = c$. (See Figure 5.) Suppose f has such an extreme value at a point $P(x_0, y_0, z_0)$. We know from the beginning of this section that ∇f is orthogonal to C at P. But we also know that ∇g is orthogonal to $g(x, y, z) = k$ and ∇h is orthogonal to $h(x, y, z) = c$, so ∇g and ∇h are both orthogonal to C. This means that the gradient vector $\nabla f(x_0, y_0, z_0)$ is in the plane determined by $\nabla g(x_0, y_0, z_0)$ and $\nabla h(x_0, y_0, z_0)$. (We assume that these gradient vectors are not zero and not parallel.) So there are numbers λ and μ (called Lagrange multipliers) such that

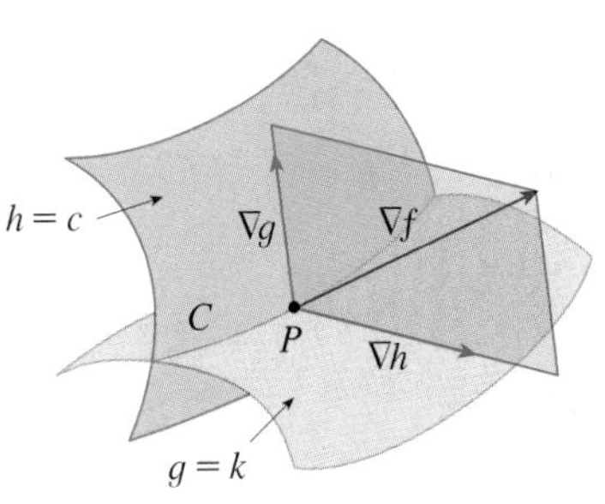

FIGURE 5

16 $$\nabla f(x_0, y_0, z_0) = \lambda \nabla g(x_0, y_0, z_0) + \mu \nabla h(x_0, y_0, z_0)$$

In this case Lagrange's method is to look for extreme values by solving five equations in the five unknowns x, y, z, λ, and μ. These equations are obtained by writing Equation 16 in terms of its components and using the constraint equations:

$$f_x = \lambda g_x + \mu h_x$$

$$f_y = \lambda g_y + \mu h_y$$

$$f_z = \lambda g_z + \mu h_z$$

$$g(x, y, z) = k$$

$$h(x, y, z) = c$$

The cylinder $x^2 + y^2 = 1$ intersects the plane $x - y + z = 1$ in an ellipse (Figure 6). Example 5 asks for the maximum value of f when (x, y, z) is restricted to lie on the ellipse.

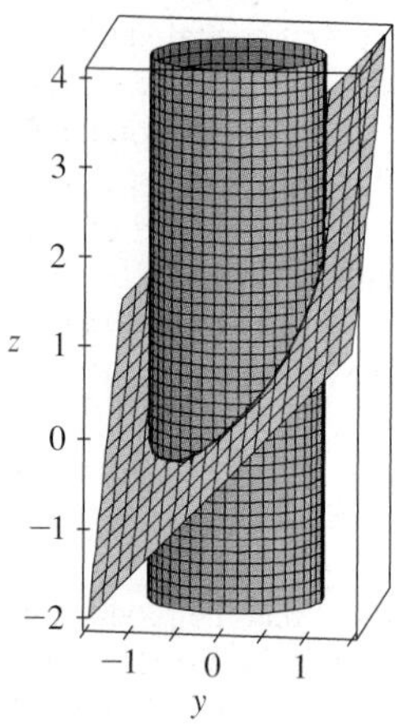

FIGURE 6

V EXAMPLE 5 A maximum problem with two constraints Find the maximum value of the function $f(x, y, z) = x + 2y + 3z$ on the curve of intersection of the plane $x - y + z = 1$ and the cylinder $x^2 + y^2 = 1$.

SOLUTION We maximize the function $f(x, y, z) = x + 2y + 3z$ subject to the constraints $g(x, y, z) = x - y + z = 1$ and $h(x, y, z) = x^2 + y^2 = 1$. The Lagrange condition is $\nabla f = \lambda \nabla g + \mu \nabla h$, so we solve the equations

$$1 = \lambda + 2x\mu \tag{17}$$

$$2 = -\lambda + 2y\mu \tag{18}$$

$$3 = \lambda \tag{19}$$

$$x - y + z = 1 \tag{20}$$

$$x^2 + y^2 = 1 \tag{21}$$

Putting $\lambda = 3$ [from (19)] in (17), we get $2x\mu = -2$, so $x = -1/\mu$. Similarly, (18) gives $y = 5/(2\mu)$. Substitution in (21) then gives

$$\frac{1}{\mu^2} + \frac{25}{4\mu^2} = 1$$

and so $\mu^2 = \frac{29}{4}$, $\mu = \pm\sqrt{29}/2$. Then $x = \mp 2/\sqrt{29}$, $y = \pm 5/\sqrt{29}$, and, from (20), $z = 1 - x + y = 1 \pm 7/\sqrt{29}$. The corresponding values of f are

$$\mp\frac{2}{\sqrt{29}} + 2\left(\pm\frac{5}{\sqrt{29}}\right) + 3\left(1 \pm \frac{7}{\sqrt{29}}\right) = 3 \pm \sqrt{29}$$

Therefore the maximum value of f on the given curve is $3 + \sqrt{29}$.

11.8 Exercises

1. Pictured are a contour map of f and a curve with equation $g(x, y) = 8$. Estimate the maximum and minimum values of f subject to the constraint that $g(x, y) = 8$. Explain your reasoning.

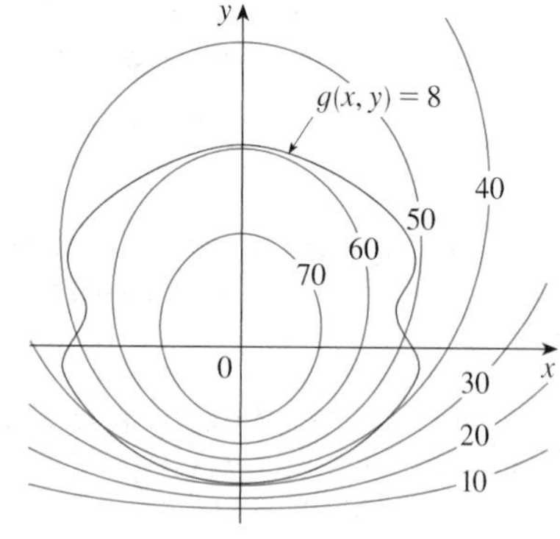

2. (a) Use a graphing calculator or computer to graph the circle $x^2 + y^2 = 1$. On the same screen, graph several curves of the form $x^2 + y = c$ until you find two that just touch the circle. What is the significance of the values of c for these two curves?
   (b) Use Lagrange multipliers to find the extreme values of $f(x, y) = x^2 + y$ subject to the constraint $x^2 + y^2 = 1$. Compare your answers with those in part (a).

3–17 Use Lagrange multipliers to find the maximum and minimum values of the function subject to the given constraint(s).

3. $f(x, y) = x^2 + y^2$; $xy = 1$

4. $f(x, y) = 4x + 6y$; $x^2 + y^2 = 13$

5. $f(x, y) = x^2y$; $x^2 + 2y^2 = 6$

6. $f(x, y) = e^{xy}; \quad x^3 + y^3 = 16$

7. $f(x, y, z) = 2x + 6y + 10z; \quad x^2 + y^2 + z^2 = 35$

8. $f(x, y, z) = 8x - 4z; \quad x^2 + 10y^2 + z^2 = 5$

9. $f(x, y, z) = xyz; \quad x^2 + 2y^2 + 3z^2 = 6$

10. $f(x, y, z) = x^2y^2z^2; \quad x^2 + y^2 + z^2 = 1$

11. $f(x, y, z) = x^2 + y^2 + z^2; \quad x^4 + y^4 + z^4 = 1$

12. $f(x, y, z) = x^4 + y^4 + z^4; \quad x^2 + y^2 + z^2 = 1$

13. $f(x, y, z, t) = x + y + z + t; \quad x^2 + y^2 + z^2 + t^2 = 1$

14. $f(x_1, x_2, \ldots, x_n) = x_1 + x_2 + \cdots + x_n;$

$x_1^2 + x_2^2 + \cdots + x_n^2 = 1$

15. $f(x, y, z) = x + 2y; \quad x + y + z = 1, \quad y^2 + z^2 = 4$

16. $f(x, y, z) = 3x - y - 3z;$
$x + y - z = 0, \quad x^2 + 2z^2 = 1$

17. $f(x, y, z) = yz + xy; \quad xy = 1, \quad y^2 + z^2 = 1$

18–19 Find the extreme values of f on the region described by the inequality.

18. $f(x, y) = 2x^2 + 3y^2 - 4x - 5, \quad x^2 + y^2 \leqslant 16$

19. $f(x, y) = e^{-xy}, \quad x^2 + 4y^2 \leqslant 1$

---

20. Consider the problem of maximizing the function $f(x, y) = 2x + 3y$ subject to the constraint $\sqrt{x} + \sqrt{y} = 5$.
(a) Try using Lagrange multipliers to solve the problem.
(b) Does $f(25, 0)$ give a larger value than the one in part (a)?
(c) Solve the problem by graphing the constraint equation and several level curves of f.
(d) Explain why the method of Lagrange multipliers fails to solve the problem.
(e) What is the significance of $f(9, 4)$?

21. Consider the problem of minimizing the function $f(x, y) = x$ on the curve $y^2 + x^4 - x^3 = 0$ (a piriform).
(a) Try using Lagrange multipliers to solve the problem.
(b) Show that the minimum value is $f(0, 0) = 0$ but the Lagrange condition $\nabla f(0, 0) = \lambda \nabla g(0, 0)$ is not satisfied for any value of λ.
(c) Explain why Lagrange multipliers fail to find the minimum value in this case.

CAS **22.** (a) If your computer algebra system plots implicitly defined curves, use it to estimate the minimum and maximum values of $f(x, y) = x^3 + y^3 + 3xy$ subject to the constraint $(x - 3)^2 + (y - 3)^2 = 9$ by graphical methods.
(b) Solve the problem in part (a) with the aid of Lagrange multipliers. Use your CAS to solve the equations numerically. Compare your answers with those in part (a).

23. The total production P of a certain product depends on the amount L of labor used and the amount K of capital investment. In Sections 11.1 and 11.3 we discussed how the Cobb-Douglas model $P = bL^{\alpha}K^{1-\alpha}$ follows from certain economic assumptions, where b and α are positive constants and $\alpha < 1$. If the cost of a unit of labor is m and the cost of a unit of capital is n, and the company can spend only p dollars as its total budget, then maximizing the production P is subject to the constraint $mL + nK = p$. Show that the maximum production occurs when

$$L = \frac{\alpha p}{m} \quad \text{and} \quad K = \frac{(1 - \alpha)p}{n}$$

24. Referring to Exercise 23, we now suppose that the production is fixed at $bL^{\alpha}K^{1-\alpha} = Q$, where Q is a constant. What values of L and K minimize the cost function $C(L, K) = mL + nK$?

25. Use Lagrange multipliers to prove that the rectangle with maximum area that has a given perimeter p is a square.

26. Use Lagrange multipliers to prove that the triangle with maximum area that has a given perimeter p is equilateral.
Hint: Use Heron's formula for the area:

$$A = \sqrt{s(s - x)(s - y)(s - z)}$$

where $s = p/2$ and x, y, z are the lengths of the sides.

27–39 Use Lagrange multipliers to give an alternate solution to the indicated exercise in Section 11.7.

27. Exercise 35 **28.** Exercise 36

29. Exercise 37 **30.** Exercise 38

31. Exercise 39 **32.** Exercise 40

33. Exercise 41 **34.** Exercise 42

35. Exercise 43 **36.** Exercise 44

37. Exercise 45 **38.** Exercise 46

39. Exercise 49

---

40. Find the maximum and minimum volumes of a rectangular box whose surface area is 1500 cm^2 and whose total edge length is 200 cm.

41. The plane $x + y + 2z = 2$ intersects the paraboloid $z = x^2 + y^2$ in an ellipse. Find the points on this ellipse that are nearest to and farthest from the origin.

42. The plane $4x - 3y + 8z = 5$ intersects the cone $z^2 = x^2 + y^2$ in an ellipse.

(a) Graph the cone, the plane, and the ellipse.

(b) Use Lagrange multipliers to find the highest and lowest points on the ellipse.

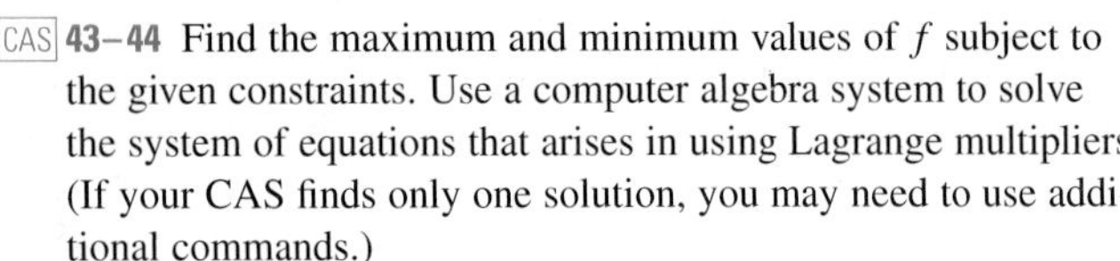

CAS **43–44** Find the maximum and minimum values of f subject to the given constraints. Use a computer algebra system to solve the system of equations that arises in using Lagrange multipliers. (If your CAS finds only one solution, you may need to use additional commands.)

43. $f(x, y, z) = ye^{x-z}$; $9x^2 + 4y^2 + 36z^2 = 36$, $xy + yz = 1$

44. $f(x, y, z) = x + y + z$; $x^2 - y^2 = z$, $x^2 + z^2 = 4$

---

45. (a) Find the maximum value of

$$f(x_1, x_2, \ldots, x_n) = \sqrt[n]{x_1 x_2 \cdots x_n}$$

given that $x_1, x_2, \ldots, x_n$ are positive numbers and $x_1 + x_2 + \cdots + x_n = c$, where c is a constant.

(b) Deduce from part (a) that if $x_1, x_2, \ldots, x_n$ are positive numbers, then

$$\sqrt[n]{x_1 x_2 \cdots x_n} \leqslant \frac{x_1 + x_2 + \cdots + x_n}{n}$$

This inequality says that the geometric mean of n numbers is no larger than the arithmetic mean of the numbers. Under what circumstances are these two means equal?

46. (a) Maximize $\Sigma_{i=1}^{n} x_i y_i$ subject to the constraints $\Sigma_{i=1}^{n} x_i^2 = 1$ and $\Sigma_{i=1}^{n} y_i^2 = 1$.

(b) Put

$$x_i = \frac{a_i}{\sqrt{\Sigma\, a_j^2}} \qquad \text{and} \qquad y_i = \frac{b_i}{\sqrt{\Sigma\, b_j^2}}$$

to show that

$$\sum a_i b_i \leqslant \sqrt{\Sigma\, a_j^2}\,\sqrt{\Sigma\, b_j^2}$$

for any numbers $a_1, \ldots, a_n, b_1, \ldots, b_n$. This inequality is known as the Cauchy-Schwarz Inequality.

APPLIED PROJECT Rocket Science

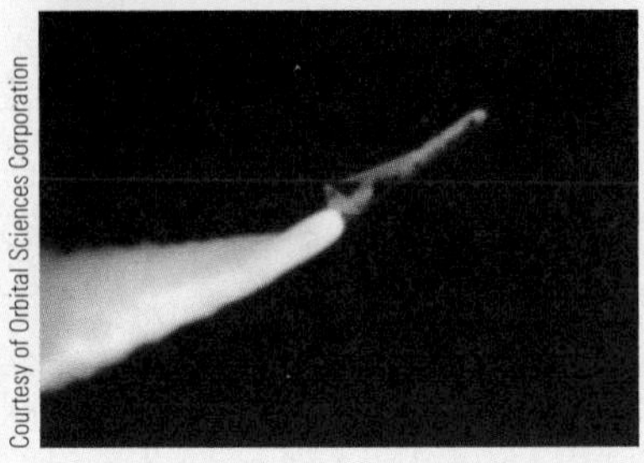

Courtesy of Orbital Sciences Corporation

Many rockets, such as the *Pegasus XL* currently used to launch satellites and the *Saturn V* that first put men on the moon, are designed to use three stages in their ascent into space. A large first stage initially propels the rocket until its fuel is consumed, at which point the stage is jettisoned to reduce the mass of the rocket. The smaller second and third stages function similarly in order to place the rocket's payload into orbit about the earth. (With this design, at least two stages are required in order to reach the necessary velocities, and using three stages has proven to be a good compromise between cost and performance.) Our goal here is to determine the individual masses of the three stages, which are to be designed in such a way as to minimize the total mass of the rocket while enabling it to reach a desired velocity.

For a single-stage rocket consuming fuel at a constant rate, the change in velocity resulting from the acceleration of the rocket vehicle has been modeled by

$$\Delta V = -c \ln\left(1 - \frac{(1 - S)M_r}{P + M_r}\right)$$

where M_r is the mass of the rocket engine including initial fuel, P is the mass of the payload, S is a *structural factor* determined by the design of the rocket (specifically, it is the ratio of the mass of the rocket vehicle without fuel to the total mass of the rocket with payload), and c is the (constant) speed of exhaust relative to the rocket.

Now consider a rocket with three stages and a payload of mass A. Assume that outside forces are negligible and that c and S remain constant for each stage. If M_i is the mass of the ith stage, we can initially consider the rocket engine to have mass M_1 and its payload to have mass $M_2 + M_3 + A$; the second and third stages can be handled similarly.

1. Show that the velocity attained after all three stages have been jettisoned is given by

$$v_f = c\left[\ln\left(\frac{M_1 + M_2 + M_3 + A}{SM_1 + M_2 + M_3 + A}\right) + \ln\left(\frac{M_2 + M_3 + A}{SM_2 + M_3 + A}\right) + \ln\left(\frac{M_3 + A}{SM_3 + A}\right)\right]$$

2. We wish to minimize the total mass $M = M_1 + M_2 + M_3$ of the rocket engine subject to the constraint that the desired velocity v_f from Problem 1 is attained. The method of

Lagrange multipliers is appropriate here, but difficult to implement using the current expressions. To simplify, we define variables N_i so that the constraint equation may be expressed as $v_f = c(\ln N_1 + \ln N_2 + \ln N_3)$. Since M is now difficult to express in terms of the N_i's, we wish to use a simpler function that will be minimized at the same place as M. Show that

$$\frac{M_1 + M_2 + M_3 + A}{M_2 + M_3 + A} = \frac{(1 - S)N_1}{1 - SN_1}$$

$$\frac{M_2 + M_3 + A}{M_3 + A} = \frac{(1 - S)N_2}{1 - SN_2}$$

$$\frac{M_3 + A}{A} = \frac{(1 - S)N_3}{1 - SN_3}$$

and conclude that

$$\frac{M + A}{A} = \frac{(1 - S)^3 N_1 N_2 N_3}{(1 - SN_1)(1 - SN_2)(1 - SN_3)}$$

3. Verify that $\ln((M + A)/A)$ is minimized at the same location as M; use Lagrange multipliers and the results of Problem 2 to find expressions for the values of N_i where the minimum occurs subject to the constraint $v_f = c(\ln N_1 + \ln N_2 + \ln N_3)$. [*Hint:* Use properties of logarithms to help simplify the expressions.]

4. Find an expression for the minimum value of M as a function of v_f.

5. If we want to put a three-stage rocket into orbit 100 miles above the earth's surface, a final velocity of approximately 17,500 mi/h is required. Suppose that each stage is built with a structural factor $S = 0.2$ and an exhaust speed of $c = 6000$ mi/h.
(a) Find the minimum total mass M of the rocket engines as a function of A.
(b) Find the mass of each individual stage as a function of A. (They are not equally sized!)

6. The same rocket would require a final velocity of approximately 24,700 mi/h in order to escape earth's gravity. Find the mass of each individual stage that would minimize the total mass of the rocket engines and allow the rocket to propel a 500-pound probe into deep space.

APPLIED PROJECT

Hydro-Turbine Optimization

The Katahdin Paper Company in Millinocket, Maine, operates a hydroelectric generating station on the Penobscot River. Water is piped from a dam to the power station. The rate at which the water flows through the pipe varies, depending on external conditions.

The power station has three different hydroelectric turbines, each with a known (and unique) power function that gives the amount of electric power generated as a function of the water flow arriving at the turbine. The incoming water can be apportioned in different volumes to each turbine, so the goal is to determine how to distribute water among the turbines to give the maximum total energy production for any rate of flow.

Using experimental evidence and *Bernoulli's equation*, the following quadratic models were determined for the power output of each turbine, along with the allowable flows of operation:

$$KW_1 = (-18.89 + 0.1277Q_1 - 4.08 \cdot 10^{-5}Q_1^2)(170 - 1.6 \cdot 10^{-6}Q_T^2)$$

$$KW_2 = (-24.51 + 0.1358Q_2 - 4.69 \cdot 10^{-5}Q_2^2)(170 - 1.6 \cdot 10^{-6}Q_T^2)$$

$$KW_3 = (-27.02 + 0.1380Q_3 - 3.84 \cdot 10^{-5}Q_3^2)(170 - 1.6 \cdot 10^{-6}Q_T^2)$$

$$250 \leqslant Q_1 \leqslant 1110, \quad 250 \leqslant Q_2 \leqslant 1110, \quad 250 \leqslant Q_3 \leqslant 1225$$

where

$$Q_i = \text{flow through turbine } i \text{ in cubic feet per second}$$

$$KW_i = \text{power generated by turbine } i \text{ in kilowatts}$$

$$Q_T = \text{total flow through the station in cubic feet per second}$$

1. If all three turbines are being used, we wish to determine the flow Q_i to each turbine that will give the maximum total energy production. Our limitations are that the flows must sum to the total incoming flow and the given domain restrictions must be observed. Consequently, use Lagrange multipliers to find the values for the individual flows (as functions of Q_T) that maximize the total energy production $KW_1 + KW_2 + KW_3$ subject to the constraints $Q_1 + Q_2 + Q_3 = Q_T$ and the domain restrictions on each Q_i.

2. For which values of Q_T is your result valid?

3. For an incoming flow of 2500 ft^3/s, determine the distribution to the turbines and verify (by trying some nearby distributions) that your result is indeed a maximum.

4. Until now we have assumed that all three turbines are operating; is it possible in some situations that more power could be produced by using only one turbine? Make a graph of the three power functions and use it to help decide if an incoming flow of 1000 ft^3/s should be distributed to all three turbines or routed to just one. (If you determine that only one turbine should be used, which one would it be?) What if the flow is only 600 ft^3/s?

5. Perhaps for some flow levels it would be advantageous to use two turbines. If the incoming flow is 1500 ft^3/s, which two turbines would you recommend using? Use Lagrange multipliers to determine how the flow should be distributed between the two turbines to maximize the energy produced. For this flow, is using two turbines more efficient than using all three?

6. If the incoming flow is 3400 ft^3/s, what would you recommend to the company?

11 Review

Concept Check

1. (a) What is a function of two variables?
   (b) Describe two methods for visualizing a function of two variables. What is the connection between them?

2. What is a function of three variables? How can you visualize such a function?

3. What does

$$\lim_{(x,y)\to(a,b)} f(x, y) = L$$

mean? How can you show that such a limit does not exist?

4. (a) What does it mean to say that f is continuous at (a, b)?
   (b) If f is continuous on $\mathbb{R}^2$, what can you say about its graph?

5. (a) Write expressions for the partial derivatives $f_x(a, b)$ and $f_y(a, b)$ as limits.
   (b) How do you interpret $f_x(a, b)$ and $f_y(a, b)$ geometrically? How do you interpret them as rates of change?
   (c) If $f(x, y)$ is given by a formula, how do you calculate f_x and f_y?

6. What does Clairaut's Theorem say?

7. How do you find a tangent plane to each of the following types of surfaces?
   (a) A graph of a function of two variables, $z = f(x, y)$
   (b) A level surface of a function of three variables, $F(x, y, z) = k$
   (c) A parametric surface given by a vector function $\mathbf{r}(u, v)$

8. Define the linearization of f at (a, b). What is the corresponding linear approximation? What is the geometric interpretation of the linear approximation?

9. (a) What does it mean to say that f is differentiable at (a, b)?
   (b) How do you usually verify that f is differentiable?

10. If $z = f(x, y)$, what are the differentials dx, dy, and dz?

11. State the Chain Rule for the case where $z = f(x, y)$ and x and y are functions of one variable. What if x and y are functions of two variables?

12. If z is defined implicitly as a function of x and y by an equation of the form $F(x, y, z) = 0$, how do you find $\partial z/\partial x$ and $\partial z/\partial y$?

13. (a) Write an expression as a limit for the directional derivative of f at (x_0, y_0) in the direction of a unit vector $\mathbf{u} = \langle a, b \rangle$. How do you interpret it as a rate? How do you interpret it geometrically?
    (b) If f is differentiable, write an expression for $D_{\mathbf{u}} f(x_0, y_0)$ in terms of f_x and f_y.

14. (a) Define the gradient vector ∇f for a function f of two or three variables.
    (b) Express $D_{\mathbf{u}} f$ in terms of ∇f.
    (c) Explain the geometric significance of the gradient.

15. What do the following statements mean?
    (a) f has a local maximum at (a, b).
    (b) f has an absolute maximum at (a, b).
    (c) f has a local minimum at (a, b).
    (d) f has an absolute minimum at (a, b).
    (e) f has a saddle point at (a, b).

16. (a) If f has a local maximum at (a, b), what can you say about its partial derivatives at (a, b)?
    (b) What is a critical point of f?

17. State the Second Derivatives Test.

18. (a) What is a closed set in $\mathbb{R}^2$? What is a bounded set?
    (b) State the Extreme Value Theorem for functions of two variables.
    (c) How do you find the values that the Extreme Value Theorem guarantees?

19. Explain how the method of Lagrange multipliers works in finding the extreme values of $f(x, y, z)$ subject to the constraint $g(x, y, z) = k$. What if there is a second constraint $h(x, y, z) = c$?

True-False Quiz

Determine whether the statement is true or false. If it is true, explain why. If it is false, explain why or give an example that disproves the statement.

1. $f_y(a, b) = \lim_{y \to b} \dfrac{f(a, y) - f(a, b)}{y - b}$

2. There exists a function f with continuous second-order partial derivatives such that $f_x(x, y) = x + y^2$ and $f_y(x, y) = x - y^2$.

3. $f_{xy} = \dfrac{\partial^2 f}{\partial x \, \partial y}$

4. $D_{\mathbf{k}} f(x, y, z) = f_z(x, y, z)$

5. If $f(x, y) \to L$ as $(x, y) \to (a, b)$ along every straight line through (a, b), then $\lim_{(x, y) \to (a, b)} f(x, y) = L$.

6. If $f_x(a, b)$ and $f_y(a, b)$ both exist, then f is differentiable at (a, b).

7. If f has a local minimum at (a, b) and f is differentiable at (a, b), then $\nabla f(a, b) = \mathbf{0}$.

8. If f is a function, then
$$\lim_{(x, y) \to (2, 5)} f(x, y) = f(2, 5)$$

9. If $f(x, y) = \ln y$, then $\nabla f(x, y) = 1/y$.

10. If $(2, 1)$ is a critical point of f and
$$f_{xx}(2, 1)\, f_{yy}(2, 1) < [f_{xy}(2, 1)]^2$$
then f has a saddle point at $(2, 1)$.

11. If $f(x, y) = \sin x + \sin y$, then $-\sqrt{2} \leqslant D_{\mathbf{u}} f(x, y) \leqslant \sqrt{2}$.

12. If $f(x, y)$ has two local maxima, then f must have a local minimum.

Exercises

1–2 Find and sketch the domain of the function.

1. $f(x, y) = \ln(x + y + 1)$

2. $f(x, y) = \sqrt{4 - x^2 - y^2} + \sqrt{1 - x^2}$

3–4 Sketch the graph of the function.

3. $f(x, y) = 1 - y^2$

4. $f(x, y) = x^2 + (y - 2)^2$

Graphing calculator or computer with graphing software required

5–6 Sketch several level curves of the function.

5. $f(x, y) = \sqrt{4x^2 + y^2}$ **6.** $f(x, y) = e^x + y$

7. Make a rough sketch of a contour map for the function whose graph is shown.

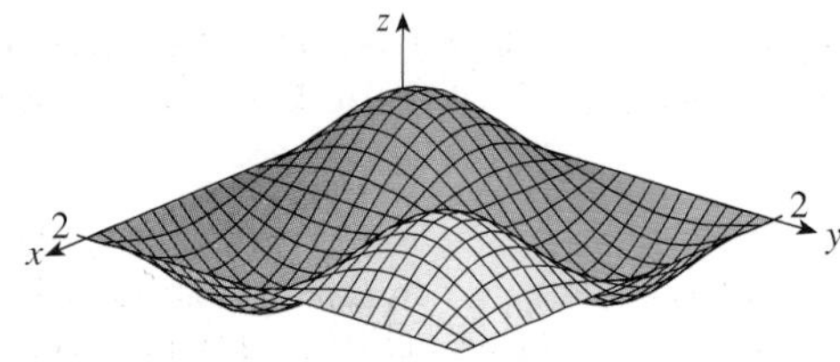

8. A contour map of a function f is shown. Use it to make a rough sketch of the graph of f.

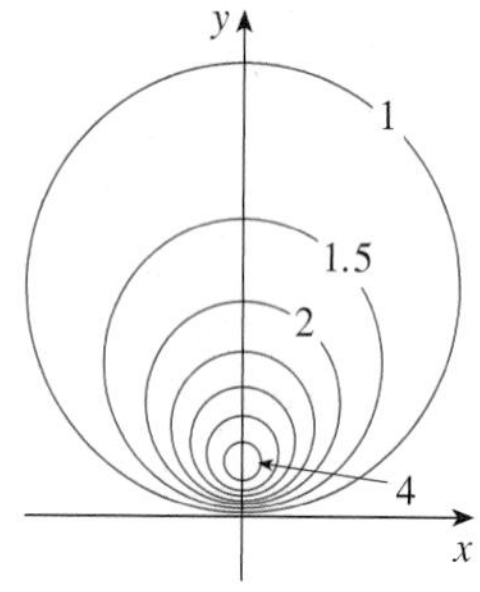

9–10 Evaluate the limit or show that it does not exist.

9. $\lim_{(x, y)\to(1, 1)} \dfrac{2xy}{x^2 + 2y^2}$ **10.** $\lim_{(x, y)\to(0, 0)} \dfrac{2xy}{x^2 + 2y^2}$

11. A metal plate is situated in the xy-plane and occupies the rectangle $0 \leqslant x \leqslant 10$, $0 \leqslant y \leqslant 8$, where x and y are measured in meters. The temperature at the point (x, y) in the plate is $T(x, y)$, where T is measured in degrees Celsius. Temperatures at equally spaced points were measured and recorded in the table.

(a) Estimate the values of the partial derivatives $T_x(6, 4)$ and $T_y(6, 4)$. What are the units?

(b) Estimate the value of $D_{\mathbf{u}} T(6, 4)$, where $\mathbf{u} = (\mathbf{i} + \mathbf{j})/\sqrt{2}$. Interpret your result.

(c) Estimate the value of $T_{xy}(6, 4)$.

x \ y	0	2	4	6	8
0	30	38	45	51	55
2	52	56	60	62	61
4	78	74	72	68	66
6	98	87	80	75	71
8	96	90	86	80	75
10	92	92	91	87	78

12. Find a linear approximation to the temperature function $T(x, y)$ in Exercise 11 near the point $(6, 4)$. Then use it to estimate the temperature at the point $(5, 3.8)$.

13–17 Find the first partial derivatives.

13. $f(x, y) = \sqrt{2x + y^2}$ **14.** $u = e^{-r} \sin 2\theta$

15. $g(u, v) = u \tan^{-1} v$ **16.** $w = \dfrac{x}{y - z}$

17. $T(p, q, r) = p \ln(q + e^r)$

18. The speed of sound traveling through ocean water is a function of temperature, salinity, and pressure. It has been modeled by the function

$$C = 1449.2 + 4.6T - 0.055T^2 + 0.00029T^3 + (1.34 - 0.01T)(S - 35) + 0.016D$$

where C is the speed of sound (in meters per second), T is the temperature (in degrees Celsius), S is the salinity (the concentration of salts in parts per thousand, which means the number of grams of dissolved solids per 1000 g of water), and D is the depth below the ocean surface (in meters). Compute $\partial C/\partial T$, $\partial C/\partial S$, and $\partial C/\partial D$ when $T = 10°\text{C}$, $S = 35$ parts per thousand, and $D = 100$ m. Explain the physical significance of these partial derivatives.

19–22 Find all second partial derivatives of f.

19. $f(x, y) = 4x^3 - xy^2$ **20.** $z = xe^{-2y}$

21. $f(x, y, z) = x^k y^l z^m$ **22.** $v = r\cos(s + 2t)$

23. If $z = xy + xe^{y/x}$, show that $x\dfrac{\partial z}{\partial x} + y\dfrac{\partial z}{\partial y} = xy + z$.

24. If $z = \sin(x + \sin t)$, show that

$$\frac{\partial z}{\partial x}\frac{\partial^2 z}{\partial x\,\partial t} = \frac{\partial z}{\partial t}\frac{\partial^2 z}{\partial x^2}$$

25–29 Find equations of (a) the tangent plane and (b) the normal line to the given surface at the specified point.

25. $z = 3x^2 - y^2 + 2x$, $(1, -2, 1)$

26. $z = e^x \cos y$, $(0, 0, 1)$

27. $x^2 + 2y^2 - 3z^2 = 3$, $(2, -1, 1)$

28. $xy + yz + zx = 3$, $(1, 1, 1)$

29. $\mathbf{r}(u, v) = (u + v)\,\mathbf{i} + u^2\,\mathbf{j} + v^2\,\mathbf{k}$, $(3, 4, 1)$

30. Use a computer to graph the surface $z = x^2 + y^4$ and its tangent plane and normal line at $(1, 1, 2)$ on the same screen. Choose the domain and viewpoint so that you get a good view of all three objects.

31. Find the points on the hyperboloid $x^2 + 4y^2 - z^2 = 4$ where the tangent plane is parallel to the plane $2x + 2y + z = 5$.

32. Find du if $u = \ln(1 + se^{2t})$.

33. Find the linear approximation of the function $f(x, y, z) = x^3\sqrt{y^2 + z^2}$ at the point (2, 3, 4) and use it to estimate the number $(1.98)^3\sqrt{(3.01)^2 + (3.97)^2}$.

34. The two legs of a right triangle are measured as 5 m and 12 m with a possible error in measurement of at most 0.2 cm in each. Use differentials to estimate the maximum error in the calculated value of (a) the area of the triangle and (b) the length of the hypotenuse.

35. If $u = x^2y^3 + z^4$, where $x = p + 3p^2$, $y = pe^p$, and $z = p \sin p$, use the Chain Rule to find du/dp.

36. If $v = x^2 \sin y + ye^{xy}$, where $x = s + 2t$ and $y = st$, use the Chain Rule to find $\partial v/\partial s$ and $\partial v/\partial t$ when $s = 0$ and $t = 1$.

37. Suppose $z = f(x, y)$, where $x = g(s, t)$, $y = h(s, t)$, $g(1, 2) = 3$, $g_s(1, 2) = -1$, $g_t(1, 2) = 4$, $h(1, 2) = 6$, $h_s(1, 2) = -5$, $h_t(1, 2) = 10$, $f_x(3, 6) = 7$, and $f_y(3, 6) = 8$. Find $\partial z/\partial s$ and $\partial z/\partial t$ when $s = 1$ and $t = 2$.

38. Use a tree diagram to write out the Chain Rule for the case where $w = f(t, u, v)$, $t = t(p, q, r, s)$, $u = u(p, q, r, s)$, and $v = v(p, q, r, s)$ are all differentiable functions.

39. If $z = y + f(x^2 - y^2)$, where f is differentiable, show that

$$y\frac{\partial z}{\partial x} + x\frac{\partial z}{\partial y} = x$$

40. The length x of a side of a triangle is increasing at a rate of 3 in/s, the length y of another side is decreasing at a rate of 2 in/s, and the contained angle θ is increasing at a rate of 0.05 radian/s. How fast is the area of the triangle changing when $x = 40$ in, $y = 50$ in, and $\theta = \pi/6$?

41. If $z = f(u, v)$, where $u = xy$, $v = y/x$, and f has continuous second partial derivatives, show that

$$x^2\frac{\partial^2 z}{\partial x^2} - y^2\frac{\partial^2 z}{\partial y^2} = -4uv\frac{\partial^2 z}{\partial u\,\partial v} + 2v\frac{\partial z}{\partial v}$$

42. If $\cos(xyz) = 1 + x^2y^2 + z^2$, find $\dfrac{\partial z}{\partial x}$ and $\dfrac{\partial z}{\partial y}$.

43. Find the gradient of the function $f(x, y, z) = x^2e^{yz^2}$.

44. (a) When is the directional derivative of f a maximum?
(b) When is it a minimum?
(c) When is it 0?
(d) When is it half of its maximum value?

45–46 Find the directional derivative of f at the given point in the indicated direction.

45. $f(x, y) = x^2e^{-y}$, $(-2, 0)$, in the direction toward the point $(2, -3)$

46. $f(x, y, z) = x^2y + x\sqrt{1 + z}$, $(1, 2, 3)$, in the direction of $\mathbf{v} = 2\mathbf{i} + \mathbf{j} - 2\mathbf{k}$

47. Find the maximum rate of change of $f(x, y) = x^2y + \sqrt{y}$ at the point (2, 1). In which direction does it occur?

48. Find the direction in which $f(x, y, z) = ze^{xy}$ increases most rapidly at the point (0, 1, 2). What is the maximum rate of increase?

49. The contour map shows wind speed in knots during Hurricane Andrew on August 24, 1992. Use it to estimate the value of the directional derivative of the wind speed at Homestead, Florida, in the direction of the eye of the hurricane.

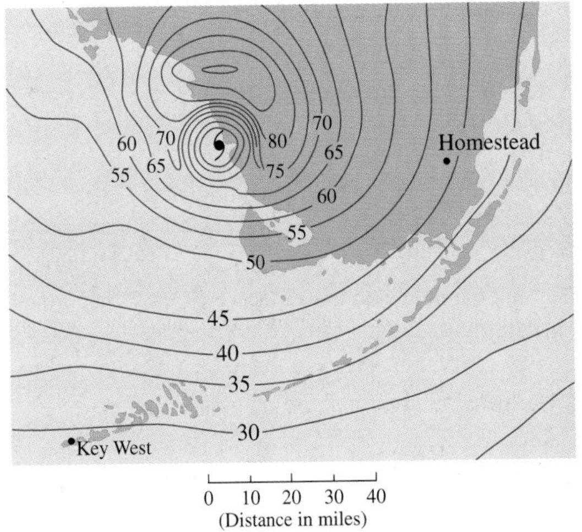

50. Find parametric equations of the tangent line at the point $(-2, 2, 4)$ to the curve of intersection of the surface $z = 2x^2 - y^2$ and the plane $z = 4$.

51–54 Find the local maximum and minimum values and saddle points of the function. If you have three-dimensional graphing software, graph the function with a domain and viewpoint that reveal all the important aspects of the function.

51. $f(x, y) = x^2 - xy + y^2 + 9x - 6y + 10$

52. $f(x, y) = x^3 - 6xy + 8y^3$

53. $f(x, y) = 3xy - x^2y - xy^2$

54. $f(x, y) = (x^2 + y)e^{y/2}$

55–56 Find the absolute maximum and minimum values of f on the set D.

55. $f(x, y) = 4xy^2 - x^2y^2 - xy^3$; D is the closed triangular region in the xy-plane with vertices (0, 0), (0, 6), and (6, 0)

56. $f(x, y) = e^{-x^2-y^2}(x^2 + 2y^2)$; D is the disk $x^2 + y^2 \leq 4$

57. Use a graph or level curves or both to estimate the local maximum and minimum values and saddle points of $f(x, y) = x^3 - 3x + y^4 - 2y^2$. Then use calculus to find these values precisely.

58. Use a graphing calculator or computer (or Newton's method or a computer algebra system) to find the critical points of $f(x, y) = 12 + 10y - 2x^2 - 8xy - y^4$ correct to three decimal places. Then classify the critical points and find the highest point on the graph.

59–62 Use Lagrange multipliers to find the maximum and minimum values of f subject to the given constraint(s).

59. $f(x, y) = x^2y; \quad x^2 + y^2 = 1$

60. $f(x, y) = \dfrac{1}{x} + \dfrac{1}{y}; \quad \dfrac{1}{x^2} + \dfrac{1}{y^2} = 1$

61. $f(x, y, z) = xyz; \quad x^2 + y^2 + z^2 = 3$

62. $f(x, y, z) = x^2 + 2y^2 + 3z^2;$
$x + y + z = 1, \quad x - y + 2z = 2$

63. Find the points on the surface $xy^2z^3 = 2$ that are closest to the origin.

64. A package in the shape of a rectangular box can be mailed by the US Postal Service if the sum of its length and girth (the perimeter of a cross-section perpendicular to the length) is at most 108 in. Find the dimensions of the package with largest volume that can be mailed.

65. A pentagon is formed by placing an isosceles triangle on a rectangle, as shown in the figure. If the pentagon has fixed perimeter P, find the lengths of the sides of the pentagon that maximize the area of the pentagon.

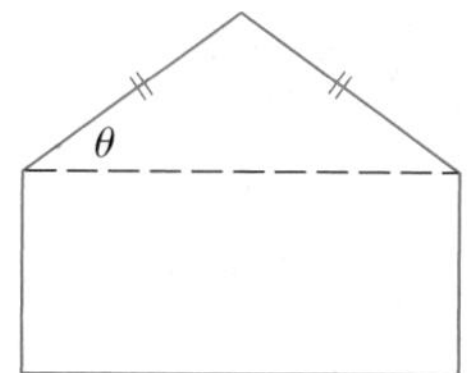

66. A particle of mass m moves on the surface $z = f(x, y)$. Let $x = x(t)$ and $y = y(t)$ be the x- and y-coordinates of the particle at time t.

(a) Find the velocity vector $\mathbf{v}$ and the kinetic energy $K = \frac{1}{2}m|\mathbf{v}|^2$ of the particle.

(b) Determine the acceleration vector $\mathbf{a}$.

(c) Let $z = x^2 + y^2$ and $x(t) = t\cos t$, $y(t) = t\sin t$. Find the velocity vector, the kinetic energy, and the acceleration vector.

Focus on Problem Solving

1. A rectangle with length L and width W is cut into four smaller rectangles by two lines parallel to the sides. Find the maximum and minimum values of the sum of the squares of the areas of the smaller rectangles.

2. Marine biologists have determined that when a shark detects the presence of blood in the water, it will swim in the direction in which the concentration of the blood increases most rapidly. Based on certain tests, the concentration of blood (in parts per million) at a point $P(x, y)$ on the surface of seawater is approximated by

$$C(x, y) = e^{-(x^2+2y^2)/10^4}$$

where x and y are measured in meters in a rectangular coordinate system with the blood source at the origin.
   (a) Identify the level curves of the concentration function and sketch several members of this family together with a path that a shark will follow to the source.
   (b) Suppose a shark is at the point (x_0, y_0) when it first detects the presence of blood in the water. Find an equation of the shark's path by setting up and solving a differential equation.

3. A long piece of galvanized sheet metal with width w is to be bent into a symmetric form with three straight sides to make a rain gutter. A cross-section is shown in the figure.
   (a) Determine the dimensions that allow the maximum possible flow; that is, find the dimensions that give the maximum possible cross-sectional area.
   (b) Would it be better to bend the metal into a gutter with a semicircular cross-section?

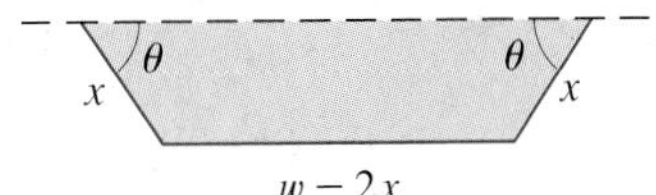

4. For what values of the number r is the function

$$f(x, y, z) = \begin{cases} \dfrac{(x + y + z)^r}{x^2 + y^2 + z^2} & \text{if } (x, y, z) \neq (0, 0, 0) \\ 0 & \text{if } (x, y, z) = (0, 0, 0) \end{cases}$$

continuous on $\mathbb{R}^3$?

5. Suppose f is a differentiable function of one variable. Show that all tangent planes to the surface $z = xf(y/x)$ intersect in a common point.

6. (a) Newton's method for approximating a root of an equation $f(x) = 0$ (see Section 4.7) can be adapted to approximating a solution of a system of equations $f(x, y) = 0$ and $g(x, y) = 0$. The surfaces $z = f(x, y)$ and $z = g(x, y)$ intersect in a curve that intersects the xy-plane at the point (r, s), which is the solution of the system. If an initial approximation (x_1, y_1) is close to this point, then the tangent planes to the surfaces at (x_1, y_1) intersect in a straight line that intersects the xy-plane in a point (x_2, y_2), which should be closer to (r, s). (Compare with Figure 2 in Section 4.7.) Show that

$$x_2 = x_1 - \frac{fg_y - f_y g}{f_x g_y - f_y g_x} \quad \text{and} \quad y_2 = y_1 - \frac{f_x g - fg_x}{f_x g_y - f_y g_x}$$

where f, g, and their partial derivatives are evaluated at (x_1, y_1). If we continue this procedure, we obtain successive approximations (x_n, y_n).

(b) It was Thomas Simpson (1710–1761) who formulated Newton's method as we know it today and who extended it to functions of two variables as in part (a). (See the biography of Simpson on page 408.) The example that he gave to illustrate the method was to solve the system of equations

$$x^x + y^y = 1000 \qquad x^y + y^x = 100$$

In other words, he found the points of intersection of the curves in the figure. Use the method of part (a) to find the coordinates of the points of intersection correct to six decimal places.

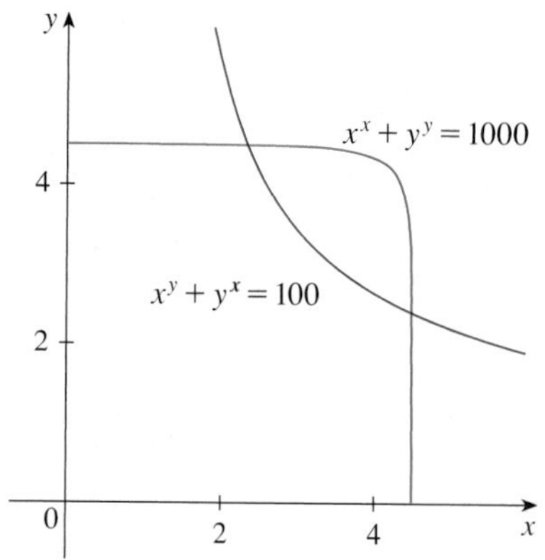

7. (a) Show that when Laplace's equation

$$\frac{\partial^2 u}{\partial x^2} + \frac{\partial^2 u}{\partial y^2} + \frac{\partial^2 u}{\partial z^2} = 0$$

is written in cylindrical coordinates, it becomes

$$\frac{\partial^2 u}{\partial r^2} + \frac{1}{r}\frac{\partial u}{\partial r} + \frac{1}{r^2}\frac{\partial^2 u}{\partial \theta^2} + \frac{\partial^2 u}{\partial z^2} = 0$$

(b) Show that when Laplace's equation is written in spherical coordinates, it becomes

$$\frac{\partial^2 u}{\partial \rho^2} + \frac{2}{\rho}\frac{\partial u}{\partial \rho} + \frac{\cot \phi}{\rho^2}\frac{\partial u}{\partial \phi} + \frac{1}{\rho^2}\frac{\partial^2 u}{\partial \phi^2} + \frac{1}{\rho^2 \sin^2\phi}\frac{\partial^2 u}{\partial \theta^2} = 0$$

8. Among all planes that are tangent to the surface $xy^2z^2 = 1$, find the ones that are farthest from the origin.

9. If the ellipse $x^2/a^2 + y^2/b^2 = 1$ is to enclose the circle $x^2 + y^2 = 2y$, what values of a and b minimize the area of the ellipse?

33–40 Solve the inequality.

33. $|x| < 3$

34. $|x| \geq 3$

35. $|x - 4| < 1$

36. $|x - 6| < 0.1$

37. $|x + 5| \geq 2$

38. $|x + 1| \geq 3$

39. $|2x - 3| \leq 0.4$

40. $|5x - 2| < 6$

41. Solve the inequality $a(bx - c) \geq bc$ for x, assuming that a, b, and c are positive constants.

42. Solve the inequality $ax + b < c$ for x, assuming that a, b, and c are negative constants.

43. Prove that $|ab| = |a||b|$. [*Hint:* Use Equation 3.]

44. Show that if $0 < a < b$, then $a^2 < b^2$.

B Coordinate Geometry

The points in a plane can be identified with ordered pairs of real numbers. We start by drawing two perpendicular coordinate lines that intersect at the origin O on each line. Usually one line is horizontal with positive direction to the right and is called the x-axis; the other line is vertical with positive direction upward and is called the y-axis.

Any point P in the plane can be located by a unique ordered pair of numbers as follows. Draw lines through P perpendicular to the x- and y-axes. These lines intersect the axes in points with coordinates a and b as shown in Figure 1. Then the point P is assigned the ordered pair (a, b). The first number a is called the **x-coordinate** of P; the second number b is called the **y-coordinate** of P. We say that P is the point with coordinates (a, b), and we denote the point by the symbol $P(a, b)$. Several points are labeled with their coordinates in Figure 2.

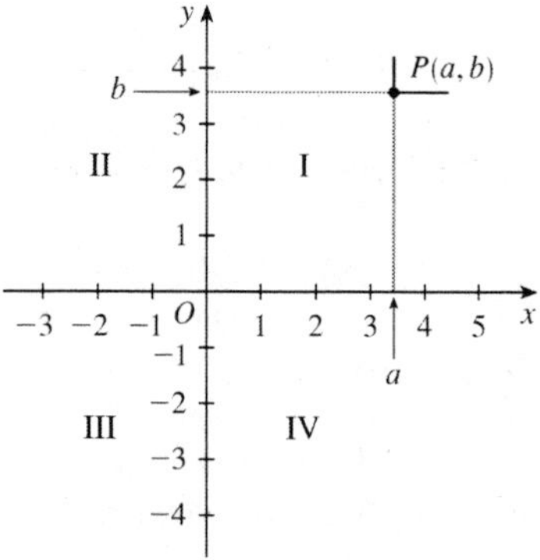

FIGURE 1

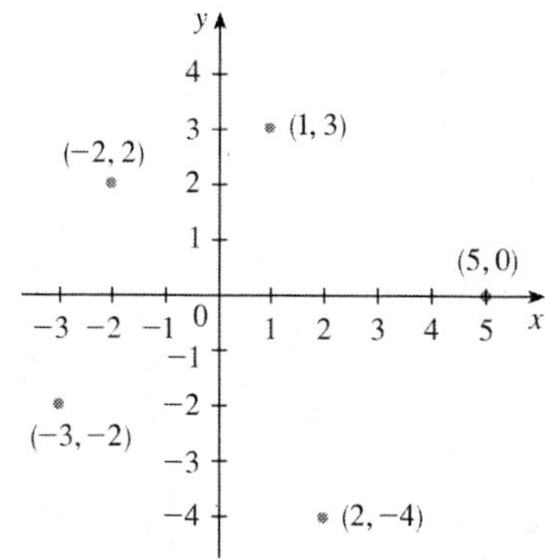

FIGURE 2

By reversing the preceding process we can start with an ordered pair (a, b) and arrive at the corresponding point P. Often we identify the point P with the ordered pair (a, b) and refer to "the point (a, b)." [Although the notation used for an open interval (a, b) is the same as the notation used for a point (a, b), you will be able to tell from the context which meaning is intended.]

This coordinate system is called the **rectangular coordinate system** or the **Cartesian coordinate system** in honor of the French mathematician René Descartes (1596–1650), even though another Frenchman, Pierre Fermat (1601–1665), invented the principles of analytic geometry at about the same time as Descartes. The plane supplied with this coordinate system is called the **coordinate plane** or the **Cartesian plane** and is denoted by $\mathbb{R}^2$.

The x- and y-axes are called the **coordinate axes** and divide the Cartesian plane into four quadrants, which are labeled I, II, III, and IV in Figure 1. Notice that the first quadrant consists of those points whose x- and y-coordinates are both positive.

EXAMPLE 1 Describe and sketch the regions given by the following sets.

(a) $\{(x, y) \mid x \geqslant 0\}$ (b) $\{(x, y) \mid y = 1\}$ (c) $\{(x, y) \mid |y| < 1\}$

SOLUTION

(a) The points whose x-coordinates are 0 or positive lie on the y-axis or to the right of it as indicated by the shaded region in Figure 3(a).

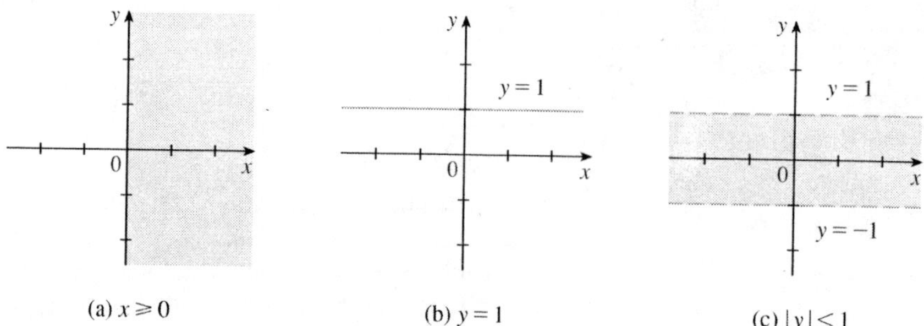

FIGURE 3 (a) $x \geqslant 0$ (b) $y = 1$ (c) $|y| < 1$

(b) The set of all points with y-coordinate 1 is a horizontal line one unit above the x-axis [see Figure 3(b)].

(c) Recall from Appendix A that

$$|y| < 1 \quad \text{if and only if} \quad -1 < y < 1$$

The given region consists of those points in the plane whose y-coordinates lie between -1 and 1. Thus the region consists of all points that lie between (but not on) the horizontal lines $y = 1$ and $y = -1$. [These lines are shown as dashed lines in Figure 3(c) to indicate that the points on these lines don't lie in the set.]

Recall from Appendix A that the distance between points a and b on a number line is $|a - b| = |b - a|$. Thus the distance between points $P_1(x_1, y_1)$ and $P_3(x_2, y_1)$ on a horizontal line must be $|x_2 - x_1|$ and the distance between $P_2(x_2, y_2)$ and $P_3(x_2, y_1)$ on a vertical line must be $|y_2 - y_1|$. (See Figure 4.)

To find the distance $|P_1P_2|$ between any two points $P_1(x_1, y_1)$ and $P_2(x_2, y_2)$, we note that triangle $P_1P_2P_3$ in Figure 4 is a right triangle, and so by the Pythagorean Theorem we have

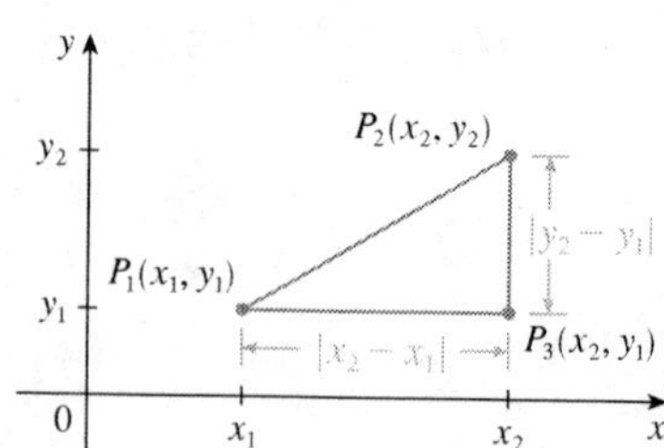

FIGURE 4

$$|P_1P_2| = \sqrt{|P_1P_3|^2 + |P_2P_3|^2} = \sqrt{|x_2 - x_1|^2 + |y_2 - y_1|^2}$$

$$= \sqrt{(x_2 - x_1)^2 + (y_2 - y_1)^2}$$

Distance Formula The distance between the points $P_1(x_1, y_1)$ and $P_2(x_2, y_2)$ is

$$|P_1P_2| = \sqrt{(x_2 - x_1)^2 + (y_2 - y_1)^2}$$

For instance, the distance between $(1, -2)$ and $(5, 3)$ is

$$\sqrt{(5 - 1)^2 + [3 - (-2)]^2} = \sqrt{4^2 + 5^2} = \sqrt{41}$$

Circles

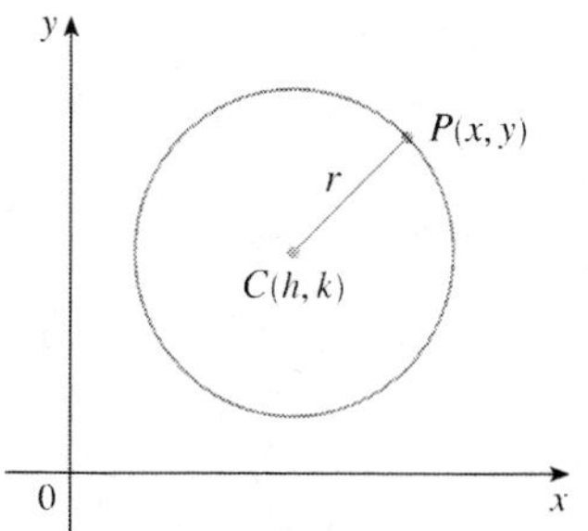

FIGURE 5

An **equation of a curve** is an equation satisfied by the coordinates of the points on the curve and by no other points. Let's use the distance formula to find the equation of a circle with radius r and center (h, k). By definition, the circle is the set of all points $P(x, y)$ whose distance from the center $C(h, k)$ is r. (See Figure 5.) Thus P is on the circle if and only if $|PC| = r$. From the distance formula, we have

$$\sqrt{(x - h)^2 + (y - k)^2} = r$$

or equivalently, squaring both sides, we get

$$(x - h)^2 + (y - k)^2 = r^2$$

This is the desired equation.

Equation of a Circle An equation of the circle with center (h, k) and radius r is

$$(x - h)^2 + (y - k)^2 = r^2$$

In particular, if the center is the origin $(0, 0)$, the equation is

$$x^2 + y^2 = r^2$$

For instance, an equation of the circle with radius 3 and center $(2, -5)$ is

$$(x - 2)^2 + (y + 5)^2 = 9$$

EXAMPLE 2 Sketch the graph of the equation $x^2 + y^2 + 2x - 6y + 7 = 0$ by first showing that it represents a circle and then finding its center and radius.

SOLUTION We first group the x-terms and y-terms as follows:

$$(x^2 + 2x) + (y^2 - 6y) = -7$$

Then we complete the square within each grouping, adding the appropriate constants (the squares of half the coefficients of x and y) to both sides of the equation:

$$(x^2 + 2x + 1) + (y^2 - 6y + 9) = -7 + 1 + 9$$

or

$$(x + 1)^2 + (y - 3)^2 = 3$$

Comparing this equation with the standard equation of a circle, we see that $h = -1$, $k = 3$, and $r = \sqrt{3}$, so the given equation represents a circle with center $(-1, 3)$ and radius $\sqrt{3}$. It is sketched in Figure 6.

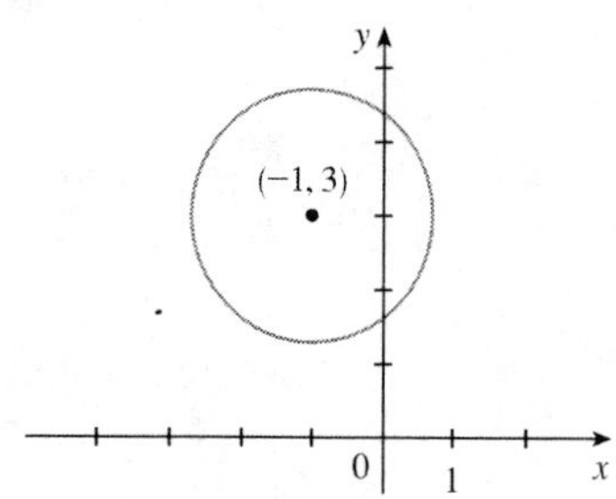

FIGURE 6
$x^2 + y^2 + 2x - 6y + 7 = 0$

Lines

To find the equation of a line L we use its *slope*, which is a measure of the steepness of the line.

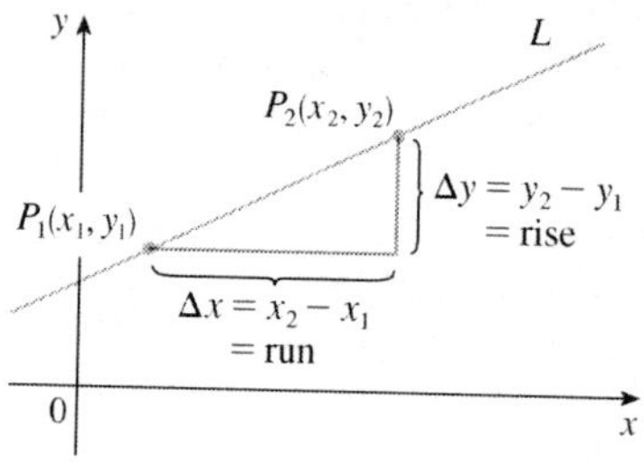

FIGURE 7

Definition The **slope** of a nonvertical line that passes through the points $P_1(x_1, y_1)$ and $P_2(x_2, y_2)$ is

$$m = \frac{\Delta y}{\Delta x} = \frac{y_2 - y_1}{x_2 - x_1}$$

The slope of a vertical line is not defined.

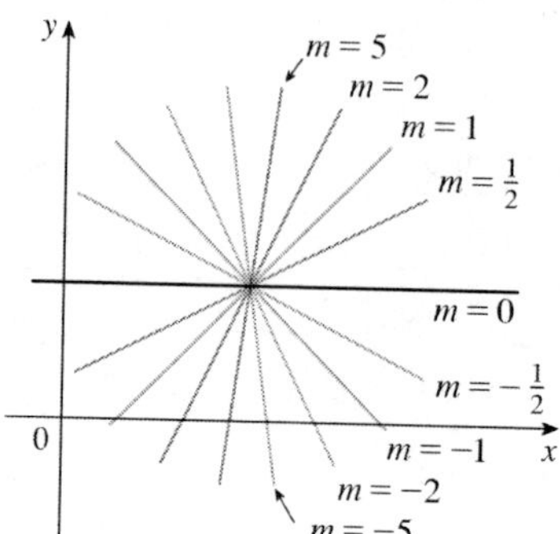
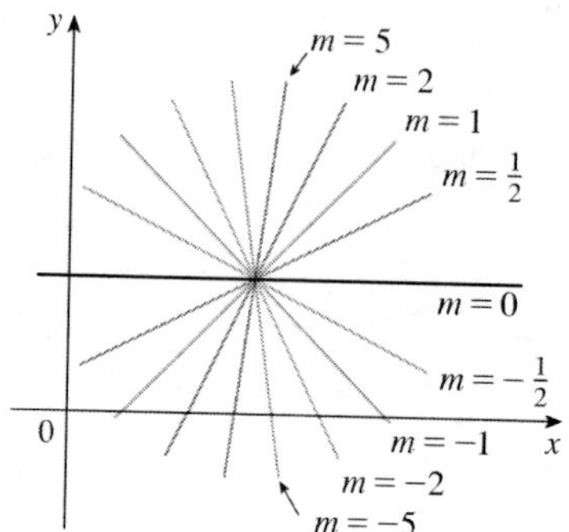

FIGURE 8

Thus the slope of a line is the ratio of the change in y, Δy, to the change in x, Δx. (See Figure 7.) The slope is therefore the rate of change of y with respect to x. The fact that the line is straight means that the rate of change is constant.

Figure 8 shows several lines labeled with their slopes. Notice that lines with positive slope slant upward to the right, whereas lines with negative slope slant downward to the right. Notice also that the steepest lines are the ones for which the absolute value of the slope is largest, and a horizontal line has slope 0.

Now let's find an equation of the line that passes through a given point $P_1(x_1, y_1)$ and has slope m. A point $P(x, y)$ with $x \neq x_1$ lies on this line if and only if the slope of the line through P_1 and P is equal to m; that is,

$$\frac{y - y_1}{x - x_1} = m$$

This equation can be rewritten in the form

$$y - y_1 = m(x - x_1)$$

and we observe that this equation is also satisfied when $x = x_1$ and $y = y_1$. Therefore it is an equation of the given line.

Point-Slope Form of the Equation of a Line An equation of the line passing through the point $P_1(x_1, y_1)$ and having slope m is

$$y - y_1 = m(x - x_1)$$

EXAMPLE 3 Find an equation of the line through the points $(-1, 2)$ and $(3, -4)$.

SOLUTION The slope of the line is

$$m = \frac{-4 - 2}{3 - (-1)} = -\frac{3}{2}$$

Using the point-slope form with $x_1 = -1$ and $y_1 = 2$, we obtain

$$y - 2 = -\tfrac{3}{2}(x + 1)$$

which simplifies to

$$3x + 2y = 1$$

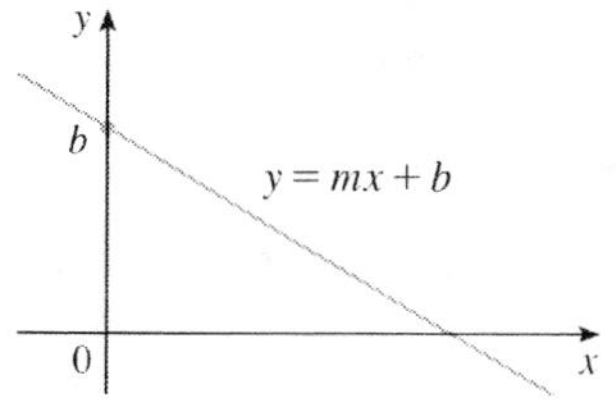

FIGURE 9

Suppose a nonvertical line has slope m and y-intercept b. (See Figure 9.) This means it intersects the y-axis at the point $(0, b)$, so the point-slope form of the equation of the line, with $x_1 = 0$ and $y_1 = b$, becomes

$$y - b = m(x - 0)$$

This simplifies as follows.

Slope-Intercept Form of the Equation of a Line An equation of the line with slope m and y-intercept b is

$$y = mx + b$$

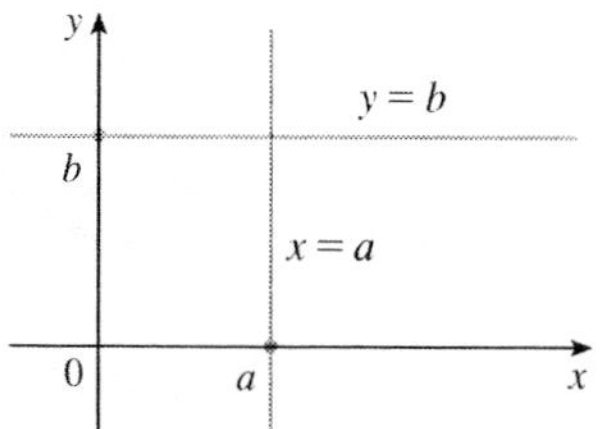

FIGURE 10

In particular, if a line is horizontal, its slope is $m = 0$, so its equation is $y = b$, where b is the y-intercept (see Figure 10). A vertical line does not have a slope, but we can write its equation as $x = a$, where a is the x-intercept, because the x-coordinate of every point on the line is a.

EXAMPLE 4 Graph the inequality $x + 2y > 5$.

SOLUTION We are asked to sketch the graph of the set $\{(x, y) \mid x + 2y > 5\}$ and we begin by solving the inequality for y:

$$x + 2y > 5$$

$$2y > -x + 5$$

$$y > -\tfrac{1}{2}x + \tfrac{5}{2}$$

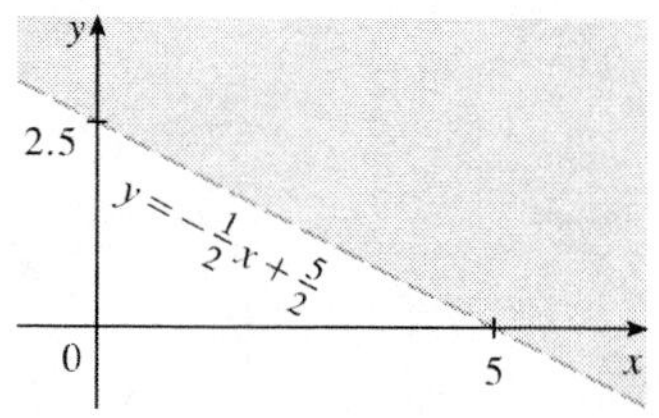

FIGURE 11

Compare this inequality with the equation $y = -\frac{1}{2}x + \frac{5}{2}$, which represents a line with slope $-\frac{1}{2}$ and y-intercept $\frac{5}{2}$. We see that the given graph consists of points whose y-coordinates are *larger* than those on the line $y = -\frac{1}{2}x + \frac{5}{2}$. Thus the graph is the region that lies *above* the line, as illustrated in Figure 11.

Parallel and Perpendicular Lines

Slopes can be used to show that lines are parallel or perpendicular. The following facts are proved, for instance, in *Precalculus: Mathematics for Calculus, Fifth Edition* by Stewart, Redlin, and Watson (Belmont, CA, 2006).

Parallel and Perpendicular Lines

1. Two nonvertical lines are parallel if and only if they have the same slope.
2. Two lines with slopes m_1 and m_2 are perpendicular if and only if $m_1 m_2 = -1$; that is, their slopes are negative reciprocals:

$$m_2 = -\frac{1}{m_1}$$

EXAMPLE 5 Find an equation of the line through the point $(5, 2)$ that is parallel to the line $4x + 6y + 5 = 0$.

SOLUTION The given line can be written in the form

$$y = -\tfrac{2}{3}x - \tfrac{5}{6}$$

which is in slope-intercept form with $m = -\frac{2}{3}$. Parallel lines have the same slope, so the required line has slope $-\frac{2}{3}$ and its equation in point-slope form is

$$y - 2 = -\tfrac{2}{3}(x - 5)$$

We can write this equation as $2x + 3y = 16$.

EXAMPLE 6 Show that the lines $2x + 3y = 1$ and $6x - 4y - 1 = 0$ are perpendicular.

SOLUTION The equations can be written as

$$y = -\tfrac{2}{3}x + \tfrac{1}{3} \qquad \text{and} \qquad y = \tfrac{3}{2}x - \tfrac{1}{4}$$

from which we see that the slopes are

$$m_1 = -\tfrac{2}{3} \qquad \text{and} \qquad m_2 = \tfrac{3}{2}$$

Since $m_1 m_2 = -1$, the lines are perpendicular.

Conic Sections

Here we review the geometric definitions of parabolas, ellipses, and hyperbolas and their standard equations. They are called **conic sections**, or **conics**, because they result from intersecting a cone with a plane as shown in Figure 12.

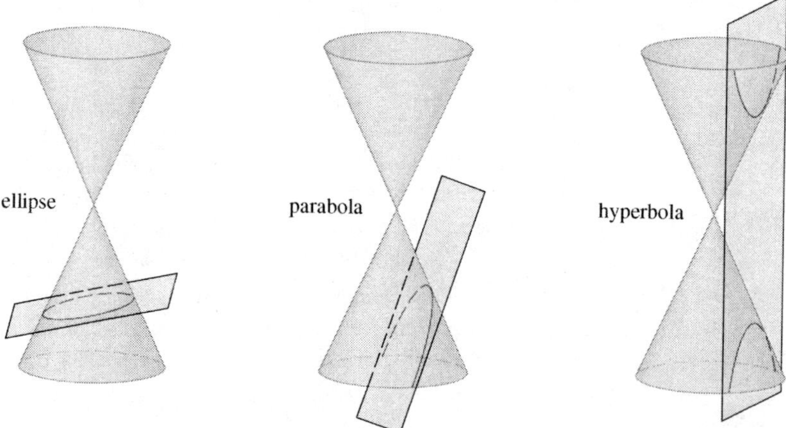

FIGURE 12
Conics

Parabolas

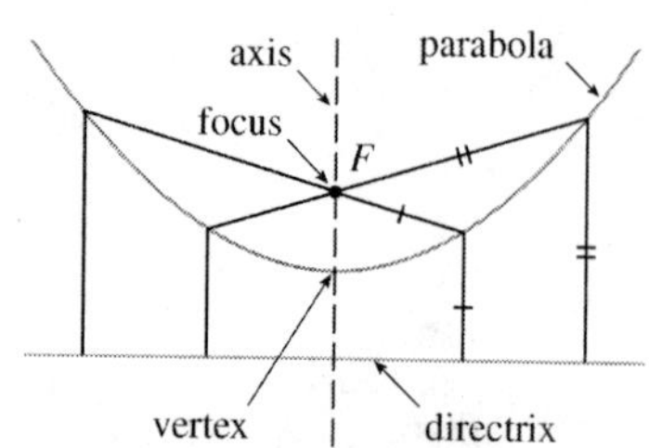

FIGURE 13

A **parabola** is the set of points in a plane that are equidistant from a fixed point F (called the **focus**) and a fixed line (called the **directrix**). This definition is illustrated by Figure 13. Notice that the point halfway between the focus and the directrix lies on the parabola; it is called the **vertex**. The line through the focus perpendicular to the directrix is called the **axis** of the parabola.

In the 16th century Galileo showed that the path of a projectile that is shot into the air at an angle to the ground is a parabola. Since then, parabolic shapes have been used in designing automobile headlights, reflecting telescopes, and suspension bridges. (See Problem 18 on page 254 for the reflection property of parabolas that makes them so useful.)

We obtain a particularly simple equation for a parabola if we place its vertex at the origin O and its directrix parallel to the x-axis as in Figure 14. If the focus is the point

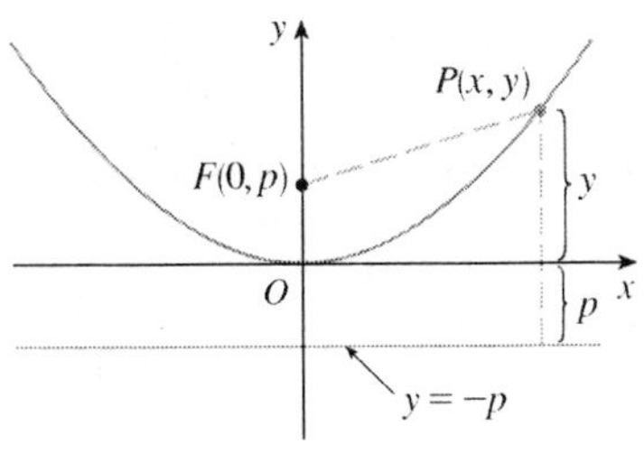

FIGURE 14

$(0, p)$, then the directrix has the equation $y = -p$ and the parabola has the equation

$$x^2 = 4py$$

(See Exercise 47.)

If we write $a = 1/(4p)$, then the equation of the parabola becomes

$$\boxed{y = ax^2}$$

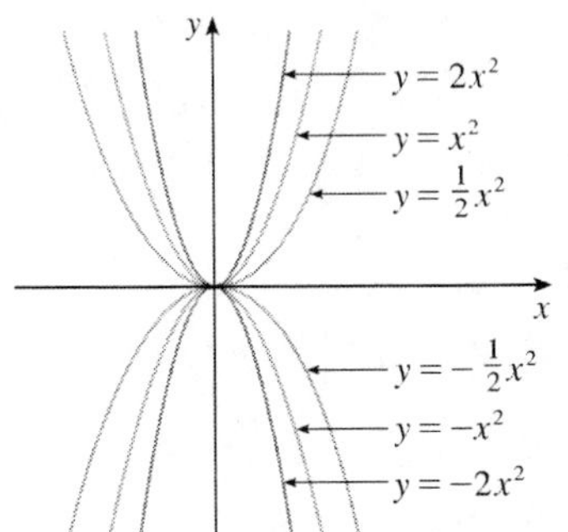

FIGURE 15

Figure 15 shows the graphs of several parabolas with equations of the form $y = ax^2$ for various values of the number a. We see that the parabola $y = ax^2$ opens upward if $a > 0$ and downward if $a < 0$ (as in Figure 16). The graph is symmetric with respect to the y-axis because its equation is unchanged when x is replaced by $-x$. This corresponds to the fact that the function $f(x) = ax^2$ is an even function.

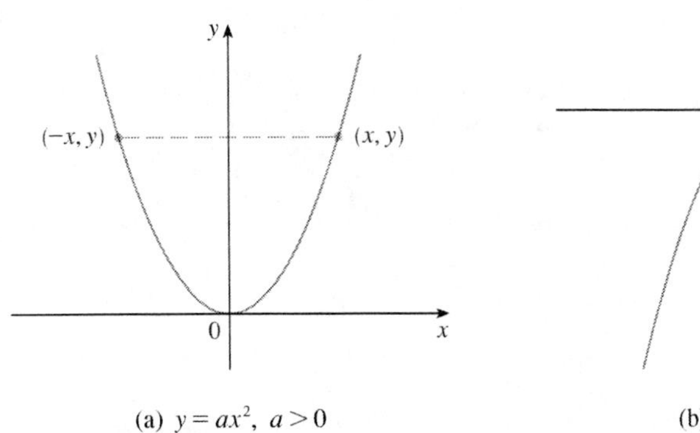

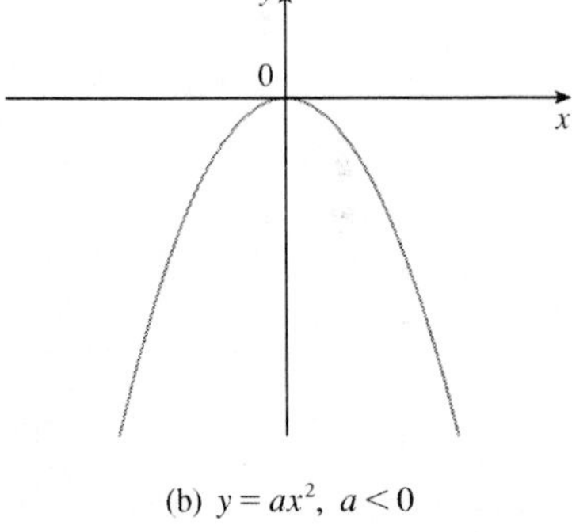

FIGURE 16 (a) $y = ax^2$, $a > 0$ (b) $y = ax^2$, $a < 0$

If we interchange x and y in the equation $y = ax^2$, the result is $x = ay^2$, which also represents a parabola. (Interchanging x and y amounts to reflecting about the diagonal line $y = x$.) The parabola $x = ay^2$ opens to the right if $a > 0$ and to the left if $a < 0$. (See Figure 17.) This time the parabola is symmetric with respect to the x-axis because the equation is unchanged when y is replaced by $-y$.

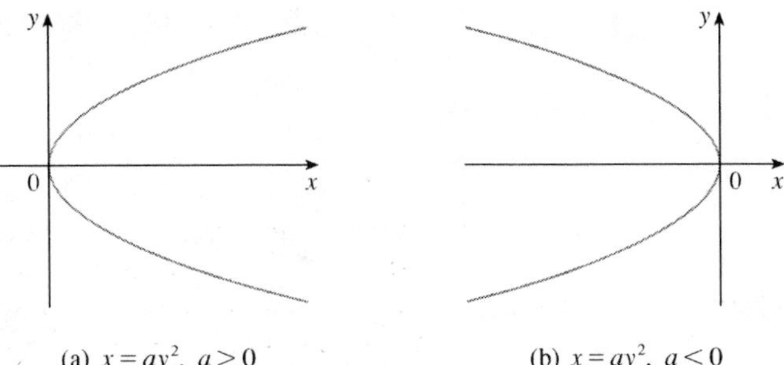

FIGURE 17 (a) $x = ay^2$, $a > 0$ (b) $x = ay^2$, $a < 0$

EXAMPLE 7 Sketch the region bounded by the parabola $x = 1 - y^2$ and the line $x + y + 1 = 0$.

SOLUTION First we find the points of intersection by solving the two equations. Substituting $x = -y - 1$ into the equation $x = 1 - y^2$, we get $-y - 1 = 1 - y^2$, which gives

$$0 = y^2 - y - 2 = (y - 2)(y + 1)$$

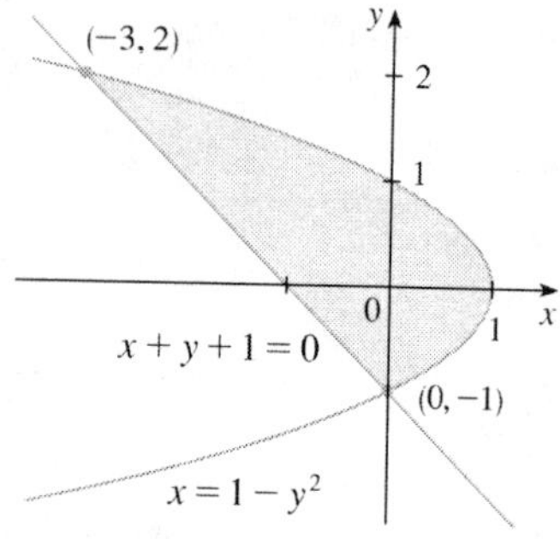
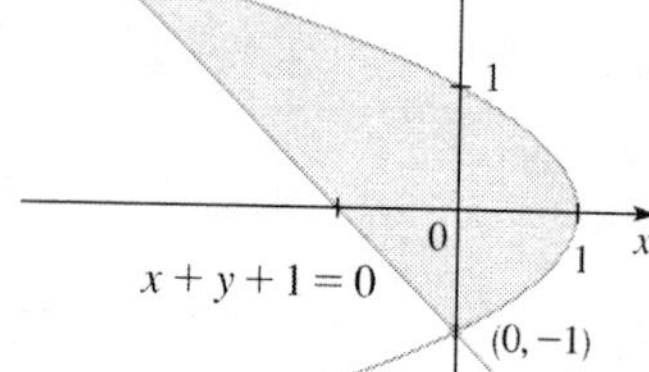

FIGURE 18

so $y = 2$ or -1. Thus the points of intersection are $(-3, 2)$ and $(0, -1)$, and we draw the line $x + y + 1 = 0$ passing through these points.

To sketch the parabola $x = 1 - y^2$ we start with the parabola $x = -y^2$ in Figure 17(b) and shift one unit to the right. We also make sure it passes through the points $(-3, 2)$ and $(0, -1)$. The region bounded by $x = 1 - y^2$ and $x + y + 1 = 0$ means the finite region whose boundaries are these curves. It is sketched in Figure 18.

Ellipses

An **ellipse** is the set of points in a plane the sum of whose distances from two fixed points F_1 and F_2 is a constant (see Figure 19). These two fixed points are called the **foci** (plural of **focus**). One of Kepler's laws is that the orbits of the planets in the solar system are ellipses with the sun at one focus.

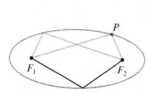

FIGURE 19

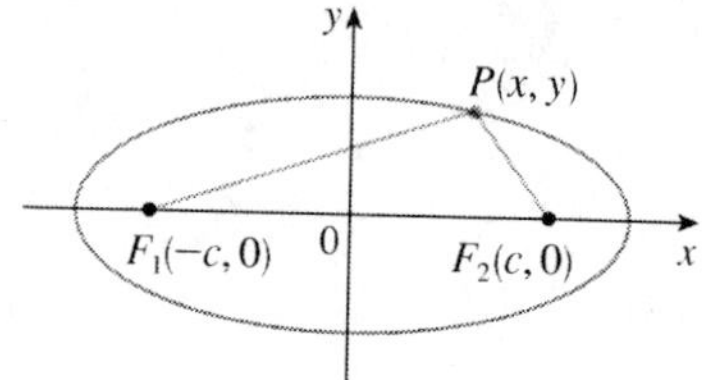

FIGURE 20

In order to obtain the simplest equation for an ellipse, we place the foci on the x-axis at the points $(-c, 0)$ and $(c, 0)$ as in Figure 20, so that the origin is halfway between the foci. If we let the sum of the distances from a point on the ellipse to the foci be $2a$, then we can write an equation of the ellipse as

$$\boxed{1} \qquad \frac{x^2}{a^2} + \frac{y^2}{b^2} = 1$$

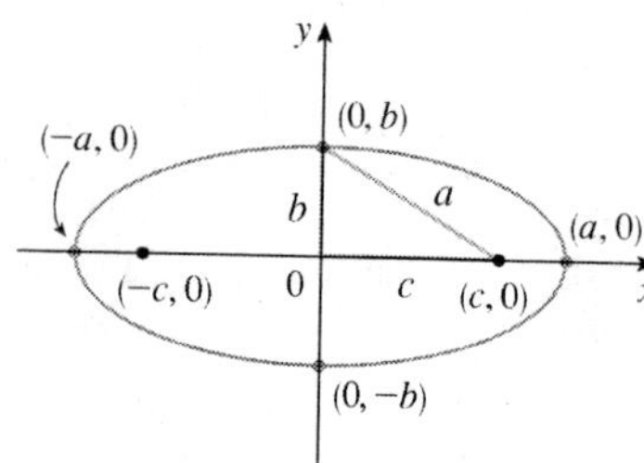

FIGURE 21

$\dfrac{x^2}{a^2} + \dfrac{y^2}{b^2} = 1, \; a \geq b$

where $c^2 = a^2 - b^2$. (See Exercise 49 and Figure 21.) Notice that the x-intercepts are $\pm a$, the y-intercepts are $\pm b$, the foci are $(\pm c, 0)$, and the ellipse is symmetric with respect to both axes. If the foci of an ellipse are located on the y-axis at $(0, \pm c)$, then we can find its equation by interchanging x and y in (1).

EXAMPLE 8 Sketch the graph of $9x^2 + 16y^2 = 144$ and locate the foci.

SOLUTION Divide both sides of the equation by 144:

$$\frac{x^2}{16} + \frac{y^2}{9} = 1$$

The equation is now in the standard form for an ellipse, so we have $a^2 = 16$, $b^2 = 9$, $a = 4$, and $b = 3$. The x-intercepts are ± 4 and the y-intercepts are ± 3. Also, $c^2 = a^2 - b^2 = 7$, so $c = \sqrt{7}$ and the foci are $(\pm\sqrt{7}, 0)$. The graph is sketched in Figure 22.

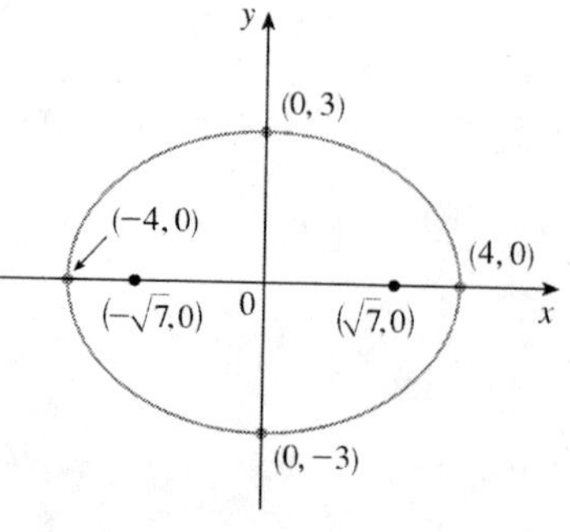

FIGURE 22

$9x^2 + 16y^2 = 144$

Like parabolas, ellipses have an interesting reflection property that has practical consequences. If a source of light or sound is placed at one focus of a surface with elliptical cross-sections, then all the light or sound is reflected off the surface to the other focus (see Exercise 55). This principle is used in *lithotripsy*, a treatment for kidney stones. A reflector with elliptical cross-section is placed in such a way that the kidney stone is at one focus. High-intensity sound waves generated at the other focus are reflected to the stone and destroy it without damaging surrounding tissue. The patient is spared the trauma of surgery and recovers within a few days.

Hyperbolas

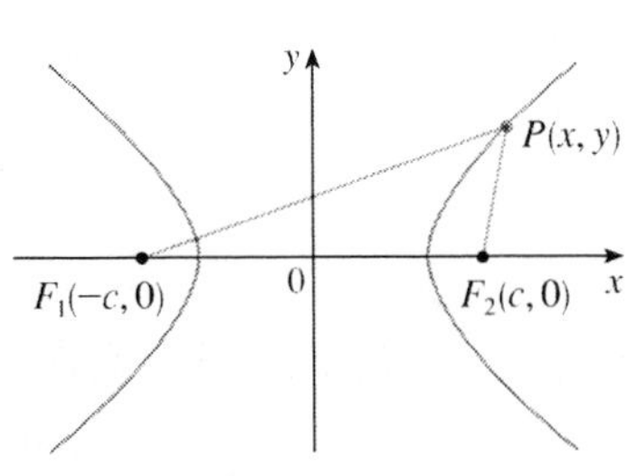

FIGURE 23
P is on the hyperbola when $|PF_1| - |PF_2| = \pm 2a$.

A **hyperbola** is the set of all points in a plane the difference of whose distances from two fixed points F_1 and F_2 (the foci) is a constant. This definition is illustrated in Figure 23.

Notice that the definition of a hyperbola is similar to that of an ellipse; the only change is that the sum of distances has become a difference of distances. It is left as Exercise 51 to show that when the foci are on the x-axis at $(\pm c, 0)$ and the difference of distances is $|PF_1| - |PF_2| = \pm 2a$, then the equation of the hyperbola is

$$\boxed{2} \qquad \frac{x^2}{a^2} - \frac{y^2}{b^2} = 1$$

where $c^2 = a^2 + b^2$. Notice that the x-intercepts are again $\pm a$. But if we put $x = 0$ in Equation 2 we get $y^2 = -b^2$, which is impossible, so there is no y-intercept. The hyperbola is symmetric with respect to both axes.

To analyze the hyperbola further, we look at Equation 2 and obtain

$$\frac{x^2}{a^2} = 1 + \frac{y^2}{b^2} \geqslant 1$$

This shows that $x^2 \geqslant a^2$, so $|x| = \sqrt{x^2} \geqslant a$. Therefore we have $x \geqslant a$ or $x \leqslant -a$. This means that the hyperbola consists of two parts, called its *branches*.

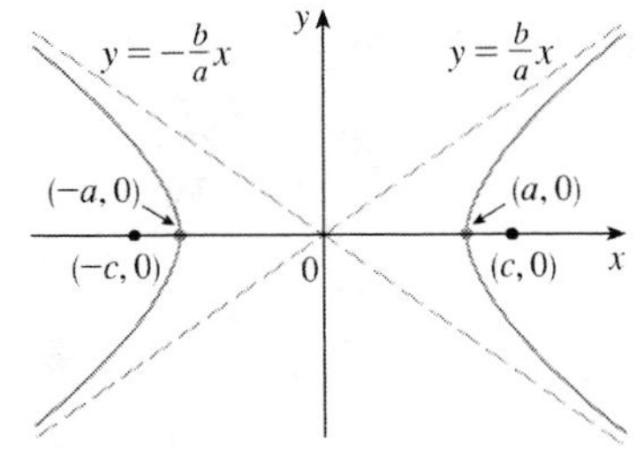

FIGURE 24
$\frac{x^2}{a^2} - \frac{y^2}{b^2} = 1$

When we draw a hyperbola it is useful to first draw its *asymptotes*, which are the lines $y = (b/a)x$ and $y = -(b/a)x$ shown in Figure 24. Both branches of the hyperbola approach the asymptotes; that is, they come arbitrarily close to the asymptotes. If the foci of a hyperbola are on the y-axis, we find its equation by reversing the roles of x and y.

EXAMPLE 9 Find the foci and asymptotes of the hyperbola $9x^2 - 16y^2 = 144$ and sketch its graph.

SOLUTION If we divide both sides of the equation by 144, it becomes

$$\frac{x^2}{16} - \frac{y^2}{9} = 1$$

which is of the form given in (2) with $a = 4$ and $b = 3$. Since $c^2 = 16 + 9 = 25$, the foci are $(\pm 5, 0)$. The asymptotes are the lines $y = \frac{3}{4}x$ and $y = -\frac{3}{4}x$. The graph is shown in Figure 25.

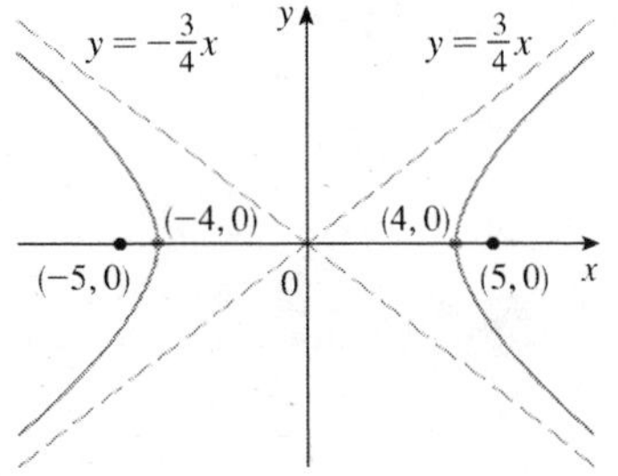

FIGURE 25
$9x^2 - 16y^2 = 144$

B Exercises

1–2 Find the distance between the points.

1. (1, 1), (4, 5)
2. (1, −3), (5, 7)

3–4 Find the slope of the line through P and Q.

3. $P(-3, 3)$, $Q(-1, -6)$
4. $P(-1, -4)$, $Q(6, 0)$

5. Show that the points $(-2, 9)$, $(4, 6)$, $(1, 0)$, and $(-5, 3)$ are the vertices of a square.

6. (a) Show that the points $A(-1, 3)$, $B(3, 11)$, and $C(5, 15)$ are collinear (lie on the same line) by showing that $|AB| + |BC| = |AC|$.
   (b) Use slopes to show that A, B, and C are collinear.

7–10 Sketch the graph of the equation.

7. $x = 3$
8. $y = -2$
9. $xy = 0$
10. $|y| = 1$

11–24 Find an equation of the line that satisfies the given conditions.

11. Through $(2, -3)$, slope 6
12. Through $(-3, -5)$, slope $-\frac{7}{2}$
13. Through (2, 1) and (1, 6)
14. Through $(-1, -2)$ and (4, 3)
15. Slope 3, y-intercept -2
16. Slope $\frac{2}{5}$, y-intercept 4
17. x-intercept 1, y-intercept -3
18. x-intercept -8, y-intercept 6
19. Through (4, 5), parallel to the x-axis
20. Through (4, 5), parallel to the y-axis
21. Through $(1, -6)$, parallel to the line $x + 2y = 6$
22. y-intercept 6, parallel to the line $2x + 3y + 4 = 0$
23. Through $(-1, -2)$, perpendicular to the line $2x + 5y + 8 = 0$
24. Through $(\frac{1}{2}, -\frac{2}{3})$, perpendicular to the line $4x - 8y = 1$

25–28 Find the slope and y-intercept of the line and draw its graph.

25. $x + 3y = 0$
26. $2x - 3y + 6 = 0$
27. $3x - 4y = 12$
28. $4x + 5y = 10$

29–36 Sketch the region in the xy-plane.

29. $\{(x, y) \mid x < 0\}$
30. $\{(x, y) \mid x \geqslant 1 \text{ and } y < 3\}$
31. $\{(x, y) \mid |x| \leqslant 2\}$
32. $\{(x, y) \mid |x| < 3 \text{ and } |y| < 2\}$
33. $\{(x, y) \mid 0 \leqslant y \leqslant 4 \text{ and } x \leqslant 2\}$
34. $\{(x, y) \mid y > 2x - 1\}$
35. $\{(x, y) \mid 1 + x \leqslant y \leqslant 1 - 2x\}$
36. $\{(x, y) \mid -x \leqslant y < \frac{1}{2}(x + 3)\}$

37–38 Find an equation of a circle that satisfies the given conditions.

37. Center $(3, -1)$, radius 5
38. Center $(-1, 5)$, passes through $(-4, -6)$

39–40 Show that the equation represents a circle and find the center and radius.

39. $x^2 + y^2 - 4x + 10y + 13 = 0$
40. $x^2 + y^2 + 6y + 2 = 0$

41. Show that the lines $2x - y = 4$ and $6x - 2y = 10$ are not parallel and find their point of intersection.

42. Show that the lines $3x - 5y + 19 = 0$ and $10x + 6y - 50 = 0$ are perpendicular and find their point of intersection.

43. Show that the midpoint of the line segment from $P_1(x_1, y_1)$ to $P_2(x_2, y_2)$ is
$$\left(\frac{x_1 + x_2}{2}, \frac{y_1 + y_2}{2}\right)$$

44. Find the midpoint of the line segment joining the points (1, 3) and (7, 15).

45. Find an equation of the perpendicular bisector of the line segment joining the points $A(1, 4)$ and $B(7, -2)$.

46. (a) Show that if the x- and y-intercepts of a line are nonzero numbers a and b, then the equation of the line can be put in the form
$$\frac{x}{a} + \frac{y}{b} = 1$$
   This equation is called the **two-intercept form** of an equation of a line.
   (b) Use part (a) to find an equation of the line whose x-intercept is 6 and whose y-intercept is -8.

47. Suppose that $P(x, y)$ is any point on the parabola with focus $(0, p)$ and directrix $y = -p$. (See Figure 14.) Use the definition of a parabola to show that $x^2 = 4py$.

48. Find the focus and directrix of the parabola $y = x^2$. Illustrate with a diagram.

49. Suppose an ellipse has foci $(\pm c, 0)$ and the sum of the distances from any point $P(x, y)$ on the ellipse to the foci is $2a$. Show that the coordinates of P satisfy Equation 1.

50. Find the foci of the ellipse $x^2 + 4y^2 = 4$ and sketch its graph.

51. Use the definition of a hyperbola to derive Equation 2 for a hyperbola with foci $(\pm c, 0)$.

52. (a) Find the foci and asymptotes of the hyperbola $x^2 - y^2 = 1$ and sketch its graph.
(b) Sketch the graph of $y^2 - x^2 = 1$.

53–54 Sketch the region bounded by the curves.

53. $x + 4y = 8$ and $x = 2y^2 - 8$

54. $y = 4 - x^2$ and $x - 2y = 2$

55. Let $P(x_1, y_1)$ be a point on the ellipse $x^2/a^2 + y^2/b^2 = 1$ with foci F_1 and F_2 and let α and β be the angles between the lines PF_1, PF_2 and the ellipse as shown in the figure. Prove that $\alpha = \beta$. This explains how whispering galleries and lithotripsy work. Sound coming from one focus is reflected and passes through the other focus. [*Hint:* Use the formula in Problem 17 on page 253 to show that $\tan \alpha = \tan \beta$.]

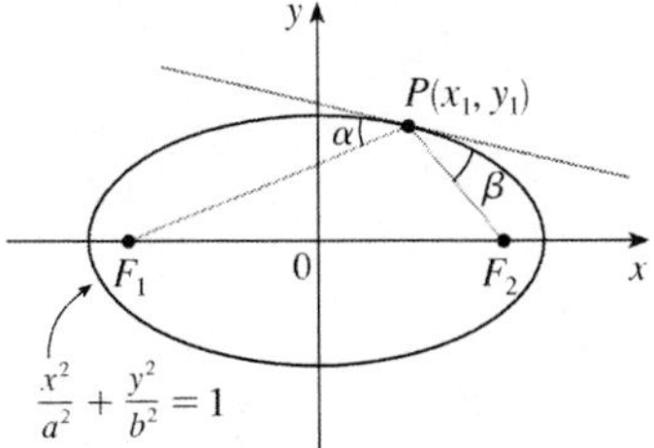

C Trigonometry

Here we review the aspects of trigonometry that are used in calculus: radian measure, trigonometric functions, trigonometric identities, and inverse trigonometric functions.

Angles

Angles can be measured in degrees or in radians (abbreviated as rad). The angle given by a complete revolution contains 360°, which is the same as 2π rad. Therefore

1 $$\pi \text{ rad} = 180°$$

and

2 $$1 \text{ rad} = \left(\frac{180}{\pi}\right)^\circ \approx 57.3° \qquad 1° = \frac{\pi}{180} \text{ rad} \approx 0.017 \text{ rad}$$

EXAMPLE 1
(a) Find the radian measure of 60°. (b) Express $5\pi/4$ rad in degrees.

SOLUTION
(a) From Equation 1 or 2 we see that to convert from degrees to radians we multiply by $\pi/180$. Therefore

$$60° = 60\left(\frac{\pi}{180}\right) = \frac{\pi}{3} \text{ rad}$$

(b) To convert from radians to degrees we multiply by $180/\pi$. Thus

$$\frac{5\pi}{4} \text{ rad} = \frac{5\pi}{4}\left(\frac{180}{\pi}\right) = 225°$$

41. Prove the **Law of Cosines**: If a triangle has sides with lengths a, b, and c, and θ is the angle between the sides with lengths a and b, then

$$c^2 = a^2 + b^2 - 2ab \cos \theta$$

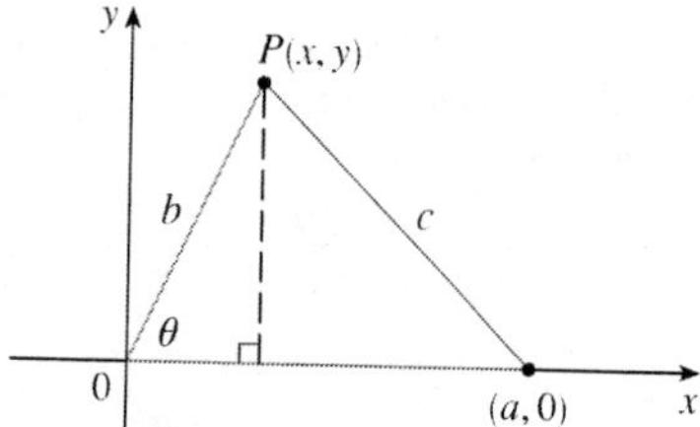

[*Hint:* Introduce a coordinate system so that θ is in standard position, as in the figure. Express x and y in terms of θ and then use the distance formula to compute c.]

42. In order to find the distance $|AB|$ across a small inlet, a point C was located as in the figure and the following measurements were recorded:

$$\angle C = 103^\circ \qquad |AC| = 820 \text{ m} \qquad |BC| = 910 \text{ m}$$

Use the Law of Cosines from Exercise 41 to find the required distance.

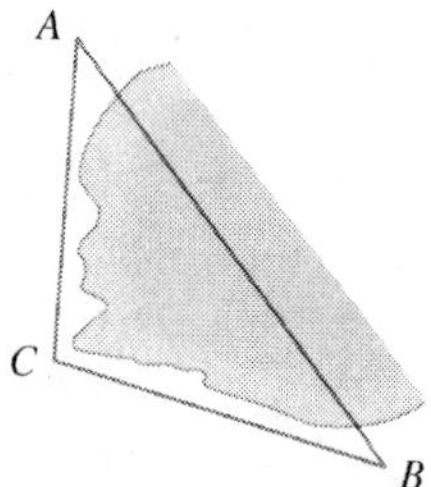

43. Use the figure to prove the subtraction formula

$$\cos(\alpha - \beta) = \cos \alpha \cos \beta + \sin \alpha \sin \beta$$

[*Hint:* Compute c^2 in two ways (using the Law of Cosines from Exercise 41 and also using the distance formula) and compare the two expressions.]

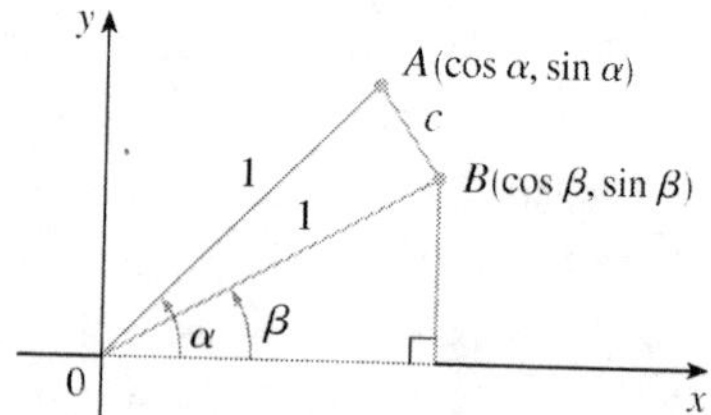

44. Use the formula in Exercise 43 to prove the addition formula for cosine (12b).

45. Use the addition formula for cosine and the identities

$$\cos\left(\frac{\pi}{2} - \theta\right) = \sin \theta \qquad \sin\left(\frac{\pi}{2} - \theta\right) = \cos \theta$$

to prove the subtraction formula (13a) for the sine function.

46. (a) Show that the area of a triangle with sides of lengths a and b and with included angle θ is

$$A = \tfrac{1}{2}ab \sin \theta$$

(b) Find the area of triangle ABC, correct to five decimal places, if

$$|AB| = 10 \text{ cm} \qquad |BC| = 3 \text{ cm} \qquad \angle ABC = 107^\circ$$

D Precise Definitions of Limits

The definitions of limits that have been given in this book are appropriate for intuitive understanding of the basic concepts of calculus. For the purposes of deeper understanding and rigorous proofs, however, the precise definitions of this appendix are necessary. In particular, the definition of a limit given here is used in Appendix E to prove that the limit of a sum is the sum of the limits.

When we say that $f(x)$ has a limit L as x approaches a, we mean, according to the intuitive definition in Section 2.2, that we can make $f(x)$ arbitrarily close to L by taking x close enough to a (but not equal to a). A more precise definition is based on the idea of specifying just how small we need to make the distance $|x - a|$ in order to make the distance $|f(x) - L|$ less than some given number. The following example illustrates the idea.

It is traditional to use the Greek letter δ (delta) in this situation.

EXAMPLE 1 Use a graph to find a number δ such that

$$\text{if} \quad |x - 1| < \delta \quad \text{then} \quad |(x^3 - 5x + 6) - 2| < 0.2$$

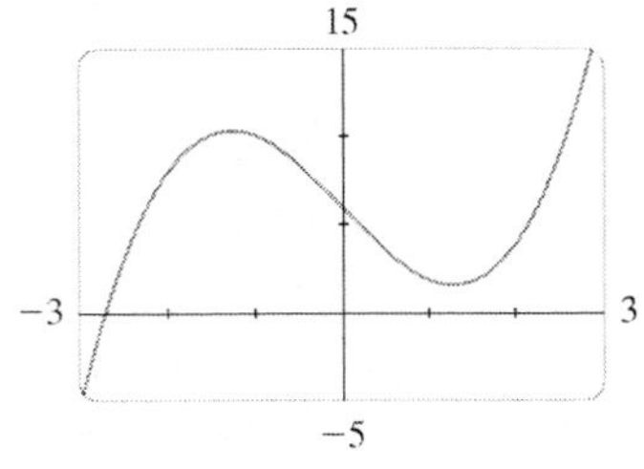

FIGURE 1

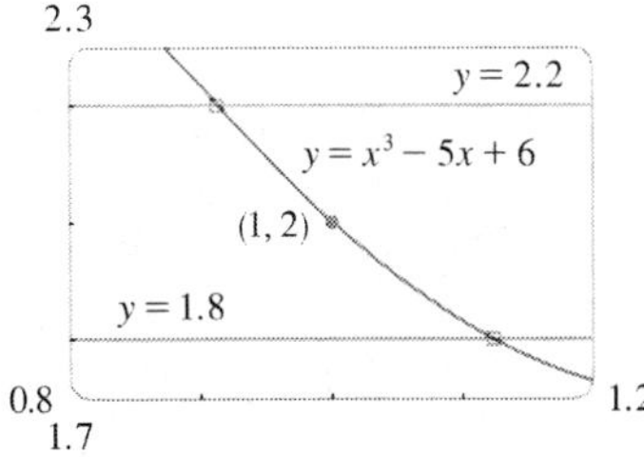

FIGURE 2

SOLUTION A graph of $f(x) = x^3 - 5x + 6$ is shown in Figure 1; we are interested in the region near the point $(1, 2)$. Notice that we can rewrite the inequality

$$|(x^3 - 5x + 6) - 2| < 0.2$$

as

$$1.8 < x^3 - 5x + 6 < 2.2$$

So we need to determine the values of x for which the curve $y = x^3 - 5x + 6$ lies between the horizontal lines $y = 1.8$ and $y = 2.2$. Therefore we graph the curves $y = x^3 - 5x + 6$, $y = 1.8$, and $y = 2.2$ near the point $(1, 2)$ in Figure 2. Then we use the cursor to estimate that the x-coordinate of the point of intersection of the line $y = 2.2$ and the curve $y = x^3 - 5x + 6$ is about 0.911. Similarly, $y = x^3 - 5x + 6$ intersects the line $y = 1.8$ when $x \approx 1.124$. So, rounding to be safe, we can say that

$$\text{if} \quad 0.92 < x < 1.12 \quad \text{then} \quad 1.8 < x^3 - 5x + 6 < 2.2$$

This interval $(0.92, 1.12)$ is not symmetric about $x = 1$. The distance from $x = 1$ to the left endpoint is $1 - 0.92 = 0.08$ and the distance to the right endpoint is 0.12. We can choose δ to be the smaller of these numbers, that is, $\delta = 0.08$. Then we can rewrite our inequalities in terms of distances as follows:

$$\text{if} \quad |x - 1| < 0.08 \quad \text{then} \quad |(x^3 - 5x + 6) - 2| < 0.2$$

This just says that by keeping x within 0.08 of 1, we are able to keep $f(x)$ within 0.2 of 2.

Although we chose $\delta = 0.08$, any smaller positive value of δ would also have worked.

Using the same graphical procedure as in Example 1, but replacing the number 0.2 by smaller numbers, we find that

$$\text{if} \quad |x - 1| < 0.046 \quad \text{then} \quad |(x^3 - 5x + 6) - 2| < 0.1$$

$$\text{if} \quad |x - 1| < 0.024 \quad \text{then} \quad |(x^3 - 5x + 6) - 2| < 0.05$$

$$\text{if} \quad |x - 1| < 0.004 \quad \text{then} \quad |(x^3 - 5x + 6) - 2| < 0.01$$

In each case we have found a number δ such that the values of the function $f(x) = x^3 - 5x + 6$ lie in successively smaller intervals centered at 2 if the distance from x to 1 is less than δ. It turns out that it is always possible to find such a number δ, no matter how small the interval is. In other words, for *any* positive number ε, no matter how small, there exists a positive number δ such that

$$\text{if} \quad |x - 1| < \delta \quad \text{then} \quad |(x^3 - 5x + 6) - 2| < \varepsilon$$

This indicates that

$$\lim_{x \to 1} (x^3 - 5x + 6) = 2$$

and suggests a more precise way of defining the limit of a general function.

1 Definition Let f be a function defined on some open interval that contains the number a, except possibly at a itself. Then we say that the **limit of $f(x)$ as x approaches a is L**, and we write

$$\lim_{x \to a} f(x) = L$$

if for every number $\varepsilon > 0$ there is a corresponding number $\delta > 0$ such that

$$\text{if} \quad 0 < |x - a| < \delta \quad \text{then} \quad |f(x) - L| < \varepsilon$$

The condition $0 < |x - a|$ is just another way of saying that $x \neq a$.

Definition 1 is illustrated in Figures 3–5. If a number $\varepsilon > 0$ is given, then we draw the horizontal lines $y = L + \varepsilon$ and $y = L - \varepsilon$ and the graph of f. (See Figure 3.) If $\lim_{x \to a} f(x) = L$, then we can find a number $\delta > 0$ such that if we restrict x to lie in the interval $(a - \delta, a + \delta)$ and take $x \neq a$, then the curve $y = f(x)$ lies between the lines $y = L - \varepsilon$ and $y = L + \varepsilon$. (See Figure 4.) You can see that if such a δ has been found, then any smaller δ will also work.

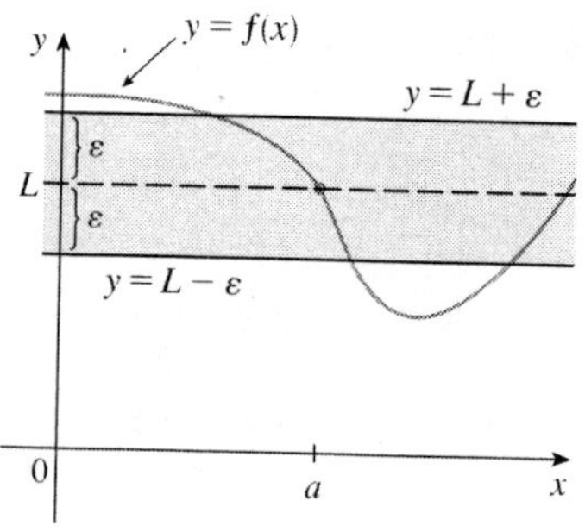

FIGURE 3

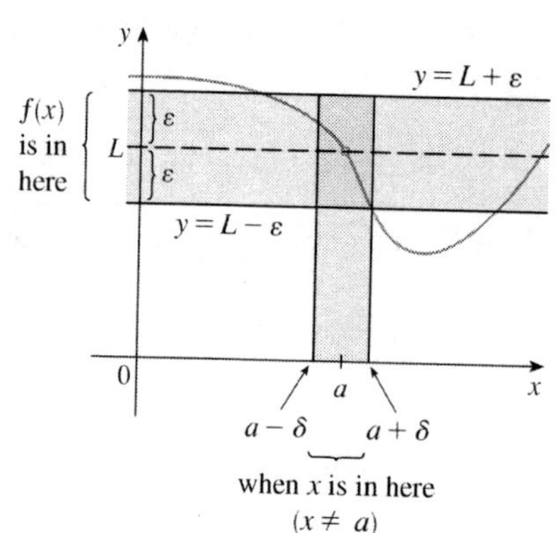

FIGURE 4

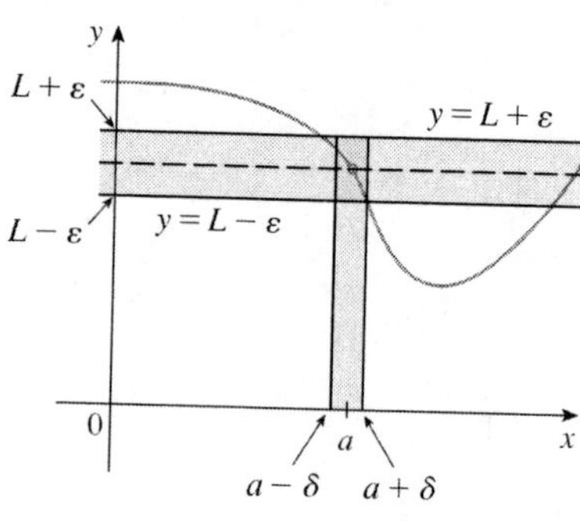

FIGURE 5

It's important to realize that the process illustrated in Figures 3 and 4 must work for *every* positive number ε no matter how small it is chosen. Figure 5 shows that if a smaller ε is chosen, then a smaller δ may be required.

EXAMPLE 2 Use the ε, δ definition to prove that $\lim_{x \to 0} x^2 = 0$.

SOLUTION Let ε be a given positive number. According to Definition 1 with $a = 0$ and $L = 0$, we need to find a number δ such that

$$\text{if} \quad 0 < |x - 0| < \delta \quad \text{then} \quad |x^2 - 0| < \varepsilon$$

that is,

$$\text{if} \quad 0 < |x| < \delta \quad \text{then} \quad x^2 < \varepsilon$$

But, since the square root function is an increasing function, we know that

$$x^2 < \varepsilon \iff \sqrt{x^2} < \sqrt{\varepsilon} \iff |x| < \sqrt{\varepsilon}$$

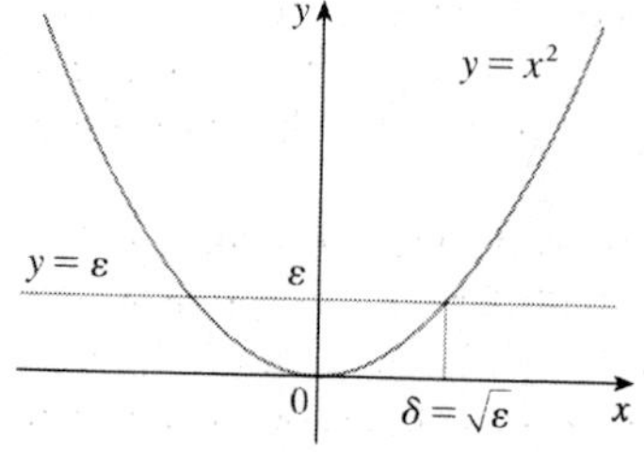

FIGURE 6

So if we choose $\delta = \sqrt{\varepsilon}$, then $x^2 < \varepsilon \iff |x| < \delta$. (See Figure 6.) This shows that $\lim_{x \to 0} x^2 = 0$.

In proving limit statements it may be helpful to think of the definition of a limit as a challenge. First it challenges you with a number ε. Then you must be able to produce a suitable δ. You have to be able to do this for *every* $\varepsilon > 0$, not just a particular ε.

TEC In Module D you can explore the precise definition of a limit both graphically and numerically.

Imagine a contest between two people, A and B, and imagine yourself to be B. Person A stipulates that the fixed number L should be approximated by the values of $f(x)$ to within a degree of accuracy ε (say, 0.01). Person B then responds by finding a number δ such that $|f(x) - L| < \varepsilon$ whenever $0 < |x - a| < \delta$. Then A may become more exacting and challenge B with a smaller value of ε (say, 0.0001). Again B has to respond by finding a corresponding δ. Usually the smaller the value of ε, the smaller the corresponding value of δ must be. If B always wins, no matter how small A makes ε, then $\lim_{x \to a} f(x) = L$.

V EXAMPLE 3 Prove that $\lim\limits_{x \to 3} (4x - 5) = 7$.

SOLUTION

1. *Preliminary analysis of the problem (guessing a value for δ).* Let ε be a given positive number. We want to find a number δ such that

$$\text{if} \quad 0 < |x - 3| < \delta \quad \text{then} \quad |(4x - 5) - 7| < \varepsilon$$

But $|(4x - 5) - 7| = |4x - 12| = |4(x - 3)| = 4|x - 3|$. Therefore we want δ such that

$$\text{if} \quad 0 < |x - 3| < \delta \quad \text{then} \quad 4|x - 3| < \varepsilon$$

that is,
$$\text{if} \quad 0 < |x - 3| < \delta \quad \text{then} \quad |x - 3| < \frac{\varepsilon}{4}$$

This suggests that we should choose $\delta = \varepsilon/4$.

2. *Proof (showing that this δ works).* Given $\varepsilon > 0$, choose $\delta = \varepsilon/4$. If $0 < |x - 3| < \delta$, then

$$|(4x - 5) - 7| = |4x - 12| = 4|x - 3| < 4\delta = 4\left(\frac{\varepsilon}{4}\right) = \varepsilon$$

Thus

$$\text{if} \quad 0 < |x - 3| < \delta \quad \text{then} \quad |(4x - 5) - 7| < \varepsilon$$

Therefore, by the definition of a limit,

$$\lim_{x \to 3} (4x - 5) = 7$$

This example is illustrated by Figure 7.

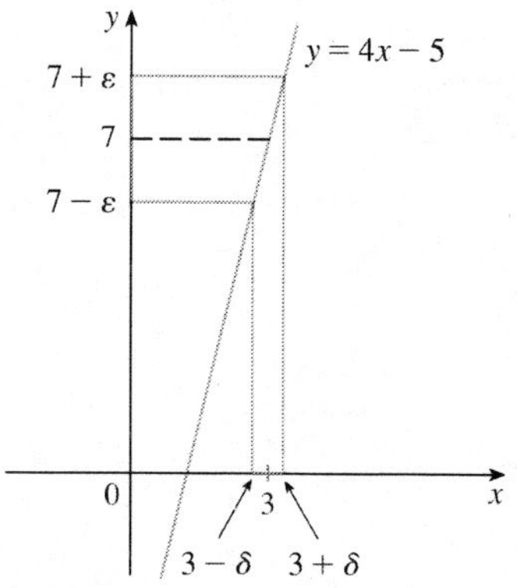

FIGURE 7

Note that in the solution of Example 3 there were two stages—guessing and proving. We made a preliminary analysis that enabled us to guess a value for δ. But then in the second stage we had to go back and prove in a careful, logical fashion that we had made a correct guess. This procedure is typical of much of mathematics. Sometimes it is necessary to first make an intelligent guess about the answer to a problem and then prove that the guess is correct.

It's not always easy to prove that limit statements are true using the ε, δ definition. For a more complicated function such as $f(x) = (6x^2 - 8x + 9)/(2x^2 - 1)$, a proof would require a great deal of ingenuity. Fortunately, this is not necessary because the Limit Laws stated in Section 2.3 can be proved using Definition 1, and then the limits of complicated functions can be found rigorously from the Limit Laws without resorting to the definition directly.

Limits at Infinity

Infinite limits and limits at infinity can also be defined in a precise way. The following is a precise version of Definition 4 in Section 2.5.

2 Definition Let f be a function defined on some interval (a, ∞). Then

$$\lim_{x \to \infty} f(x) = L$$

means that for every $\varepsilon > 0$ there is a corresponding number N such that

$$\text{if} \quad x > N \quad \text{then} \quad |f(x) - L| < \varepsilon$$

In words, this says that the values of $f(x)$ can be made arbitrarily close to L (within a distance ε, where ε is any positive number) by taking x sufficiently large (larger than N, where N depends on ε). Graphically it says that by choosing x large enough (larger than some number N) we can make the graph of f lie between the given horizontal lines $y = L - \varepsilon$ and $y = L + \varepsilon$ as in Figure 8. This must be true no matter how small we choose ε. If a smaller value of ε is chosen, then a larger value of N may be required.

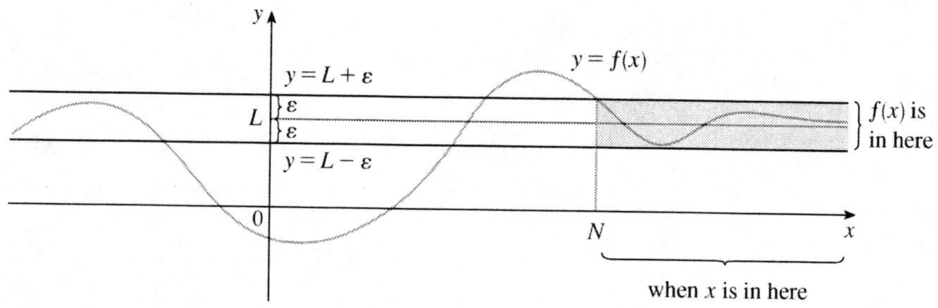

FIGURE 8
$\lim_{x \to \infty} f(x) = L$

In Example 5 in Section 2.5 we calculated that

$$\lim_{x \to \infty} \frac{3x^2 - x - 2}{5x^2 + 4x + 1} = \frac{3}{5}$$

In the next example we use a graphing device to relate this statement to Definition 2 with $L = \frac{3}{5}$ and $\varepsilon = 0.1$.

EXAMPLE 4 Use a graph to find a number N such that

$$\text{if} \quad x > N \quad \text{then} \quad \left| \frac{3x^2 - x - 2}{5x^2 + 4x + 1} - 0.6 \right| < 0.1$$

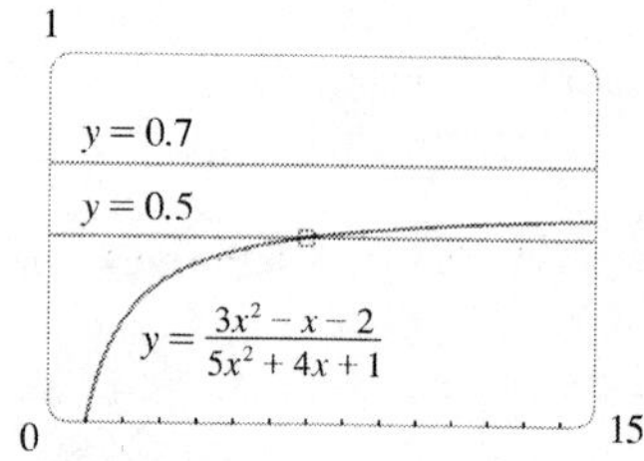

FIGURE 9

SOLUTION We rewrite the given inequality as

$$0.5 < \frac{3x^2 - x - 2}{5x^2 + 4x + 1} < 0.7$$

We need to determine the values of x for which the given curve lies between the horizontal lines $y = 0.5$ and $y = 0.7$. So we graph the curve and these lines in Figure 9. Then we use the cursor to estimate that the curve crosses the line $y = 0.5$ when $x \approx 6.7$. To the right of this number it seems that the curve stays between the lines $y = 0.5$ and $y = 0.7$. Rounding to be safe, we can say that

$$\text{if} \quad x > 7 \qquad \text{then} \qquad \left| \frac{3x^2 - x - 2}{5x^2 + 4x + 1} - 0.6 \right| < 0.1$$

In other words, for $\varepsilon = 0.1$ we can choose $N = 7$ (or any larger number) in Definition 2.

EXAMPLE 5 Use Definition 2 to prove that $\displaystyle\lim_{x \to \infty} \frac{1}{x} = 0$.

SOLUTION Given $\varepsilon > 0$, we want to find N such that

$$\text{if} \quad x > N \qquad \text{then} \qquad \left| \frac{1}{x} - 0 \right| < \varepsilon$$

In computing the limit we may assume that $x > 0$. Then $1/x < \varepsilon \iff x > 1/\varepsilon$. Let's choose $N = 1/\varepsilon$. So

$$\text{if} \quad x > N = \frac{1}{\varepsilon} \qquad \text{then} \qquad \left| \frac{1}{x} - 0 \right| = \frac{1}{x} < \varepsilon$$

Therefore, by Definition 2,

$$\lim_{x \to \infty} \frac{1}{x} = 0$$

Figure 10 illustrates the proof by showing some values of ε and the corresponding values of N.

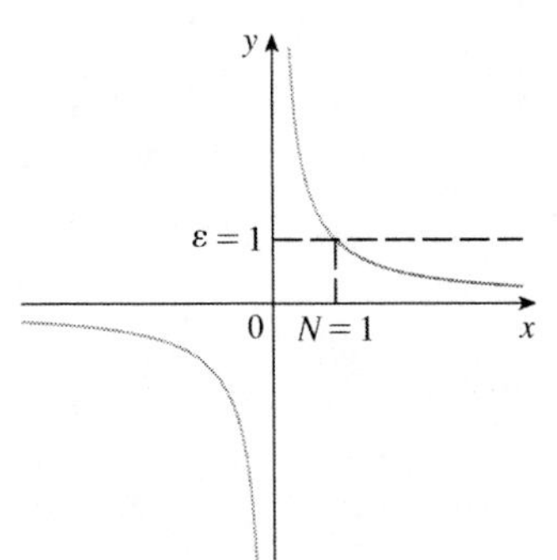

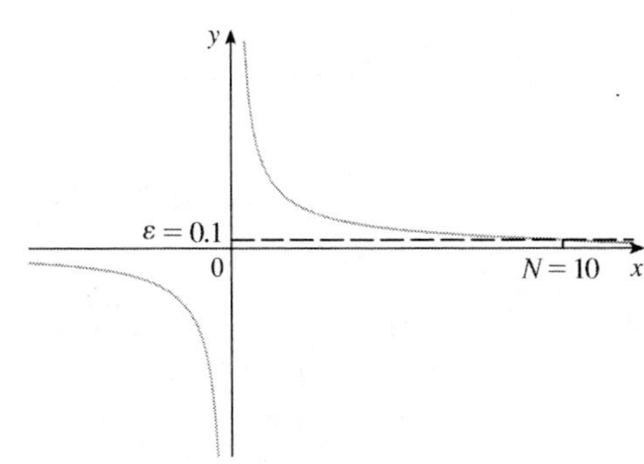

FIGURE 10

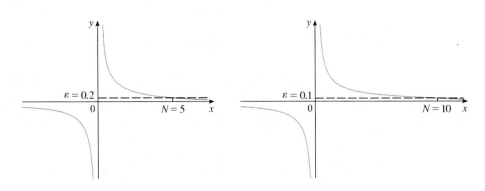

Infinite limits can also be formulated precisely. See Exercise 20.

Definite Integrals

In Section 5.2 we defined the definite integral of a function f on an interval $[a, b]$ as

$$\int_a^b f(x)\,dx = \lim_{n \to \infty} \sum_{i=1}^{n} f(x_i^*)\,\Delta x$$

where, at the nth stage, we have divided $[a, b]$ into n subintervals of equal width,

$\Delta x = (b - a)/n$, and x_i^* is any sample point in the ith subinterval. The precise meaning of this limit that defines the integral is as follows:

For every number $\varepsilon > 0$ there is an integer N such that

$$\left| \int_a^b f(x)\,dx - \sum_{i=1}^{n} f(x_i^*)\,\Delta x \right| < \varepsilon$$

for every integer $n > N$ and for every choice of x_i^* in the ith subinterval.

This means that a definite integral can be approximated to within any desired degree of accuracy by a Riemann sum.

Sequences

In Section 8.1 we used the notation

$$\lim_{n \to \infty} a_n = L$$

to mean that the terms of the sequence $\{a_n\}$ approach L as n becomes large. Notice that the following precise definition of the limit of a sequence is very similar to the definition of a limit of a function at infinity (Definition 2).

3 Definition A sequence $\{a_n\}$ has the **limit** L and we write

$$\lim_{n \to \infty} a_n = L \qquad \text{or} \qquad a_n \to L \text{ as } n \to \infty$$

if for every $\varepsilon > 0$ there is a corresponding integer N such that

$$\text{if} \quad n > N \quad \text{then} \quad |a_n - L| < \varepsilon$$

Definition 3 is illustrated by Figure 11, in which the terms $a_1, a_2, a_3, \ldots$ are plotted on a number line. No matter how small an interval $(L - \varepsilon, L + \varepsilon)$ is chosen, there exists an N such that all terms of the sequence from a_{N+1} onward must lie in that interval.

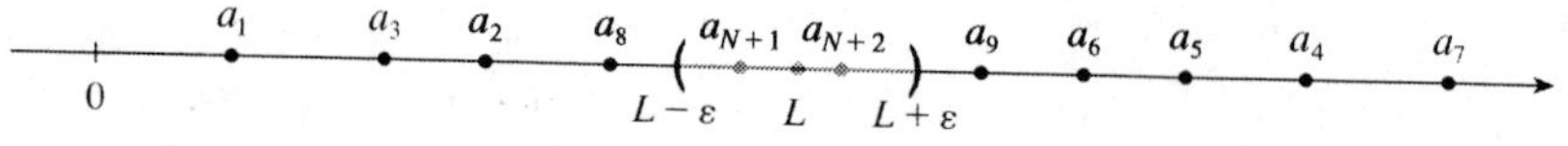

a_1 a_3 a_2 a_8 a_{N+1} a_{N+2} a_9 a_6 a_5 a_4 a_7

0 $L-\varepsilon$ L $L+\varepsilon$

FIGURE 11

Another illustration of Definition 3 is given in Figure 12. The points on the graph of $\{a_n\}$ must lie between the horizontal lines $y = L + \varepsilon$ and $y = L - \varepsilon$ if $n > N$. This picture must be valid no matter how small ε is chosen, but usually a smaller ε requires a larger N.

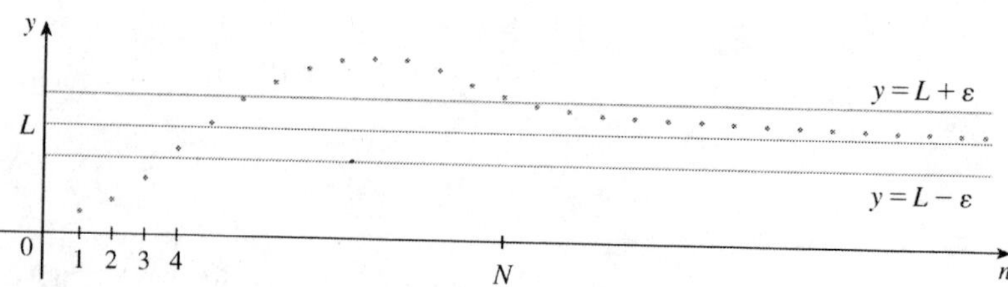

FIGURE 12

If you compare Definition 2 with Definition 3 you will see that the only difference between $\lim_{n\to\infty} a_n = L$ and $\lim_{x\to\infty} f(x) = L$ is that n is required to be an integer. The following definition shows how to make precise the idea that $\{a_n\}$ becomes infinite as n becomes infinite.

4 Definition The notation $\lim_{n\to\infty} a_n = \infty$ means that for every positive number M there is an integer N such that

$$\text{if} \quad n > N \quad \text{then} \quad a_n > M$$

EXAMPLE 6 Prove that $\lim_{n\to\infty} \sqrt{n} = \infty$.

SOLUTION Let M be any positive number. (Think of it as being very large.) Then

$$\sqrt{n} > M \iff n > M^2$$

So if we take $N = M^2$, then Definition 4 shows that $\lim_{n\to\infty} \sqrt{n} = \infty$.

Functions of Two Variables

Here is a precise version of Definition 1 in Section 11.2:

5 Definition Let f be a function of two variables whose domain D includes points arbitrarily close to (a, b). Then we say that the **limit of $f(x, y)$ as (x, y) approaches (a, b)** is L and we write

$$\lim_{(x,y)\to(a,b)} f(x, y) = L$$

if for every number $\varepsilon > 0$ there is a corresponding number $\delta > 0$ such that

$$\text{if} \quad (x, y) \in D \quad \text{and} \quad 0 < \sqrt{(x-a)^2 + (y-b)^2} < \delta \quad \text{then} \quad |f(x, y) - L| < \varepsilon$$

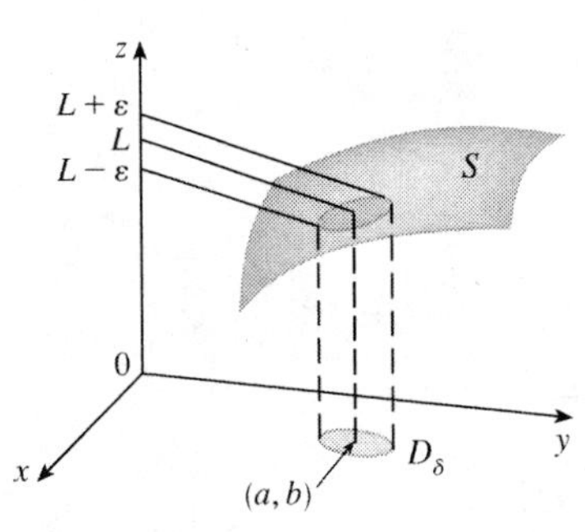

FIGURE 13

Notice that $|f(x, y) - L|$ is the distance between the numbers $f(x, y)$ and L, and $\sqrt{(x-a)^2 + (y-b)^2}$ is the distance between the point (x, y) and the point (a, b). Thus Definition 5 says that the distance between $f(x, y)$ and L can be made arbitrarily small by making the distance from (x, y) to (a, b) sufficiently small (but not 0). An illustration of Definition 5 is given in Figure 13 where the surface S is the graph of f. If $\varepsilon > 0$ is given, we can find $\delta > 0$ such that if (x, y) is restricted to lie in the disk D_δ with center (a, b) and radius δ, and if $(x, y) \neq (a, b)$, then the corresponding part of S lies between the horizontal planes $z = L - \varepsilon$ and $z = L + \varepsilon$.

EXAMPLE 7 Prove that $\displaystyle\lim_{(x,y)\to(0,0)} \frac{3x^2y}{x^2 + y^2} = 0$.

SOLUTION Let $\varepsilon > 0$. We want to find $\delta > 0$ such that

$$\text{if} \quad 0 < \sqrt{x^2 + y^2} < \delta \quad \text{then} \quad \left| \frac{3x^2y}{x^2 + y^2} - 0 \right| < \varepsilon$$

that is, if $0 < \sqrt{x^2 + y^2} < \delta$ then $\dfrac{3x^2|y|}{x^2 + y^2} < \varepsilon$

But $x^2 \leqslant x^2 + y^2$ since $y^2 \geqslant 0$, so $x^2/(x^2 + y^2) \leqslant 1$ and therefore

$$\frac{3x^2|y|}{x^2 + y^2} \leqslant 3|y| = 3\sqrt{y^2} \leqslant 3\sqrt{x^2 + y^2}$$

Thus if we choose $\delta = \varepsilon/3$ and let $0 < \sqrt{x^2 + y^2} < \delta$, then

$$\left|\frac{3x^2y}{x^2 + y^2} - 0\right| \leqslant 3\sqrt{x^2 + y^2} < 3\delta = 3\left(\frac{\varepsilon}{3}\right) = \varepsilon$$

Hence, by Definition 5,

$$\lim_{(x, y) \to (0, 0)} \frac{3x^2y}{x^2 + y^2} = 0$$

D Exercises

1. Use the given graph of $f(x) = 1/x$ to find a number δ such that

if $|x - 2| < \delta$ then $\left|\dfrac{1}{x} - 0.5\right| < 0.2$

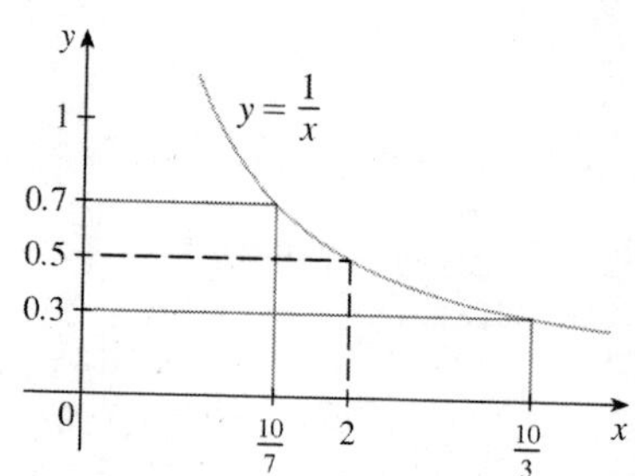

2. Use the given graph of f to find a number δ such that

if $0 < |x - 5| < \delta$ then $|f(x) - 3| < 0.6$

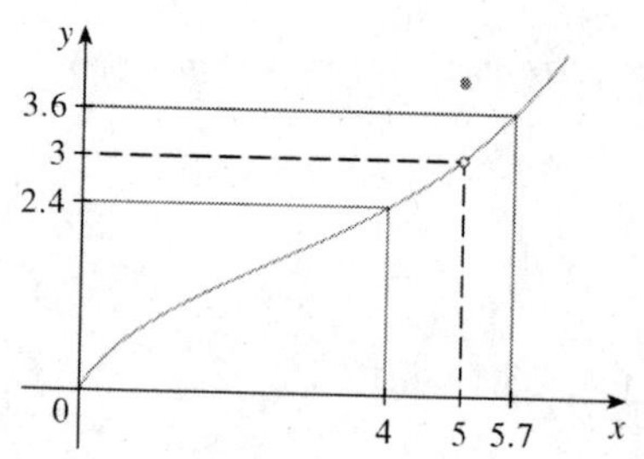

3. Use the given graph of $f(x) = \sqrt{x}$ to find a number δ such that

if $|x - 4| < \delta$ then $|\sqrt{x} - 2| < 0.4$

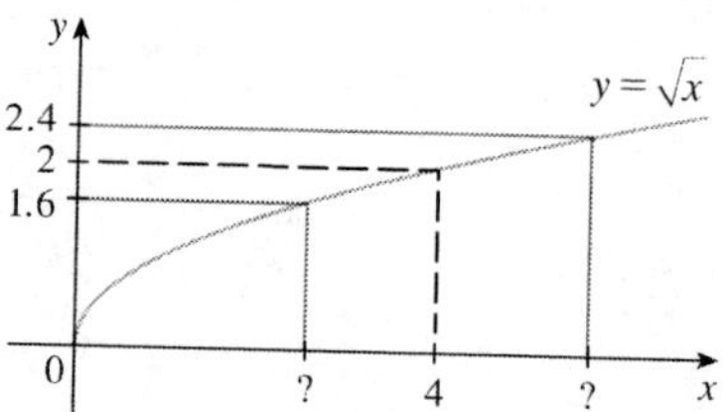

4. Use the given graph of $f(x) = x^2$ to find a number δ such that

if $|x - 1| < \delta$ then $|x^2 - 1| < \frac{1}{2}$

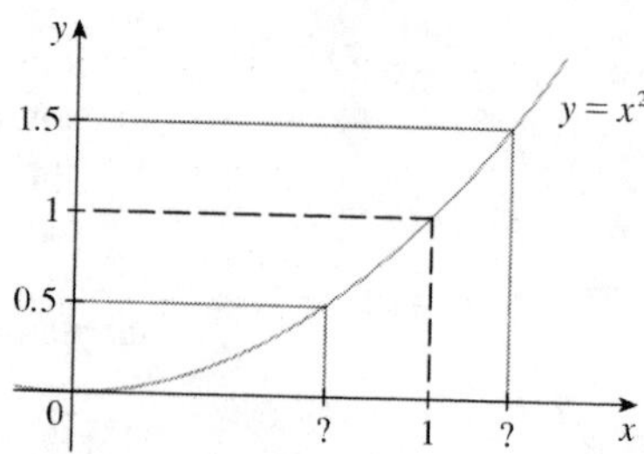

5. Use a graph to find a number δ such that

if $\left|x - \dfrac{\pi}{4}\right| < \delta$ then $|\tan x - 1| < 0.2$

Graphing calculator or computer with graphing software required

1. Homework Hints available in TEC

6. Use a graph to find a number δ such that

$$\text{if} \quad |x - 1| < \delta \quad \text{then} \quad \left| \frac{2x}{x^2 + 4} - 0.4 \right| < 0.1$$

7. For the limit

$$\lim_{x \to 1} (4 + x - 3x^3) = 2$$

illustrate Definition 1 by finding values of δ that correspond to $\varepsilon = 1$ and $\varepsilon = 0.1$.

8. For the limit

$$\lim_{x \to 0} \frac{e^x - 1}{x} = 1$$

illustrate Definition 1 by finding values of δ that correspond to $\varepsilon = 0.5$ and $\varepsilon = 0.1$.

9. Use Definition 1 to prove that $\lim_{x \to 0} x^3 = 0$.

10. (a) How would you formulate an ε, δ definition of the one-sided limit $\lim_{x \to a^+} f(x) = L$?
(b) Use your definition in part (a) to prove that $\lim_{x \to 0^+} \sqrt{x} = 0$.

11. A machinist is required to manufacture a circular metal disk with area 1000 cm^2.
(a) What radius produces such a disk?
(b) If the machinist is allowed an error tolerance of $\pm 5 \text{ cm}^2$ in the area of the disk, how close to the ideal radius in part (a) must the machinist control the radius?
(c) In terms of the ε, δ definition of $\lim_{x \to a} f(x) = L$, what is x? What is $f(x)$? What is a? What is L? What value of ε is given? What is the corresponding value of δ?

12. A crystal growth furnace is used in research to determine how best to manufacture crystals used in electronic components for the space shuttle. For proper growth of the crystal, the temperature must be controlled accurately by adjusting the input power. Suppose the relationship is given by

$$T(w) = 0.1w^2 + 2.155w + 20$$

where T is the temperature in degrees Celsius and w is the power input in watts.
(a) How much power is needed to maintain the temperature at 200°C ?
(b) If the temperature is allowed to vary from 200°C by up to ±1°C, what range of wattage is allowed for the input power?
(c) In terms of the ε, δ definition of $\lim_{x \to a} f(x) = L$, what is x? What is $f(x)$? What is a? What is L? What value of ε is given? What is the corresponding value of δ?

13. (a) Find a number δ such that if $|x - 2| < \delta$, then $|4x - 8| < \varepsilon$, where $\varepsilon = 0.1$.
(b) Repeat part (a) with $\varepsilon = 0.01$.

14. Given that $\lim_{x \to 2}(5x - 7) = 3$, illustrate Definition 1 by finding values of δ that correspond to $\varepsilon = 0.1$, $\varepsilon = 0.05$, and $\varepsilon = 0.01$.

15–16 Prove the statement using the ε, δ definition of a limit and illustrate with a diagram like Figure 7.

15. $\lim_{x \to -3} (1 - 4x) = 13$ **16.** $\lim_{x \to -2} \left(\frac{1}{2}x + 3\right) = 2$

17. Use a graph to find a number N such that

$$\text{if} \quad x > N \quad \text{then} \quad \left| \frac{6x^2 + 5x - 3}{2x^2 - 1} - 3 \right| < 0.2$$

18. For the limit

$$\lim_{x \to \infty} \frac{\sqrt{4x^2 + 1}}{x + 1} = 2$$

illustrate Definition 2 by finding values of N that correspond to $\varepsilon = 0.5$ and $\varepsilon = 0.1$.

19. (a) Determine how large we have to take x so that

$$1/x^2 < 0.0001$$

(b) Use Definition 2 to prove that

$$\lim_{x \to \infty} \frac{1}{x^2} = 0$$

20. (a) For what values of x is it true that

$$\frac{1}{x^2} > 1{,}000{,}000$$

(b) The precise definition of $\lim_{x \to a} f(x) = \infty$ states that for every positive number M (no matter how large) there is a corresponding positive number δ such that if $0 < |x - a| < \delta$, then $f(x) > M$. Use this definition to prove that $\lim_{x \to 0} (1/x^2) = \infty$.

21. (a) Use a graph to guess the value of the limit

$$\lim_{n \to \infty} \frac{n^5}{n!}$$

(b) Use a graph of the sequence in part (a) to find the smallest values of N that correspond to $\varepsilon = 0.1$ and $\varepsilon = 0.001$ in Definition 3.

22. Use Definition 3 to prove that $\lim_{n \to \infty} r^n = 0$ when $|r| < 1$.

23. Use Definition 3 to prove that if $\lim\limits_{n \to \infty} |a_n| = 0$, then $\lim\limits_{n \to \infty} a_n = 0$.

24. Use Definition 4 to prove that $\lim\limits_{n \to \infty} n^3 = \infty$.

25. Use Definition 5 to prove that $\displaystyle\lim_{(x, y) \to (0, 0)} \frac{xy}{\sqrt{x^2 + y^2}} = 0$.

E A Few Proofs

In this appendix we present proofs of some theorems that were stated in the main body of the text. We start by proving the Triangle Inequality, which is an important property of absolute value.

The Triangle Inequality If a and b are any real numbers, then

$$|a + b| \leqslant |a| + |b|$$

Observe that if the numbers a and b are both positive or both negative, then the two sides in the Triangle Inequality are actually equal. But if a and b have opposite signs, the left side involves a subtraction and the right side does not. This makes the Triangle Inequality seem reasonable, but we can prove it as follows.

Notice that

$$-|a| \leqslant a \leqslant |a|$$

is always true because a equals either $|a|$ or $-|a|$. The corresponding statement for b is

$$-|b| \leqslant b \leqslant |b|$$

Adding these inequalities, we get

$$-(|a| + |b|) \leqslant a + b \leqslant |a| + |b|$$

When combined, Properties 4 and 5 of absolute value (see Appendix A) say that

$$|x| \leqslant a \iff -a \leqslant x \leqslant a$$

If we now apply Properties 4 and 5 of absolute value from Appendix A (with x replaced by $a + b$ and a by $|a| + |b|$), we obtain

$$|a + b| \leqslant |a| + |b|$$

which is what we wanted to show. □

Next we use the Triangle Inequality to prove the Sum Law for limits.

The Sum Law was first stated in Section 2.3.

Sum Law If $\lim_{x \to a} f(x) = L$ and $\lim_{x \to a} g(x) = M$ both exist, then

$$\lim_{x \to a} [f(x) + g(x)] = L + M$$

PROOF Let $\varepsilon > 0$ be given. According to Definition 1 in Appendix D, we must find $\delta > 0$ such that

$$\text{if} \quad 0 < |x - a| < \delta \quad \text{then} \quad |f(x) + g(x) - (L + M)| < \varepsilon$$

Using the Triangle Inequality we can write

$$\boxed{1} \qquad \begin{aligned} |f(x) + g(x) - (L + M)| &= |(f(x) - L) + (g(x) - M)| \\ &\leqslant |f(x) - L| + |g(x) - M| \end{aligned}$$

We will make $|f(x) + g(x) - (L + M)|$ less than ε by making each of the terms $|f(x) - L|$ and $|g(x) - M|$ less than $\varepsilon/2$.

Since $\varepsilon/2 > 0$ and $\lim_{x \to a} f(x) = L$, there exists a number $\delta_1 > 0$ such that

$$\text{if} \quad 0 < |x - a| < \delta_1 \quad \text{then} \quad |f(x) - L| < \frac{\varepsilon}{2}$$

Similarly, since $\lim_{x \to a} g(x) = M$, there exists a number $\delta_2 > 0$ such that

$$\text{if} \quad 0 < |x - a| < \delta_2 \quad \text{then} \quad |g(x) - M| < \frac{\varepsilon}{2}$$

Let $\delta = \min\{\delta_1, \delta_2\}$, the smaller of the numbers δ_1 and δ_2. Notice that

$$\text{if} \quad 0 < |x - a| < \delta \quad \text{then} \quad 0 < |x - a| < \delta_1 \quad \text{and} \quad 0 < |x - a| < \delta_2$$

and so

$$|f(x) - L| < \frac{\varepsilon}{2} \quad \text{and} \quad |g(x) - M| < \frac{\varepsilon}{2}$$

Therefore, by (1),

$$\begin{aligned} |f(x) + g(x) - (L + M)| &\leqslant |f(x) - L| + |g(x) - M| \\ &< \frac{\varepsilon}{2} + \frac{\varepsilon}{2} = \varepsilon \end{aligned}$$

To summarize,

$$\text{if} \quad 0 < |x - a| < \delta \quad \text{then} \quad |f(x) + g(x) - (L + M)| < \varepsilon$$

Thus, by the definition of a limit,

$$\lim_{x \to a} [f(x) + g(x)] = L + M$$

□

Fermat's Theorem was discussed in Section 4.2.

Fermat's Theorem If f has a local maximum or minimum at c, and if $f'(c)$ exists, then $f'(c) = 0$.

PROOF Suppose, for the sake of definiteness, that f has a local maximum at c. Then, $f(c) \geqslant f(x)$ if x is sufficiently close to c. This implies that if h is sufficiently close to 0, with h being positive or negative, then

$$f(c) \geqslant f(c + h)$$

and therefore

$$\boxed{2} \qquad f(c + h) - f(c) \leqslant 0$$

We can divide both sides of an inequality by a positive number. Thus, if $h > 0$ and h is sufficiently small, we have

$$\frac{f(c + h) - f(c)}{h} \leqslant 0$$

Taking the right-hand limit of both sides of this inequality (using Theorem 2.3.2), we get

$$\lim_{h\to 0^+} \frac{f(c+h)-f(c)}{h} \leqslant \lim_{h\to 0^+} 0 = 0$$

But since $f'(c)$ exists, we have

$$f'(c) = \lim_{h\to 0} \frac{f(c+h)-f(c)}{h} = \lim_{h\to 0^+} \frac{f(c+h)-f(c)}{h}$$

and so we have shown that $f'(c) \leqslant 0$.

If $h < 0$, then the direction of the inequality (2) is reversed when we divide by h:

$$\frac{f(c+h)-f(c)}{h} \geqslant 0 \qquad h < 0$$

So, taking the left-hand limit, we have

$$f'(c) = \lim_{h\to 0} \frac{f(c+h)-f(c)}{h} = \lim_{h\to 0^-} \frac{f(c+h)-f(c)}{h} \geqslant 0$$

We have shown that $f'(c) \geqslant 0$ and also that $f'(c) \leqslant 0$. Since both of these inequalities must be true, the only possibility is that $f'(c) = 0$.

We have proved Fermat's Theorem for the case of a local maximum. The case of a local minimum can be proved in a similar manner. ☐

This theorem was stated and used in Section 8.1.

Theorem If $\lim_{n\to\infty} a_n = L$ and the function f is continuous at L, then

$$\lim_{n\to\infty} f(a_n) = f(L)$$

PROOF We must show that, given a number $\varepsilon > 0$, there is an integer N such that if $n > N$, then $|f(a_n) - f(L)| < \varepsilon$.

Suppose $\varepsilon > 0$. Since f is continuous at L, there is a number $\delta > 0$ such that if $|x - L| < \delta$, then $|f(x) - f(L)| < \varepsilon$. Because $\lim_{n\to\infty} a_n = L$, there is an integer N such that if $n > N$, then $|a_n - L| < \delta$. Suppose $n > N$. Then $|a_n - L| < \delta$ and so $|f(a_n) - f(L)| < \varepsilon$.

This shows that $\lim_{n\to\infty} f(a_n) = f(L)$. ☐

Clairaut's Theorem was discussed in Section 11.3.

Clairaut's Theorem Suppose f is defined on a disk D that contains the point (a, b). If the functions f_{xy} and f_{yx} are both continuous on D, then $f_{xy}(a, b) = f_{yx}(a, b)$.

PROOF For small values of h, $h \neq 0$, consider the difference

$$\Delta(h) = [f(a+h, b+h) - f(a+h, b)] - [f(a, b+h) - f(a, b)]$$

Notice that if we let $g(x) = f(x, b+h) - f(x, b)$, then

$$\Delta(h) = g(a+h) - g(a)$$

By the Mean Value Theorem, there is a number c between a and $a + h$ such that

$$g(a + h) - g(a) = g'(c)h = h[f_x(c, b + h) - f_x(c, b)]$$

Applying the Mean Value Theorem again, this time to f_x, we get a number d between b and $b + h$ such that

$$f_x(c, b + h) - f_x(c, b) = f_{xy}(c, d)h$$

Combining these equations, we obtain

$$\Delta(h) = h^2 f_{xy}(c, d)$$

If $h \to 0$, then $(c, d) \to (a, b)$, so the continuity of f_{xy} at (a, b) gives

$$\lim_{h \to 0} \frac{\Delta(h)}{h^2} = \lim_{(c, d) \to (a, b)} f_{xy}(c, d) = f_{xy}(a, b)$$

Similarly, by writing

$$\Delta(h) = [f(a + h, b + h) - f(a, b + h)] - [f(a + h, b) - f(a, b)]$$

and using the Mean Value Theorem twice and the continuity of f_{yx} at (a, b), we obtain

$$\lim_{h \to 0} \frac{\Delta(h)}{h^2} = f_{yx}(a, b)$$

It follows that $f_{xy}(a, b) = f_{yx}(a, b)$. ☐

This was stated as Theorem 8 in Section 11.4.

Theorem If the partial derivatives f_x and f_y exist near (a, b) and are continuous at (a, b), then f is differentiable at (a, b).

PROOF Let

$$\Delta z = f(a + \Delta x, b + \Delta y) - f(a, b)$$

According to (11.4.7), to prove that f is differentiable at (a, b) we have to show that we can write Δz in the form

$$\Delta z = f_x(a, b)\,\Delta x + f_y(a, b)\,\Delta y + \varepsilon_1\,\Delta x + \varepsilon_2\,\Delta y$$

where ε_1 and $\varepsilon_2 \to 0$ as $(\Delta x, \Delta y) \to (0, 0)$.

Referring to Figure 1, we write

$$\boxed{3} \quad \Delta z = [f(a + \Delta x, b + \Delta y) - f(a, b + \Delta y)] + [f(a, b + \Delta y) - f(a, b)]$$

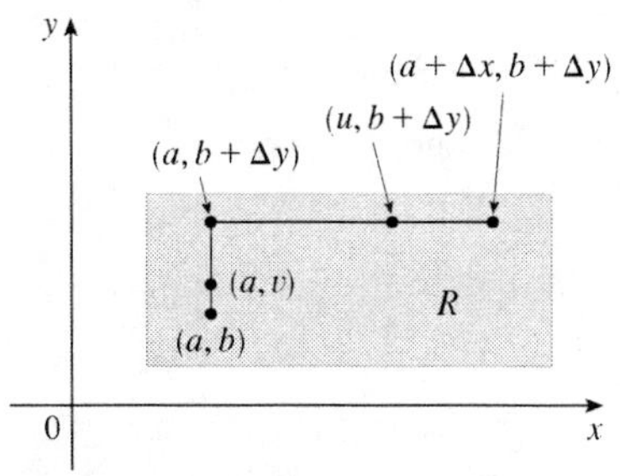

FIGURE 1

Observe that the function of a single variable

$$g(x) = f(x, b + \Delta y)$$

is defined on the interval $[a, a + \Delta x]$ and $g'(x) = f_x(x, b + \Delta y)$. If we apply the Mean Value Theorem to g, we get

$$g(a + \Delta x) - g(a) = g'(u)\,\Delta x$$

where u is some number between a and $a + \Delta x$. In terms of f, this equation becomes

$$f(a + \Delta x, b + \Delta y) - f(a, b + \Delta y) = f_x(u, b + \Delta y)\,\Delta x$$

This gives us an expression for the first part of the right side of Equation 3. For the second part we let $h(y) = f(a, y)$. Then h is a function of a single variable defined on the interval $[b, b + \Delta y]$ and $h'(y) = f_y(a, y)$. A second application of the Mean Value Theorem then gives

$$h(b + \Delta y) - h(b) = h'(v)\,\Delta y$$

where v is some number between b and $b + \Delta y$. In terms of f, this becomes

$$f(a, b + \Delta y) - f(a, b) = f_y(a, v)\,\Delta y$$

We now substitute these expressions into Equation 3 and obtain

$$\begin{aligned}\Delta z &= f_x(u, b + \Delta y)\,\Delta x + f_y(a, v)\,\Delta y \\ &= f_x(a, b)\,\Delta x + [f_x(u, b + \Delta y) - f_x(a, b)]\,\Delta x + f_y(a, b)\,\Delta y \\ &\qquad + [f_y(a, v) - f_y(a, b)]\,\Delta y \\ &= f_x(a, b)\,\Delta x + f_y(a, b)\,\Delta y + \varepsilon_1\,\Delta x + \varepsilon_2\,\Delta y\end{aligned}$$

where

$$\varepsilon_1 = f_x(u, b + \Delta y) - f_x(a, b)$$

$$\varepsilon_2 = f_y(a, v) - f_y(a, b)$$

Since $(u, b + \Delta y) \to (a, b)$ and $(a, v) \to (a, b)$ as $(\Delta x, \Delta y) \to (0, 0)$ and since f_x and f_y are continuous at (a, b), we see that $\varepsilon_1 \to 0$ and $\varepsilon_2 \to 0$ as $(\Delta x, \Delta y) \to (0, 0)$.

Therefore f is differentiable at (a, b). ☐

The Second Derivatives Test was discussed in Section 11.7. Parts (b) and (c) have similar proofs.

Second Derivatives Test Suppose the second partial derivatives of f are continuous on a disk with center (a, b), and suppose that $f_x(a, b) = 0$ and $f_y(a, b) = 0$ [that is, (a, b) is a critical point of f]. Let

$$D = D(a, b) = f_{xx}(a, b)f_{yy}(a, b) - [f_{xy}(a, b)]^2$$

(a) If $D > 0$ and $f_{xx}(a, b) > 0$, then $f(a, b)$ is a local minimum.

(b) If $D > 0$ and $f_{xx}(a, b) < 0$, then $f(a, b)$ is a local maximum.

(c) If $D < 0$, then $f(a, b)$ is not a local maximum or minimum.

PROOF OF PART (A) We compute the second-order directional derivative of f in the direction of $\mathbf{u} = \langle h, k \rangle$. The first-order derivative is given by Theorem 11.6.3:

$$D_{\mathbf{u}} f = f_x h + f_y k$$

Applying this theorem a second time, we have

$$D_{\mathbf{u}}^2 f = D_{\mathbf{u}}(D_{\mathbf{u}} f) = \frac{\partial}{\partial x}(D_{\mathbf{u}} f)h + \frac{\partial}{\partial y}(D_{\mathbf{u}} f)k$$

$$= (f_{xx}h + f_{yx}k)h + (f_{xy}h + f_{yy}k)k$$

$$= f_{xx}h^2 + 2f_{xy}hk + f_{yy}k^2 \qquad \text{(by Clairaut's Theorem)}$$

If we complete the square in this expression, we obtain

4 $$D_{\mathbf{u}}^2 f = f_{xx}\left(h + \frac{f_{xy}}{f_{xx}}k\right)^2 + \frac{k^2}{f_{xx}}(f_{xx}f_{yy} - f_{xy}^2)$$

We are given that $f_{xx}(a, b) > 0$ and $D(a, b) > 0$. But f_{xx} and $D = f_{xx}f_{yy} - f_{xy}^2$ are continuous functions, so there is a disk B with center (a, b) and radius $\delta > 0$ such that $f_{xx}(x, y) > 0$ and $D(x, y) > 0$ whenever (x, y) is in B. Therefore, by looking at Equation 4, we see that $D_{\mathbf{u}}^2 f(x, y) > 0$ whenever (x, y) is in B. This means that if C is the curve obtained by intersecting the graph of f with the vertical plane through $P(a, b, f(a, b))$ in the direction of $\mathbf{u}$, then C is concave upward on an interval of length 2δ. This is true in the direction of every vector $\mathbf{u}$, so if we restrict (x, y) to lie in B, the graph of f lies above its horizontal tangent plane at P. Thus $f(x, y) \geqslant f(a, b)$ whenever (x, y) is in B. This shows that $f(a, b)$ is a local minimum. ∎

F Sigma Notation

A convenient way of writing sums uses the Greek letter Σ (capital sigma, corresponding to our letter S) and is called **sigma notation**.

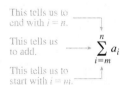

This tells us to end with $i = n$.

This tells us to add. $\displaystyle\sum_{i=m}^{n} a_i$

This tells us to start with $i = m$.

1 Definition If $a_m, a_{m+1}, \ldots, a_n$ are real numbers and m and n are integers such that $m \leqslant n$, then

$$\sum_{i=m}^{n} a_i = a_m + a_{m+1} + a_{m+2} + \cdots + a_{n-1} + a_n$$

With function notation, Definition 1 can be written as

$$\sum_{i=m}^{n} f(i) = f(m) + f(m+1) + f(m+2) + \cdots + f(n-1) + f(n)$$

Thus the symbol $\Sigma_{i=m}^{n}$ indicates a summation in which the letter i (called the **index of summation**) takes on consecutive integer values beginning with m and ending with n, that is, $m, m+1, \ldots, n$. Other letters can also be used as the index of summation.

EXAMPLE 1

(a) $\sum_{i=1}^{4} i^2 = 1^2 + 2^2 + 3^2 + 4^2 = 30$

(b) $\sum_{i=3}^{n} i = 3 + 4 + 5 + \cdots + (n-1) + n$

(c) $\sum_{j=0}^{5} 2^j = 2^0 + 2^1 + 2^2 + 2^3 + 2^4 + 2^5 = 63$

(d) $\sum_{k=1}^{n} \frac{1}{k} = 1 + \frac{1}{2} + \frac{1}{3} + \cdots + \frac{1}{n}$

(e) $\sum_{i=1}^{3} \frac{i-1}{i^2+3} = \frac{1-1}{1^2+3} + \frac{2-1}{2^2+3} + \frac{3-1}{3^2+3} = 0 + \frac{1}{7} + \frac{1}{6} = \frac{13}{42}$

(f) $\sum_{i=1}^{4} 2 = 2 + 2 + 2 + 2 = 8$

EXAMPLE 2 Write the sum $2^3 + 3^3 + \cdots + n^3$ in sigma notation.

SOLUTION There is no unique way of writing a sum in sigma notation. We could write

$$2^3 + 3^3 + \cdots + n^3 = \sum_{i=2}^{n} i^3$$

or

$$2^3 + 3^3 + \cdots + n^3 = \sum_{j=1}^{n-1} (j+1)^3$$

or

$$2^3 + 3^3 + \cdots + n^3 = \sum_{k=0}^{n-2} (k+2)^3$$

The following theorem gives three simple rules for working with sigma notation.

2 Theorem If c is any constant (that is, it does not depend on i), then

(a) $\sum_{i=m}^{n} ca_i = c \sum_{i=m}^{n} a_i$

(b) $\sum_{i=m}^{n} (a_i + b_i) = \sum_{i=m}^{n} a_i + \sum_{i=m}^{n} b_i$

(c) $\sum_{i=m}^{n} (a_i - b_i) = \sum_{i=m}^{n} a_i - \sum_{i=m}^{n} b_i$

PROOF To see why these rules are true, all we have to do is write both sides in expanded form. Rule (a) is just the distributive property of real numbers:

$$ca_m + ca_{m+1} + \cdots + ca_n = c(a_m + a_{m+1} + \cdots + a_n)$$

Rule (b) follows from the associative and commutative properties:

$$\begin{aligned}(a_m + b_m) + (a_{m+1} + b_{m+1}) + \cdots + (a_n + b_n) \\ = (a_m + a_{m+1} + \cdots + a_n) + (b_m + b_{m+1} + \cdots + b_n)\end{aligned}$$

Rule (c) is proved similarly.

EXAMPLE 3 Find $\sum_{i=1}^{n} 1$.

SOLUTION

$$\sum_{i=1}^{n} 1 = \underbrace{1 + 1 + \cdots + 1}_{n \text{ terms}} = n$$

EXAMPLE 4 Prove the formula for the sum of the first n positive integers:

$$\sum_{i=1}^{n} i = 1 + 2 + 3 + \cdots + n = \frac{n(n+1)}{2}$$

SOLUTION This formula can be proved by mathematical induction (see page 84) or by the following method used by the German mathematician Karl Friedrich Gauss (1777–1855) when he was ten years old.

Write the sum S twice, once in the usual order and once in reverse order:

$$S = 1 + \quad 2 \quad + \quad 3 \quad + \cdots + (n-1) + n$$

$$S = n + (n-1) + (n-2) + \cdots + \quad 2 \quad + 1$$

Adding all columns vertically, we get

$$2S = (n+1) + (n+1) + (n+1) + \cdots + (n+1) + (n+1)$$

On the right side there are n terms, each of which is $n + 1$, so

$$2S = n(n+1) \qquad \text{or} \qquad S = \frac{n(n+1)}{2}$$

EXAMPLE 5 Prove the formula for the sum of the squares of the first n positive integers:

$$\sum_{i=1}^{n} i^2 = 1^2 + 2^2 + 3^2 + \cdots + n^2 = \frac{n(n+1)(2n+1)}{6}$$

SOLUTION 1 Let S be the desired sum. We start with the *telescoping sum* (or collapsing sum):

Most terms cancel in pairs.

$$\sum_{i=1}^{n} [(1+i)^3 - i^3] = (2^3 - 1^3) + (3^3 - 2^3) + (4^3 - 3^3) + \cdots + [(n+1)^3 - n^3]$$

$$= (n+1)^3 - 1^3 = n^3 + 3n^2 + 3n$$

On the other hand, using Theorem 2 and Examples 3 and 4, we have

$$\sum_{i=1}^{n} [(1+i)^3 - i^3] = \sum_{i=1}^{n} [3i^2 + 3i + 1] = 3\sum_{i=1}^{n} i^2 + 3\sum_{i=1}^{n} i + \sum_{i=1}^{n} 1$$

$$= 3S + 3\,\frac{n(n+1)}{2} + n = 3S + \tfrac{3}{2}n^2 + \tfrac{5}{2}n$$

Thus we have

$$n^3 + 3n^2 + 3n = 3S + \tfrac{3}{2}n^2 + \tfrac{5}{2}n$$

Solving this equation for S, we obtain

$$3S = n^3 + \tfrac{3}{2}n^2 + \tfrac{1}{2}n$$

or

$$S = \frac{2n^3 + 3n^2 + n}{6} = \frac{n(n+1)(2n+1)}{6}$$

Principle of Mathematical Induction
Let S_n be a statement involving the positive integer n. Suppose that
1. S_1 is true.
2. If S_k is true, then S_{k+1} is true.
Then S_n is true for all positive integers n.

See pages 84 and 87 for a more thorough discussion of mathematical induction.

SOLUTION 2 Let S_n be the given formula.

1. S_1 is true because $\quad 1^2 = \dfrac{1(1+1)(2 \cdot 1 + 1)}{6}$

2. Assume that S_k is true; that is,

$$1^2 + 2^2 + 3^2 + \cdots + k^2 = \frac{k(k+1)(2k+1)}{6}$$

Then

$$\begin{aligned}
1^2 + 2^2 + 3^2 + \cdots + (k+1)^2 &= (1^2 + 2^2 + 3^2 + \cdots + k^2) + (k+1)^2 \\
&= \frac{k(k+1)(2k+1)}{6} + (k+1)^2 \\
&= (k+1)\frac{k(2k+1) + 6(k+1)}{6} \\
&= (k+1)\frac{2k^2 + 7k + 6}{6} \\
&= \frac{(k+1)(k+2)(2k+3)}{6} \\
&= \frac{(k+1)[(k+1)+1][2(k+1)+1]}{6}
\end{aligned}$$

So S_{k+1} is true.

By the Principle of Mathematical Induction, S_n is true for all n.

We list the results of Examples 3, 4, and 5 together with a similar result for cubes (see Exercises 37–40) as Theorem 3. These formulas are needed for finding areas and evaluating integrals in Chapter 5.

3 Theorem Let c be a constant and n a positive integer. Then

(a) $\displaystyle\sum_{i=1}^{n} 1 = n$

(b) $\displaystyle\sum_{i=1}^{n} c = nc$

(c) $\displaystyle\sum_{i=1}^{n} i = \frac{n(n+1)}{2}$

(d) $\displaystyle\sum_{i=1}^{n} i^2 = \frac{n(n+1)(2n+1)}{6}$

(e) $\displaystyle\sum_{i=1}^{n} i^3 = \left[\frac{n(n+1)}{2}\right]^2$

EXAMPLE 6 Evaluate $\sum_{i=1}^{n} i(4i^2 - 3)$.

SOLUTION Using Theorems 2 and 3, we have

$$\sum_{i=1}^{n} i(4i^2 - 3) = \sum_{i=1}^{n} (4i^3 - 3i) = 4\sum_{i=1}^{n} i^3 - 3\sum_{i=1}^{n} i$$

$$= 4\left[\frac{n(n+1)}{2}\right]^2 - 3\,\frac{n(n+1)}{2}$$

$$= \frac{n(n+1)[2n(n+1) - 3]}{2}$$

$$= \frac{n(n+1)(2n^2 + 2n - 3)}{2}$$

The type of calculation in Example 7 arises in Chapter 5 when we compute areas.

EXAMPLE 7 Find $\lim_{n\to\infty} \sum_{i=1}^{n} \frac{3}{n}\left[\left(\frac{i}{n}\right)^2 + 1\right]$.

SOLUTION

$$\lim_{n\to\infty} \sum_{i=1}^{n} \frac{3}{n}\left[\left(\frac{i}{n}\right)^2 + 1\right] = \lim_{n\to\infty} \sum_{i=1}^{n} \left[\frac{3}{n^3}i^2 + \frac{3}{n}\right]$$

$$= \lim_{n\to\infty} \left[\frac{3}{n^3}\sum_{i=1}^{n} i^2 + \frac{3}{n}\sum_{i=1}^{n} 1\right]$$

$$= \lim_{n\to\infty} \left[\frac{3}{n^3}\,\frac{n(n+1)(2n+1)}{6} + \frac{3}{n}\cdot n\right]$$

$$= \lim_{n\to\infty} \left[\frac{1}{2}\cdot\frac{n}{n}\cdot\left(\frac{n+1}{n}\right)\left(\frac{2n+1}{n}\right) + 3\right]$$

$$= \lim_{n\to\infty} \left[\frac{1}{2}\cdot 1\left(1 + \frac{1}{n}\right)\left(2 + \frac{1}{n}\right) + 3\right]$$

$$= \tfrac{1}{2}\cdot 1\cdot 1\cdot 2 + 3 = 4$$

F Exercises

1–10 Write the sum in expanded form.

1. $\sum_{i=1}^{5} \sqrt{i}$

2. $\sum_{i=1}^{6} \frac{1}{i+1}$

3. $\sum_{i=4}^{6} 3^i$

4. $\sum_{i=4}^{6} i^3$

5. $\sum_{k=0}^{4} \frac{2k-1}{2k+1}$

6. $\sum_{k=5}^{8} x^k$

7. $\sum_{i=1}^{n} i^{10}$

8. $\sum_{j=n}^{n+3} j^2$

9. $\sum_{j=0}^{n-1} (-1)^j$

10. $\sum_{i=1}^{n} f(x_i)\,\Delta x_i$

11–20 Write the sum in sigma notation.

11. $1 + 2 + 3 + 4 + \cdots + 10$

12. $\sqrt{3} + \sqrt{4} + \sqrt{5} + \sqrt{6} + \sqrt{7}$

13. $\frac{1}{2} + \frac{2}{3} + \frac{3}{4} + \frac{4}{5} + \cdots + \frac{19}{20}$

14. $\frac{3}{7} + \frac{4}{8} + \frac{5}{9} + \frac{6}{10} + \cdots + \frac{23}{27}$

15. $2 + 4 + 6 + 8 + \cdots + 2n$

16. $1 + 3 + 5 + 7 + \cdots + (2n - 1)$

17. $1 + 2 + 4 + 8 + 16 + 32$

18. $\frac{1}{1} + \frac{1}{4} + \frac{1}{9} + \frac{1}{16} + \frac{1}{25} + \frac{1}{36}$

19. $x + x^2 + x^3 + \cdots + x^n$

20. $1 - x + x^2 - x^3 + \cdots + (-1)^n x^n$

21–35 Find the value of the sum.

21. $\sum_{i=4}^{8} (3i - 2)$

22. $\sum_{i=3}^{6} i(i + 2)$

23. $\sum_{j=1}^{6} 3^{j+1}$

24. $\sum_{k=0}^{8} \cos k\pi$

25. $\sum_{n=1}^{20} (-1)^n$

26. $\sum_{i=1}^{100} 4$

27. $\sum_{i=0}^{4} (2^i + i^2)$

28. $\sum_{i=-2}^{4} 2^{3-i}$

29. $\sum_{i=1}^{n} 2i$

30. $\sum_{i=1}^{n} (2 - 5i)$

31. $\sum_{i=1}^{n} (i^2 + 3i + 4)$

32. $\sum_{i=1}^{n} (3 + 2i)^2$

33. $\sum_{i=1}^{n} (i + 1)(i + 2)$

34. $\sum_{i=1}^{n} i(i + 1)(i + 2)$

35. $\sum_{i=1}^{n} (i^3 - i - 2)$

36. Find the number n such that $\sum_{i=1}^{n} i = 78$.

37. Prove formula (b) of Theorem 3.

38. Prove formula (e) of Theorem 3 using mathematical induction.

39. Prove formula (e) of Theorem 3 using a method similar to that of Example 5, Solution 1 [start with $(1 + i)^4 - i^4$].

40. Prove formula (e) of Theorem 3 using the following method published by Abu Bekr Mohammed ibn Alhusain Alkarchi in about AD 1010. The figure shows a square $ABCD$ in which sides AB and AD have been divided into segments of lengths 1, 2, 3, . . . , n. Thus the side of the square has length $n(n + 1)/2$ so the area is $[n(n + 1)/2]^2$. But the area is also the sum of the areas of the n "gnomons" $G_1, G_2, \ldots, G_n$ shown in the figure. Show that the area of G_i is i^3 and conclude that formula (e) is true.

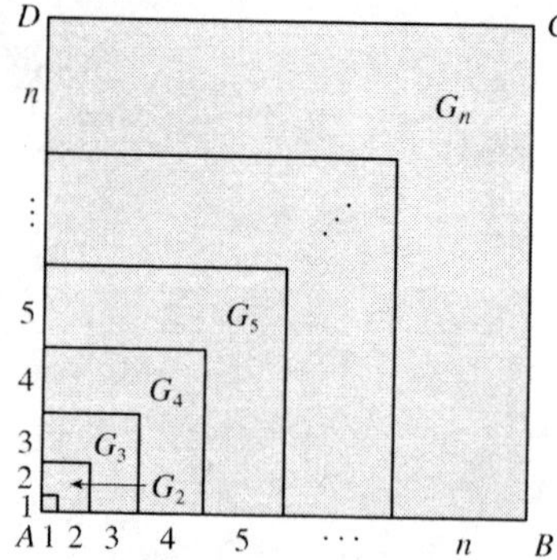

41. Evaluate each telescoping sum.

(a) $\sum_{i=1}^{n} [i^4 - (i - 1)^4]$ (b) $\sum_{i=1}^{100} (5^i - 5^{i-1})$

(c) $\sum_{i=3}^{99} \left(\frac{1}{i} - \frac{1}{i + 1}\right)$ (d) $\sum_{i=1}^{n} (a_i - a_{i-1})$

42. Prove the generalized triangle inequality:

$$\left|\sum_{i=1}^{n} a_i\right| \leqslant \sum_{i=1}^{n} |a_i|$$

43–46 Find the limit.

43. $\lim_{n\to\infty} \sum_{i=1}^{n} \frac{1}{n}\left(\frac{i}{n}\right)^2$

44. $\lim_{n\to\infty} \sum_{i=1}^{n} \frac{1}{n}\left[\left(\frac{i}{n}\right)^3 + 1\right]$

45. $\lim_{n\to\infty} \sum_{i=1}^{n} \frac{2}{n}\left[\left(\frac{2i}{n}\right)^3 + 5\left(\frac{2i}{n}\right)\right]$

46. $\lim_{n\to\infty} \sum_{i=1}^{n} \frac{3}{n}\left[\left(1 + \frac{3i}{n}\right)^3 - 2\left(1 + \frac{3i}{n}\right)\right]$

47. Prove the formula for the sum of a finite geometric series with first term a and common ratio $r \neq 1$:

$$\sum_{i=1}^{n} ar^{i-1} = a + ar + ar^2 + \cdots + ar^{n-1} = \frac{a(r^n - 1)}{r - 1}$$

48. Evaluate $\sum_{i=1}^{n} \frac{3}{2^{i-1}}$.

49. Evaluate $\sum_{i=1}^{n} (2i + 2^i)$.

50. Evaluate $\sum_{i=1}^{m} \left[\sum_{j=1}^{n} (i + j)\right]$.

41. One method of slowing the growth of an insect population without using pesticides is to introduce into the population a number of sterile males that mate with fertile females but produce no offspring. If P represents the number of female insects in a population, S the number of sterile males introduced each generation, and r the population's natural growth rate, then the female population is related to time t by

$$t = \int \frac{P + S}{P[(r - 1)P - S]}\, dP$$

Suppose an insect population with 10,000 females grows at a rate of $r = 0.10$ and 900 sterile males are added. Evaluate the integral to give an equation relating the female population to time. (Note that the resulting equation can't be solved explicitly for P.)

42. The region under the curve

$$y = \frac{1}{x^2 + 3x + 2}$$

from $x = 0$ to $x = 1$ is rotated about the x-axis. Find the volume of the resulting solid.

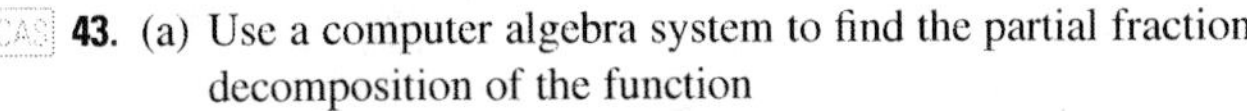

CAS **43.** (a) Use a computer algebra system to find the partial fraction decomposition of the function

$$f(x) = \frac{4x^3 - 27x^2 + 5x - 32}{30x^5 - 13x^4 + 50x^3 - 286x^2 - 299x - 70}$$

(b) Use part (a) to find $\int f(x)\, dx$ (by hand) and compare with the result of using the CAS to integrate f directly. Comment on any discrepancy.

CAS **44.** (a) Find the partial fraction decomposition of the function

$$f(x) = \frac{12x^5 - 7x^3 - 13x^2 + 8}{100x^6 - 80x^5 + 116x^4 - 80x^3 + 41x^2 - 20x + 4}$$

(b) Use part (a) to find $\int f(x)\, dx$ and graph f and its indefinite integral on the same screen.

(c) Use the graph of f to discover the main features of the graph of $\int f(x)\, dx$.

45. Suppose that F, G, and Q are polynomials and

$$\frac{F(x)}{Q(x)} = \frac{G(x)}{Q(x)}$$

for all x except when $Q(x) = 0$. Prove that $F(x) = G(x)$ for all x. [*Hint:* Use continuity.]

46. If f is a quadratic function such that $f(0) = 1$ and

$$\int \frac{f(x)}{x^2(x + 1)^3}\, dx$$

is a rational function, find the value of $f'(0)$.

H Polar Coordinates

Polar coordinates offer an alternative way of locating points in a plane. They are useful because, for certain types of regions and curves, polar coordinates provide very simple descriptions and equations. The principal applications of this idea occur in multivariable calculus: the evaluation of double integrals and the derivation of Kepler's laws of planetary motion.

H.1 Curves in Polar Coordinates

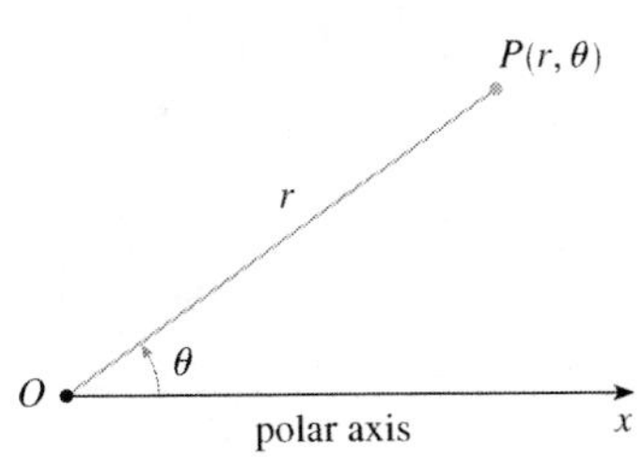

FIGURE 1

A coordinate system represents a point in the plane by an ordered pair of numbers called coordinates. Usually we use Cartesian coordinates, which are directed distances from two perpendicular axes. Here we describe a coordinate system introduced by Newton, called the **polar coordinate system**, which is more convenient for many purposes.

We choose a point in the plane that is called the **pole** (or origin) and is labeled O. Then we draw a ray (half-line) starting at O called the **polar axis**. This axis is usually drawn horizontally to the right and corresponds to the positive x-axis in Cartesian coordinates.

If P is any other point in the plane, let r be the distance from O to P and let θ be the angle (usually measured in radians) between the polar axis and the line OP as in Figure 1. Then the point P is represented by the ordered pair (r, θ) and r, θ are called **polar coordinates** of P. We use the convention that an angle is positive if measured in the counterclock-

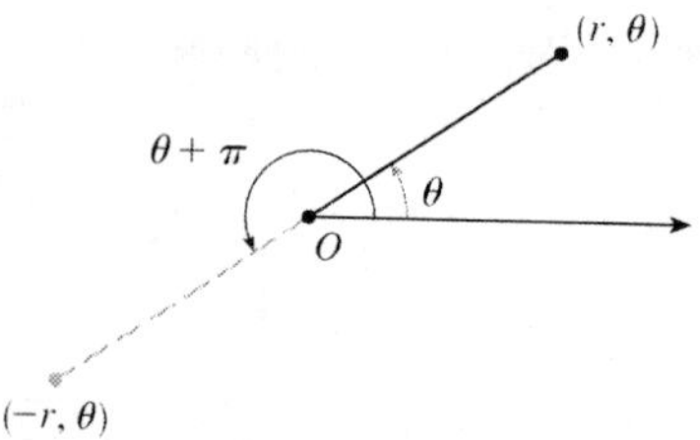

FIGURE 2

wise direction from the polar axis and negative in the clockwise direction. If $P = O$, then $r = 0$ and we agree that $(0, \theta)$ represents the pole for any value of θ.

We extend the meaning of polar coordinates (r, θ) to the case in which r is negative by agreeing that, as in Figure 2, the points $(-r, \theta)$ and (r, θ) lie on the same line through O and at the same distance $|r|$ from O, but on opposite sides of O. If $r > 0$, the point (r, θ) lies in the same quadrant as θ; if $r < 0$, it lies in the quadrant on the opposite side of the pole. Notice that $(-r, \theta)$ represents the same point as $(r, \theta + \pi)$.

EXAMPLE 1 Plot the points whose polar coordinates are given.

(a) $(1, 5\pi/4)$ (b) $(2, 3\pi)$ (c) $(2, -2\pi/3)$ (d) $(-3, 3\pi/4)$

SOLUTION The points are plotted in Figure 3. In part (d) the point $(-3, 3\pi/4)$ is located three units from the pole in the fourth quadrant because the angle $3\pi/4$ is in the second quadrant and $r = -3$ is negative.

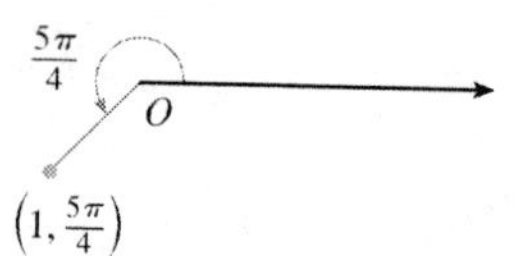

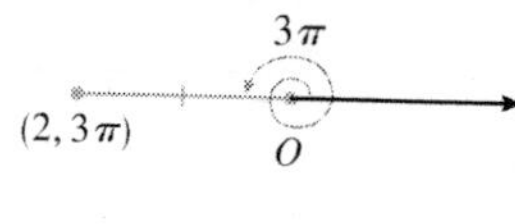

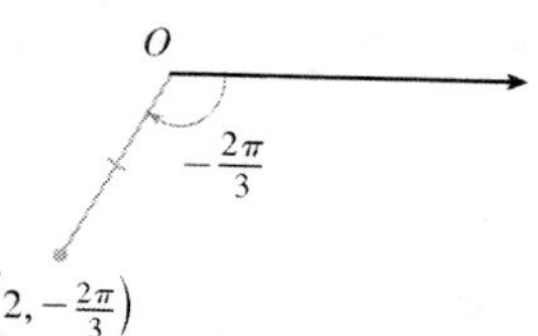

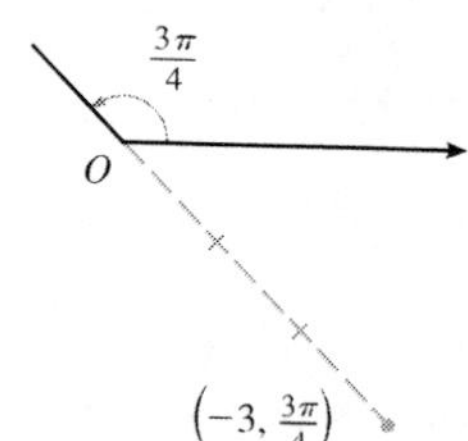

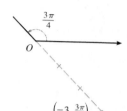

FIGURE 3

In the Cartesian coordinate system every point has only one representation, but in the polar coordinate system each point has many representations. For instance, the point $(1, 5\pi/4)$ in Example 1(a) could be written as $(1, -3\pi/4)$ or $(1, 13\pi/4)$ or $(-1, \pi/4)$. (See Figure 4.)

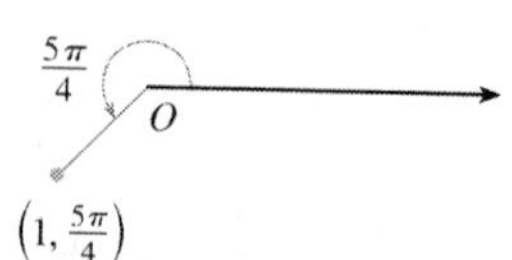

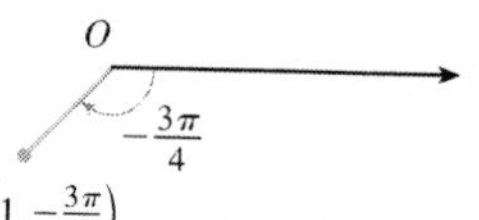

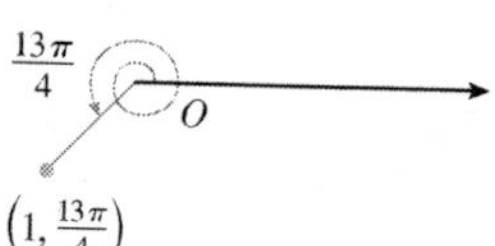

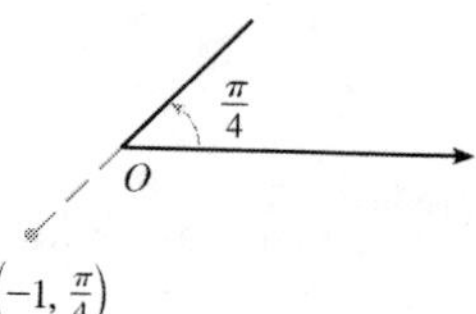

FIGURE 4

In fact, since a complete counterclockwise rotation is given by an angle 2π, the point represented by polar coordinates (r, θ) is also represented by

$$(r, \theta + 2n\pi) \qquad \text{and} \qquad (-r, \theta + (2n + 1)\pi)$$

where n is any integer.

The connection between polar and Cartesian coordinates can be seen from Figure 5, in which the pole corresponds to the origin and the polar axis coincides with the positive x-axis. If the point P has Cartesian coordinates (x, y) and polar coordinates (r, θ), then, from the figure, we have

FIGURE 5

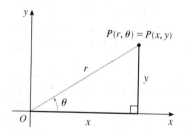

$$\cos \theta = \frac{x}{r} \qquad \sin \theta = \frac{y}{r}$$

and so

1 $$x = r \cos \theta \qquad y = r \sin \theta$$

Although Equations 1 were deduced from Figure 5, which illustrates the case where $r > 0$ and $0 < \theta < \pi/2$, these equations are valid for all values of r and θ. (See the general definition of $\sin \theta$ and $\cos \theta$ in Appendix C.)

Equations 1 allow us to find the Cartesian coordinates of a point when the polar coordinates are known. To find r and θ when x and y are known, we use the equations

2
$$r^2 = x^2 + y^2 \qquad \tan \theta = \frac{y}{x}$$

which can be deduced from Equations 1 or simply read from Figure 5.

EXAMPLE 2 Convert the point $(2, \pi/3)$ from polar to Cartesian coordinates.

SOLUTION Since $r = 2$ and $\theta = \pi/3$, Equations 1 give

$$x = r \cos \theta = 2 \cos \frac{\pi}{3} = 2 \cdot \frac{1}{2} = 1$$

$$y = r \sin \theta = 2 \sin \frac{\pi}{3} = 2 \cdot \frac{\sqrt{3}}{2} = \sqrt{3}$$

Therefore the point is $(1, \sqrt{3})$ in Cartesian coordinates.

EXAMPLE 3 Represent the point with Cartesian coordinates $(1, -1)$ in terms of polar coordinates.

SOLUTION If we choose r to be positive, then Equations 2 give

$$r = \sqrt{x^2 + y^2} = \sqrt{1^2 + (-1)^2} = \sqrt{2}$$

$$\tan \theta = \frac{y}{x} = -1$$

Since the point $(1, -1)$ lies in the fourth quadrant, we can choose $\theta = -\pi/4$ or $\theta = 7\pi/4$. Thus one possible answer is $(\sqrt{2}, -\pi/4)$; another is $(\sqrt{2}, 7\pi/4)$.

Note: Equations 2 do not uniquely determine θ when x and y are given because, as θ increases through the interval $0 \leqslant \theta < 2\pi$, each value of $\tan \theta$ occurs twice. Therefore, in converting from Cartesian to polar coordinates, it's not good enough just to find r and θ that satisfy Equations 2. As in Example 3, we must choose θ so that the point (r, θ) lies in the correct quadrant.

The **graph of a polar equation** $r = f(\theta)$, or more generally $F(r, \theta) = 0$, consists of all points P that have at least one polar representation (r, θ) whose coordinates satisfy the equation.

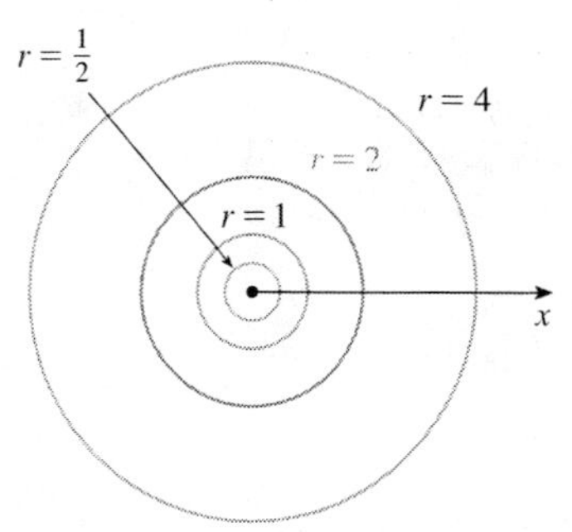

FIGURE 6

V EXAMPLE 4 What curve is represented by the polar equation $r = 2$?

SOLUTION The curve consists of all points (r, θ) with $r = 2$. Since r represents the distance from the point to the pole, the curve $r = 2$ represents the circle with center O and radius 2. In general, the equation $r = a$ represents a circle with center O and radius $|a|$. (See Figure 6.)

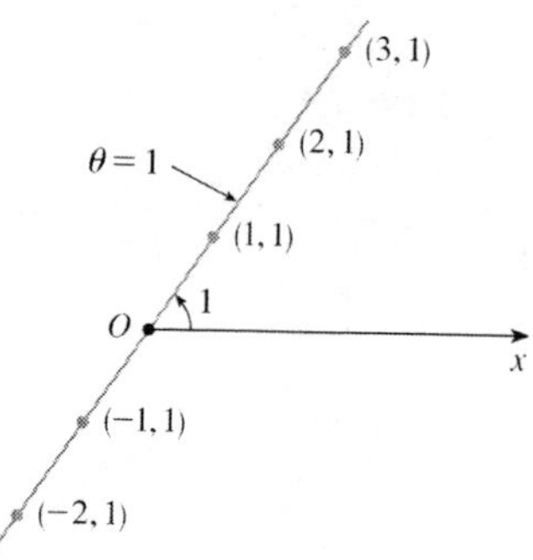

FIGURE 7

EXAMPLE 5 Sketch the polar curve $\theta = 1$.

SOLUTION This curve consists of all points (r, θ) such that the polar angle θ is 1 radian. It is the straight line that passes through O and makes an angle of 1 radian with the polar axis (see Figure 7). Notice that the points $(r, 1)$ on the line with $r > 0$ are in the first quadrant, whereas those with $r < 0$ are in the third quadrant.

EXAMPLE 6

(a) Sketch the curve with polar equation $r = 2\cos\theta$.
(b) Find a Cartesian equation for this curve.

SOLUTION

(a) In Figure 8 we find the values of r for some convenient values of θ and plot the corresponding points (r, θ). Then we join these points to sketch the curve, which appears to be a circle. We have used only values of θ between 0 and π, since if we let θ increase beyond π, we obtain the same points again.

θ	$r = 2\cos\theta$
0	2
$\pi/6$	$\sqrt{3}$
$\pi/4$	$\sqrt{2}$
$\pi/3$	1
$\pi/2$	0
$2\pi/3$	-1
$3\pi/4$	$-\sqrt{2}$
$5\pi/6$	$-\sqrt{3}$
π	-2

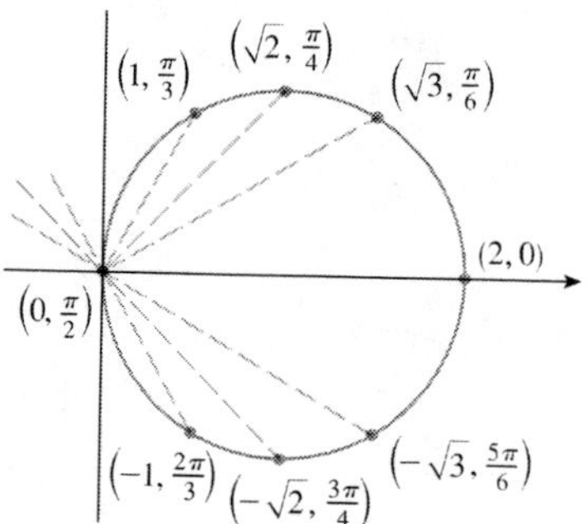

FIGURE 8
Table of values and graph of $r = 2\cos\theta$

(b) To convert the given equation into a Cartesian equation we use Equations 1 and 2. From $x = r\cos\theta$ we have $\cos\theta = x/r$, so the equation $r = 2\cos\theta$ becomes $r = 2x/r$, which gives

$$2x = r^2 = x^2 + y^2 \qquad \text{or} \qquad x^2 + y^2 - 2x = 0$$

Completing the square, we obtain

$$(x - 1)^2 + y^2 = 1$$

which is an equation of a circle with center $(1, 0)$ and radius 1.

Figure 9 shows a geometrical illustration that the circle in Example 6 has the equation $r = 2\cos\theta$. The angle OPQ is a right angle (Why?) and so $r/2 = \cos\theta$.

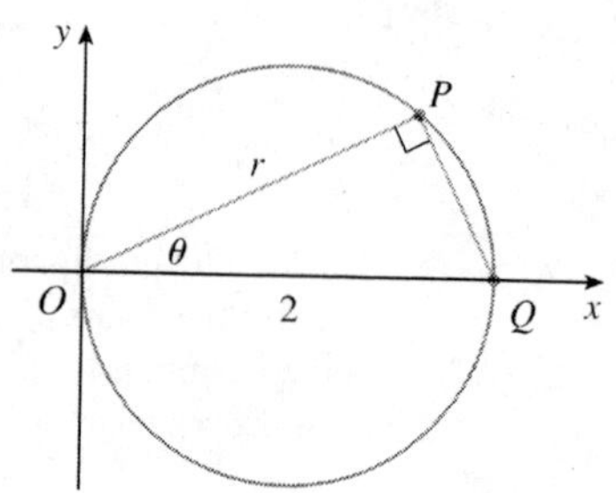

FIGURE 9

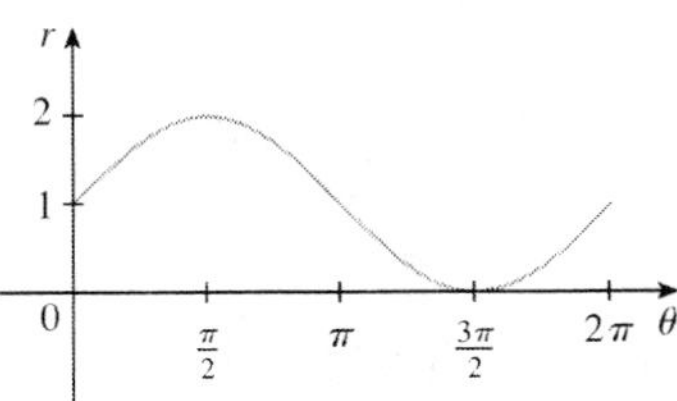

FIGURE 10
$r = 1 + \sin\theta$ in Cartesian coordinates, $0 \leqslant \theta \leqslant 2\pi$

V EXAMPLE 7 Sketch the curve $r = 1 + \sin\theta$.

SOLUTION Instead of plotting points as in Example 6, we first sketch the graph of $r = 1 + \sin\theta$ in *Cartesian* coordinates in Figure 10 by shifting the sine curve up one unit. This enables us to read at a glance the values of r that correspond to increasing values of θ. For instance, we see that as θ increases from 0 to $\pi/2$, r (the distance from O) increases from 1 to 2, so we sketch the corresponding part of the polar curve in Figure 11(a). As θ increases from $\pi/2$ to π, Figure 10 shows that r decreases from 2 to 1, so we sketch the next part of the curve as in Figure 11(b). As θ increases from π to $3\pi/2$, r decreases from 1 to 0 as shown in part (c). Finally, as θ increases from $3\pi/2$ to 2π, r increases from 0 to 1 as shown in part (d). If we let θ increase beyond 2π or decrease beyond 0, we would simply retrace our path. Putting together the parts of the curve from Figure 11(a)–(d), we sketch the complete curve in part (e). It is called a **cardioid** because it's shaped like a heart.

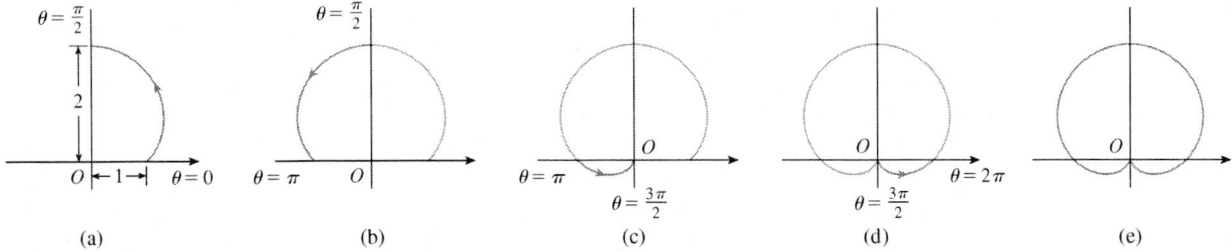

FIGURE 11 Stages in sketching the cardioid $r = 1 + \sin\theta$

EXAMPLE 8 Sketch the curve $r = \cos 2\theta$.

TEC Module H helps you see how polar curves are traced out by showing animations similar to Figures 10–13.

SOLUTION As in Example 7, we first sketch $r = \cos 2\theta$, $0 \leqslant \theta \leqslant 2\pi$, in Cartesian coordinates in Figure 12. As θ increases from 0 to $\pi/4$, Figure 12 shows that r decreases from 1 to 0 and so we draw the corresponding portion of the polar curve in Figure 13 (indicated by ①). As θ increases from $\pi/4$ to $\pi/2$, r goes from 0 to -1. This means that the distance from O increases from 0 to 1, but instead of being in the first quadrant this portion of the polar curve (indicated by ②) lies on the opposite side of the pole in the third quadrant. The remainder of the curve is drawn in a similar fashion, with the arrows and numbers indicating the order in which the portions are traced out. The resulting curve has four loops and is called a **four-leaved rose**.

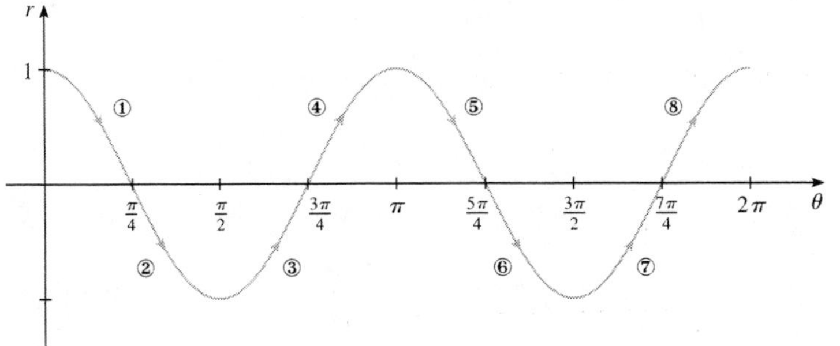

FIGURE 12
$r = \cos 2\theta$ in Cartesian coordinates

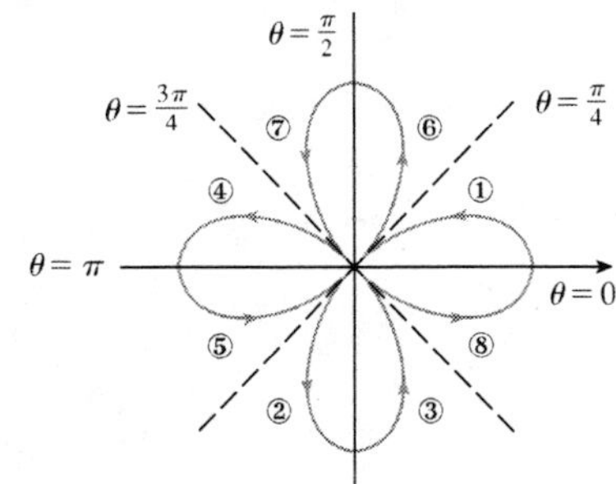

FIGURE 13
Four-leaved rose $r = \cos 2\theta$

When we sketch polar curves it is sometimes helpful to take advantage of symmetry. The following three rules are explained by Figure 14.

(a) If a polar equation is unchanged when θ is replaced by $-\theta$, the curve is symmetric about the polar axis.

(b) If the equation is unchanged when r is replaced by $-r$, or when θ is replaced by $\theta + \pi$, the curve is symmetric about the pole. (This means that the curve remains unchanged if we rotate it through 180° about the origin.)

(c) If the equation is unchanged when θ is replaced by $\pi - \theta$, the curve is symmetric about the vertical line $\theta = \pi/2$.

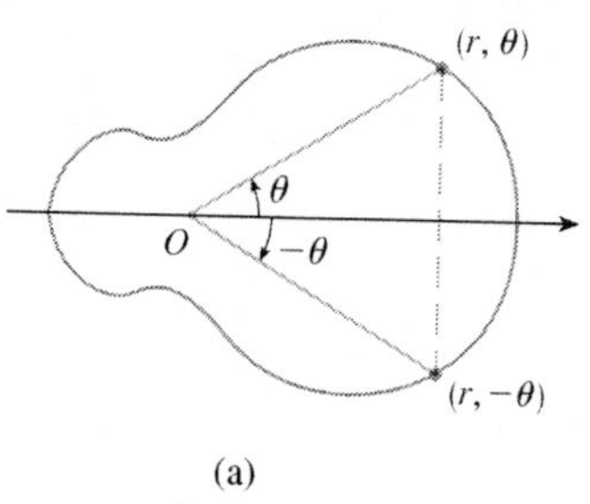

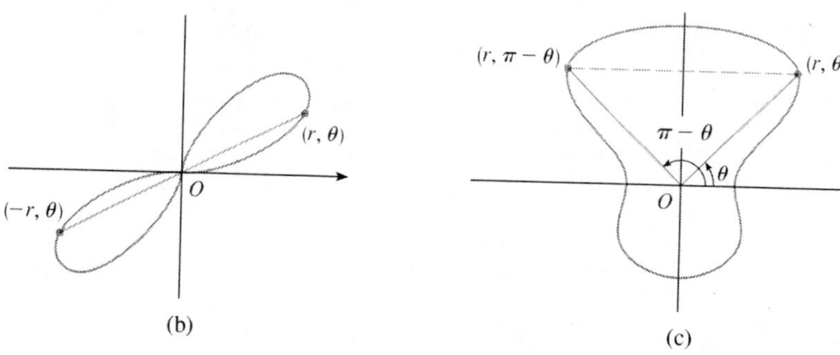

FIGURE 14

The curves sketched in Examples 6 and 8 are symmetric about the polar axis, since $\cos(-\theta) = \cos\theta$. The curves in Examples 7 and 8 are symmetric about $\theta = \pi/2$ because $\sin(\pi - \theta) = \sin\theta$ and $\cos 2(\pi - \theta) = \cos 2\theta$. The four-leaved rose is also symmetric about the pole. These symmetry properties could have been used in sketching the curves. For instance, in Example 6 we need only have plotted points for $0 \leqslant \theta \leqslant \pi/2$ and then reflected about the polar axis to obtain the complete circle.

Tangents to Polar Curves

To find a tangent line to a polar curve $r = f(\theta)$ we regard θ as a parameter and write its parametric equations as

$$x = r\cos\theta = f(\theta)\cos\theta \qquad y = r\sin\theta = f(\theta)\sin\theta$$

Then, using the method for finding slopes of parametric curves (Equation 3.4.7) and the Product Rule, we have

3
$$\frac{dy}{dx} = \frac{\dfrac{dy}{d\theta}}{\dfrac{dx}{d\theta}} = \frac{\dfrac{dr}{d\theta}\sin\theta + r\cos\theta}{\dfrac{dr}{d\theta}\cos\theta - r\sin\theta}$$

We locate horizontal tangents by finding the points where $dy/d\theta = 0$ (provided that $dx/d\theta \neq 0$). Likewise, we locate vertical tangents at the points where $dx/d\theta = 0$ (provided that $dy/d\theta \neq 0$).

Notice that if we are looking for tangent lines at the pole, then $r = 0$ and Equation 3 simplifies to

$$\frac{dy}{dx} = \tan\theta \qquad \text{if} \quad \frac{dr}{d\theta} \neq 0$$

For instance, in Example 8 we found that $r = \cos 2\theta = 0$ when $\theta = \pi/4$ or $3\pi/4$. This means that the lines $\theta = \pi/4$ and $\theta = 3\pi/4$ (or $y = x$ and $y = -x$) are tangent lines to $r = \cos 2\theta$ at the origin.

EXAMPLE 9

(a) For the cardioid $r = 1 + \sin\theta$ of Example 7, find the slope of the tangent line when $\theta = \pi/3$.

(b) Find the points on the cardioid where the tangent line is horizontal or vertical.

SOLUTION Using Equation 3 with $r = 1 + \sin\theta$, we have

$$\frac{dy}{dx} = \frac{\dfrac{dr}{d\theta}\sin\theta + r\cos\theta}{\dfrac{dr}{d\theta}\cos\theta - r\sin\theta} = \frac{\cos\theta\,\sin\theta + (1+\sin\theta)\cos\theta}{\cos\theta\,\cos\theta - (1+\sin\theta)\sin\theta}$$

$$= \frac{\cos\theta\,(1 + 2\sin\theta)}{1 - 2\sin^2\theta - \sin\theta} = \frac{\cos\theta\,(1+2\sin\theta)}{(1+\sin\theta)(1-2\sin\theta)}$$

(a) The slope of the tangent at the point where $\theta = \pi/3$ is

$$\left.\frac{dy}{dx}\right|_{\theta=\pi/3} = \frac{\cos(\pi/3)(1 + 2\sin(\pi/3))}{(1+\sin(\pi/3))(1-2\sin(\pi/3))} = \frac{\frac{1}{2}(1+\sqrt{3})}{(1+\sqrt{3}/2)(1-\sqrt{3})}$$

$$= \frac{1+\sqrt{3}}{(2+\sqrt{3})(1-\sqrt{3})} = \frac{1+\sqrt{3}}{-1-\sqrt{3}} = -1$$

(b) Observe that

$$\frac{dy}{d\theta} = \cos\theta\,(1+2\sin\theta) = 0 \qquad \text{when } \theta = \frac{\pi}{2}, \frac{3\pi}{2}, \frac{7\pi}{6}, \frac{11\pi}{6}$$

$$\frac{dx}{d\theta} = (1+\sin\theta)(1-2\sin\theta) = 0 \qquad \text{when } \theta = \frac{3\pi}{2}, \frac{\pi}{6}, \frac{5\pi}{6}$$

Therefore there are horizontal tangents at the points $(2, \pi/2)$, $(\frac{1}{2}, 7\pi/6)$, $(\frac{1}{2}, 11\pi/6)$ and vertical tangents at $(\frac{3}{2}, \pi/6)$ and $(\frac{3}{2}, 5\pi/6)$. When $\theta = 3\pi/2$, both $dy/d\theta$ and $dx/d\theta$ are 0, so we must be careful. Using l'Hospital's Rule, we have

$$\lim_{\theta\to(3\pi/2)^-}\frac{dy}{dx} = \left(\lim_{\theta\to(3\pi/2)^-}\frac{1+2\sin\theta}{1-2\sin\theta}\right)\left(\lim_{\theta\to(3\pi/2)^-}\frac{\cos\theta}{1+\sin\theta}\right)$$

$$= -\frac{1}{3}\lim_{\theta\to(3\pi/2)^-}\frac{\cos\theta}{1+\sin\theta} = -\frac{1}{3}\lim_{\theta\to(3\pi/2)^-}\frac{-\sin\theta}{\cos\theta} = \infty$$

By symmetry,
$$\lim_{\theta\to(3\pi/2)^+}\frac{dy}{dx} = -\infty$$

Thus there is a vertical tangent line at the pole (see Figure 15).

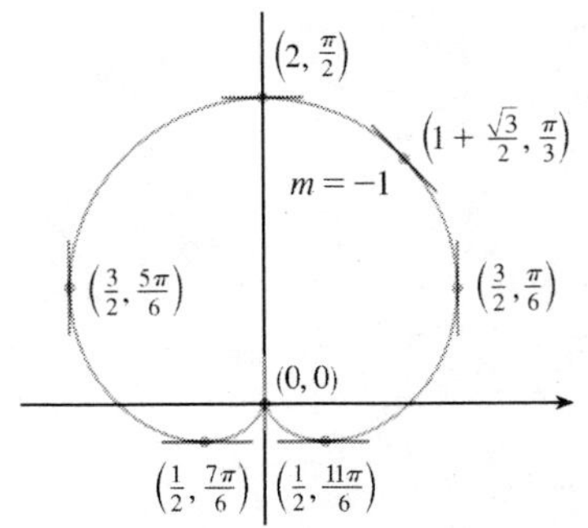

FIGURE 15
Tangent lines for $r = 1 + \sin\theta$

Note: Instead of having to remember Equation 3, we could employ the method used to derive it. For instance, in Example 9 we could have written

$$x = r\cos\theta = (1 + \sin\theta)\cos\theta = \cos\theta + \tfrac{1}{2}\sin 2\theta$$

$$y = r\sin\theta = (1 + \sin\theta)\sin\theta = \sin\theta + \sin^2\theta$$

Then we have

$$\frac{dy}{dx} = \frac{dy/d\theta}{dx/d\theta} = \frac{\cos\theta + 2\sin\theta\cos\theta}{-\sin\theta + \cos 2\theta} = \frac{\cos\theta + \sin 2\theta}{-\sin\theta + \cos 2\theta}$$

which is equivalent to our previous expression.

Graphing Polar Curves with Graphing Devices

Although it's useful to be able to sketch simple polar curves by hand, we need to use a graphing calculator or computer when we are faced with a curve as complicated as the ones shown in Figures 16 and 17.

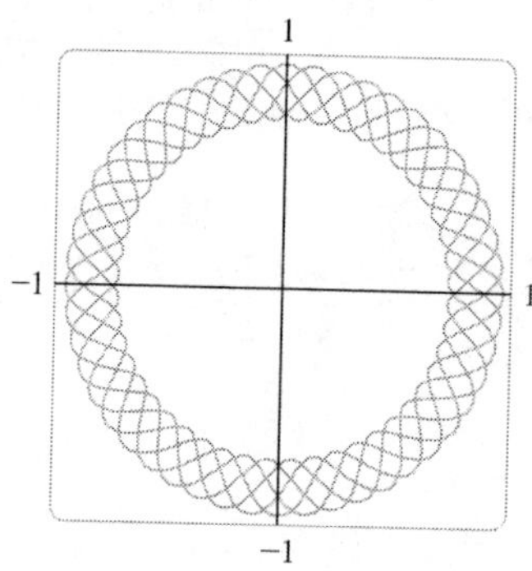

FIGURE 16
$r = \sin^2(2.4\theta) + \cos^4(2.4\theta)$

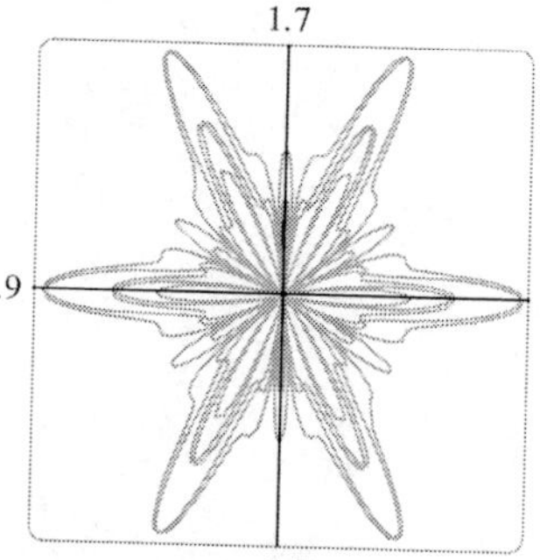

FIGURE 17
$r = \sin^2(1.2\theta) + \cos^3(6\theta)$

Some graphing devices have commands that enable us to graph polar curves directly. With other machines we need to convert to parametric equations first. In this case we take the polar equation $r = f(\theta)$ and write its parametric equations as

$$x = r\cos\theta = f(\theta)\cos\theta \qquad y = r\sin\theta = f(\theta)\sin\theta$$

Some machines require that the parameter be called t rather than θ.

EXAMPLE 10 Graph the curve $r = \sin(8\theta/5)$.

SOLUTION Let's assume that our graphing device doesn't have a built-in polar graphing command. In this case we need to work with the corresponding parametric equations, which are

$$x = r\cos\theta = \sin(8\theta/5)\cos\theta \qquad y = r\sin\theta = \sin(8\theta/5)\sin\theta$$

In any case we need to determine the domain for θ. So we ask ourselves: How many complete rotations are required until the curve starts to repeat itself? If the answer is n, then

$$\sin\frac{8(\theta + 2n\pi)}{5} = \sin\left(\frac{8\theta}{5} + \frac{16n\pi}{5}\right) = \sin\frac{8\theta}{5}$$

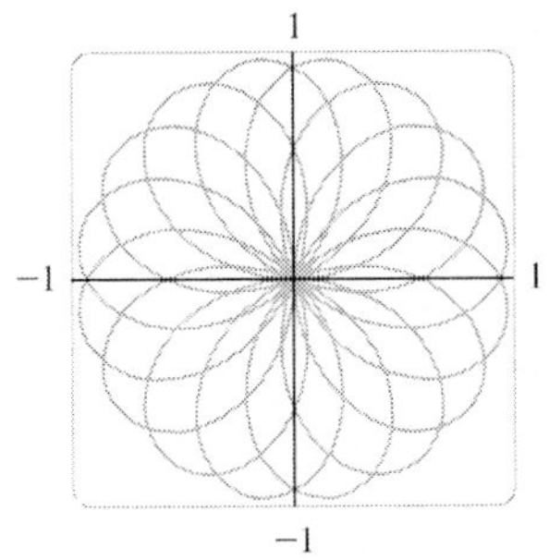

FIGURE 18
$r = \sin(8\theta/5)$

and so we require that $16n\pi/5$ be an even multiple of π. This will first occur when $n = 5$. Therefore we will graph the entire curve if we specify that $0 \leqslant \theta \leqslant 10\pi$. Switching from θ to t, we have the equations

$$x = \sin(8t/5)\cos t \qquad y = \sin(8t/5)\sin t \qquad 0 \leqslant t \leqslant 10\pi$$

and Figure 18 shows the resulting curve. Notice that this rose has 16 loops.

EXAMPLE 11 Investigate the family of polar curves given by $r = 1 + c \sin \theta$. How does the shape change as c changes? (These curves are called **limaçons**, after a French word for snail, because of the shape of the curves for certain values of c.)

In Exercise 47 you are asked to prove analytically what we have discovered from the graphs in Figure 19.

SOLUTION Figure 19 shows computer-drawn graphs for various values of c. For $c > 1$ there is a loop that decreases in size as c decreases. When $c = 1$ the loop disappears and the curve becomes the cardioid that we sketched in Example 7. For c between 1 and $\frac{1}{2}$ the cardioid's cusp is smoothed out and becomes a "dimple." When c decreases from $\frac{1}{2}$ to 0, the limaçon is shaped like an oval. This oval becomes more circular as $c \to 0$, and when $c = 0$ the curve is just the circle $r = 1$.

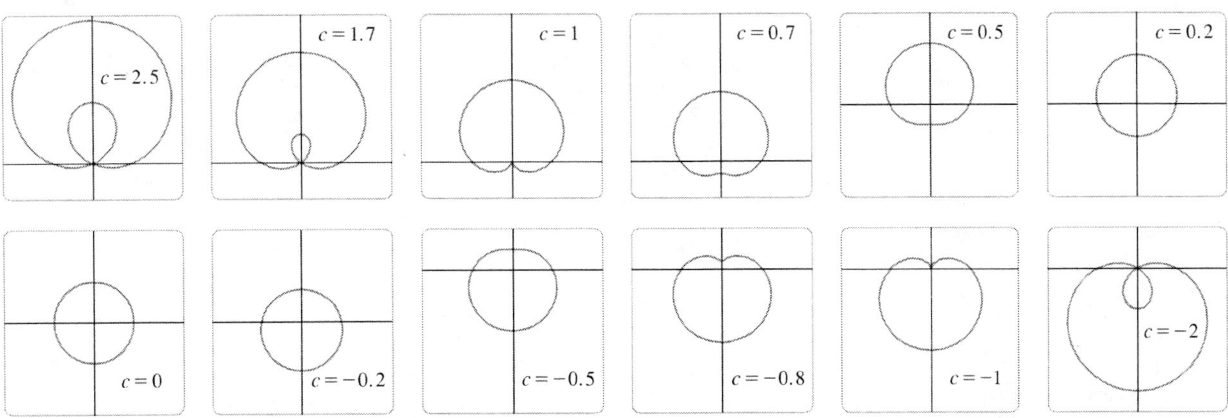

FIGURE 19
Members of the family of limaçons $r = 1 + c \sin \theta$

The remaining parts of Figure 19 show that as c becomes negative, the shapes change in reverse order. In fact, these curves are reflections about the horizontal axis of the corresponding curves with positive c.

H.1 Exercises

1–2 Plot the point whose polar coordinates are given. Then find two other pairs of polar coordinates of this point, one with $r > 0$ and one with $r < 0$.

1. (a) $(2, \pi/3)$ (b) $(1, -3\pi/4)$ (c) $(-1, \pi/2)$

2. (a) $(1, 7\pi/4)$ (b) $(-3, \pi/6)$ (c) $(1, -1)$

3–4 Plot the point whose polar coordinates are given. Then find the Cartesian coordinates of the point.

3. (a) $(1, \pi)$ (b) $(2, -2\pi/3)$ (c) $(-2, 3\pi/4)$

4. (a) $(-\sqrt{2}, 5\pi/4)$ (b) $(1, 5\pi/2)$ (c) $(2, -7\pi/6)$

5–6 The Cartesian coordinates of a point are given.
(i) Find polar coordinates (r, θ) of the point, where $r > 0$ and $0 \leqslant \theta < 2\pi$.
(ii) Find polar coordinates (r, θ) of the point, where $r < 0$ and $0 \leqslant \theta < 2\pi$.

5. (a) $(2, -2)$ (b) $(-1, \sqrt{3})$

6. (a) $(3\sqrt{3}, 3)$ (b) $(1, -2)$

7–12 Sketch the region in the plane consisting of points whose polar coordinates satisfy the given conditions.

7. $1 \leqslant r \leqslant 2$

8. $r \geqslant 0, \quad \pi/3 \leqslant \theta \leqslant 2\pi/3$

9. $0 \leqslant r < 4, \quad -\pi/2 \leqslant \theta < \pi/6$

10. $2 < r \leqslant 5, \quad 3\pi/4 < \theta < 5\pi/4$

11. $2 < r < 3, \quad 5\pi/3 \leqslant \theta \leqslant 7\pi/3$

12. $r \geqslant 1, \quad \pi \leqslant \theta \leqslant 2\pi$

13–16 Identify the curve by finding a Cartesian equation for the curve.

13. $r = 3 \sin \theta$

14. $r = 2 \sin \theta + 2 \cos \theta$

15. $r = \csc \theta$

16. $r = \tan \theta \sec \theta$

17–20 Find a polar equation for the curve represented by the given Cartesian equation.

17. $x = -y^2$

18. $x + y = 9$

19. $x^2 + y^2 = 2cx$

20. $xy = 4$

21–22 For each of the described curves, decide if the curve would be more easily given by a polar equation or a Cartesian equation. Then write an equation for the curve.

21. (a) A line through the origin that makes an angle of $\pi/6$ with the positive x-axis
(b) A vertical line through the point (3, 3)

22. (a) A circle with radius 5 and center (2, 3)
(b) A circle centered at the origin with radius 4

23–42 Sketch the curve with the given polar equation.

23. $\theta = -\pi/6$

24. $r^2 - 3r + 2 = 0$

25. $r = \sin \theta$

26. $r = -3 \cos \theta$

27. $r = 2(1 - \sin \theta), \ \theta \geqslant 0$

28. $r = 1 - 3 \cos \theta$

29. $r = \theta, \ \theta \geqslant 0$

30. $r = \ln \theta, \ \theta \geqslant 1$

31. $r = 4 \sin 3\theta$

32. $r = \cos 5\theta$

33. $r = 2 \cos 4\theta$

34. $r = 3 \cos 6\theta$

35. $r = 1 - 2 \sin \theta$

36. $r = 2 + \sin \theta$

37. $r^2 = 9 \sin 2\theta$

38. $r^2 = \cos 4\theta$

39. $r = 2 \cos(3\theta/2)$

40. $r^2\theta = 1$

41. $r = 1 + 2 \cos 2\theta$

42. $r = 1 + 2 \cos(\theta/2)$

43–44 The figure shows a graph of r as a function of θ in Cartesian coordinates. Use it to sketch the corresponding polar curve.

43.

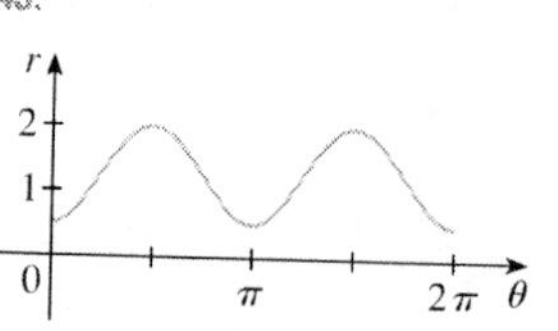

44.

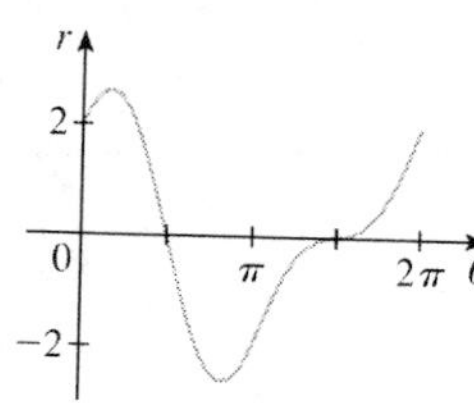

45. Show that the polar curve $r = 4 + 2 \sec \theta$ (called a **conchoid**) has the line $x = 2$ as a vertical asymptote by showing that $\lim_{r \to \pm\infty} x = 2$. Use this fact to help sketch the conchoid.

46. Show that the curve $r = \sin \theta \tan \theta$ (called a **cissoid of Diocles**) has the line $x = 1$ as a vertical asymptote. Show also that the curve lies entirely within the vertical strip $0 \leqslant x < 1$. Use these facts to help sketch the cissoid.

47. (a) In Example 11 the graphs suggest that the limaçon $r = 1 + c \sin \theta$ has an inner loop when $|c| > 1$. Prove that this is true, and find the values of θ that correspond to the inner loop.
(b) From Figure 19 it appears that the limaçon loses its dimple when $c = \frac{1}{2}$. Prove this.

48. Match the polar equations with the graphs labeled I–VI. Give reasons for your choices. (Don't use a graphing device.)
(a) $r = \sqrt{\theta}, \quad 0 \leqslant \theta \leqslant 16\pi$
(b) $r = \theta^2, \quad 0 \leqslant \theta \leqslant 16\pi$
(c) $r = \cos(\theta/3)$
(d) $r = 1 + 2 \cos \theta$
(e) $r = 2 + \sin 3\theta$
(f) $r = 1 + 2 \sin 3\theta$

I

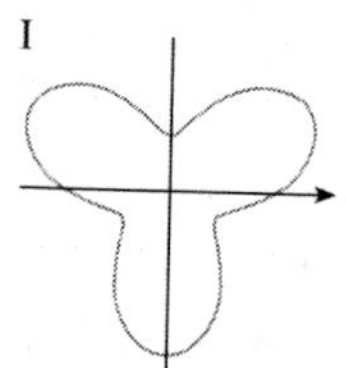

II

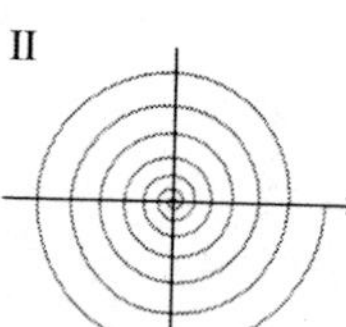

III

IV

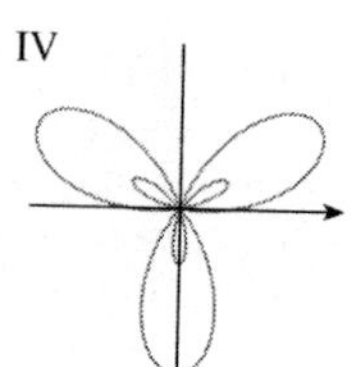

V

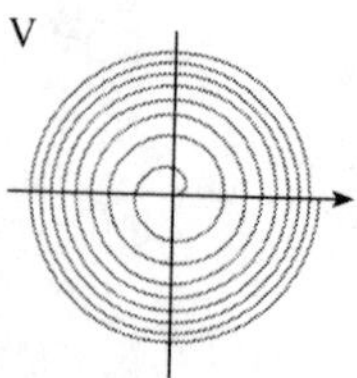

VI

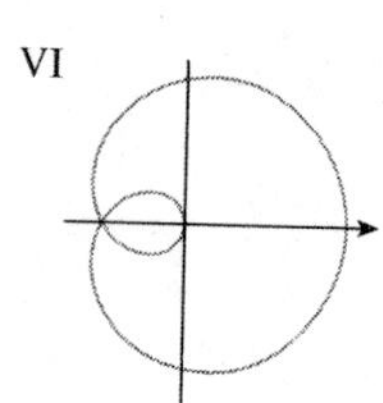

49–52 Find the slope of the tangent line to the given polar curve at the point specified by the value of θ.

49. $r = 1/\theta, \quad \theta = \pi$

50. $r = 2 - \sin\theta, \quad \theta = \pi/3$

51. $r = \cos 2\theta, \quad \theta = \pi/4$

52. $r = \cos(\theta/3), \quad \theta = \pi$

53–56 Find the points on the given curve where the tangent line is horizontal or vertical.

53. $r = 3\cos\theta$

54. $r = e^{\theta}$

55. $r = 1 + \cos\theta$

56. $r = 1 - \sin\theta$

57. Show that the polar equation $r = a\sin\theta + b\cos\theta$, where $ab \neq 0$, represents a circle, and find its center and radius.

58. Show that the curves $r = a\sin\theta$ and $r = a\cos\theta$ intersect at right angles.

59–62 Use a graphing device to graph the polar curve. Choose the parameter interval carefully to make sure that you produce an appropriate curve.

59. $r = e^{\sin\theta} - 2\cos(4\theta)$ (butterfly curve)

60. $r = |\tan\theta|^{|\cot\theta|}$ (valentine curve)

61. $r = 2 - 5\sin(\theta/6)$

62. $r = \cos(\theta/2) + \cos(\theta/3)$

63. How are the graphs of $r = 1 + \sin(\theta - \pi/6)$ and $r = 1 + \sin(\theta - \pi/3)$ related to the graph of $r = 1 + \sin\theta$? In general, how is the graph of $r = f(\theta - \alpha)$ related to the graph of $r = f(\theta)$?

64. Use a graph to estimate the y-coordinate of the highest points on the curve $r = \sin 2\theta$. Then use calculus to find the exact value.

65. (a) Investigate the family of curves defined by the polar equations $r = \sin n\theta$, where n is a positive integer. How is the number of loops related to n?
(b) What happens if the equation in part (a) is replaced by $r = |\sin n\theta|$?

66. A family of curves is given by the equations $r = 1 + c\sin n\theta$, where c is a real number and n is a positive integer. How does the graph change as n increases? How does it change as c changes? Illustrate by graphing enough members of the family to support your conclusions.

67. A family of curves has polar equations

$$r = \frac{1 - a\cos\theta}{1 + a\cos\theta}$$

Investigate how the graph changes as the number a changes. In particular, you should identify the transitional values of a for which the basic shape of the curve changes.

68. The astronomer Giovanni Cassini (1625–1712) studied the family of curves with polar equations

$$r^4 - 2c^2r^2\cos 2\theta + c^4 - a^4 = 0$$

where a and c are positive real numbers. These curves are called the **ovals of Cassini** even though they are oval shaped only for certain values of a and c. (Cassini thought that these curves might represent planetary orbits better than Kepler's ellipses.) Investigate the variety of shapes that these curves may have. In particular, how are a and c related to each other when the curve splits into two parts?

69. Let P be any point (except the origin) on the curve $r = f(\theta)$. If ψ is the angle between the tangent line at P and the radial line OP, show that

$$\tan\psi = \frac{r}{dr/d\theta}$$

[*Hint:* Observe that $\psi = \phi - \theta$ in the figure.]

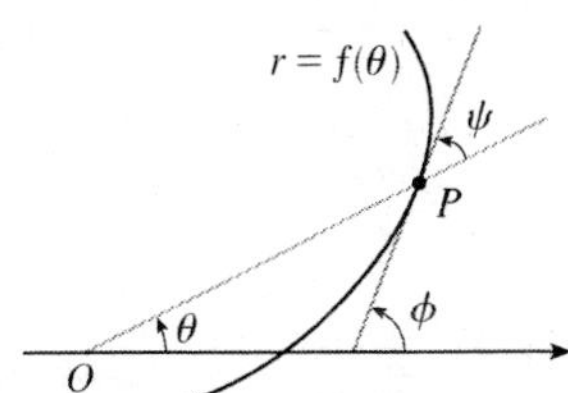

70. (a) Use Exercise 69 to show that the angle between the tangent line and the radial line is $\psi = \pi/4$ at every point on the curve $r = e^{\theta}$.
(b) Illustrate part (a) by graphing the curve and the tangent lines at the points where $\theta = 0$ and $\pi/2$.
(c) Prove that any polar curve $r = f(\theta)$ with the property that the angle ψ between the radial line and the tangent line is a constant must be of the form $r = Ce^{k\theta}$, where C and k are constants.

H.2 Areas and Lengths in Polar Coordinates

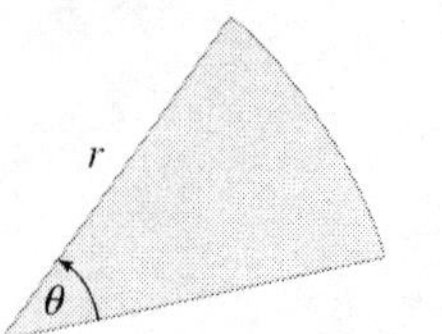

FIGURE 1

In this section we develop the formula for the area of a region whose boundary is given by a polar equation. We need to use the formula for the area of a sector of a circle

$$A = \tfrac{1}{2}r^2\theta \tag{1}$$

where, as in Figure 1, r is the radius and θ is the radian measure of the central angle. Formula 1 follows from the fact that the area of a sector is proportional to its central angle: $A = (\theta/2\pi)\pi r^2 = \frac{1}{2}r^2\theta$.

Let $\mathcal{R}$ be the region, illustrated in Figure 2, bounded by the polar curve $r = f(\theta)$ and by the rays $\theta = a$ and $\theta = b$, where f is a positive continuous function and where $0 < b - a \leqslant 2\pi$. We divide the interval $[a, b]$ into subintervals with endpoints θ_0, $\theta_1, \theta_2, \ldots, \theta_n$ and equal width $\Delta\theta$. The rays $\theta = \theta_i$ then divide $\mathcal{R}$ into n smaller regions with central angle $\Delta\theta = \theta_i - \theta_{i-1}$. If we choose θ_i^* in the ith subinterval $[\theta_{i-1}, \theta_i]$, then the area ΔA_i of the ith region is approximated by the area of the sector of a circle with central angle $\Delta\theta$ and radius $f(\theta_i^*)$. (See Figure 3.)

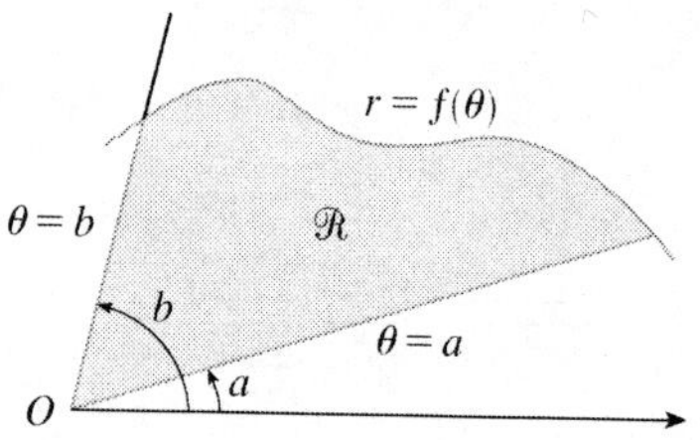

FIGURE 2

Thus from Formula 1 we have

$$\Delta A_i \approx \tfrac{1}{2}[f(\theta_i^*)]^2\,\Delta\theta$$

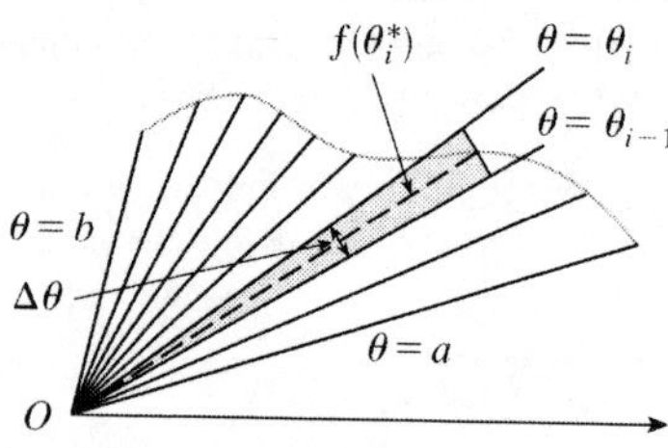

FIGURE 3

and so an approximation to the total area A of $\mathcal{R}$ is

$$A \approx \sum_{i=1}^{n} \tfrac{1}{2}[f(\theta_i^*)]^2\,\Delta\theta \tag{2}$$

It appears from Figure 3 that the approximation in (2) improves as $n \to \infty$. But the sums in (2) are Riemann sums for the function $g(\theta) = \frac{1}{2}[f(\theta)]^2$, so

$$\lim_{n\to\infty} \sum_{i=1}^{n} \tfrac{1}{2}[f(\theta_i^*)]^2\,\Delta\theta = \int_a^b \tfrac{1}{2}[f(\theta)]^2\,d\theta$$

It therefore appears plausible (and can in fact be proved) that the formula for the area A of the polar region $\mathcal{R}$ is

$$A = \int_a^b \tfrac{1}{2}[f(\theta)]^2\,d\theta \tag{3}$$

Formula 3 is often written as

$$A = \int_a^b \tfrac{1}{2}r^2\,d\theta \tag{4}$$

with the understanding that $r = f(\theta)$. Note the similarity between Formulas 1 and 4.

When we apply Formula 3 or 4 it is helpful to think of the area as being swept out by a rotating ray through O that starts with angle a and ends with angle b.

V EXAMPLE 1 Find the area enclosed by one loop of the four-leaved rose $r = \cos 2\theta$.

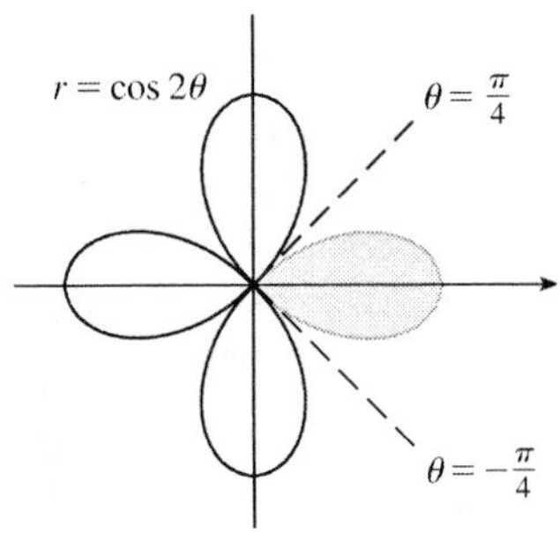

FIGURE 4

SOLUTION The curve $r = \cos 2\theta$ was sketched in Example 8 in Section H.1. Notice from Figure 4 that the region enclosed by the right loop is swept out by a ray that rotates from $\theta = -\pi/4$ to $\theta = \pi/4$. Therefore Formula 4 gives

$$A = \int_{-\pi/4}^{\pi/4} \tfrac{1}{2} r^2 \, d\theta = \tfrac{1}{2} \int_{-\pi/4}^{\pi/4} \cos^2 2\theta \, d\theta = \int_{0}^{\pi/4} \cos^2 2\theta \, d\theta$$

We could evaluate the integral using Formula 64 in the Table of Integrals. Or, as in Section 5.7, we could use the identity $\cos^2 x = \frac{1}{2}(1 + \cos 2x)$ to write

$$A = \int_{0}^{\pi/4} \tfrac{1}{2}(1 + \cos 4\theta) \, d\theta = \tfrac{1}{2}\Big[\theta + \tfrac{1}{4} \sin 4\theta\Big]_0^{\pi/4} = \frac{\pi}{8}$$

V EXAMPLE 2 Find the area of the region that lies inside the circle $r = 3 \sin \theta$ and outside the cardioid $r = 1 + \sin \theta$.

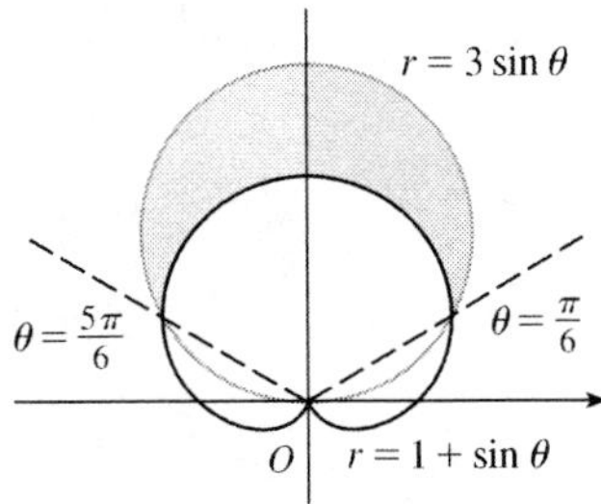

FIGURE 5

SOLUTION The cardioid (see Example 7 in Section H.1) and the circle are sketched in Figure 5 and the desired region is shaded. The values of a and b in Formula 4 are determined by finding the points of intersection of the two curves. They intersect when $3 \sin \theta = 1 + \sin \theta$, which gives $\sin \theta = \frac{1}{2}$, so $\theta = \pi/6, 5\pi/6$. The desired area can be found by subtracting the area inside the cardioid between $\theta = \pi/6$ and $\theta = 5\pi/6$ from the area inside the circle from $\pi/6$ to $5\pi/6$. Thus

$$A = \tfrac{1}{2} \int_{\pi/6}^{5\pi/6} (3 \sin \theta)^2 \, d\theta - \tfrac{1}{2} \int_{\pi/6}^{5\pi/6} (1 + \sin \theta)^2 \, d\theta$$

Since the region is symmetric about the vertical axis $\theta = \pi/2$, we can write

$$\begin{aligned} A &= 2\left[\tfrac{1}{2} \int_{\pi/6}^{\pi/2} 9 \sin^2\theta \, d\theta - \tfrac{1}{2} \int_{\pi/6}^{\pi/2} (1 + 2 \sin \theta + \sin^2\theta) \, d\theta\right] \\ &= \int_{\pi/6}^{\pi/2} (8 \sin^2\theta - 1 - 2 \sin \theta) \, d\theta \\ &= \int_{\pi/6}^{\pi/2} (3 - 4 \cos 2\theta - 2 \sin \theta) \, d\theta \qquad \left[\text{because } \sin^2\theta = \tfrac{1}{2}(1 - \cos 2\theta)\right] \\ &= 3\theta - 2 \sin 2\theta + 2 \cos \theta \Big]_{\pi/6}^{\pi/2} = \pi \end{aligned}$$

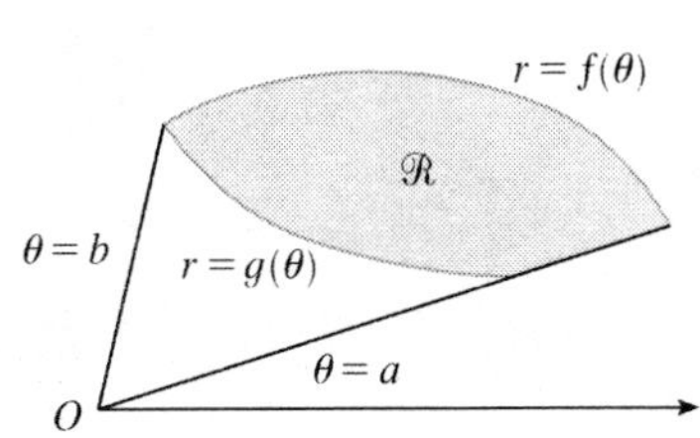

FIGURE 6

Example 2 illustrates the procedure for finding the area of the region bounded by two polar curves. In general, let $\mathcal{R}$ be a region, as illustrated in Figure 6, that is bounded by curves with polar equations $r = f(\theta)$, $r = g(\theta)$, $\theta = a$, and $\theta = b$, where $f(\theta) \geqslant g(\theta) \geqslant 0$ and $0 < b - a \leqslant 2\pi$. The area A of $\mathcal{R}$ is found by subtracting the area inside $r = g(\theta)$ from the area inside $r = f(\theta)$, so using Formula 3 we have

$$\begin{aligned} A &= \int_a^b \tfrac{1}{2}[f(\theta)]^2 \, d\theta - \int_a^b \tfrac{1}{2}[g(\theta)]^2 \, d\theta \\ &= \tfrac{1}{2} \int_a^b \left([f(\theta)]^2 - [g(\theta)]^2\right) d\theta \end{aligned}$$

CAUTION The fact that a single point has many representations in polar coordinates sometimes makes it difficult to find all the points of intersection of two polar curves. For instance, it is obvious from Figure 5 that the circle and the cardioid have three points of intersection; however, in Example 2 we solved the equations $r = 3 \sin \theta$ and $r = 1 + \sin \theta$

and found only two such points, $(\frac{3}{2}, \pi/6)$ and $(\frac{3}{2}, 5\pi/6)$. The origin is also a point of intersection, but we can't find it by solving the equations of the curves because the origin has no single representation in polar coordinates that satisfies both equations. Notice that, when represented as $(0, 0)$ or $(0, \pi)$, the origin satisfies $r = 3\sin\theta$ and so it lies on the circle; when represented as $(0, 3\pi/2)$, it satisfies $r = 1 + \sin\theta$ and so it lies on the cardioid. Think of two points moving along the curves as the parameter value θ increases from 0 to 2π. On one curve the origin is reached at $\theta = 0$ and $\theta = \pi$; on the other curve it is reached at $\theta = 3\pi/2$. The points don't collide at the origin because they reach the origin at different times, but the curves intersect there nonetheless.

Thus, to find *all* points of intersection of two polar curves, it is recommended that you draw the graphs of both curves. It is especially convenient to use a graphing calculator or computer to help with this task.

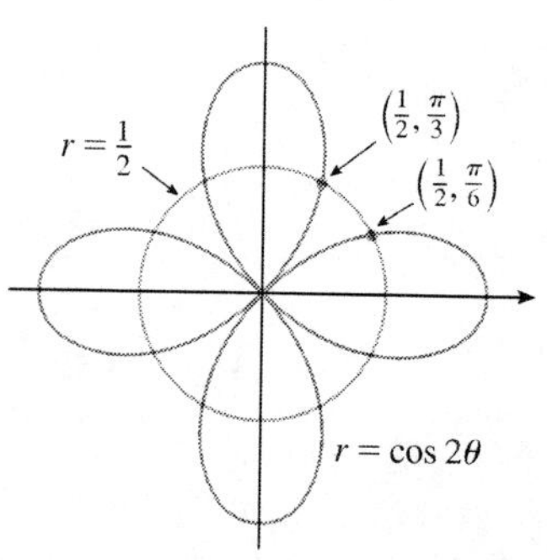

FIGURE 7

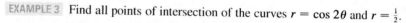

EXAMPLE 3 Find all points of intersection of the curves $r = \cos 2\theta$ and $r = \frac{1}{2}$.

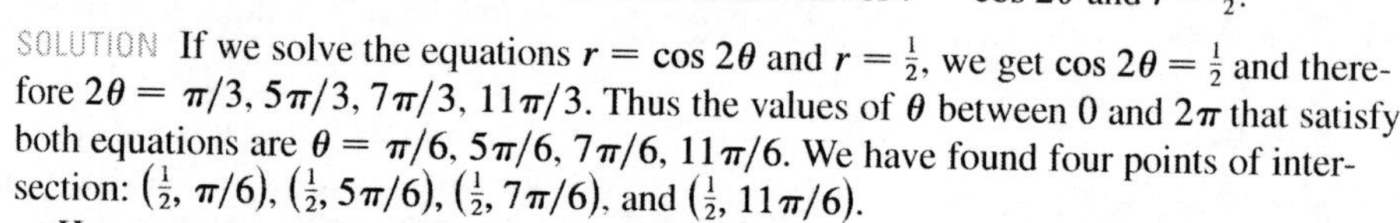

SOLUTION If we solve the equations $r = \cos 2\theta$ and $r = \frac{1}{2}$, we get $\cos 2\theta = \frac{1}{2}$ and therefore $2\theta = \pi/3, 5\pi/3, 7\pi/3, 11\pi/3$. Thus the values of θ between 0 and 2π that satisfy both equations are $\theta = \pi/6, 5\pi/6, 7\pi/6, 11\pi/6$. We have found four points of intersection: $(\frac{1}{2}, \pi/6)$, $(\frac{1}{2}, 5\pi/6)$, $(\frac{1}{2}, 7\pi/6)$, and $(\frac{1}{2}, 11\pi/6)$.

However, you can see from Figure 7 that the curves have four other points of intersection—namely, $(\frac{1}{2}, \pi/3)$, $(\frac{1}{2}, 2\pi/3)$, $(\frac{1}{2}, 4\pi/3)$, and $(\frac{1}{2}, 5\pi/3)$. These can be found using symmetry or by noticing that another equation of the circle is $r = -\frac{1}{2}$ and then solving the equations $r = \cos 2\theta$ and $r = -\frac{1}{2}$.

Arc Length

To find the length of a polar curve $r = f(\theta)$, $a \leqslant \theta \leqslant b$, we regard θ as a parameter and write the parametric equations of the curve as

$$x = r\cos\theta = f(\theta)\cos\theta \qquad y = r\sin\theta = f(\theta)\sin\theta$$

Using the Product Rule and differentiating with respect to θ, we obtain

$$\frac{dx}{d\theta} = \frac{dr}{d\theta}\cos\theta - r\sin\theta \qquad \frac{dy}{d\theta} = \frac{dr}{d\theta}\sin\theta + r\cos\theta$$

so, using $\cos^2\theta + \sin^2\theta = 1$, we have

$$\begin{aligned}\left(\frac{dx}{d\theta}\right)^2 + \left(\frac{dy}{d\theta}\right)^2 &= \left(\frac{dr}{d\theta}\right)^2 \cos^2\theta - 2r\frac{dr}{d\theta}\cos\theta\sin\theta + r^2\sin^2\theta \\ &\quad + \left(\frac{dr}{d\theta}\right)^2 \sin^2\theta + 2r\frac{dr}{d\theta}\sin\theta\cos\theta + r^2\cos^2\theta \\ &= \left(\frac{dr}{d\theta}\right)^2 + r^2\end{aligned}$$

Assuming that f' is continuous, we can use Formula 6.4.1 to write the arc length as

$$L = \int_a^b \sqrt{\left(\frac{dx}{d\theta}\right)^2 + \left(\frac{dy}{d\theta}\right)^2}\, d\theta$$

Therefore the length of a curve with polar equation $r = f(\theta)$, $a \leqslant \theta \leqslant b$, is

5
$$L = \int_a^b \sqrt{r^2 + \left(\frac{dr}{d\theta}\right)^2}\, d\theta$$

V EXAMPLE 4 Find the length of the cardioid $r = 1 + \sin\theta$.

SOLUTION The cardioid is shown in Figure 8. (We sketched it in Example 7 in Section H.1.) Its full length is given by the parameter interval $0 \leqslant \theta \leqslant 2\pi$, so Formula 5 gives

$$L = \int_0^{2\pi} \sqrt{r^2 + \left(\frac{dr}{d\theta}\right)^2}\, d\theta = \int_0^{2\pi} \sqrt{(1 + \sin\theta)^2 + \cos^2\theta}\, d\theta$$

$$= \int_0^{2\pi} \sqrt{2 + 2\sin\theta}\, d\theta$$

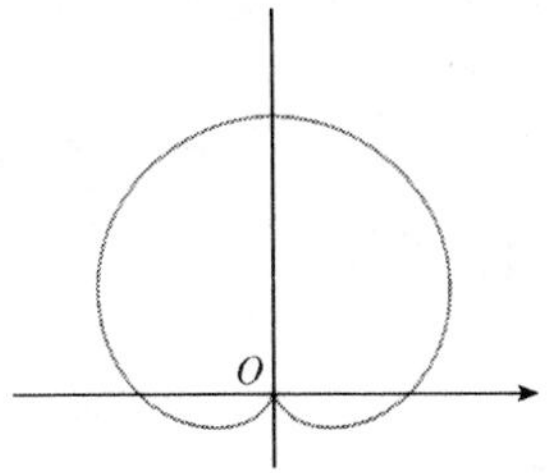

FIGURE 8
$r = 1 + \sin\theta$

We could evaluate this integral by multiplying and dividing the integrand by $\sqrt{2 - 2\sin\theta}$, or we could use a computer algebra system. In any event, we find that the length of the cardioid is $L = 8$.

H.2 Exercises

1–4 Find the area of the region that is bounded by the given curve and lies in the specified sector.

1. $r = \theta^2$, $0 \leqslant \theta \leqslant \pi/4$

2. $r = e^{\theta/2}$, $\pi \leqslant \theta \leqslant 2\pi$

3. $r = \sin\theta$, $\pi/3 \leqslant \theta \leqslant 2\pi/3$

4. $r = \sqrt{\sin\theta}$, $0 \leqslant \theta \leqslant \pi$

5–8 Find the area of the shaded region.

5.

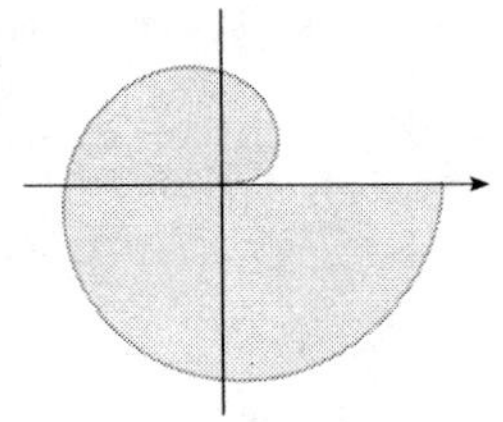

$r = \sqrt{\theta}$

6.

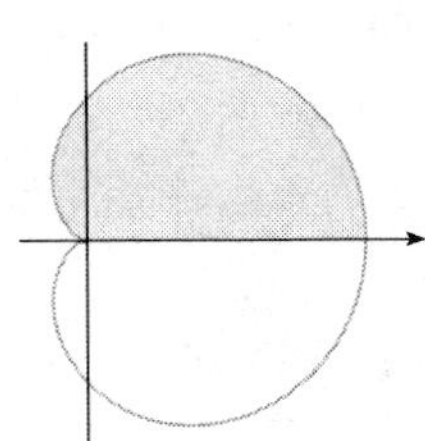

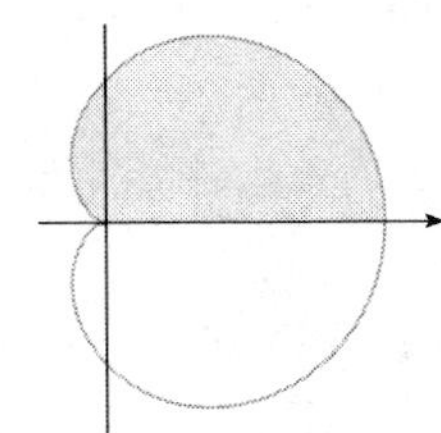

$r = 1 + \cos\theta$

7.

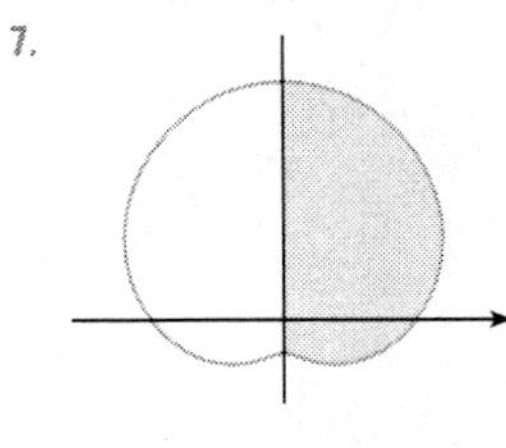

$r = 4 + 3\sin\theta$

8.

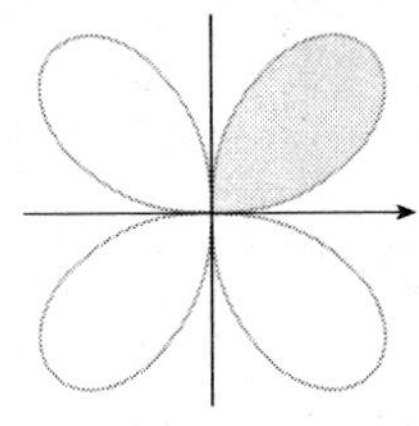

$r = \sin 2\theta$

9–12 Sketch the curve and find the area that it encloses.

9. $r^2 = 4\cos 2\theta$

10. $r = 2 - \sin\theta$

11. $r = 2\cos 3\theta$

12. $r = 2 + \cos 2\theta$

13–14 Graph the curve and find the area that it encloses.

13. $r = 1 + 2\sin 6\theta$

14. $r = 2\sin\theta + 3\sin 9\theta$

15–18 Find the area of the region enclosed by one loop of the curve.

15. $r = \sin 2\theta$

16. $r = 4\sin 3\theta$

17. $r = 1 + 2\sin\theta$ (inner loop)

18. $r = 2\cos\theta - \sec\theta$

19–22 Find the area of the region that lies inside the first curve and outside the second curve.

19. $r = 2\cos\theta$, $r = 1$

20. $r = 1 - \sin\theta$, $r = 1$

21. $r = 3\cos\theta$, $r = 1 + \cos\theta$

22. $r = 3\sin\theta$, $r = 2 - \sin\theta$

Graphing calculator or computer with graphing software required

1. Homework Hints available in TEC

23–26 Find the area of the region that lies inside both curves.

23. $r = \sqrt{3} \cos \theta, \quad r = \sin \theta$

24. $r = 1 + \cos \theta, \quad r = 1 - \cos \theta$

25. $r = \sin 2\theta, \quad r = \cos 2\theta$

26. $r = 3 + 2 \cos \theta, \quad r = 3 + 2 \sin \theta$

27. Find the area inside the larger loop and outside the smaller loop of the limaçon $r = \frac{1}{2} + \cos \theta$.

28. When recording live performances, sound engineers often use a microphone with a cardioid pickup pattern because it suppresses noise from the audience. Suppose the microphone is placed 4 m from the front of the stage (as in the figure) and the boundary of the optimal pickup region is given by the cardioid $r = 8 + 8 \sin \theta$, where r is measured in meters and the microphone is at the pole. The musicians want to know the area they will have on stage within the optimal pickup range of the microphone. Answer their question.

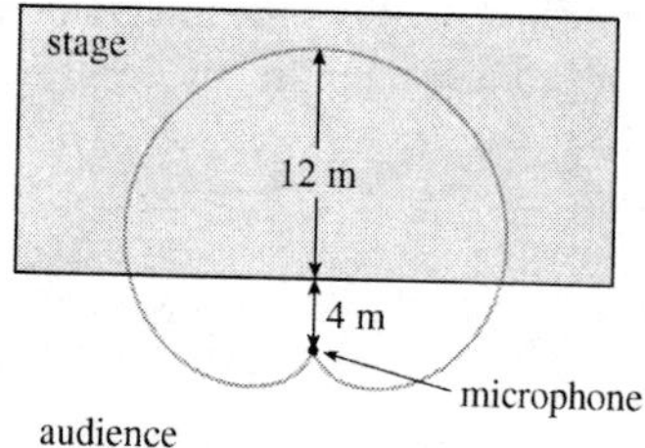

29–32 Find all points of intersection of the given curves.

29. $r = 2 \sin 2\theta, \quad r = 1$

30. $r = \cos 3\theta, \quad r = \sin 3\theta$

31. $r = \sin \theta, \quad r = \sin 2\theta$

32. $r^2 = \sin 2\theta, \quad r^2 = \cos 2\theta$

33. The points of intersection of the cardioid $r = 1 + \sin \theta$ and the spiral loop $r = 2\theta, -\pi/2 \leqslant \theta \leqslant \pi/2$, can't be found exactly. Use a graphing device to find the approximate values of θ at which they intersect. Then use these values to estimate the area that lies inside both curves.

34. Use a graph to estimate the values of θ for which the curves $r = 3 + \sin 5\theta$ and $r = 6 \sin \theta$ intersect. Then estimate the area that lies inside both curves.

35–38 Find the exact length of the polar curve.

35. $r = 3 \sin \theta, \quad 0 \leqslant \theta \leqslant \pi/3$

36. $r = e^{2\theta}, \quad 0 \leqslant \theta \leqslant 2\pi$

37. $r = \theta^2, \quad 0 \leqslant \theta \leqslant 2\pi$

38. $r = \theta, \quad 0 \leqslant \theta \leqslant 2\pi$

39–40 Use a calculator to find the length of the curve correct to four decimal places.

39. $r = 3 \sin 2\theta$

40. $r = 4 \sin 3\theta$

DISCOVERY PROJECT Conic Sections in Polar Coordinates

In this project we give a unified treatment of all three types of conic sections in terms of a focus and directrix. We will see that if we place the focus at the origin, then a conic section has a simple polar equation. In Chapter 10 we will use the polar equation of an ellipse to derive Kepler's laws of planetary motion.

Let F be a fixed point (called the **focus**) and l be a fixed line (called the **directrix**) in a plane. Let e be a fixed positive number (called the **eccentricity**). Let C be the set of all points P in the plane such that

$$\frac{|PF|}{|Pl|} = e$$

(that is, the ratio of the distance from F to the distance from l is the constant e). Notice that if the eccentricity is $e = 1$, then $|PF| = |Pl|$ and so the given condition simply becomes the definition of a parabola as given in Appendix B.

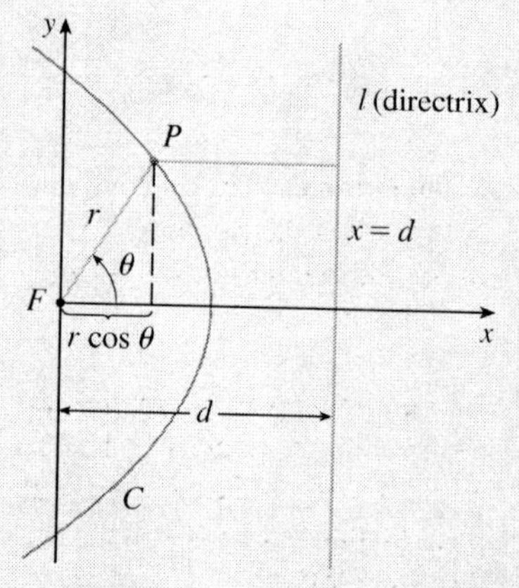

FIGURE 1

1. If we place the focus F at the origin and the directrix parallel to the y-axis and d units to the right, then the directrix has equation $x = d$ and is perpendicular to the polar axis. If the point P has polar coordinates (r, θ), use Figure 1 to show that

$$r = e(d - r \cos \theta)$$

2. By converting the polar equation in Problem 1 to rectangular coordinates, show that the curve C is an ellipse if $e < 1$. (See Appendix B for a discussion of ellipses.)

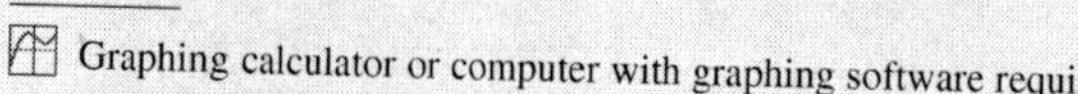
Graphing calculator or computer with graphing software required

3. Show that C is a hyperbola if $e > 1$.

4. Show that the polar equation

$$r = \frac{ed}{1 + e\cos\theta}$$

represents an ellipse if $e < 1$, a parabola if $e = 1$, or a hyperbola if $e > 1$.

5. For each of the following conics, find the eccentricity and directrix. Then identify and sketch the conic.

(a) $r = \dfrac{4}{1 + 3\cos\theta}$ (b) $r = \dfrac{8}{3 + 3\cos\theta}$ (c) $r = \dfrac{2}{2 + \cos\theta}$

6. Graph the conics $r = e/(1 - e\cos\theta)$ with $e = 0.4, 0.6, 0.8$, and 1.0 on a common screen. How does the value of e affect the shape of the curve?

7. (a) Show that the polar equation of an ellipse with directrix $x = d$ can be written in the form

$$r = \frac{a(1 - e^2)}{1 - e\cos\theta}$$

(b) Find an approximate polar equation for the elliptical orbit of the planet Earth around the sun (at one focus) given that the eccentricity is about 0.017 and the length of the major axis is about 2.99×10^8 km.

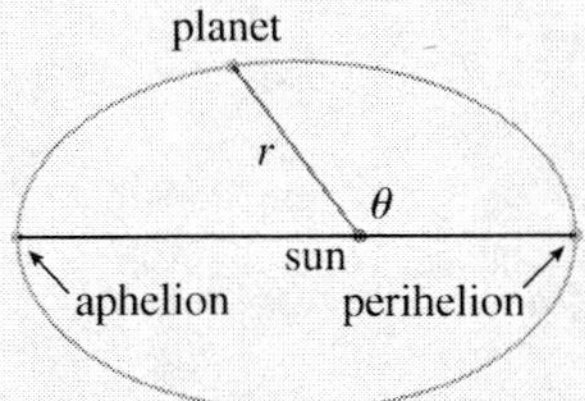

FIGURE 2

8. (a) The planets move around the sun in elliptical orbits with the sun at one focus. The positions of a planet that are closest to and farthest from the sun are called its *perihelion* and *aphelion*, respectively. (See Figure 2.) Use Problem 7(a) to show that the perihelion distance from a planet to the sun is $a(1 - e)$ and the aphelion distance is $a(1 + e)$.

(b) Use the data of Problem 7(b) to find the distances from the planet Earth to the sun at perihelion and at aphelion.

9. (a) The planet Mercury travels in an elliptical orbit with eccentricity 0.206. Its minimum distance from the sun is 4.6×10^7 km. Use the results of Problem 8(a) to find its maximum distance from the sun.

(b) Find the distance traveled by the planet Mercury during one complete orbit around the sun. (Use your calculator or computer algebra system to evaluate the definite integral.)

I Complex Numbers

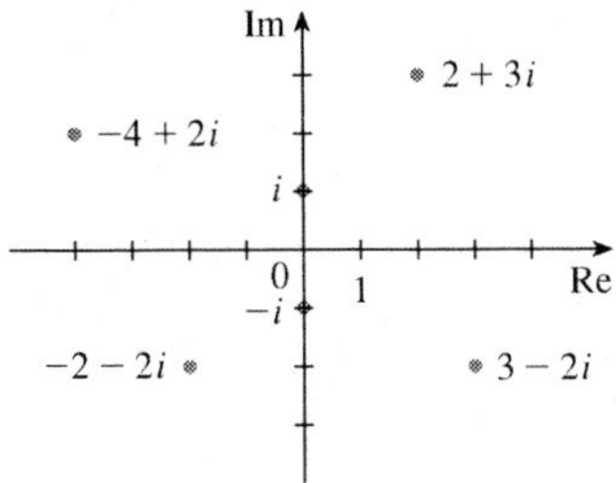

FIGURE 1
Complex numbers as points in the Argand plane

A **complex number** can be represented by an expression of the form $a + bi$, where a and b are real numbers and i is a symbol with the property that $i^2 = -1$. The complex number $a + bi$ can also be represented by the ordered pair (a, b) and plotted as a point in a plane (called the Argand plane) as in Figure 1. Thus the complex number $i = 0 + 1 \cdot i$ is identified with the point $(0, 1)$.

The **real part** of the complex number $a + bi$ is the real number a and the **imaginary part** is the real number b. Thus the real part of $4 - 3i$ is 4 and the imaginary part is -3. Two complex numbers $a + bi$ and $c + di$ are **equal** if $a = c$ and $b = d$, that is, their real parts are equal and their imaginary parts are equal. In the Argand plane the horizontal axis is called the real axis and the vertical axis is called the imaginary axis.

The sum and difference of two complex numbers are defined by adding or subtracting their real parts and their imaginary parts:

$$(a + bi) + (c + di) = (a + c) + (b + d)i$$

$$(a + bi) - (c + di) = (a - c) + (b - d)i$$

Answers to Odd Numbered Questions

(d)
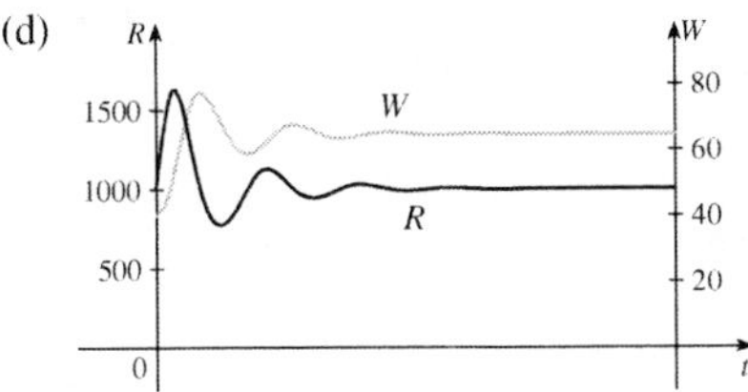

(d)
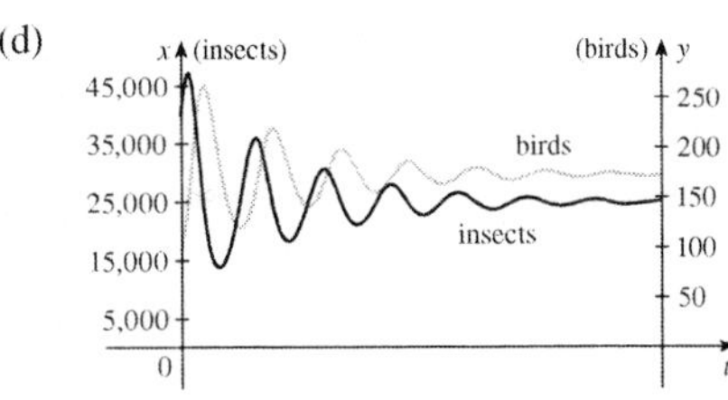

CHAPTER 7 REVIEW ■ PAGE 547

True-False Quiz

1. True **3.** False **5.** True

Exercises

1. (a)
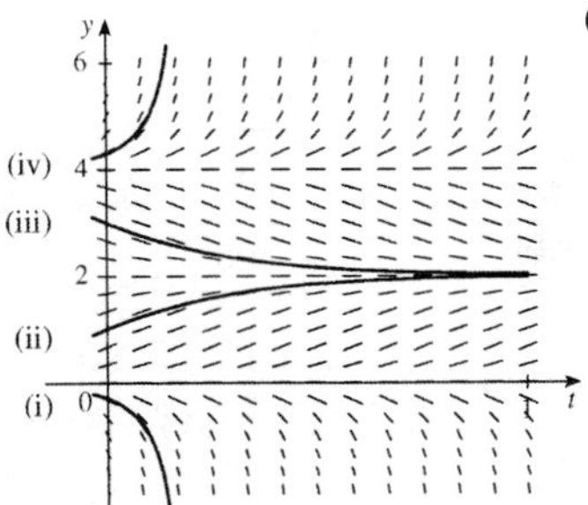

(b) $0 \leqslant c \leqslant 4$; $y = 0$, $y = 2$, $y = 4$

3. (a)
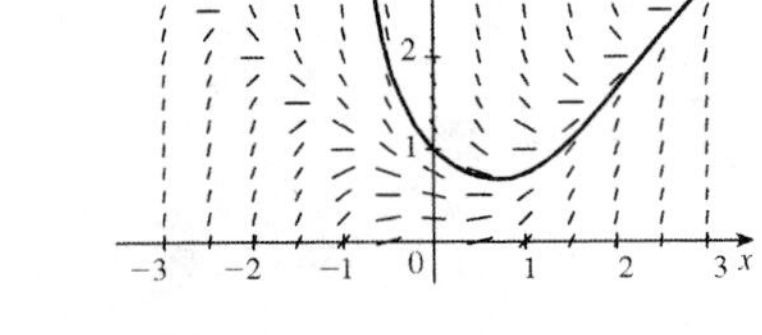

$y(0.3) \approx 0.8$

(b) 0.75676
(c) $y = x$ and $y = -x$; there is a loc max or loc min

5. $y = \pm\sqrt{\ln(x^2 + 2x^{3/2} + C)}$ **7.** $r(t) = 5e^{t-t^2}$

9. $x = C - \frac{1}{2}y^2$

11. (a) $200(3.24)^t$ (b) $\approx 22{,}040$
(c) $\approx 25{,}910$ bacteria/h (d) $(\ln 50)/(\ln 3.24) \approx 3.33$ h

13. (a) $C_0 e^{-kt}$ (b) ≈ 100 h

15. (a) $P(t) = \dfrac{2000}{1 + 19e^{-0.1t}}$; ≈ 560 (b) $t = -10 \ln \frac{2}{57} \approx 33.5$

17. (a) $L(t) = L_\infty - [L_\infty - L(0)]e^{-kt}$ (b) $L(t) = 53 - 43e^{-0.2t}$

19. 15 days **21.** $k \ln h + h = (-R/V)t + C$

23. (a) Stabilizes at 200,000
(b) (i) $x = 0$, $y = 0$: Zero populations
(ii) $x = 200{,}000$, $y = 0$: In the absence of birds, the insect population is always 200,000.
(iii) $x = 25{,}000$, $y = 175$: Both populations are stable.
(c) The populations stabilize at 25,000 insects and 175 birds.

FOCUS ON PROBLEM SOLVING ■ PAGE 551

1. $f(x) = \pm 10e^x$ **5.** $y = x^{1/n}$ **7.** 20°C

9. (b) $f(x) = \dfrac{x^2 - L^2}{4L} - \frac{1}{2}L \ln\left(\dfrac{x}{L}\right)$ (c) No

11. (a) 9.8 h (b) $31{,}900\pi$ ft²; 2000π ft²/h
(c) 5.1 h

13. $x^2 + (y - 6)^2 = 25$

CHAPTER 8

EXERCISES 8.1 ■ PAGE 562

Abbreviations: C, convergent; D, divergent

1. (a) A sequence is an ordered list of numbers. It can also be defined as a function whose domain is the set of positive integers.
(b) The terms a_n approach 8 as n becomes large.
(c) The terms a_n become large as n becomes large.

3. $\frac{1}{3}, \frac{2}{5}, \frac{3}{7}, \frac{4}{9}, \frac{5}{11}, \frac{6}{13}$; yes; $\frac{1}{2}$ **5.** $a_n = 1/(2n - 1)$

7. $a_n = 5n - 3$ **9.** $a_n = \left(-\frac{2}{3}\right)^{n-1}$ **11.** 5

13. 1 **15.** 1 **17.** 1 **19.** 0 **21.** 0 **23.** 0

25. 0 **27.** e^2 **29.** 0 **31.** D **33.** ln 2 **35.** 1

37. $\frac{1}{2}$ **39.** D

41. (a) 1060, 1123.60, 1191.02, 1262.48, 1338.23 (b) D

43. (a) $P_n = 1.08P_{n-1} - 300$ (b) 5734

45. (a) D (b) C **47.** (b) $\frac{1}{2}(1 + \sqrt{5})$

49. Decreasing; yes **51.** Not monotonic; no

53. Convergent by the Monotonic Sequence Theorem; $5 \leqslant L < 8$

55. $\frac{1}{2}(3 + \sqrt{5})$ **57.** 62

EXERCISES 8.2 ■ PAGE 572

1. (a) A sequence is an ordered list of numbers whereas a series is the *sum* of a list of numbers.
(b) A series is convergent if the sequence of partial sums is a convergent sequence. A series is divergent if it is not convergent.

3. -2.40000, -1.92000,
-2.01600, -1.99680,
-2.00064, -1.99987,
-2.00003, -1.99999,
-2.00000, -2.00000;
convergent, sum $= -2$

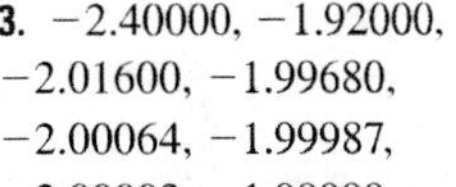

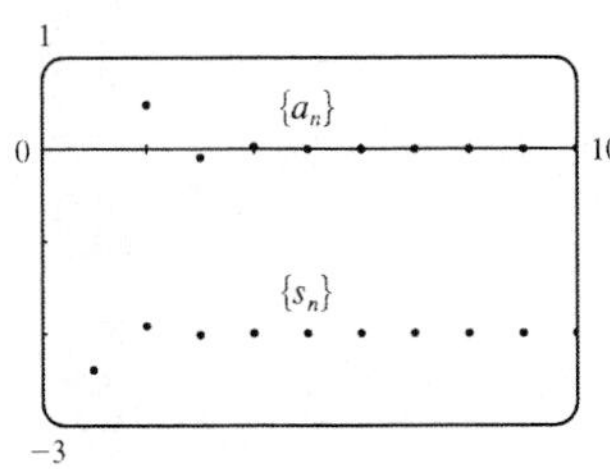

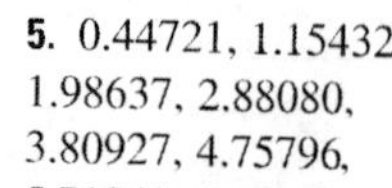

5. 0.44721, 1.15432, 1.98637, 2.88080, 3.80927, 4.75796, 5.71948, 6.68962, 7.66581, 8.64639; divergent

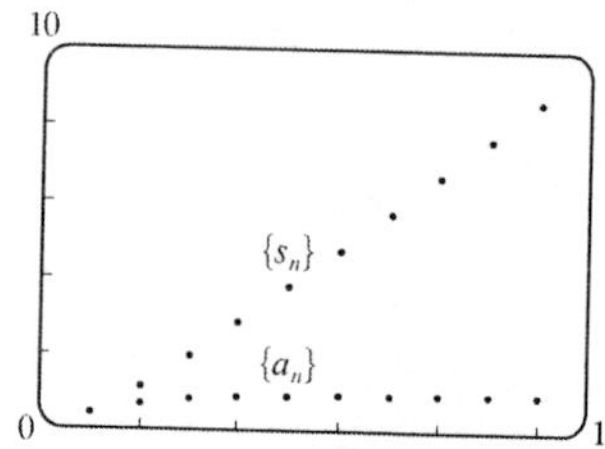

7. 0.29289, 0.42265, 0.50000, 0.55279, 0.59175, 0.62204, 0.64645, 0.66667, 0.68377, 0.69849; convergent, sum = 1

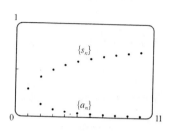

9. (a) C (b) D **11.** D **13.** $\frac{25}{3}$ **15.** 60 **17.** D **19.** D **21.** D **23.** $\frac{5}{2}$ **25.** D **27.** D **29.** $e/(e-1)$ **31.** $\frac{3}{2}$ **33.** $\frac{11}{6}$

35. (b) 1 (c) 2 (d) All rational numbers with a terminating decimal representation, except 0.

37. $\frac{2}{9}$ **39.** 5063/3300 **41.** $-3 < x < 3$; $\dfrac{x}{3-x}$

43. All x; $\dfrac{2}{2-\cos x}$ **45.** 1

47. $a_1 = 0$, $a_n = \dfrac{2}{n(n+1)}$ for $n > 1$, sum = 1

49. (a) 105.25 mg (b) $\dfrac{100(1-0.05^n)}{1-0.05}$ mg

(c) The quantity of the drug approaches $\dfrac{100}{0.95} \approx 105.26$ mg

51. (a) $S_n = \dfrac{D(1-c^n)}{1-c}$ (b) 5 **53.** $\frac{1}{2}(\sqrt{3}-1)$

57. $\dfrac{1}{n(n+1)}$ **59.** The series is divergent.

63. $\{s_n\}$ is bounded and increasing.

65. (a) $0, \frac{1}{9}, \frac{2}{9}, \frac{1}{3}, \frac{2}{3}, \frac{7}{9}, \frac{8}{9}, 1$

67. (a) $\frac{1}{2}, \frac{5}{6}, \frac{23}{24}, \frac{119}{120}$; $\dfrac{(n+1)!-1}{(n+1)!}$ (c) 1

EXERCISES 8.3 ■ PAGE 583

1. C

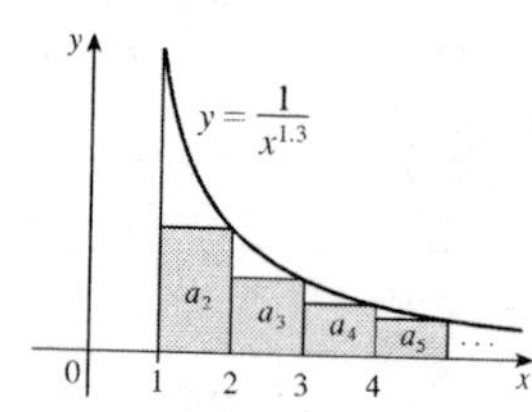

3. (a) Nothing (b) C

5. p-series; geometric series; $b < -1$; $-1 < b < 1$ **7.** D

9. C **11.** D **13.** C **15.** C **17.** D **19.** C **21.** C **23.** D **25.** D **27.** C **29.** D **31.** $p > 1$

33. (a) 1.54977, error $\leqslant 0.1$ (b) 1.64522, error $\leqslant 0.005$ (c) $n > 1000$

35. 0.00145 **37.** 1.249, error < 0.1 **43.** Yes

EXERCISES 8.4 ■ PAGE 591

1. (a) A series whose terms are alternately positive and negative (b) $0 < b_{n+1} \leqslant b_n$ and $\lim_{n\to\infty} b_n = 0$, where $b_n = |a_n|$ (c) $|R_n| \leqslant b_{n+1}$

3. C **5.** C **7.** D **9.** C

11. An underestimate **13.** $p > 0$ **15.** 5 **17.** -0.5507

19. 0.0676 **21.** No **23.** Yes **25.** Yes **27.** No

29. Yes **31.** Yes **33.** Yes **35.** D **37.** (a) and (d)

39. AC

EXERCISES 8.5 ■ PAGE 597

1. A series of the form $\sum_{n=0}^{\infty} c_n(x-a)^n$, where x is a variable and a and the c_n's are constants

3. $1, [-1, 1)$ **5.** $1, [-1, 1]$ **7.** $\infty, (-\infty, \infty)$

9. $2, (-2, 2)$ **11.** $\frac{1}{2}, (-\frac{1}{2}, \frac{1}{2}]$ **13.** $1, [1, 3]$

15. $\frac{1}{3}, \left[-\frac{13}{3}, -\frac{11}{3}\right)$ **17.** $\frac{1}{4}, \left[-\frac{1}{2}, 0\right]$ **19.** $0, \left\{\frac{1}{2}\right\}$

21. $b, (a-b, a+b)$ **23.** $\infty, (-\infty, \infty)$

25. (a) Yes (b) No **27.** k^k

29. (a) $(-\infty, \infty)$

(b), (c)

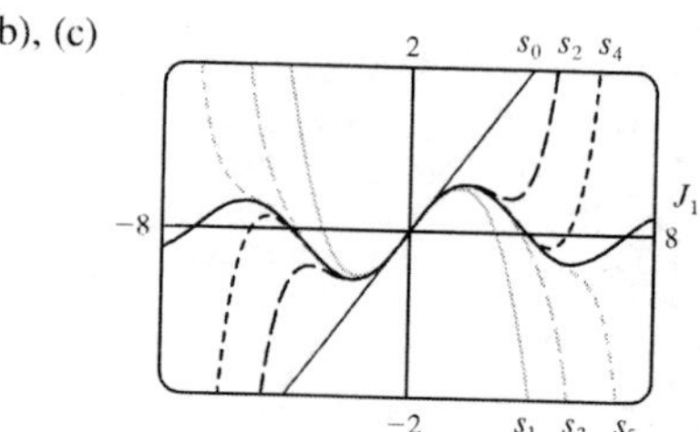

31. $(-1, 1), f(x) = (1+2x)/(1-x^2)$ **33.** 2 **35.** No

EXERCISES 8.6 ■ PAGE 603

1. 10 **3.** $\sum_{n=0}^{\infty} (-1)^n x^n, (-1, 1)$ **5.** $2\sum_{n=0}^{\infty} \dfrac{1}{3^{n+1}} x^n, (-3, 3)$

7. $\sum_{n=0}^{\infty} (-1)^n \dfrac{1}{9^{n+1}} x^{2n+1}, (-3, 3)$ **9.** $1 + 2\sum_{n=1}^{\infty} x^n, (-1, 1)$

11. (a) $\sum_{n=0}^{\infty} (-1)^n (n+1)x^n, R = 1$

(b) $\dfrac{1}{2}\sum_{n=0}^{\infty} (-1)^n (n+2)(n+1)x^n, R = 1$

(c) $\dfrac{1}{2}\sum_{n=2}^{\infty} (-1)^n n(n-1)x^n, R = 1$

13. $\ln 5 - \sum_{n=1}^{\infty} \dfrac{x^n}{n5^n}, R = 5$

15. $\sum_{n=0}^{\infty} (-1)^n 4^n (n+1) x^{n+1}$, $R = \frac{1}{4}$

17. $\sum_{n=0}^{\infty} (2n+1)x^n$, $R = 1$

19. $\sum_{n=0}^{\infty} (-1)^n \frac{1}{16^{n+1}} x^{2n+1}$, $R = 4$

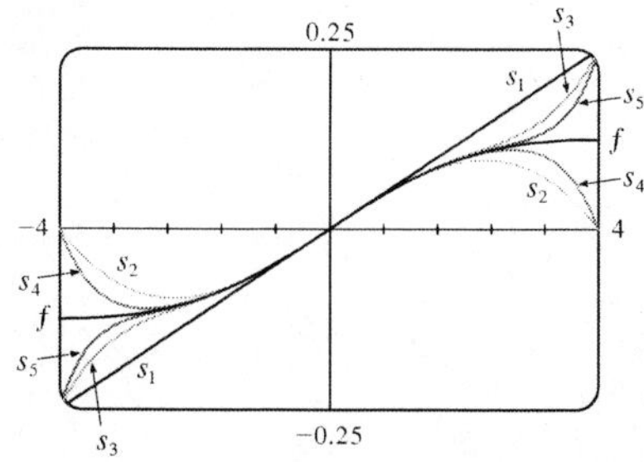

21. $\sum_{n=0}^{\infty} \frac{2x^{2n+1}}{2n+1}$, $R = 1$

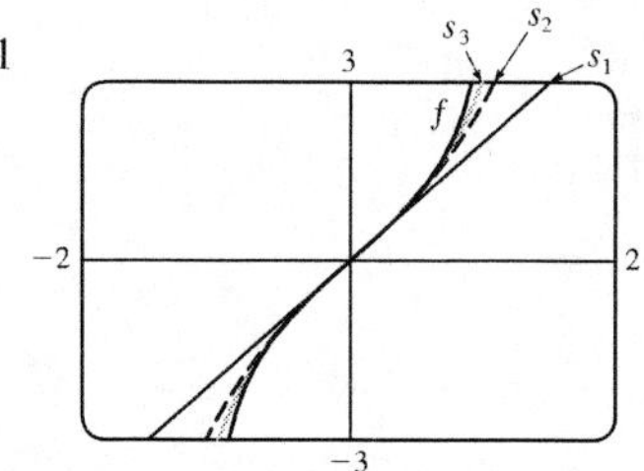

23. $C + \sum_{n=0}^{\infty} \frac{t^{8n+2}}{8n+2}$, $R = 1$

25. $C + \sum_{n=1}^{\infty} (-1)^{n+1} \frac{x^{2n-1}}{4n^2 - 1}$, $R = 1$

27. 0.199989 **29.** 0.000983 **31.** 0.19740

33. (b) 0.920 **37.** $[-1, 1]$, $[-1, 1)$, $(-1, 1)$

EXERCISES 8.7 ■ PAGE 616

1. $b_8 = f^{(8)}(5)/8!$ **3.** $\sum_{n=0}^{\infty} (n+1)x^n$, $R = 1$

5. $\sum_{n=0}^{\infty} (n+1)x^n$, $R = 1$

7. $\sum_{n=0}^{\infty} (-1)^n \frac{\pi^{2n+1}}{(2n+1)!} x^{2n+1}$, $R = \infty$

9. $\sum_{n=0}^{\infty} \frac{5^n}{n!} x^n$, $R = \infty$

11. $-1 - 2(x-1) + 3(x-1)^2 + 4(x-1)^3 + (x-1)^4$, $R = \infty$

13. $\sum_{n=0}^{\infty} \frac{e^3}{n!} (x-3)^n$, $R = \infty$

15. $\sum_{n=0}^{\infty} (-1)^{n+1} \frac{1}{(2n)!} (x-\pi)^{2n}$, $R = \infty$

17. $\frac{1}{3} + \sum_{n=1}^{\infty} (-1)^n \frac{1 \cdot 3 \cdot 5 \cdot \cdots \cdot (2n-1)}{2^n \cdot 3^{2n+1} \cdot n!} (x-9)^n$, $R = 9$

21. $1 + \frac{x}{2} + \sum_{n=2}^{\infty} (-1)^{n-1} \frac{1 \cdot 3 \cdot 5 \cdot \cdots \cdot (2n-3)}{2^n n!} x^n$, $R = 1$

23. $\sum_{n=0}^{\infty} (-1)^n \frac{(n+1)(n+2)}{2^{n+4}} x^n$, $R = 2$

25. $\sum_{n=0}^{\infty} (-1)^n \frac{\pi^{2n+1}}{(2n+1)!} x^{2n+1}$, $R = \infty$

27. $\sum_{n=0}^{\infty} \frac{2^n + 1}{n!} x^n$, $R = \infty$

29. $\sum_{n=0}^{\infty} (-1)^n \frac{1}{2^{2n}(2n)!} x^{4n+1}$, $R = \infty$

31. $\frac{1}{2}x + \sum_{n=1}^{\infty} (-1)^n \frac{1 \cdot 3 \cdot 5 \cdot \cdots \cdot (2n-1)}{n! \, 2^{3n+1}} x^{2n+1}$, $R = 2$

33. $\sum_{n=1}^{\infty} (-1)^{n+1} \frac{2^{2n-1}}{(2n)!} x^{2n}$, $R = \infty$

35. $\sum_{n=0}^{\infty} (-1)^n \frac{1}{(2n)!} x^{4n}$, $R = \infty$

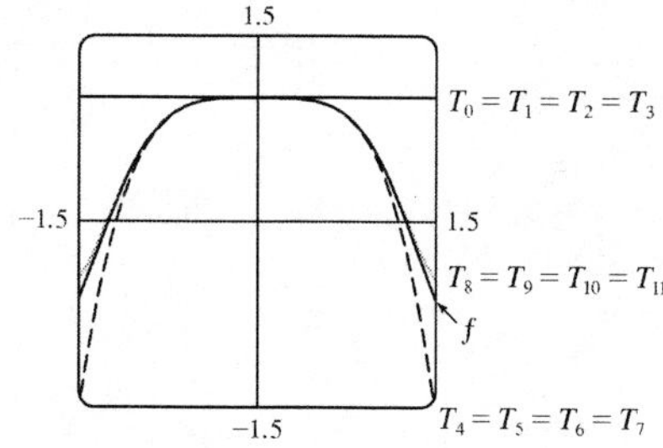

37. $\sum_{n=1}^{\infty} \frac{(-1)^{n-1}}{(n-1)!} x^n$, $R = \infty$

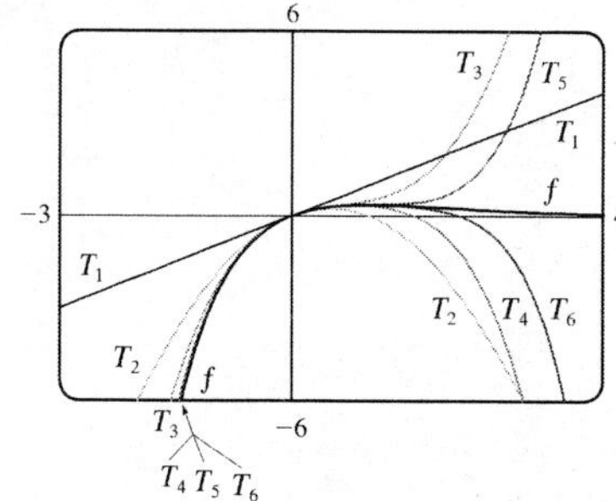

39. 0.81873

41. (a) $1 + \sum_{n=1}^{\infty} \frac{1 \cdot 3 \cdot 5 \cdot \cdots \cdot (2n-1)}{2^n n!} x^{2n}$

(b) $x + \sum_{n=1}^{\infty} \frac{1 \cdot 3 \cdot 5 \cdot \cdots \cdot (2n-1)}{(2n+1)2^n n!} x^{2n+1}$

43. $C + \sum_{n=0}^{\infty} (-1)^n \frac{x^{6n+2}}{(6n+2)(2n)!}$, $R = \infty$

45. $C + \sum_{n=1}^{\infty} (-1)^n \frac{1}{2n\,(2n)!} x^{2n}$, $R = \infty$

47. 0.440 **49.** 0.40102 **51.** $\frac{1}{2}$ **53.** $\frac{1}{120}$

55. $1 - \frac{3}{2}x^2 + \frac{25}{24}x^4$ **57.** $1 + \frac{1}{6}x^2 + \frac{7}{360}x^4$ **59.** e^{-x^4}

61. $\ln \frac{8}{5}$ **63.** $1/\sqrt{2}$ **65.** $e^3 - 1$

EXERCISES 8.8 ■ PAGE 625

1. (a) $T_0(x) = 1 = T_1(x)$, $T_2(x) = 1 - \frac{1}{2}x^2 = T_3(x)$,
$T_4(x) = 1 - \frac{1}{2}x^2 + \frac{1}{24}x^4 = T_5(x)$,
$T_6(x) = 1 - \frac{1}{2}x^2 + \frac{1}{24}x^4 - \frac{1}{720}x^6$

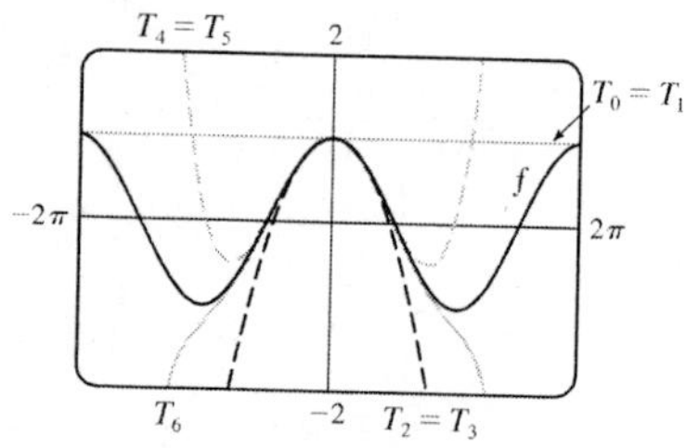

(b)

x	f	$T_0 = T_1$	$T_2 = T_3$	$T_4 = T_5$	T_6
$\frac{\pi}{4}$	0.7071	1	0.6916	0.7074	0.7071
$\frac{\pi}{2}$	0	1	−0.2337	0.0200	−0.0009
π	−1	1	−3.9348	0.1239	−1.2114

(c) As n increases, $T_n(x)$ is a good approximation to $f(x)$ on a larger and larger interval.

3. $\frac{1}{2} - \frac{1}{4}(x - 2) + \frac{1}{8}(x - 2)^2 - \frac{1}{16}(x - 2)^3$

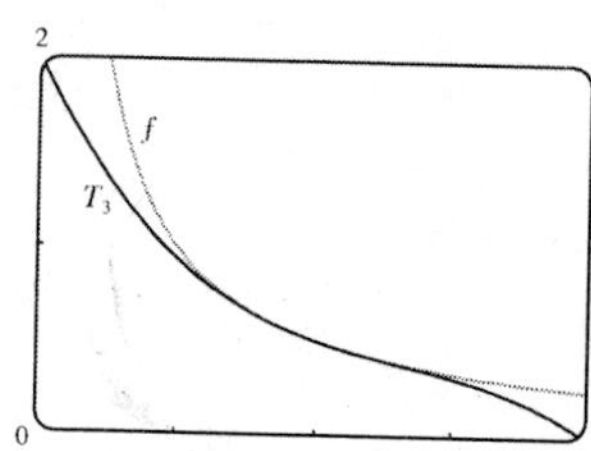

5. $-\left(x - \frac{\pi}{2}\right) + \frac{1}{6}\left(x - \frac{\pi}{2}\right)^3$

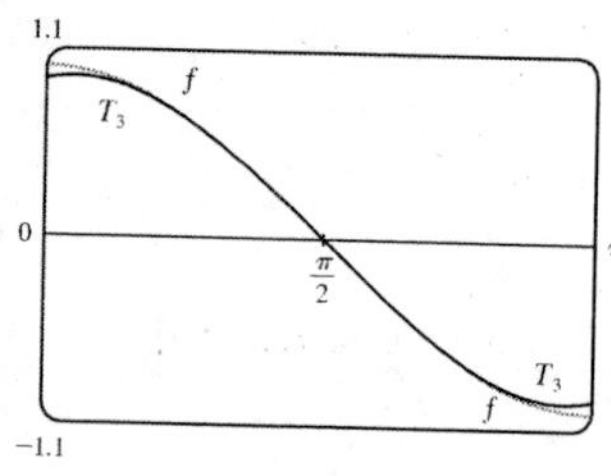

7. $x - 2x^2 + 2x^3$

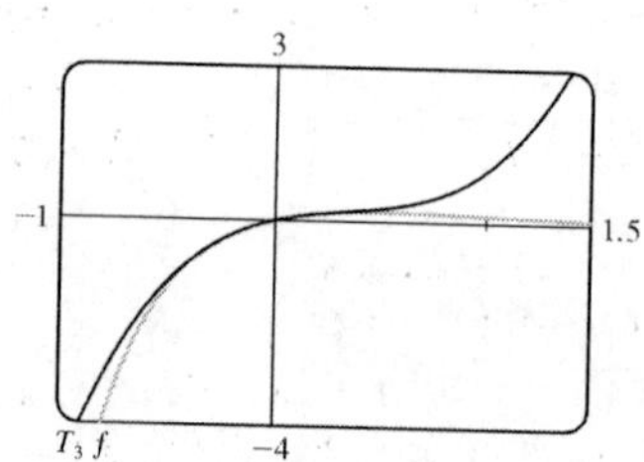

9. $T_5(x) = 1 - 2\left(x - \frac{\pi}{4}\right) + 2\left(x - \frac{\pi}{4}\right)^2 - \frac{8}{3}\left(x - \frac{\pi}{4}\right)^3 + \frac{10}{3}\left(x - \frac{\pi}{4}\right)^4 - \frac{64}{15}\left(x - \frac{\pi}{4}\right)^5$

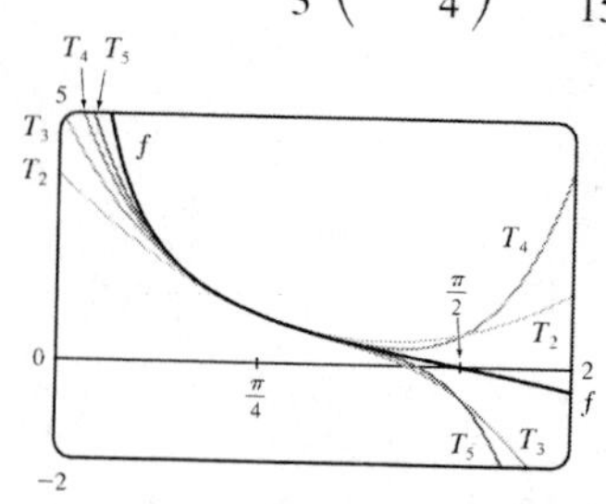

11. (a) $2 + \frac{1}{4}(x - 4) - \frac{1}{64}(x - 4)^2$ (b) 1.5625×10^{-5}

13. (a) $1 + \frac{2}{3}(x - 1) - \frac{1}{9}(x - 1)^2 + \frac{4}{81}(x - 1)^3$ (b) 0.000097

15. (a) $1 + x^2$ (b) 0.00006 **17.** (a) $x^2 - \frac{1}{6}x^4$ (b) 0.042

19. 0.17365 **21.** Four **23.** $-1.037 < x < 1.037$

25. $-0.86 < x < 0.86$ **27.** 21 m, no

31. (c) They differ by about 8×10^{-9} km.

CHAPTER 8 REVIEW ■ PAGE 629

True-False Quiz

1. False **3.** True **5.** False **7.** False **9.** False
11. True **13.** True **15.** False **17.** True **19.** True

Exercises

1. $\frac{1}{2}$ **3.** D **5.** 0 **7.** e^{12} **9.** C **11.** C **13.** D
15. C **17.** C **19.** $\frac{1}{11}$ **21.** $\pi/4$ **23.** $\frac{4111}{3330}$
25. 0.9721 **27.** 0.18976224, error $< 6.4 \times 10^{-7}$
31. 4, $[-6, 2)$ **33.** 0.5, $[2.5, 3.5)$

35. $\frac{1}{2}\sum_{n=0}^{\infty}(-1)^n\left[\frac{1}{(2n)!}\left(x - \frac{\pi}{6}\right)^{2n} + \frac{\sqrt{3}}{(2n+1)!}\left(x - \frac{\pi}{6}\right)^{2n+1}\right]$

37. $\sum_{n=0}^{\infty}(-1)^n x^{n+2}$, $R = 1$ **39.** $\ln 4 - \sum_{n=1}^{\infty}\frac{x^n}{n4^n}$, $R = 4$

41. $\sum_{n=0}^{\infty}(-1)^n\frac{x^{8n+4}}{(2n+1)!}$, $R = \infty$

43. $\frac{1}{2} + \sum_{n=1}^{\infty}\frac{1 \cdot 5 \cdot 9 \cdot \cdots \cdot (4n-3)}{n!\,2^{6n+1}}x^n$, $R = 16$

45. $C + \ln|x| + \sum_{n=1}^{\infty}\frac{x^n}{n \cdot n!}$

47. (a) $1 + \frac{1}{2}(x - 1) - \frac{1}{8}(x - 1)^2 + \frac{1}{16}(x - 1)^3$

(b)

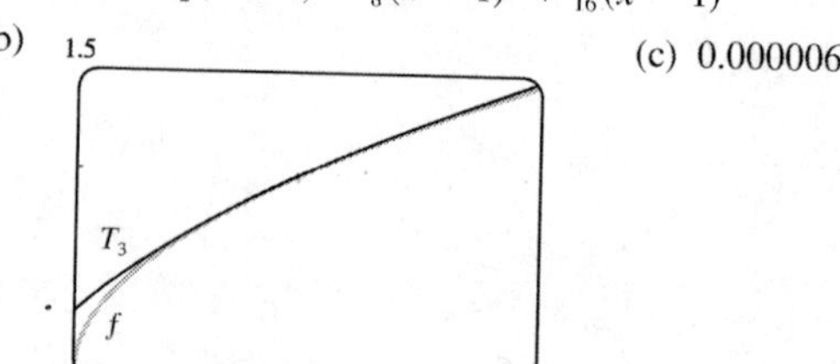

(c) 0.000006

49. $-\frac{1}{6}$

PRINCIPLES OF PROBLEM SOLVING ■ PAGE 631

1. $15!/5! = 10{,}897{,}286{,}400$
3. (a) $s_n = 3 \cdot 4^n$, $l_n = 1/3^n$, $p_n = 4^n/3^{n-1}$ (c) $\frac{2}{5}\sqrt{3}$
5. $\ln \frac{1}{2}$ **11.** $\dfrac{\pi}{2\sqrt{3}} - 1$
13. $-\left(\dfrac{\pi}{2} - \pi k\right)^2$ where k is a positive integer

CHAPTER 9

EXERCISES 9.1 ■ PAGE 638

1. $(4, 0, -3)$ **3.** Q; R
5. A vertical plane that intersects the xy-plane in the line $y = 2 - x$, $z = 0$ (see graph at right)

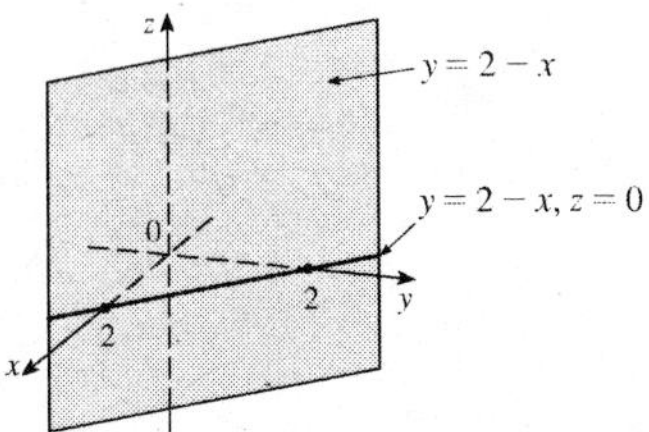

7. (a) $|PQ| = 6$, $|QR| = 2\sqrt{10}$, $|RP| = 6$; isosceles triangle
(b) $|PQ| = 3$, $|QR| = 3\sqrt{5}$, $|RP| = 6$; right triangle
9. (a) No (b) Yes
11. $(x-3)^2 + (y-8)^2 + (z-1)^2 = 30$
13. $(3, -2, 1)$, 5 **15.** $(2, 0, -6)$, $9/\sqrt{2}$
17. (b) $\frac{5}{2}, \frac{1}{2}\sqrt{94}, \frac{1}{2}\sqrt{85}$
19. (a) $(x-2)^2 + (y+3)^2 + (z-6)^2 = 36$
(b) $(x-2)^2 + (y+3)^2 + (z-6)^2 = 4$
(c) $(x-2)^2 + (y+3)^2 + (z-6)^2 = 9$
21. A plane parallel to the yz-plane and 5 units in front of it
23. A half-space consisting of all points to the left of the plane $y = 8$
25. All points on or between the horizontal planes $z = 0$ and $z = 6$
27. All points on a circle with radius 2 and center on the z-axis that is contained in the plane $z = -1$
29. All points on or inside a sphere with radius $\sqrt{3}$ and center O
31. All points on or inside a circular cylinder of radius 3 with axis the y-axis
33. $0 < x < 5$ **35.** $r^2 < x^2 + y^2 + z^2 < R^2$
37. (a) $(2, 1, 4)$ (b)

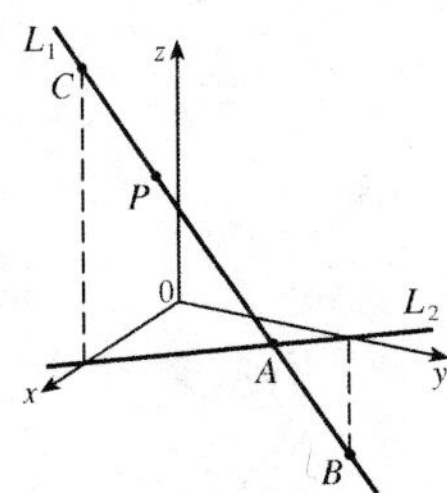

39. $14x - 6y - 10z = 9$, a plane perpendicular to AB
41. $2\sqrt{3} - 3$

EXERCISES 9.2 ■ PAGE 646

1. (a) Scalar (b) Vector (c) Vector (d) Scalar
3. $\overrightarrow{AB} = \overrightarrow{DC}$, $\overrightarrow{DA} = \overrightarrow{CB}$, $\overrightarrow{DE} = \overrightarrow{EB}$, $\overrightarrow{EA} = \overrightarrow{CE}$

5. (a)

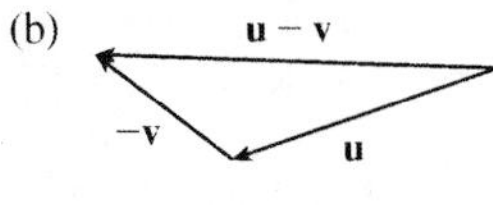

(b)

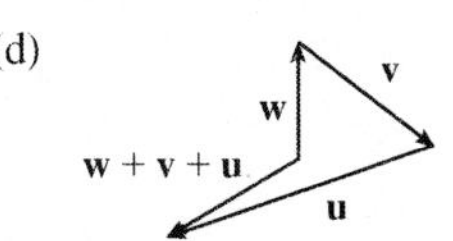

(c)

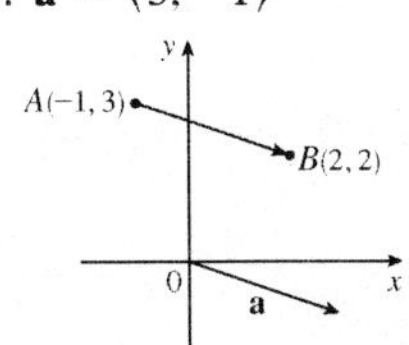

(d)

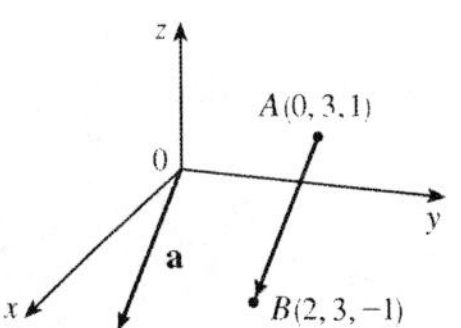

7. $\mathbf{a} = \langle 3, -1 \rangle$

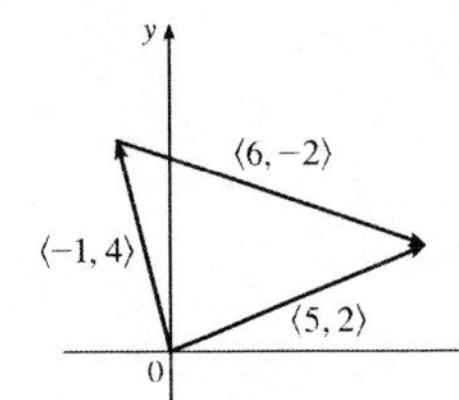

9. $\mathbf{a} = \langle 2, 0, -2 \rangle$

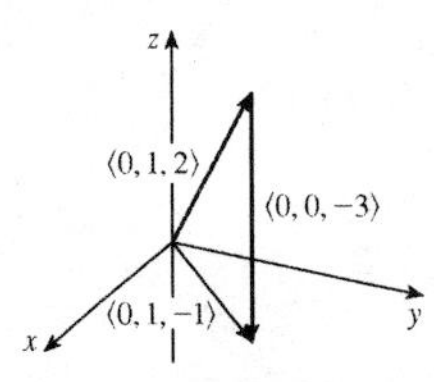

11. $\langle 5, 2 \rangle$

13. $\langle 0, 1, -1 \rangle$

15. $\langle 2, -18 \rangle$, $\langle 1, -42 \rangle$, 13, 10
17. $-\mathbf{i} + \mathbf{j} + 2\mathbf{k}$, $-4\mathbf{i} + \mathbf{j} + 9\mathbf{k}$, $\sqrt{14}$, $\sqrt{82}$
19. $-\dfrac{3}{\sqrt{58}}\mathbf{i} + \dfrac{7}{\sqrt{58}}\mathbf{j}$ **21.** $\frac{8}{9}\mathbf{i} - \frac{1}{9}\mathbf{j} + \frac{4}{9}\mathbf{k}$
23. $\langle 2, 2\sqrt{3} \rangle$ **25.** ≈ 45.96 ft/s, ≈ 38.57 ft/s
27. $100\sqrt{7} \approx 264.6$ N, $\approx 139.1°$
29. $\sqrt{493} \approx 22.2$ mi/h, N8°W
31. $\mathbf{T}_1 = -196\,\mathbf{i} + 3.92\,\mathbf{j}$, $\mathbf{T}_2 = 196\,\mathbf{i} + 3.92\,\mathbf{j}$
33. $\pm(\mathbf{i} + 4\,\mathbf{j})/\sqrt{17}$
35. (a), (b)

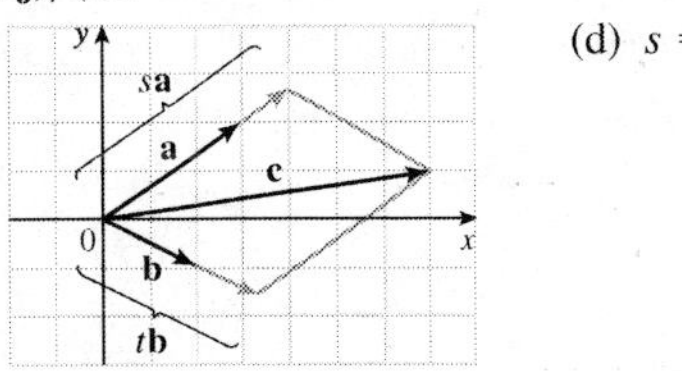

(d) $s = \frac{9}{7}$, $t = \frac{11}{7}$

37. $\mathbf{a} \approx \langle 0.50, 0.31, 0.81 \rangle$
39. A sphere with radius 1, centered at (x_0, y_0, z_0)

EXERCISES 9.3 ■ PAGE 653

1. (b), (c), (d) are meaningful **3.** -15
5. 14 **7.** 19 **9.** 1 **11.** $\mathbf{u} \cdot \mathbf{v} = \frac{1}{2}$, $\mathbf{u} \cdot \mathbf{w} = -\frac{1}{2}$
15. $\cos^{-1}\left(\dfrac{9 - 4\sqrt{7}}{20}\right) \approx 95°$ **17.** $\cos^{-1}\left(\dfrac{-1}{2\sqrt{7}}\right) \approx 101°$
19. 45°, 45°, 90°
21. (a) Neither (b) Orthogonal
(c) Orthogonal (d) Parallel
23. Yes **25.** $(\mathbf{i} - \mathbf{j} - \mathbf{k})/\sqrt{3}$ $[\text{or } (-\mathbf{i} + \mathbf{j} + \mathbf{k})/\sqrt{3}]$
27. 45° **29.** 3, $\langle \frac{9}{5}, -\frac{12}{5} \rangle$ **31.** $1/\sqrt{21}$, $\frac{2}{21}\mathbf{i} - \frac{1}{21}\mathbf{j} + \frac{4}{21}\mathbf{k}$

35. $\langle 0, 0, -2\sqrt{10} \rangle$ or any vector of the form $\langle s, t, 3s - 2\sqrt{10} \rangle$, $s, t \in \mathbb{R}$
37. 144 J **39.** $2400 \cos(40^\circ) \approx 1839$ ft-lb
41. $\frac{13}{5}$ **43.** $\cos^{-1}(1/\sqrt{3}) \approx 55^\circ$

EXERCISES 9.4 ■ PAGE 661

1. (a) Scalar (b) Meaningless (c) Vector (d) Meaningless (e) Meaningless (f) Scalar
3. $96\sqrt{3}$; into the page **5.** $10.8 \sin 80^\circ \approx 10.6$ N·m
7. $16\,\mathbf{i} + 48\,\mathbf{k}$ **9.** $15\,\mathbf{i} - 3\,\mathbf{j} + 3\,\mathbf{k}$ **11.** $\frac{1}{2}\mathbf{i} - \mathbf{j} + \frac{3}{2}\mathbf{k}$
13. $t^4\mathbf{i} - 2t^3\mathbf{j} + t^2\mathbf{k}$ **15.** $\mathbf{0}$ **17.** $\mathbf{i} + \mathbf{j} + \mathbf{k}$
19. $\langle -2/\sqrt{6}, -1/\sqrt{6}, 1/\sqrt{6} \rangle$, $\langle 2/\sqrt{6}, 1/\sqrt{6}, -1/\sqrt{6} \rangle$
21. 16 **23.** (a) $\langle 13, -14, 5 \rangle$ (b) $\frac{1}{2}\sqrt{390}$
25. ≈ 417 N **27.** 82 **29.** 3
33. (b) $\sqrt{97/3}$ **39.** (a) No (b) No (c) Yes

EXERCISES 9.5 ■ PAGE 670

1. (a) True (b) False (c) True (d) False (e) False (f) True (g) False (h) True (i) True (j) False (k) True
3. $\mathbf{r} = (2\,\mathbf{i} + 2.4\,\mathbf{j} + 3.5\,\mathbf{k}) + t(3\,\mathbf{i} + 2\,\mathbf{j} - \mathbf{k})$;
$x = 2 + 3t, y = 2.4 + 2t, z = 3.5 - t$
5. $\mathbf{r} = (\mathbf{i} + 6\mathbf{k}) + t(\mathbf{i} + 3\,\mathbf{j} + \mathbf{k})$;
$x = 1 + t, y = 3t, z = 6 + t$
7. $x = 2 + 2t, y = 1 + \frac{1}{2}t$,
$z = -3 - 4t$;
$(x - 2)/2 = 2y - 2 = (z + 3)/(-4)$
9. $x = 1 + t, y = -1 + 2t, z = 1 + t$;
$x - 1 = (y + 1)/2 = z - 1$
11. Yes
13. (a) $(x - 1)/(-1) = (y + 5)/2 = (z - 6)/(-3)$
(b) $(-1, -1, 0)$, $(-\frac{3}{2}, 0, -\frac{3}{2})$, $(0, -3, 3)$
15. $\mathbf{r}(t) = (2\mathbf{i} - \mathbf{j} + 4\mathbf{k}) + t(2\mathbf{i} + 7\mathbf{j} - 3\mathbf{k}), 0 \le t \le 1$
17. Parallel **19.** Skew **21.** $-2x + y + 5z = 1$
23. $3x - 7z = -9$ **25.** $x + y + z = 2$
27. $33x + 10y + 4z = 190$ **29.** $x - 2y + 4z = -1$
31. $3x - 8y - z = -38$

33.

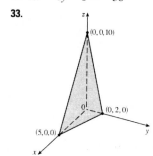

35.

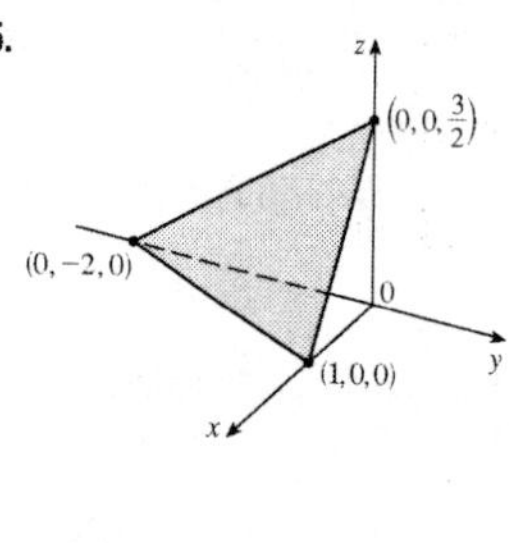

37. $(2, 3, 5)$ **39.** Perpendicular
41. Neither, $\cos^{-1}(\frac{1}{3}) \approx 70.5^\circ$

43. (a) $x = 1, y = -t, z = t$ (b) $\cos^{-1}\left(\dfrac{5}{3\sqrt{3}}\right) \approx 15.8^\circ$

45. $x = 1, y - 2 = -z$ **47.** $(x/a) + (y/b) + (z/c) = 1$
49. $x = 3t, y = 1 - t, z = 2 - 2t$
51. P_2 and P_3 are parallel, P_1 and P_4 are identical
53. $\sqrt{61/14}$ **55.** $\frac{18}{7}$ **57.** $5/(2\sqrt{14})$ **61.** $1/\sqrt{6}$

EXERCISES 9.6 ■ PAGE 680

1. (a) 25; a 40-knot wind blowing in the open sea for 15 h will create waves about 25 ft high.
(b) $f(30, t)$ is a function of t giving the wave heights produced by 30-knot winds blowing for t hours.
(c) $f(v, 30)$ is a function of v giving the wave heights produced by winds of speed v blowing for 30 hours.
3. (a) 1 (b) $\mathbb{R}^2$ (c) $[-1, 1]$
5. $\{(x, y) \mid y \ge x^2, x \ne \pm 1\}$

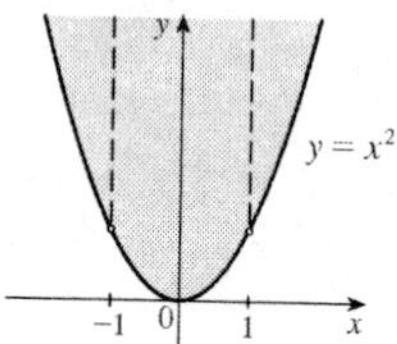

7. $\{(x, y) \mid -1 \le x \le 1, -1 \le y \le 1\}$

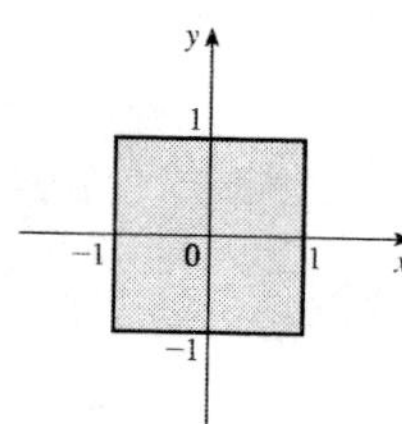

9. $z = 3$, horizontal plane

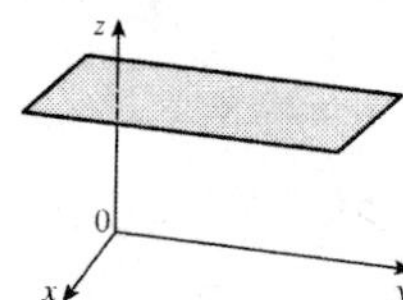

11. $3x + 2y + z = 6$, plane

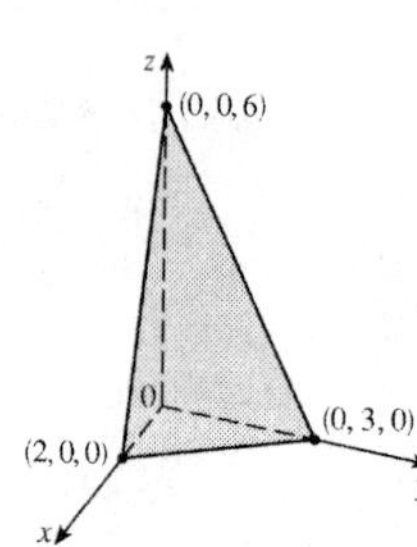

13. $z = y^2 + 1$, parabolic cylinder

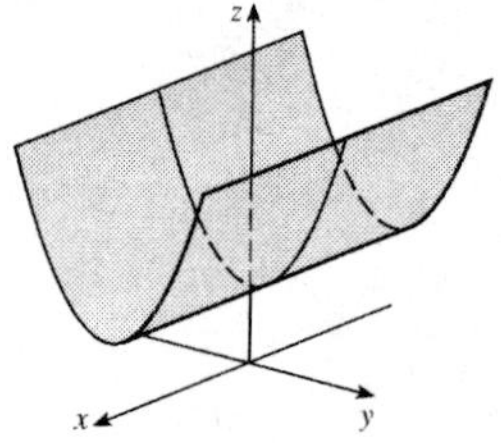

15. (a) VI (b) V (c) I (d) IV (e) II (f) III

17. $z = \sqrt{4x^2 + y^2}$

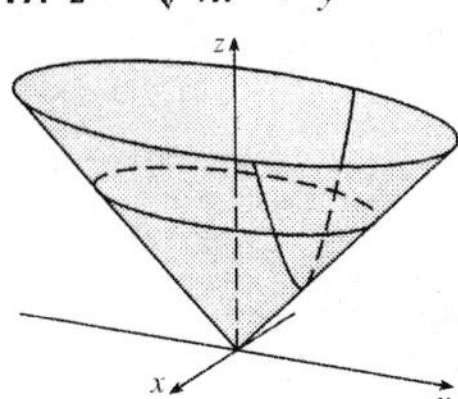

19.

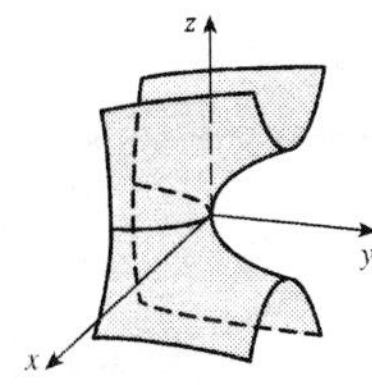

21. $x^2 + \dfrac{(y-2)^2}{4} + (z-3)^2 = 1$

Ellipsoid with center $(0, 2, 3)$

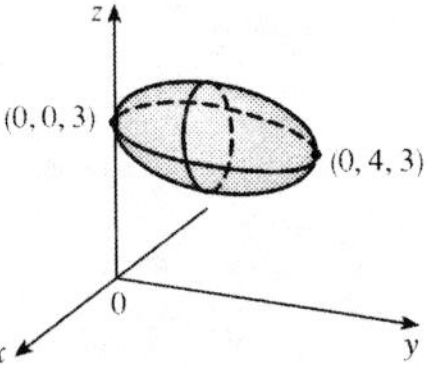

23. (a) A circle of radius 1 centered at the origin
(b) A circular cylinder of radius 1 with axis the z-axis
(c) A circular cylinder of radius 1 with axis the y-axis

25. (a) $x = k$, $y^2 - z^2 = 1 - k^2$, hyperbola $(k \neq \pm 1)$;
$y = k$, $x^2 - z^2 = 1 - k^2$, hyperbola $(k \neq \pm 1)$;
$z = k$, $x^2 + y^2 = 1 + k^2$, circle
(b) The hyperboloid is rotated so that it has axis the y-axis
(c) The hyperboloid is shifted one unit in the negative y-direction

27. III

29. 

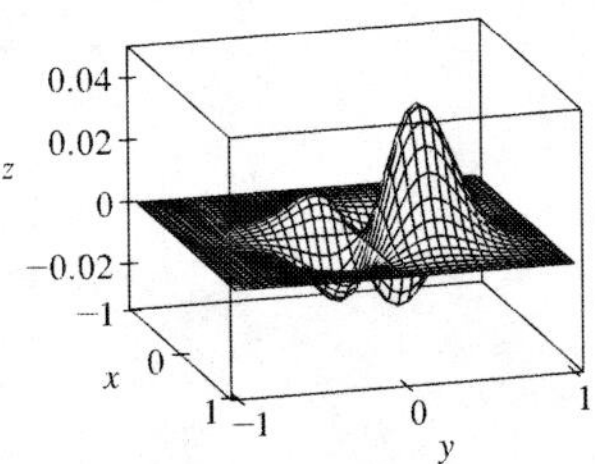

f appears to have a maximum value of about 0.044. There are two local maximum points and two local minimum points.

31.

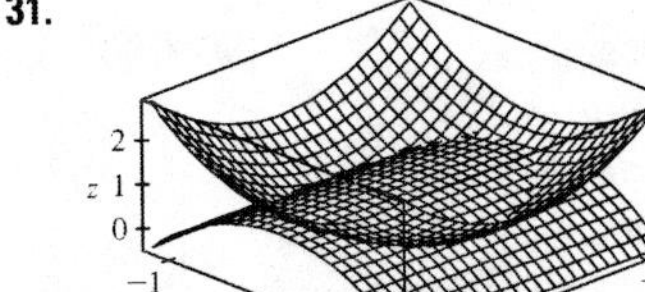

EXERCISES 9.7 ■ PAGE 686

1. See pages 682–83.

3. (a)

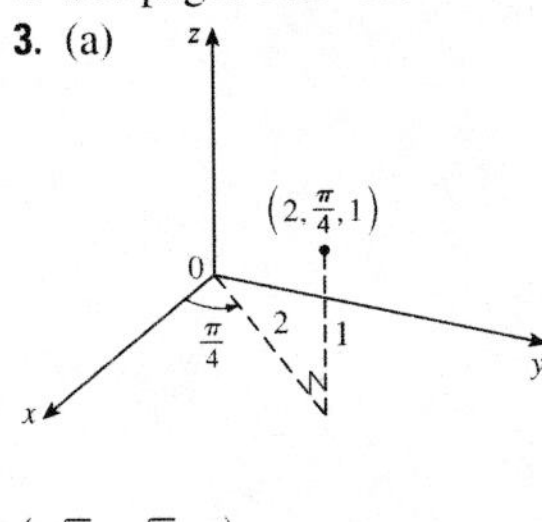

$(\sqrt{2}, \sqrt{2}, 1)$

(b)

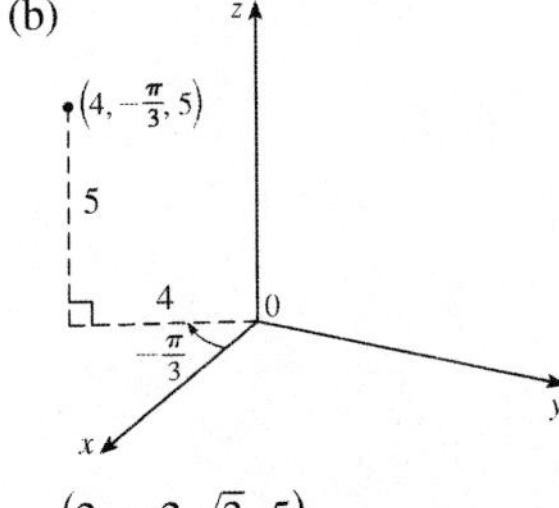

$(2, -2\sqrt{3}, 5)$

5. (a) $(\sqrt{2}, 7\pi/4, 4)$ (b) $(2, 4\pi/3, 2)$

7. (a) (b)

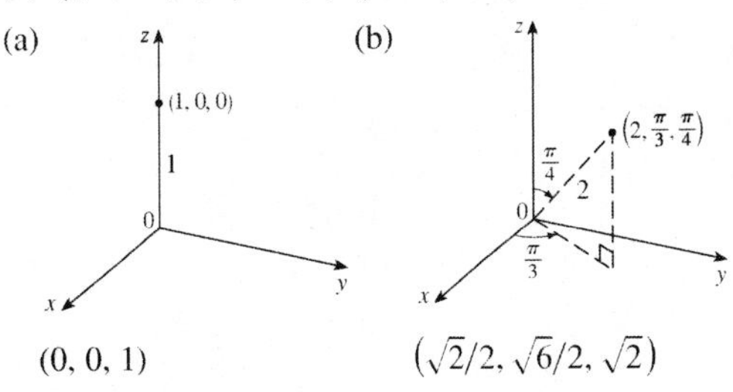

(a) $(0, 0, 1)$ (b) $(\sqrt{2}/2, \sqrt{6}/2, \sqrt{2})$

9. (a) $(4, \pi/3, \pi/6)$ (b) $(\sqrt{2}, 3\pi/2, 3\pi/4)$

11. Vertical half-plane through the z-axis **13.** Half-cone

15. Circular paraboloid

17. Circular cylinder, radius 1, axis parallel to the z-axis

19. Sphere, radius $\frac{1}{2}$, center $(0, \frac{1}{2}, 0)$

21. (a) $r = 2 \sin \theta$ (b) $\rho \sin \phi = 2 \sin \theta$

23. (a) $z = 6 - r(3 \cos \theta + 2 \sin \theta)$
(b) $\rho(3 \sin \phi \cos \theta + 2 \sin \phi \sin \theta + \cos \phi) = 6$

25. 

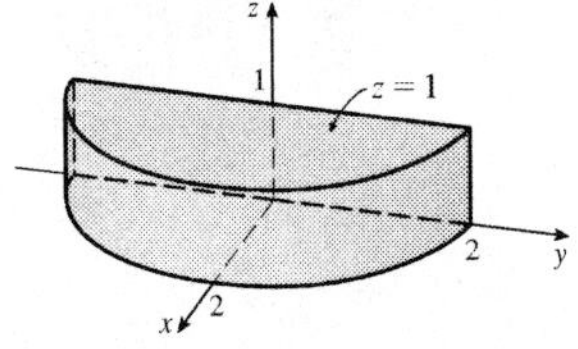

27. 

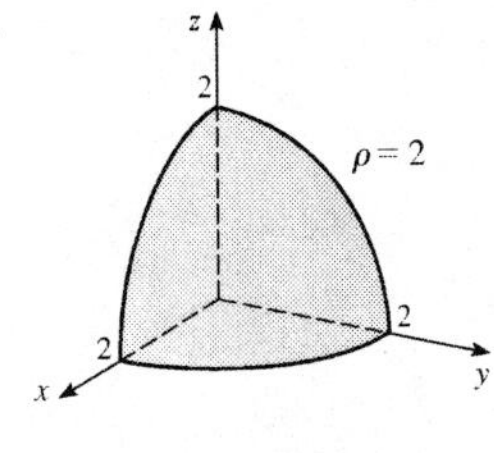

29.

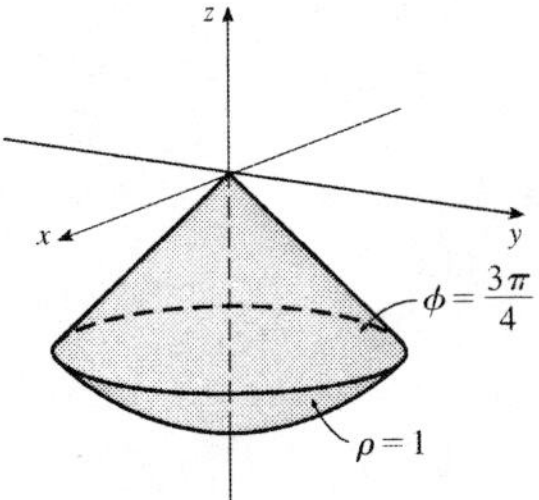

31. Cylindrical coordinates: $6 \leqslant r \leqslant 7$, $0 \leqslant \theta \leqslant 2\pi$, $0 \leqslant z \leqslant 20$

33. $0 \leqslant \phi \leqslant \pi/4$, $0 \leqslant \rho \leqslant \cos \phi$

35.

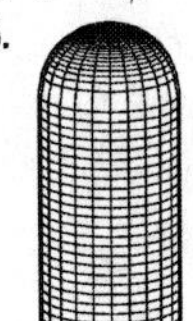

CHAPTER 9 REVIEW ■ PAGE 688

True-False Quiz

1. True **3.** True **5.** True **7.** True **9.** True
11. False **13.** False **15.** False **17.** True

Exercises

1. (a) $(x + 1)^2 + (y - 2)^2 + (z - 1)^2 = 69$
(b) $(y - 2)^2 + (z - 1)^2 = 68$, $x = 0$
(c) Center $(4, -1, -3)$, radius 5

3. $\mathbf{u} \cdot \mathbf{v} = 3\sqrt{2}$; $|\mathbf{u} \times \mathbf{v}| = 3\sqrt{2}$; out of the page
5. $-2, -4$ **7.** (a) 2 (b) -2 (c) -2 (d) 0
9. $\cos^{-1}(\frac{1}{3}) \approx 71°$ **11.** (a) $\langle 4, -3, 4 \rangle$ (b) $\sqrt{41}/2$
13. 166 N, 114 N
15. $x = 4 - 3t, y = -1 + 2t, z = 2 + 3t$
17. $x = -2 + 2t, y = 2 - t, z = 4 + 5t$
19. $-4x + 3y + z = -14$ **21.** $x + y + z = 4$
23. Skew **25.** (a) $22/\sqrt{26}$ (b) $3/\sqrt{2}$
27. $\{(x, y) \mid x > y^2\}$

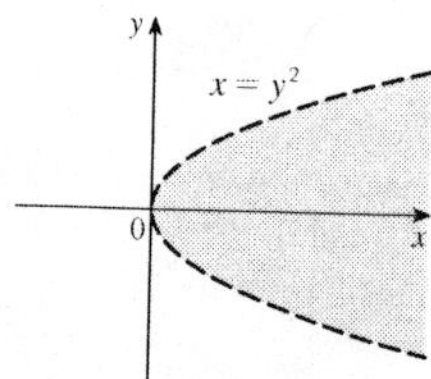

29.

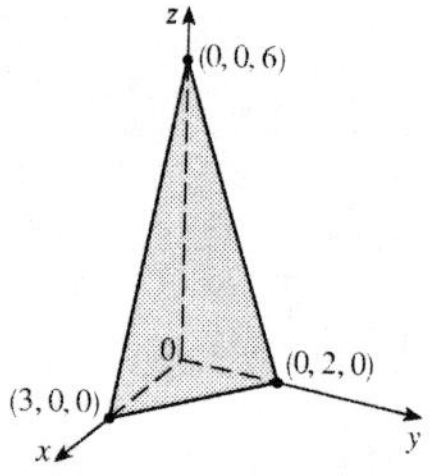

31.

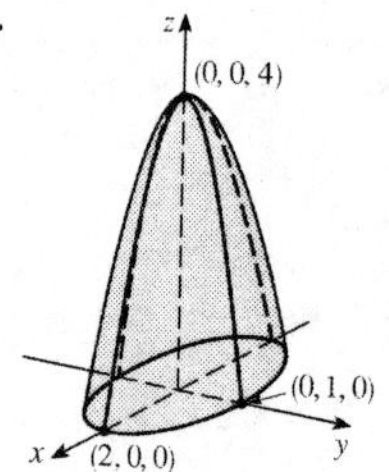

33. Ellipsoid

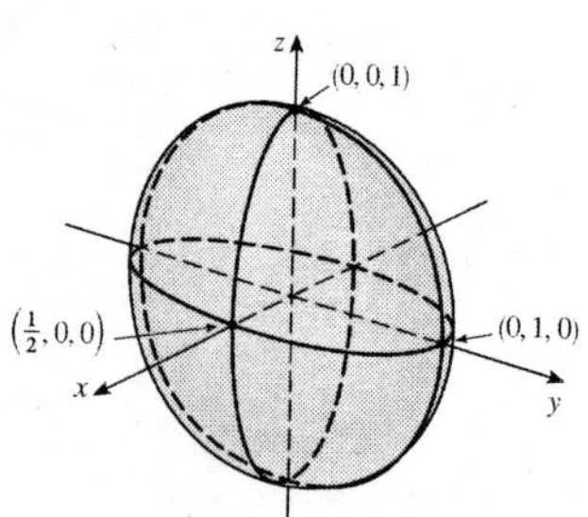

35. Circular cylinder

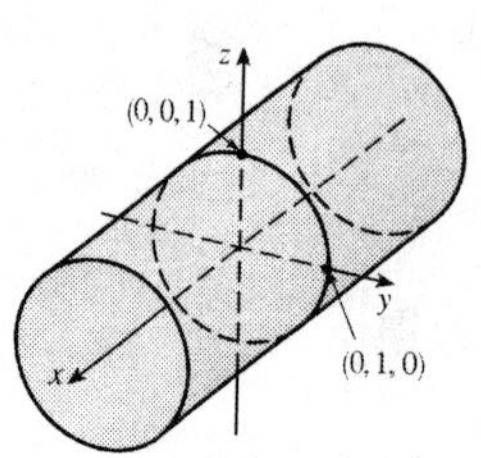

37. $(\sqrt{3}, 3, 2), (4, \pi/3, \pi/3)$
39. $(2\sqrt{2}, 2\sqrt{2}, 4\sqrt{3}), (4, \pi/4, 4\sqrt{3})$
41. $r^2 + z^2 = 4, \rho = 2$ **43.** $z = 4r^2$

FOCUS ON PROBLEM SOLVING ■ PAGE 691

1. $(\sqrt{3} - \frac{3}{2})$ m
3. (a) $(x + 1)/(-2c) = (y - c)/(c^2 - 1) = (z - c)/(c^2 + 1)$
(b) $x^2 + y^2 = t^2 + 1, z = t$ (c) $4\pi/3$
5. 20

CHAPTER 10

EXERCISES 10.1 ■ PAGE 699

1. $(-1, 2]$ **3.** $\langle -1, \pi/2, 0 \rangle$

5.

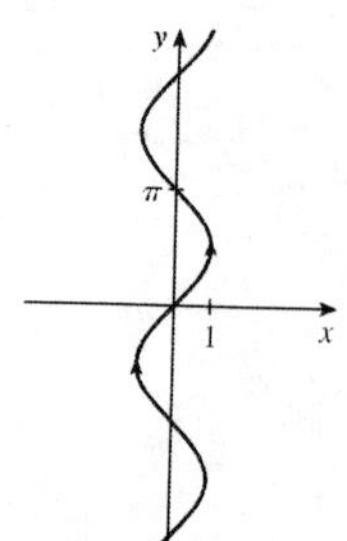

7.

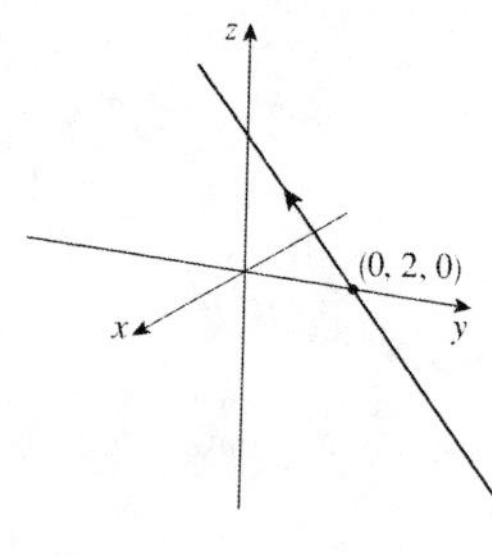

9.

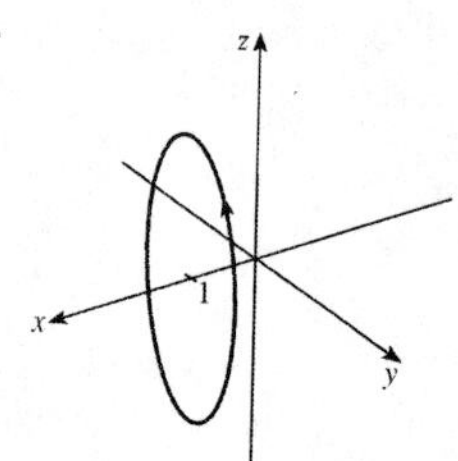

11.

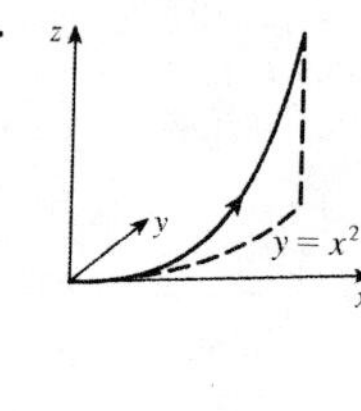

13.

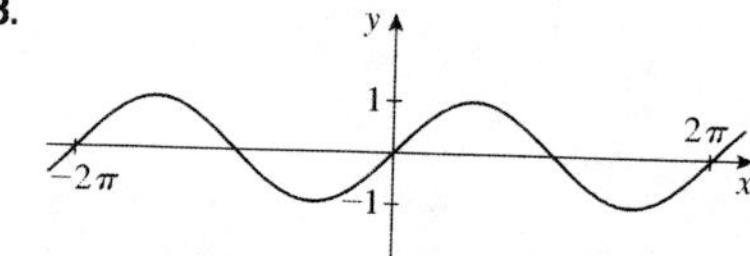

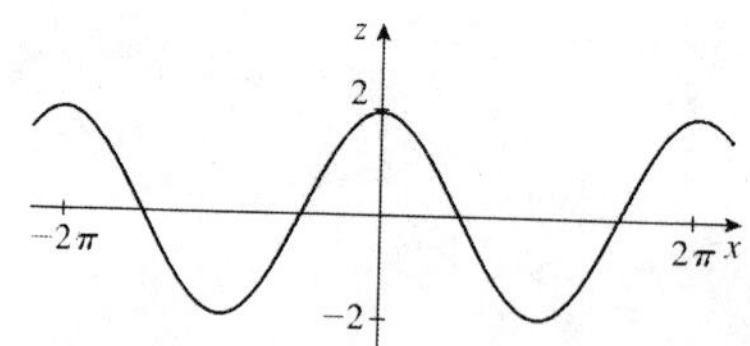

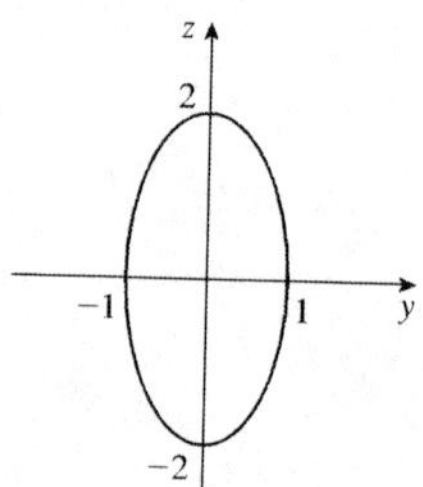

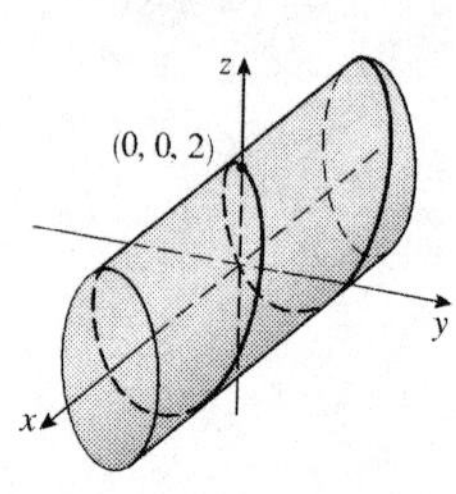

15. $\mathbf{r}(t) = \langle t, 2t, 3t \rangle, 0 \leq t \leq 1$;
$x = t, y = 2t, z = 3t, 0 \leq t \leq 1$
17. $\mathbf{r}(t) = \langle 3t + 1, 2t - 1, 5t + 2 \rangle, 0 \leq t \leq 1$;
$x = 3t + 1, y = 2t - 1, z = 5t + 2, 0 \leq t \leq 1$
19. II **21.** V **23.** IV

11.

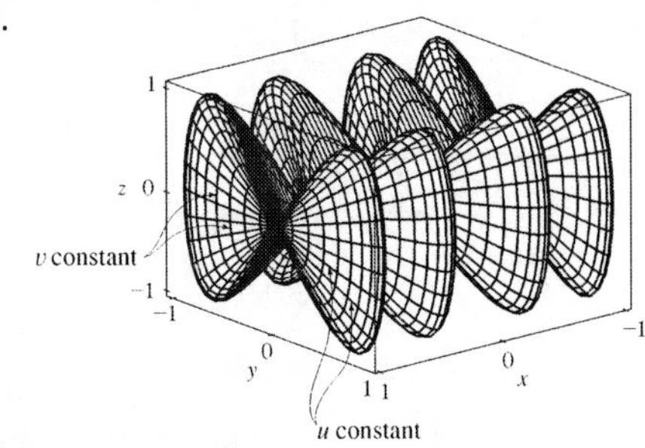

13. IV **15.** II **17.** III

19. $x = 1 + u + v, y = 2 + u - v, z = -3 - u + v$

21. $x = x, z = z, y = \sqrt{1 - x^2 + z^2}$

23. $x = 2 \sin \phi \cos \theta, y = 2 \sin \phi \sin \theta,$
$z = 2 \cos \phi, 0 \leqslant \phi \leqslant \pi/4, 0 \leqslant \theta \leqslant 2\pi$
$\left[\text{or } x = x, y = y, z = \sqrt{4 - x^2 - y^2}, x^2 + y^2 \leqslant 2\right]$

25. $x = x, y = 4 \cos \theta, z = 4 \sin \theta, 0 \leqslant x \leqslant 5, 0 \leqslant \theta \leqslant 2\pi$

29. $x = x, y = e^{-x} \cos \theta,$
$z = e^{-x} \sin \theta, 0 \leqslant x \leqslant 3,$
$0 \leqslant \theta \leqslant 2\pi$

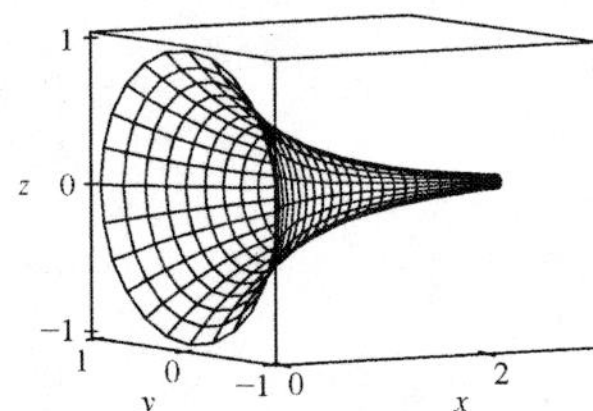

31. (b)

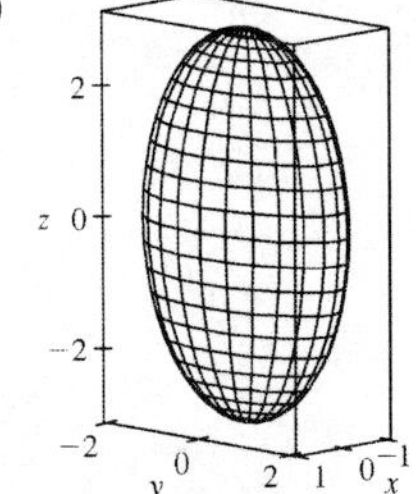

33. (a) Direction reverses (b) Number of coils doubles

CHAPTER 10 REVIEW ■ PAGE 733

True-False Quiz

1. True **3.** False **5.** False **7.** True **9.** False
11. True

Exercises

1. (a)

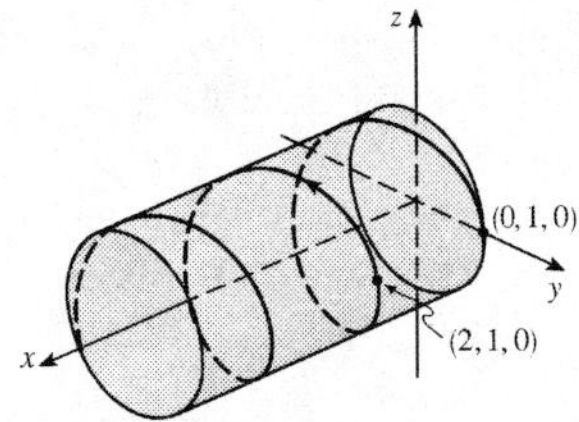

(b) $\mathbf{r}'(t) = \mathbf{i} - \pi \sin \pi t\, \mathbf{j} + \pi \cos \pi t\, \mathbf{k}$,
$\mathbf{r}''(t) = -\pi^2 \cos \pi t\, \mathbf{j} - \pi^2 \sin \pi t\, \mathbf{k}$

3. $\mathbf{r}(t) = 4 \cos t\, \mathbf{i} + 4 \sin t\, \mathbf{j} + (5 - 4 \cos t)\mathbf{k}, 0 \leqslant t \leqslant 2\pi$

5. $\frac{1}{3}\mathbf{i} - (2/\pi^2)\mathbf{j} + (2/\pi)\mathbf{k}$ **7.** 86.631 **9.** $\pi/2$

11. (a) $\langle t^2, t, 1 \rangle / \sqrt{t^4 + t^2 + 1}$
(b) $\langle 2t, 1 - t^4, -2t^3 - t \rangle / \sqrt{t^8 + 4t^6 + 2t^4 + 5t^2}$
(c) $\sqrt{t^8 + 4t^6 + 2t^4 + 5t^2}/(t^4 + t^2 + 1)^2$

13. $12/17^{3/2}$ **15.** $x - 2y + 2\pi = 0$

17. $\mathbf{v}(t) = (1 + \ln t)\mathbf{i} + \mathbf{j} - e^{-t}\mathbf{k}$,
$|\mathbf{v}(t)| = \sqrt{2 + 2 \ln t + (\ln t)^2 + e^{-2t}}, \mathbf{a}(t) = (1/t)\mathbf{i} + e^{-t}\mathbf{k}$

19. (a) About 3.8 ft above the ground, 60.8 ft from the athlete
(b) ≈21.4 ft (c) ≈64.2 ft from the athlete

21. $x = 2 \sin \phi \cos \theta, y = 2 \sin \phi \sin \theta, z = 2 \cos \phi,$
$0 \leqslant \theta \leqslant 2\pi, \pi/3 \leqslant \phi \leqslant 2\pi/3$

23. $\pi|t|$

FOCUS ON PROBLEM SOLVING ■ PAGE 735

1. (a) $\mathbf{v} = \omega R(-\sin \omega t\, \mathbf{i} + \cos \omega t\, \mathbf{j})$ (c) $\mathbf{a} = -\omega^2 \mathbf{r}$

3. (a) 90°, $v_0^2/(2g)$

5. (a) ≈0.94 ft to the right of the table's edge, ≈15 ft/s
(b) ≈7.6° (c) ≈2.13 ft to the right of the table's edge

7. 56°

9. $\mathbf{r}(u, v) = \mathbf{c} + u\,\mathbf{a} + v\,\mathbf{b}$ where $\mathbf{a} = \langle a_1, a_2, a_3 \rangle$,
$\mathbf{b} = \langle b_1, b_2, b_3 \rangle, \mathbf{c} = \langle c_1, c_2, c_3 \rangle$

CHAPTER 11

EXERCISES 11.1 ■ PAGE 745

1. (a) −27; a temperature of −15°C with wind blowing at 40 km/h feels equivalent to about −27°C without wind.
(b) When the temperature is −20°C, what wind speed gives a wind chill of −30°C? 20 km/h
(c) With a wind speed of 20 km/h, what temperature gives a wind chill of −49°C? −35°C
(d) A function of wind speed that gives wind-chill values when the temperature is −5°C
(e) A function of temperature that gives wind-chill values when the wind speed is 50 km/h

3. Yes

5. $\{(x, y) \mid \frac{1}{9}x^2 + y^2 < 1\}, (-\infty, \ln 9]$

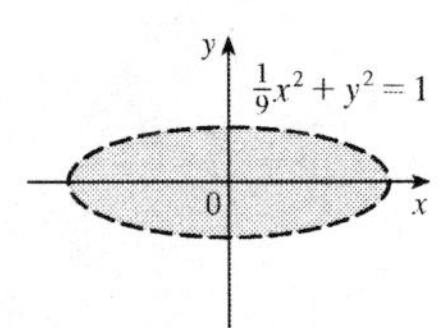

7. (a) 3 (b) $\{(x, y, z) \mid x^2 + y^2 + z^2 < 4, x \geqslant 0, y \geqslant 0, z \geqslant 0\}$, interior of a sphere of radius 2, center the origin, in the first octant

9. ≈56, ≈35 **11.** 11°C, 19.5°C **13.** Steep; nearly flat

15.

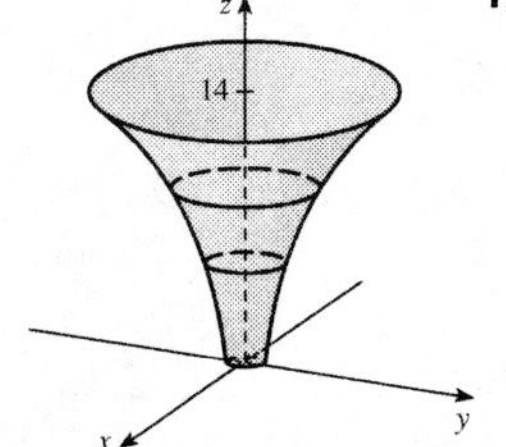

17.

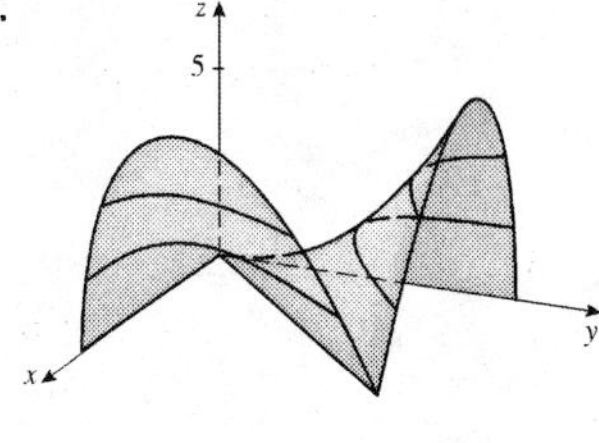

19. $(y - 2x)^2 = k$

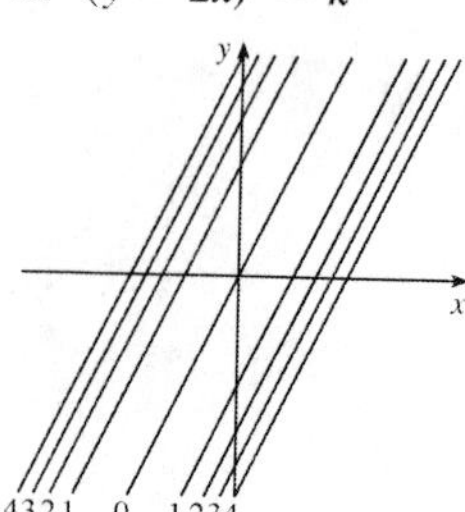

21. $y = -\sqrt{x} + k$

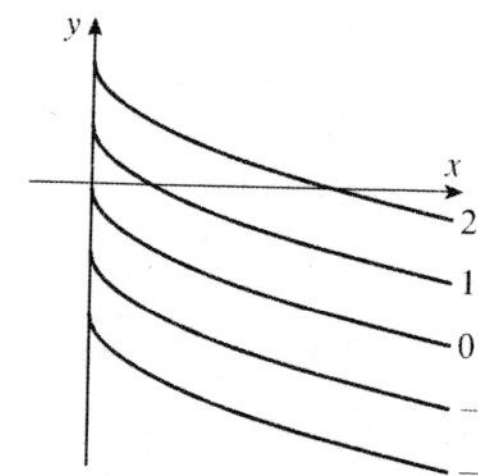

23. $y = ke^{-x}$

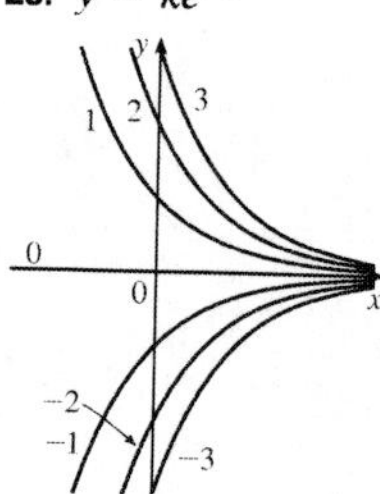

25. $y^2 - x^2 = k^2$

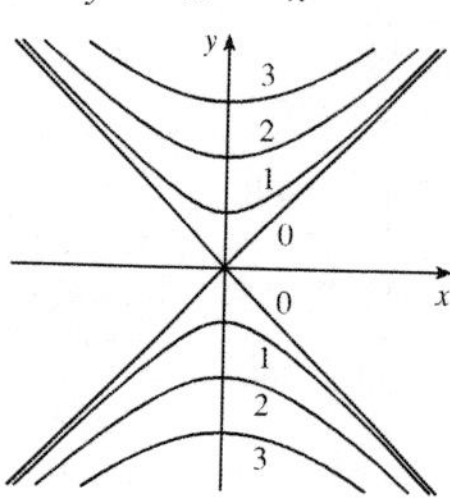

27. $x^2 + 9y^2 = k$

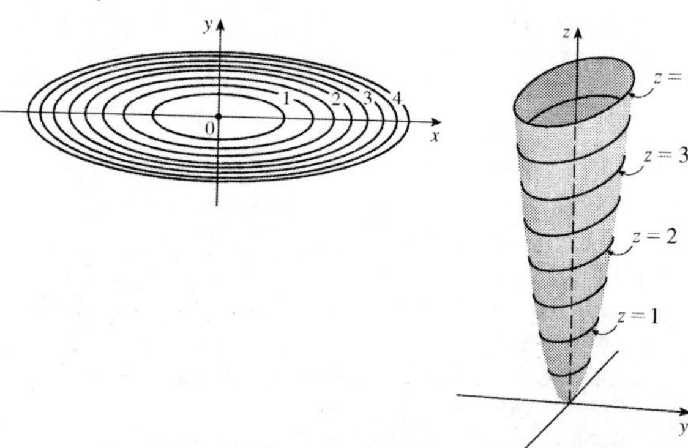

29.

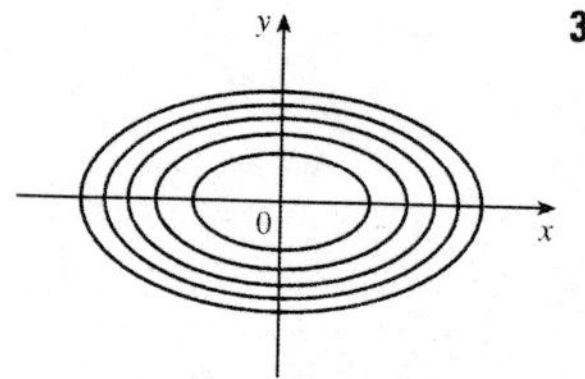

31.

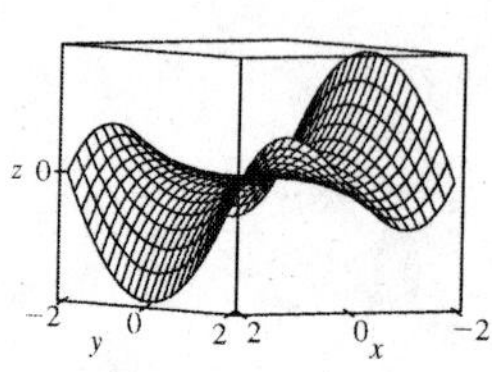

33.

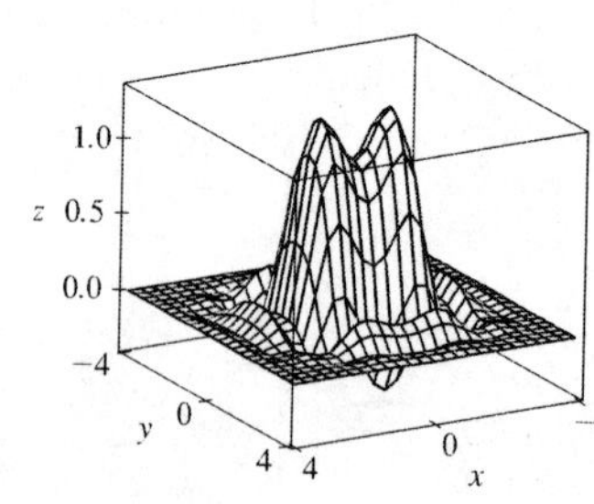

35. (a) C (b) II **37.** (a) F (b) I
39. (a) B (b) VI **41.** Family of parallel planes
43. Family of circular cylinders with axis the x-axis ($k > 0$)
45. (a) Shift the graph of f upward 2 units
(b) Stretch the graph of f vertically by a factor of 2
(c) Reflect the graph of f about the xy-plane
(d) Reflect the graph of f about the xy-plane and then shift it upward 2 units
47. If $c = 0$, the graph is a cylindrical surface. For $c > 0$, the level curves are ellipses. The graph curves upward as we leave the origin, and the steepness increases as c increases. For $c < 0$, the level curves are hyperbolas. The graph curves upward in the y-direction and downward, approaching the xy-plane, in the x-direction giving a saddle-shaped appearance near (0, 0, 1).
49. (b) $y = 0.75x + 0.01$

EXERCISES 11.2 ■ PAGE 755

1. Nothing; if f is continuous, $f(3, 1) = 6$ **3.** $-\frac{5}{2}$
5. 1 **7.** Does not exist **9.** Does not exist **11.** 0
13. Does not exist **15.** 2 **17.** 1 **19.** Does not exist
21. The graph shows that the function approaches different numbers along different lines.
23. $h(x, y) = (2x + 3y - 6)^2 + \sqrt{2x + 3y - 6}$; $\{(x, y) \mid 2x + 3y \geq 6\}$
25. Along the line $y = x$ **27.** $\{(x, y) \mid y \geq 0\}$
29. $\{(x, y) \mid x^2 + y^2 > 4\}$ **31.** $\{(x, y, z) \mid y \geq 0, y \neq \sqrt{x^2 + z^2}\}$
33. $\{(x, y) \mid (x, y) \neq (0, 0)\}$ **35.** 0
37. 0
39.

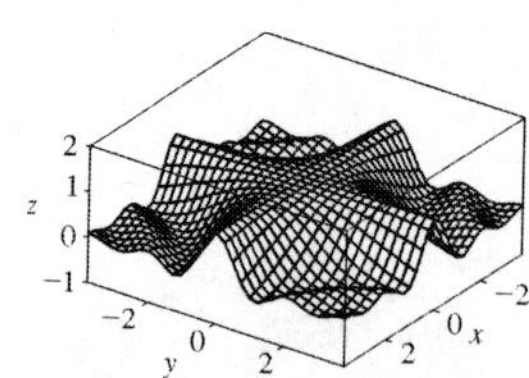

f is continuous on $\mathbb{R}^2$

EXERCISES 11.3 ■ PAGE 766

1. (a) The rate of change of temperature as longitude varies, with latitude and time fixed; the rate of change as only latitude varies; the rate of change as only time varies.
(b) Positive, negative, positive
3. (a) $f_T(-15, 30) \approx 1.3$; for a temperature of −15°C and wind speed of 30 km/h, the wind-chill index rises by 1.3°C for each degree the temperature increases. $f_v(-15, 30) \approx -0.15$; for a temperature of −15°C and wind speed of 30 km/h, the wind-chill index decreases by 0.15°C for each km/h the wind speed increases.
(b) Positive, negative (c) 0
5. (a) Positive (b) Negative
7. (a) Positive (b) Negative
9. $c = f$, $b = f_x$, $a = f_y$

11. $f_x(1, 2) = -8 =$ slope of C_1, $f_y(1, 2) = -4 =$ slope of C_2

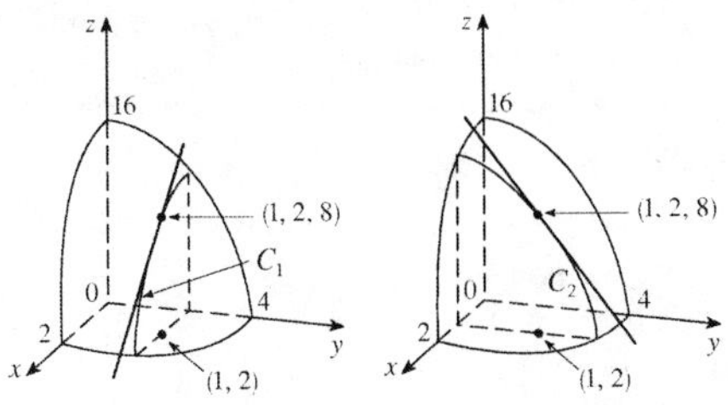

13. $f_x = 2x + 2xy$, $f_y = 2y + x^2$

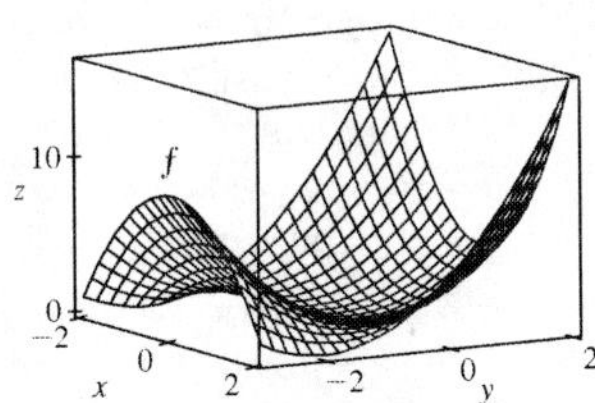

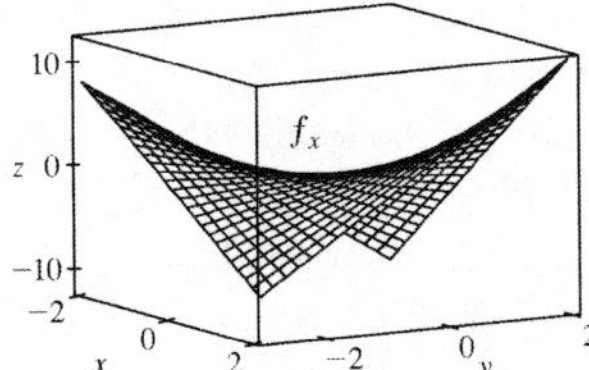

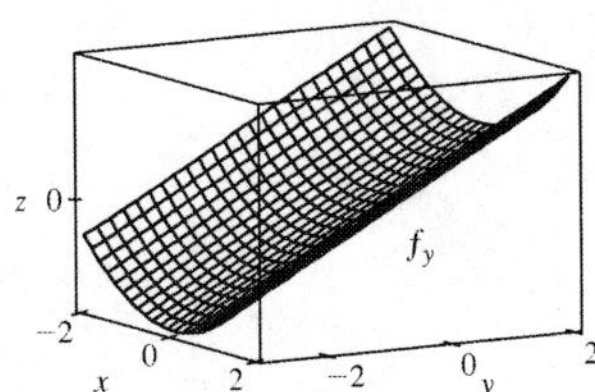

15. $f_x(x, y) = -3y$, $f_y(x, y) = 5y^4 - 3x$

17. $f_x(x, t) = -\pi e^{-t} \sin \pi x$, $f_t(x, t) = -e^{-t} \cos \pi x$

19. $\partial z/\partial x = 20(2x + 3y)^9$, $\partial z/\partial y = 30(2x + 3y)^9$

21. $f_x(x, y) = 2y/(x + y)^2$, $f_y(x, y) = -2x/(x + y)^2$

23. $\partial w/\partial \alpha = \cos \alpha \cos \beta$, $\partial w/\partial \beta = -\sin \alpha \sin \beta$

25. $f_r(r, s) = \dfrac{2r^2}{r^2 + s^2} + \ln(r^2 + s^2)$, $f_s(r, s) = \dfrac{2rs}{r^2 + s^2}$

27. $\partial u/\partial t = e^{w/t}(1 - w/t)$, $\partial u/\partial w = e^{w/t}$

29. $f_x = z - 10xy^3z^4$, $f_y = -15x^2y^2z^4$, $f_z = x - 20x^2y^3z^3$

31. $\partial w/\partial x = 1/(x + 2y + 3z)$, $\partial w/\partial y = 2/(x + 2y + 3z)$, $\partial w/\partial z = 3/(x + 2y + 3z)$

33. $\partial u/\partial x = y \sin^{-1}(yz)$, $\partial u/\partial y = x \sin^{-1}(yz) + xyz/\sqrt{1 - y^2z^2}$, $\partial u/\partial z = xy^2/\sqrt{1 - y^2z^2}$

35. $f_x = yz^2 \tan(yt)$, $f_y = xyz^2t \sec^2(yt) + xz^2 \tan(yt)$, $f_z = 2xyz \tan(yt)$, $f_t = xy^2z^2 \sec^2(yt)$

37. $\partial u/\partial x_i = x_i/\sqrt{x_1^2 + x_2^2 + \cdots + x_n^2}$

39. $\frac{1}{5}$ **41.** $\frac{1}{4}$

43. $f_x(x, y) = y^2 - 3x^2y$, $f_y(x, y) = 2xy - x^3$

45. $\dfrac{\partial z}{\partial x} = \dfrac{3yz - 2x}{2z - 3xy}$, $\dfrac{\partial z}{\partial y} = \dfrac{3xz - 2y}{2z - 3xy}$

47. $\dfrac{\partial z}{\partial x} = \dfrac{1 + y^2z^2}{1 + y + y^2z^2}$, $\dfrac{\partial z}{\partial y} = \dfrac{-z}{1 + y + y^2z^2}$

49. (a) $f'(x), g'(y)$ (b) $f'(x + y), f'(x + y)$

51. $f_{xx} = 6xy^5 + 24x^2y$, $f_{xy} = 15x^2y^4 + 8x^3 = f_{yx}$, $f_{yy} = 20x^3y^3$

53. $w_{uu} = v^2/(u^2 + v^2)^{3/2}$, $w_{uv} = -uv/(u^2 + v^2)^{3/2} = w_{vu}$, $w_{vv} = u^2/(u^2 + v^2)^{3/2}$

55. $z_{xx} = -2x/(1 + x^2)^2$, $z_{xy} = 0 = z_{yx}$, $z_{yy} = -2y/(1 + y^2)^2$

59. $12xy$, $72xy$

61. $24 \sin(4x + 3y + 2z)$, $12 \sin(4x + 3y + 2z)$

63. $\theta e^{r\theta}(2 \sin \theta + \theta \cos \theta + r\theta \sin \theta)$ **65.** $6yz^2$

67. ≈12.2, ≈16.8, ≈23.25 **79.** R^2/R_1^2

85. No **87.** $x = 1 + t$, $y = 2$, $z = 2 - 2t$ **89.** -2

91. (a)

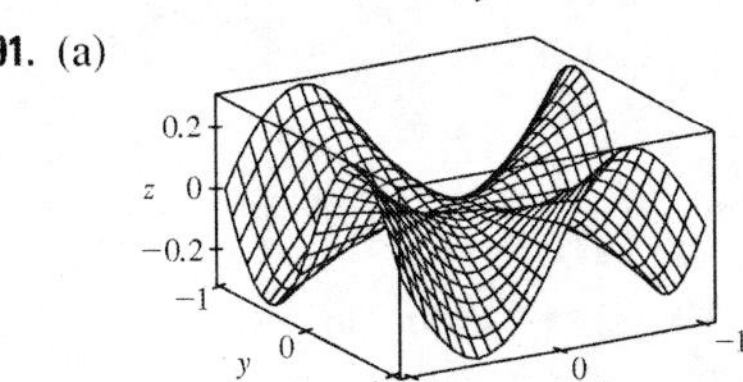

(b) $f_x(x, y) = \dfrac{x^4y + 4x^2y^3 - y^5}{(x^2 + y^2)^2}$, $f_y(x, y) = \dfrac{x^5 - 4x^3y^2 - xy^4}{(x^2 + y^2)^2}$

(c) 0, 0 (e) No, since f_{xy} and f_{yx} are not continuous.

EXERCISES 11.4 ■ PAGE 778

1. $z = -7x - 6y + 5$ **3.** $x + y - 2z = 0$ **5.** $z = y$

7.

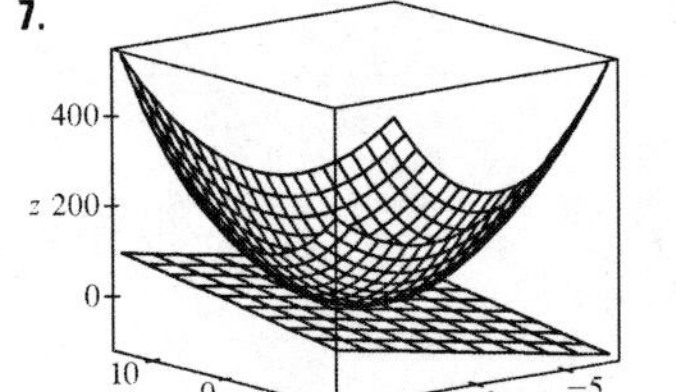

9.

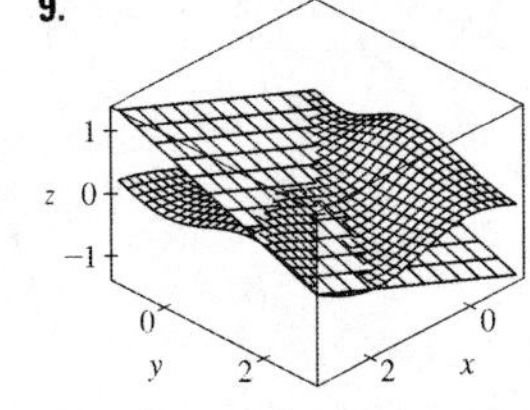

11. $2x + \frac{1}{4}y - 1$ **13.** $\frac{1}{9}x - \frac{2}{9}y + \frac{2}{3}$ **17.** 6.3

19. $\frac{3}{7}x + \frac{2}{7}y + \frac{6}{7}z$; 6.9914 **21.** $4T + H - 329$; 129°F

23. $dz = 3x^2 \ln(y^2)\, dx + (2x^3/y)\, dy$

25. $dm = 5p^4q^3\, dp + 3p^5q^2\, dq$

27. $dR = \beta^2 \cos \gamma\, d\alpha + 2\alpha\beta \cos \gamma\, d\beta - \alpha\beta^2 \sin \gamma\, d\gamma$

29. $\Delta z = 0.9225$, $dz = 0.9$ **31.** 5.4 cm² **33.** 16 cm³

35. 2.3% **37.** $\frac{1}{17} \approx 0.059\ \Omega$ **39.** $3x - y + 3z = 3$

41. $-x + 2z = 1$ **43.** $x - y + z = 2$

45. $\varepsilon_1 = \Delta x$, $\varepsilon_2 = \Delta y$

EXERCISES 11.5 ■ PAGE 786

1. $(2x + y) \cos t + (2y + x)e^t$

3. $[(x/t) - y \sin t]/\sqrt{1 + x^2 + y^2}$

5. $e^{y/z}[2t - (x/z) - (2xy/z^2)]$

7. $\partial z/\partial s = 2xy^3 \cos t + 3x^2y^2 \sin t$, $\partial z/\partial t = -2sxy^3 \sin t + 3sx^2y^2 \cos t$

9. $\partial z/\partial s = t^2 \cos \theta \cos \phi - 2st \sin \theta \sin \phi$, $\partial z/\partial t = 2st \cos \theta \cos \phi - s^2 \sin \theta \sin \phi$

11. $\dfrac{\partial z}{\partial s} = e^r\left(t\cos\theta - \dfrac{s}{\sqrt{s^2+t^2}}\sin\theta\right)$,
$\dfrac{\partial z}{\partial t} = e^r\left(s\cos\theta - \dfrac{t}{\sqrt{s^2+t^2}}\sin\theta\right)$
13. 62 **15.** 7, 2
17. $\dfrac{\partial u}{\partial r} = \dfrac{\partial u}{\partial x}\dfrac{\partial x}{\partial r} + \dfrac{\partial u}{\partial y}\dfrac{\partial y}{\partial r}$, $\dfrac{\partial u}{\partial s} = \dfrac{\partial u}{\partial x}\dfrac{\partial x}{\partial s} + \dfrac{\partial u}{\partial y}\dfrac{\partial y}{\partial s}$,
$\dfrac{\partial u}{\partial t} = \dfrac{\partial u}{\partial x}\dfrac{\partial x}{\partial t} + \dfrac{\partial u}{\partial y}\dfrac{\partial y}{\partial t}$
19. $\dfrac{\partial w}{\partial x} = \dfrac{\partial w}{\partial r}\dfrac{\partial r}{\partial x} + \dfrac{\partial w}{\partial s}\dfrac{\partial s}{\partial x} + \dfrac{\partial w}{\partial t}\dfrac{\partial t}{\partial x}$,
$\dfrac{\partial w}{\partial y} = \dfrac{\partial w}{\partial r}\dfrac{\partial r}{\partial y} + \dfrac{\partial w}{\partial s}\dfrac{\partial s}{\partial y} + \dfrac{\partial w}{\partial t}\dfrac{\partial t}{\partial y}$
21. 85, 178, 54 **23.** $\frac{9}{7}, \frac{9}{7}$ **25.** 36, 24, 30
27. $\dfrac{\sin(x-y)+e^y}{\sin(x-y)-xe^y}$ **29.** $\dfrac{3yz-2x}{2z-3xy}, \dfrac{3xz-2y}{2z-3xy}$
31. $\dfrac{1+y^2z^2}{1+y+y^2z^2}, -\dfrac{z}{1+y+y^2z^2}$
33. 2°C/s **35.** ≈ -0.33 m/s per minute
37. (a) 6 m³/s (b) 10 m²/s (c) 0 m/s
39. ≈ -0.27 L/s **41.** $-1/(12\sqrt{3})$ rad/s
43. (a) $\partial z/\partial r = (\partial z/\partial x)\cos\theta + (\partial z/\partial y)\sin\theta$,
$\partial z/\partial\theta = -(\partial z/\partial x)r\sin\theta + (\partial z/\partial y)r\cos\theta$
49. $4rs\,\partial^2 z/\partial x^2 + (4r^2+4s^2)\partial^2 z/\partial x\,\partial y + 4rs\,\partial^2 z/\partial y^2 + 2\,\partial z/\partial y$

EXERCISES 11.6 ■ PAGE 799

1. ≈ -0.08 mb/km **3.** ≈ 0.778 **5.** $2 + \sqrt{3}/2$
7. (a) $\nabla f(x, y) = \langle 2\cos(2x+3y), 3\cos(2x+3y)\rangle$
(b) $\langle 2, 3\rangle$ (c) $\sqrt{3} - \frac{3}{2}$
9. (a) $\langle e^{2yz}, 2xze^{2yz}, 2xye^{2yz}\rangle$ (b) $\langle 1, 12, 0\rangle$ (c) $-\frac{22}{3}$
11. 23/10 **13.** $-8/\sqrt{10}$ **15.** $4/\sqrt{30}$ **17.** $9/(2\sqrt{5})$
19. 2/5 **21.** 1, $\langle 0, 1\rangle$ **23.** 1, $\langle 3, 6, -2\rangle$
25. (b) $\langle -12, 92\rangle$
27. All points on the line $y = x + 1$
29. (a) $-40/(3\sqrt{3})$
31. (a) $32/\sqrt{3}$ (b) $\langle 38, 6, 12\rangle$ (c) $2\sqrt{406}$
33. $\frac{327}{13}$ **37.** $\frac{774}{25}$
39. (a) $x + y + z = 11$ (b) $x - 3 = y - 3 = z - 5$
41. (a) $4x - 5y - z = 4$ (b) $\dfrac{x-2}{4} = \dfrac{y-1}{-5} = \dfrac{z+1}{-1}$
43. (a) $x + y - z = 1$ (b) $x - 1 = y = -z$
45.

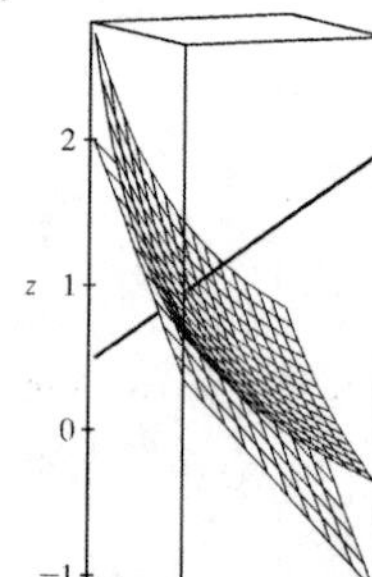

47. $\langle 2, 3\rangle$, $2x + 3y = 12$

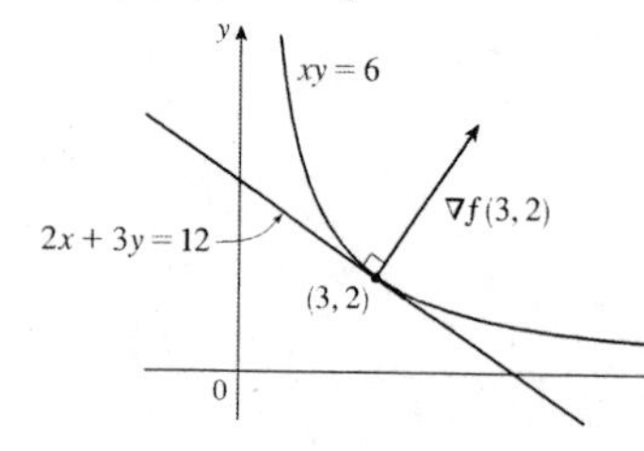

51. No **57.** $x = -1 - 10t, y = 1 - 16t, z = 2 - 12t$
61. If $\mathbf{u} = \langle a, b\rangle$ and $\mathbf{v} = \langle c, d\rangle$, then $af_x + bf_y$ and $cf_x + df_y$ are known, so we solve linear equations for f_x and f_y.

EXERCISES 11.7 ■ PAGE 809

1. (a) f has a local minimum at (1, 1).
(b) f has a saddle point at (1, 1).
3. Local minimum at (1, 1), saddle point at (0, 0)
5. Minimum $f(\frac{1}{3}, -\frac{2}{3}) = -\frac{1}{3}$
7. Minima $f(1, 1) = 0$, $f(-1, -1) = 0$, saddle point at (0, 0)
9. Minimum $f(2, 1) = -8$, saddle point at (0, 0)
11. None **13.** Minimum $f(0, 0) = 0$, saddle points at $(\pm 1, 0)$
15. Minima $f(0, 1) = f(\pi, -1) = f(2\pi, 1) = -1$,
saddle points at $(\pi/2, 0)$, $(3\pi/2, 0)$
19. Minima $f(1, \pm 1) = 3$, $f(-1, \pm 1) = 3$
21. Maximum $f(\pi/3, \pi/3) = 3\sqrt{3}/2$,
minimum $f(5\pi/3, 5\pi/3) = -3\sqrt{3}/2$, saddle point at (π, π)
23. Minima $f(-1.714, 0) \approx -9.200$, $f(1.402, 0) \approx 0.242$,
saddle point (0.312, 0), lowest point $(-1.714, 0, -9.200)$
25. Maxima $f(-1.267, 0) \approx 1.310$, $f(1.629, \pm 1.063) \approx 8.105$,
saddle points $(-0.259, 0)$, $(1.526, 0)$,
highest points $(1.629, \pm 1.063, 8.105)$
27. Maximum $f(2, 0) = 9$, minimum $f(0, 3) = -14$
29. Maximum $f(\pm 1, 1) = 7$, minimum $f(0, 0) = 4$
31. Maximum $f(1, 0) = 2$, minimum $f(-1, 0) = -2$
33.

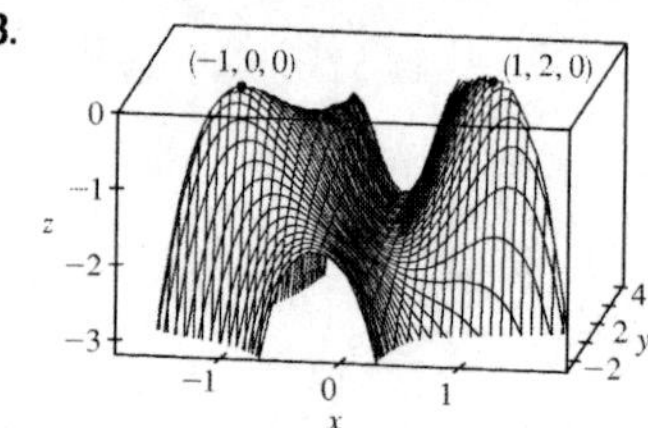

35. $\sqrt{3}$ **37.** $(2, 1, \sqrt{5})$, $(2, 1, -\sqrt{5})$ **39.** $\frac{100}{3}, \frac{100}{3}, \frac{100}{3}$
41. $8r^3/(3\sqrt{3})$ **43.** $\frac{4}{3}$ **45.** Cube, edge length $c/12$
47. Square base of side 40 cm, height 20 cm **49.** $L^3/(3\sqrt{3})$

EXERCISES 11.8 ■ PAGE 818

1. ≈ 59, 30
3. No maximum, minimum $f(1, 1) = f(-1, -1) = 2$
5. Maximum $f(\pm 2, 1) = 4$, minimum $f(\pm 2, -1) = -4$
7. Maximum $f(1, 3, 5) = 70$, minimum $f(-1, -3, -5) = -70$
9. Maximum $2/\sqrt{3}$, minimum $-2/\sqrt{3}$
11. Maximum $\sqrt{3}$, minimum 1
13. Maximum $f(\frac{1}{2}, \frac{1}{2}, \frac{1}{2}, \frac{1}{2}) = 2$,
minimum $f(-\frac{1}{2}, -\frac{1}{2}, -\frac{1}{2}, -\frac{1}{2}) = -2$
15. Maximum $f(1, \sqrt{2}, -\sqrt{2}) = 1 + 2\sqrt{2}$,
minimum $f(1, -\sqrt{2}, \sqrt{2}) = 1 - 2\sqrt{2}$
17. Maximum $\frac{3}{2}$, minimum $\frac{1}{2}$
19. Maximum $f(\pm 1/\sqrt{2}, \mp 1/(2\sqrt{2})) = e^{1/4}$,
minimum $f(\pm 1/\sqrt{2}, \pm 1/(2\sqrt{2})) = e^{-1/4}$
27–37. See Exercises 35–45 in Section 11.7.
39. $L^3/(3\sqrt{3})$

41. Nearest $\left(\frac{1}{2}, \frac{1}{2}, \frac{1}{2}\right)$, farthest $(-1, -1, 2)$
43. Maximum ≈ 9.7938, minimum ≈ -5.3506
45. (a) c/n (b) When $x_1 = x_2 = \cdots = x_n$

CHAPTER 11 REVIEW ■ PAGE 823

True-False Quiz

1. True **3.** False **5.** False **7.** True **9.** False
11. True

Exercises

1. $\{(x, y) \mid y > -x - 1\}$

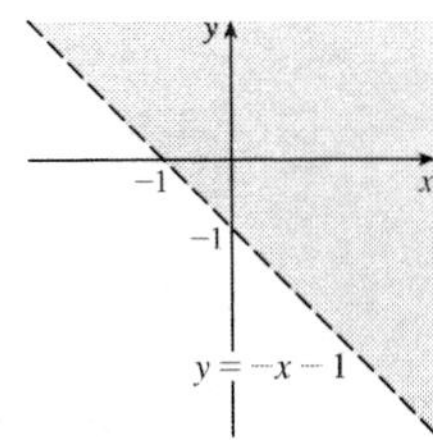

3.

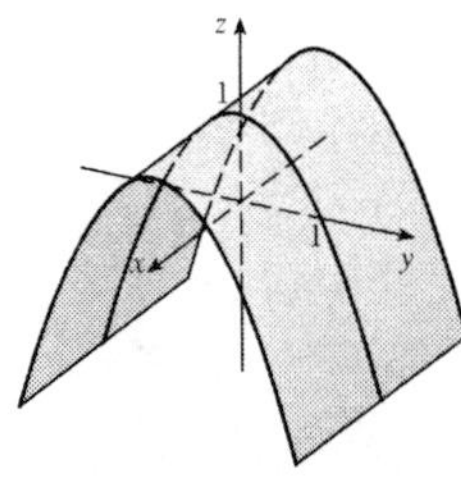

5.

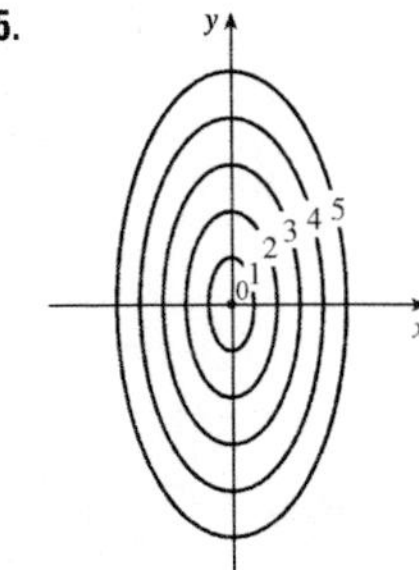

7.

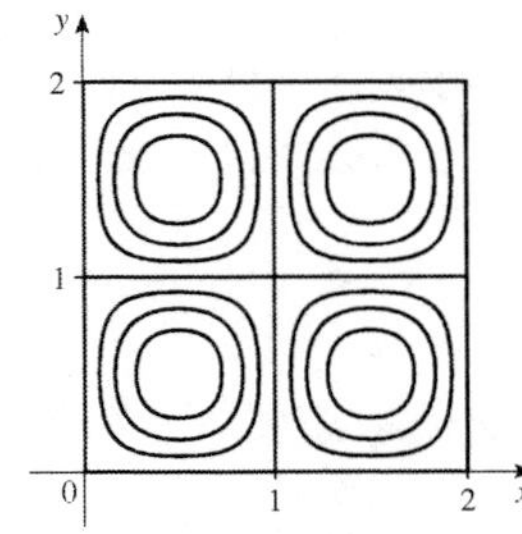

9. $\frac{2}{3}$
11. (a) $\approx 3.5°\text{C/m}, -3.0°\text{C/m}$ (b) $\approx 0.35°\text{C/m}$ by Equation 11.6.9 (Definition 11.6.2 gives $\approx 1.1°\text{C/m}$.)
(c) -0.25
13. $f_x = 1/\sqrt{2x + y^2}$, $f_y = y/\sqrt{2x + y^2}$
15. $g_u = \tan^{-1}v$, $g_v = u/(1 + v^2)$
17. $T_p = \ln(q + e^r)$, $T_q = p/(q + e^r)$, $T_r = pe^r/(q + e^r)$
19. $f_{xx} = 24x$, $f_{xy} = -2y = f_{yx}$, $f_{yy} = -2x$
21. $f_{xx} = k(k - 1)x^{k-2}y^lz^m$, $f_{xy} = klx^{k-1}y^{l-1}z^m = f_{yx}$,
$f_{xz} = kmx^{k-1}y^lz^{m-1} = f_{zx}$, $f_{yy} = l(l - 1)x^ky^{l-2}z^m$,
$f_{yz} = lmx^ky^{l-1}z^{m-1} = f_{zy}$, $f_{zz} = m(m - 1)x^ky^lz^{m-2}$
25. (a) $z = 8x + 4y + 1$ (b) $\dfrac{x - 1}{8} = \dfrac{y + 2}{4} = \dfrac{z - 1}{-1}$
27. (a) $2x - 2y - 3z = 3$ (b) $\dfrac{x - 2}{4} = \dfrac{y + 1}{-4} = \dfrac{z - 1}{-6}$
29. (a) $4x - y - 2z = 6$
(b) $x = 3 + 8t$, $y = 4 - 2t$, $z = 1 - 4t$
31. $\left(2, \frac{1}{2}, -1\right), \left(-2, -\frac{1}{2}, 1\right)$
33. $60x + \frac{24}{5}y + \frac{32}{5}z - 120$; 38.656
35. $2xy^3(1 + 6p) + 3x^2y^2(pe^p + e^p) + 4z^3(p\cos p + \sin p)$
37. $-47, 108$
43. $\langle 2xe^{yz^2}, x^2z^2e^{yz^2}, 2x^2yze^{yz^2}\rangle$ **45.** $-\frac{4}{5}$
47. $\sqrt{145}/2$, $\left\langle 4, \frac{9}{2}\right\rangle$ **49.** $\approx \frac{5}{8}$ knot/mi
51. Minimum $f(-4, 1) = -11$
53. Maximum $f(1, 1) = 1$; saddle points $(0, 0), (0, 3), (3, 0)$
55. Maximum $f(1, 2) = 4$, minimum $f(2, 4) = -64$
57. Maximum $f(-1, 0) = 2$, minima $f(1, \pm 1) = -3$, saddle points $(-1, \pm 1), (1, 0)$
59. Maximum $f\left(\pm\sqrt{2/3}, 1/\sqrt{3}\right) = 2/\left(3\sqrt{3}\right)$, minimum $f\left(\pm\sqrt{2/3}, -1/\sqrt{3}\right) = -2/\left(3\sqrt{3}\right)$
61. Maximum 1, minimum -1
63. $\left(\pm 3^{-1/4}, 3^{-1/4}\sqrt{2}, \pm 3^{1/4}\right), \left(\pm 3^{-1/4}, -3^{-1/4}\sqrt{2}, \pm 3^{1/4}\right)$
65. $P\left(2 - \sqrt{3}\right), P\left(3 - \sqrt{3}\right)/6, P\left(2\sqrt{3} - 3\right)/3$

FOCUS ON PROBLEM SOLVING ■ PAGE 827

1. $L^2W^2, \frac{1}{4}L^2W^2$ **3.** (a) $x = w/3$, base $= w/3$ (b) Yes
9. $\sqrt{3}/2, 3/\sqrt{2}$

CHAPTER 12

EXERCISES 12.1 ■ PAGE 837

1. (a) 288 (b) 144 **3.** (a) $\pi^2/2 \approx 4.935$ (b) 0
5. (a) 4 (b) -8 **7.** $U < V < L$
9. (a) ≈ 248 (b) ≈ 15.5 **11.** 60 **13.** 3
15. 1.141606, 1.143191, 1.143535, 1.143617, 1.143637, 1.143642

EXERCISES 12.2 ■ PAGE 843

1. $500y^3, 3x^2$ **3.** 10 **5.** 2 **7.** 261,632/45 **9.** $\frac{21}{2}\ln 2$
11. 0 **13.** π **15.** $\frac{21}{2}$ **17.** $9\ln 2$
19. $\frac{1}{2}\left(\sqrt{3} - 1\right) - \frac{1}{12}\pi$ **21.** $\frac{1}{2}(e^2 - 3)$
23.

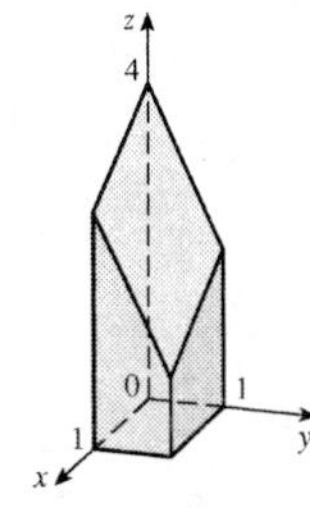

25. $\frac{95}{2}$ **27.** $\frac{166}{27}$ **29.** 2 **31.** $\frac{64}{3}$
33. $21e - 57$

35. $\frac{5}{6}$ **37.** 0
39. Fubini's Theorem does not apply. The integrand has an infinite discontinuity at the origin.

EXERCISES 12.3 ■ PAGE 850

1. 32 **3.** $\frac{3}{10}$ **5.** $e - 1$ **7.** $\frac{4}{3}$ **9.** π

Index

RP denotes Reference Page numbers.

Abel, Niels, 213
absolute maximum and minimum, 262, 802
absolute maximum and minimum values, 262, 807
absolute value, 18, A4, A72
absolute value function, 18
absolutely convergent series, 588
acceleration, 153, 228, 716
Achilles and the tortoise, 6
adaptive numerical integration, 410
addition formulas for sine and cosine, A22, RP2
addition of vectors, 640
algebra review, RP1
Airy function, 598
Airy, Sir George, 598
algebraic function, 32
allometric growth, 516
alternating harmonic series, 586
alternating series, 585
Alternating Series Estimation Theorem, 587
Alternating Series Test, 585
analytic geometry, A7
angle(s), A17
  between curves, 253
  of deviation, 270
  negative, A18
  between planes, 668
  positive, A18
  standard position, A18
  between vectors, 650
angular momentum, 725
antiderivative, 160, 317
antidifferentiation formulas, 318, RP5
aphelion, A71
approach path of an aircraft, 209
approximate integration, 401
approximating cylinder, 440
approximation
  by differentials, 243
  to *e*, 180
  linear, 241
  by the Midpoint Rule, 349, 402
  by Newton's method, 312
  quadratic, 247, 812
  by Riemann sums, 344
  by Simpson's Rule, 406
  tangent line, 241
  to a tangent plane, 770, 772
  by Taylor polynomials, 619
  by Taylor's Inequality, 607, 620
  by the Trapezoidal Rule, 402
Archimedes, 374
Archimedes' Principle, 491
arc curvature, 707
arc length, 455, 456, 707, 708
  of a polar curve, A68
arc length contest, 460
arc length formula, 456
arcsine function, 216
area, 4, 332
  of a circle, 390
  under a curve, 332, 337
  between curves, 432, 433
  by exhaustion, 4, 107
  enclosed by a parametric curve, 435
  by Green's Theorem, 936, 937
  in polar coordinates, A66
  of a sector of a circle, A66
  of a surface, 868
area function, 366
area problem, 4, 332
Argand plane, A71
argument of a complex number, A74
arrow diagram, 13
astroid, 79, 214
asymptote(s)
  in graphing,
  horizontal, 128
  of a hyperbola, A15
  vertical, 125
autonomous differential equation, 503
average cost function, 308
average rate of change, 140, 228
average speed of molecules, 422
average value of a function, 460, 461, 482, 835, 882
  of a probability density function, 481
average velocity, 6, 93, 137, 228
axes, coordinate, 634, A7
axes of ellipse, A14
axis of a parabola, A12

bacterial growth, 519, 535
Barrow, Isaac, 4, 107, 145, 367, 374
baseball and calculus, 529
base of a cylinder, 438

base of a logarithm, 65
  change of, 67
Bernoulli, James, 508
Bernoulli, John, 291, 508, 606
Bessel, Friedrich, 594
Bessel function, 216, 594, 597
Bézier, Pierre, 208
Bézier curves, 75, 208
binomial coefficients, 612
binomial series, 612, 618
  discovery by Newton, 618
Binomial Theorem, 175, RP1
binormal vector, 712
blackbody radiation, 627
blood flow, 234, 309, 477
boundary curve, 961
bounded sequence, 561
bounded set, 807
Boyle's Law, 238
brachistochrone problem, 76
Brahe, Tycho, 721
branches of a hyperbola, A15
bullet-nose curve, 52, 205

C^1 transformation, 891
cable (hanging), 227
calculator, graphing, 46, 74, 282, A58
  See also computer algebra systems
calculus, 10
  differential, 5
  integral, 5
  invention of, 374
cancellation equations
  for inverse functions, 63
  for logarithms, 65
cans, minimizing manufacturing
  cost of, 311
Cantor, Georg, 574
Cantor set, 574
capital formation, 480
cardiac output, 478
cardioid, 214, A59
carrying capacity, 160, 240, 530
Cartesian coordinate system, A7
Cartesian plane, A7
Cassini, Giovanni, A65
catenary, 227
Cavalieri, 408
Cauchy, Augustin-Louis, 840
Cauchy-Schwarz Inequality, 654
Cavalieri's Principle, 448
center of gravity, 469
center of mass, 469, 474, 859, 860, 878, 915, 951
  of a plate, 472
centripetal force, 735
centroid of a plane region, 470
centroid of a solid, 879
Chain Rule, 197, 198, 200
  for several variables, 780, 782, 783
change of base, formula for, 67
change of variables
  in a double integral, 854, 894
  in an integral, 375
  for several variables, 780, 782, 783
  in a triple integral, 884, 885, 897
charge, electric, 231, 859, 879
charge density, 859, 879
chemical reaction, 231
circle, A9
  area of, 390
  equation of, A9
circle of curvature, 713
circular cylinder, 438
circulation of a vector field, 964
cissoid of Diocles, 82, A64
Clairaut, Alexis, 763
Clairaut's Theorem, 763, A3
clipping planes, 673
closed curve, 927
closed interval, A2
Closed Interval Method, 266
closed set, 807
closed surface, 954
Cobb-Douglas production function, 738, 739, 765, 819
coefficient of friction, 196
coefficient(s)
  binomial, 612
  of friction, 269
  of inequality, 365
  of a polynomial, 29
  of a power series, 592
combinations of functions, 41
common ratio, 566
comparison properties of the integral, 352
comparison test for improper integrals, 420
Comparison Test for series, 579
Comparison Theorem for integrals, 420
complex conjugate, A72
complex exponentials, A77
complex number(s), A71
  addition of, A71
  argument of, A74
  division of, A72
  equality of, A71
  imaginary part of, A71
  modulus of, A72
  multiplication of, A72
  polar form, A73
  powers of, A75
  principal square root of, A73
  real part of, A71
  roots of, A76
  subtraction of, A71
component function, 694, 907
components of a vector, 642, 652
composition of functions, 42, 197
  continuity of, 119, 753, 754
  derivative of, 199
compound interest, 298, 526
compressibility, 232
computer algebra system, 46, 98, 397
  for integration, 397, 602
  for graphing a sequence, 559
computer, graphing with, 46, 282, A62
concavity, 159, 274
Concavity Test, 275
concentration, 231
conchoid, A64
conductivity, 958
cone, 679, A12
conic section(s), A12
  directrix, A12, A70
  eccentricity, A70
  focus, A12, A14, A70
  polar equations for, A70
conjugate, A72
connected region, 927
conservation of energy, 931
conservative vector field, 911, 932
constant function, 174
Constant Multiple Law of limits, 104
Constant Multiple Rule, 177
constraint, 813, 817
consumer surplus, 476, 477
continued fraction expansion, 564
continuity
  of a function, 113, 695, 752, 754
  on an interval, 115
  from the left, 115
  from the right, 115
continuous compounding of interest, 298, 526
continuous function, 113
continuous random variable, 480
contour map, 742
convergence
  absolute, 588
  of an improper integral, 414, 418
  interval of, 595
  radius of, 595
  of a sequence, 556
  of a series, 566
convergent improper integral, 414, 418
convergent sequence, 556
convergent series, 566
  properties of, 570–571
conversion
  cylindrical to rectangular
    coordinates, 682
  rectangular to spherical coordinates, 685
  spherical to rectangular coordinates, 684
coordinate(s), 634
  cylindrical, 682, 883, 884

polar, A6, A17
spherical, 682, 684, 885
coordinate axes, A7
coordinate plane, A7
coordinate system, A7
Cartesian, A7
polar, A59
rectangular, A7
Cornu's spiral, 460
cosine function, A19
derivative of, 193
graph of, 33, A23
power series for, 610, 611
cost function, 235, 304
Coulomb's Law, 281
critical number, 266
critical point, 802, 812
cross product, 654, 655
in component form, 657
properties of, 656
cross-section, 438, 675
cubic function, 29
curl of a vector field, 941
current, 231
curvature, 709
curve(s)
Bézier, 75, 208
boundary, 961
bullet-nose 52
closed, 927
connected, 927
Cornu's spiral, 460
demand, 476
devil's, 215
grid, 728
length of, 455, 707
level, 740, 742
open, 927
orientation of, 918, 934
orthogonal, 215
parametric, 71, 695
piecewise-smooth, 914
polar, A57
serpentine, 189
simple, 928
smooth, 455, 709
space, 694, 695, 697
swallotail catastrophe, 78
curve fitting 26
cycloid, 75
cylinder, 438
cylindrical coordinate system, 682
cylindrical coordinates, 682, 883, 884
cylindrical shell, 450
decay
law of natural, 520
radioactive, 523
decreasing function, 21, 158, 273
decreasing sequence, 560
definite integral, 343
properties of, 350
Substitution Rule for, 378
of a vector-valued function, 705
definite integration
by parts, 385
by substitution, 378
degree of a polynomial, 29
del (∇), 792
delta (Δ) notation, 139, 140
demand curve, 476
demand function, 304, 476
De Moivre, Abraham, A75
De Moivre's Theorem, A75
density
linear, 230, 361
of a lamina, 858
liquid, 468
mass vs. weight, 468
of a solid, 878, 879
dependent variable, 12, 673, 782
derivative(s), 135, 138
of a composite function, 197
of a constant function, 174
directional, 789, 790, 793
domain of , 146
of exponential functions, 180, 201
as a function, 146
higher, 153, 762
higher-order, 764
of hyperbolic functions, 227
of an integral, 368
of an inverse function, 221
of inverse trigonometric functions, 216, 218
of logarithmic functions, 221
maximization of, 794
normal, 948
notation, 150
partial, 756–758, 762
of a polynomial, 174
of a power function, 175
of a power series, 599
of a product, 183, 184
of a quotient, 186, 187
as a rate of change, 135
second, 153, 704
second partial, 762
as the slope of a tangent, 135
third, 154
of trigonometric functions, 190, 194
of a vector-valued function, 701
Descartes, René, A7
descent of aircraft, determining start of, 209
determinant, 657
devil's curve, 215
Difference Law of limits, 104
difference quotient, 14
Difference Rule, 178
differentiable function, 150, 773
differential, 243, 774, 776
differential calculus, 5
differential equation, 182, 319, 493-494, 496
autonomous, 503
family of solutions, 494, 497
first-order, 496
general solution of, 497
logistic, 531
order of, 496
partial, 764
second-order, 496
separable, 508
solution of, 496
differentiation, 150
formulas for, 188, RP5
implicit, 209, 210, 761, 784
integration of, 599
logarithmic, 223
operators, 150
partial, 756, 761
of a power series, 599
term-by-term, 600
of a vector function, 704
differentiation operator, 150
directed line segment (see vector), 639
Direct Substitution Property, 107
direction field, 499, 500, 531
direction numbers, 664
directional derivative, 789, 790, 793
estimation, 790
maximization of, 794
directrix, A12
discontinuity, 113
discontinuous function, 113
discontinuous integrand, 417
disk method for approximating volume, 440
dispersion, 271
displacement, 361
displacement of a vector, 639, 648
distance
between lines, 670
between planes, 669
between point and line, 662
between points in a plane, A8
between points in space, 636
between real numbers, A5
distance formula, A8
in three dimensions, 636
distance problem, 339
divergence
of an improper integral, 414, 418
of an infinite series, 566
of a sequence, 556
Test for, 570
of a vector field, 941, 944
Divergence Theorem, 967

Divergence, Test for, 570
divergent improper integral, 414, 418
divergent sequence, 556
divergent series, 566
division of power series, 615
DNA, 696
domain of a function, 12, 673
domain sketching, 674
dot product, 648, 649
in component form, 650
properties of, 651
double-angle formulas, A22
double integral, 832, 844
change of variable in, 894
Midpoint Rule for, 834
over general regions, 844, 845
in polar coordinates, 853, 854
properties of, 836, 849
over rectangles, 830
volume, 842
double Riemann sum, 832
dye dilution method, 478

e (the number) 57, 180
as a limit, 225
as a sum of an infinite series, 609
eccentricity, A72
electric charge, 879
electric circuit, 507, 510
electric current to a flash bulb, 91–92, 207
electric flux, 957
electric force field, 910
elementary functions, 398
elimination constant of a drug, 548
ellipse, 214, A14
foci, A14
reflection property, A14
rotated, 216
ellipsoid, 678, 679
cylindrical equation for, 683
elliptic paraboloid, 676, 679
empirical model, 26
end behavior of a function, 134
endpoint extreme values, 264
energy
conservation of, 931
kinetic, 931
potential, 931
epicycloid, 79
epitrochoid, 460
equation(s)
cancellation, 63
of a circle, A9
of a curve, A9
differential. (*See* differential equation)
of an ellipse, A14
of a graph, A9
heat, 768
of a hyperbola, A15
integral, 514
Laplace's, 764, 945
of a line, A1, A11
of a line in space, 663, 664
of a line through two points, 665
linear, 667
logistic difference, 564
logistic differential, 495, 532
Lotka-Volterra, 541
*n*th-degree, 213
of a parabola, A13
parametric, 71, 663, 695, 727
parametric for a plane, 728
parametric for a sphere, 728
of a plane, 666
of a plane through three points, 667
point-slope, 19, A10
polar, A57
predator-prey, 540, 541
of a sphere, 637
slope-intercept, A11
two-intercept form, A16
wave, 764
equation of a line through two points, 665
equation of a plane through three points, 667
equilibrium point, 542
equilibrium solution, 495, 541
equipotential curves, 747
error
in approximate integration, 403, 404
percentage, 245
relative, 244
in Taylor approximation, 620
error bounds, 405, 409
error estimate
for alternating series, 587
using differentials, 775
for the Midpoint Rule, 403
for Simpson's Rule, 409
for the Trapezoidal Rule, 403
error function, 373
estimate of the sum of a series, 580, 587
Euclid, 107
Eudoxus, 3, 107, 374
Euler, Leonhard, 58, 503, 609
Euler's formula, A78
Euler's Method, 503, 504, 532
Evaluation Theorem, 356
even function, 19
expected values, 865
exponential decay, 519
exponential function(s) 34, 52, 179, RP4
derivative of, 180, 201
graphs of, 54, 180
integration of, 348, 357, 377, 613, 614
limits of, 131
power series for, 606
exponential graph 54
exponential growth, 519, 535
exponents, laws of, 54
extrapolation, 28
extreme value, 263
Extreme Value Theorem, 264, 807

family
of epicycloids and hypocycloids 79
of exponential functions 54
of functions, 50, 279, 286
of solutions, 494, 497
of surfaces, 687
fat circle, 214, 460
Fermat, Pierre, 265, 374
Fermat's Principle, 308
Fermat's Theorem, 265, A36
Fibonacci, 555, 563
Fibonacci sequence, 555, 563
field
conservative, 911, 932
electric, 910
force, 910
gradient, 910
gravitational, 909, 910
scalar, 907
vector, 906, 907, 911
velocity, 909
First Derivative Test, 274
for Absolute Extreme Values, 302
first octant, 634
first-order differential equation, 496
first-order optics, 625
fixed point of a function, 170
flash bulb, current to, 91, 92, 207
flow lines, 912
fluid flow, 909
flux, 477, 478, 955, 957
across a sphere, 956
FM synthesis, 286
focus, A12
of a conic section, A12, A70
of an ellipse, A14
of a hyperbola, A15
of a parabola, A12
folium of Descartes, 210
force
exerted by fluid, 467, 468
force field, 910
Fourier, Joseph, 237
four-leaved rose, A59
fractions, partial, 391, A43
Frenet-Serret formulas, 715
Fresnel, Augustin, 370
Fresnel function, 370
frustum, 447
Fubini, Guido, 840
Fubini's Theorem, 840, 873
function(s), 12, 673
absolute value, 18
Airy, 598

algebraic, 32
arc length, 708
arcsine, 216
area, 366
arrow diagram of, 13
average cost, 308
average value of, 460, 461, 482, 835, 882
Bessel, 216, 594, 597
Cobb-Douglas production, 738, 739, 765, 819
combinations of, 41
component, 694, 907
composite, 42
concavity of, 159
constant, 174
continuous, 113, 695, 752–754
cost, 235, 304
cubic, 29
decreasing, 21, 158, 273
demand, 304, 476
derivative of, 138
differentiable, 150, 773
discontinuous, 113
discontinuous at origin, 753
domain of, 12, 673
elementary, 398
error, 373
even, 19
exponential, 34, 52, 179, RP4
extreme values of, 263
family of, 50, 279, 286
fixed point of, 170
Fresnel, 370
Gompertz, 537
gradient of, 792, 794
graph of, 13, 675, 740
greatest integer, 109
harmonic, 764
Heaviside, 45
hyperbolic, 227
implicit, 209, 210, 785
increasing, 21, 158, 273
inverse, 61, 62
inverse hyperbolic, RP4
inverse sine, 216
inverse trigonometric, 216, 218, A24
joint density, 863, 879
limit of, 95, 749, 750, 752
linear, 25, 675
logarithmic, 34, 65
machine diagram of, 13
marginal cost, 140, 236, 304, 361
marginal profit, 304
marginal revenue, 304
maximum and minimum value of, 262, 802, 807
of ***n*** variables, 745
natural exponential, 58
natural logarithmic, 66
nondifferentiable, 152
nonintegrable, 398
odd, 20
one-to-one, 61
piecewise defined, 18
polynomial, 29, 753
potential, 911
position, 137
power, 30, 174
probability density, 481, 863
profit, 304
quadratic, 29
ramp, 46
range of, 12, 673
rational, 32, 753, A47
reciprocal, 32
reflected, 38
representation as a power series, 598
representations of, 12, 14
revenue, 304
root, 31
of several variables, 738, 744
shifted, 38
sine integral, 374
smooth, 455
step, 19
stretched, 38
tabular 15
of three variables, 744
transformation of, 37–38
translation of, 37
trigonometric, 33, A19
of two variables, 673, 738
value of, 12
vector-valued, 694
Fundamental Theorem of Calculus, 367, 369, 371, 925

G (gravitational constant), 238, 473
Galileo, 76, A12
Galois, Evariste, 213
gas law, 769
Gause, G. F. 535
Gauss, Karl Friedrich, 967, A43
Gaussian optics, 625
Gauss's Law, 958
Gauss's Theorem, 967
geometric series, 566
geometry review, RP1
geometry of a tetrahedron, 662
global maximum and minimum, 263
Gompertz function, 537, 540
gradient, 792, 794
gradient vector, 792, 794, 798
significance of, 798
gradient vector field, 910
graph(s)
of an equation, A9
of equations in three dimensions, 635
of exponential functions, 54
of a function, 13, 675, 740
of logarithmic functions, 65, 69
of a parametric curve, 72
polar, A57, A62
of power functions, 31, RP3
of a sequence, 559
surface of, 951
of trigonometric functions, 33, A23, RP2
graphing calculator, 46, 74, 282, A62
graphing device. *See* computer algebra system
graphing equations in three dimensions, 635
gravitational acceleration, 464
gravitational field, 909, 910
gravitation law, 473
greatest integer function, 109
Green, George, 935, 966
Green's identities, 948
Green's Theorem, 934, 937
vector forms, 946, 947
Gregory, James, 198, 408, 602, 606
Gregory's series, 602
grid curves, 728
growth, law of natural, 520
growth rate, 233, 361
relative, 520

half-angle formulas, A23
half-life, 56, 523
half-space, 744
hare-lynx system, 544
harmonic function, 764
harmonic series, 569, 578
heat conductivity, 958
heat equation, 768
heat flow, 958
heat index, 774
Heaviside, Oliver, 99
Heaviside function, 45
Hecht, Eugene, 624
helix, 695
hidden line rendering, 673
higher derivatives, 153, 762
homeostasis, 516
Hooke's Law, 466
horizontal asymptote, 128
horizontal line, equation of, A11
Horizontal Line Test, 61
horizontal plane, 635
Hubble Space Telescope, 267
Huygens, Christiaan, 76
hydrostatic pressure and force, 467, 468
hydro-turbine optimization, 821
hyperbola, 214, A15
asymptotes, A15
branches, A15
equation, A15
foci, A15
hyperbolic functions, 227

hyperbolic paraboloid, 677, 679
hyperboloid, 679
hypersphere, 883
hypervolume, 883
hypocycloid, 79

i, A71
i, 644
I/D Test, 273
ideal gas law, 240
image, 891
implicit differentiation, 209, 210, 761, 784, 785
implicit function, 209, 210, 785
Implicit Function Theorem, 785, 786
implicit partial differentiation, 761
improper integral, 413
  convergence/divergence of, 414, 418
impulse of a force, 529
incompressible velocity field, 945
Increasing/Decreasing Test, 273
increasing function, 21, 158, 273
increasing sequence, 560
increment, 139, 773, 775, 776
indefinite integral(s), 357–358
  table of, 358, RP6–10
independence of path, 926
independent random variable, 864
independent variable, 12, 673, 782
indeterminate difference, 294
indeterminate forms of limits, 290
indeterminate power, 295
indeterminate product, 294
index of summation, A38
inequalities, rules for, A2
inertia (moment of), 861, 879, 924
infinite discontinuity, 114
infinite interval, 414
infinite limit, 124, 132, A30
infinite sequence. *See* sequence
infinite series. *See* series
inflection point, 160, 275
initial condition, 497
initial point of a parametric curve, 72
initial point of a vector, 639
initial-value problem, 497
instantaneous rate of change, 92, 140, 228
instantaneous rate of growth, 233
instantaneous rate of reaction, 232
instantaneous velocity, 93, 137
integral equation, 514
integral(s)
  approximations to, 349
  change of variables in, 375, 780, 782, 783, 854, 884, 885, 894, 897
  comparison properties of, 352
  definite, 343, 705, 830
  derivative of, 369
  double, 832, 836, 844, 845
  double to compute volume, 842
  evaluating, 345
  improper, 413
  indefinite, 358
  iterated, 839, 845
  line, 913, 916, 918, 920
  multiple, 873
  patterns in, 400
  properties of, 350
  surface, 949, 955
  of symmetric functions, 380
  table of, 394, RP6–10
  trigonometric, 389
  triple, 873, 874
  units for, 363
  of a vector function, 701, 705
integral calculus, 5
Integral Test, 575, 577
integrand, 343
  discontinuous, 417
integration, 343
  approximate, 401
  by computer algebra system, 397
  of exponential functions, 348, 357, 377
  formulas, RP6–10
  indefinite, 357
  limits of, 343
  numerical, 401
  over a solid, 884
  partial, 838
  by partial fractions, 391, A43
  by parts, 383–385
  of a power series, 599
  of rational functions, A43
  reversing order of, 849
  by substitution, 375–376, 390
  term-by-term, 600
  tables, use of, 394
  by trigonometric substitution, 390
interest compunded continuously, 526
Intermediate Value Theorem, 120
intermediate variable, 782
interpolation, 28
intersection of planes, 668
intersection of polar graphs, A67
interval, A2
interval of convergence, 595
inverse function(s), 61, 62
  steps of finding, 64
inverse hyperbolic function, RP4
inverse sine function, 216
inverse transformation, 892
inverse trigonometric functions, 216, 218, A24
involute of the circle, 492
irrotational vector field, 944
isobars, 741
isothermal compressibility, 232
isothermals, 741, 747
iterated integral, 839, 845

j, 644
Jacobi, Carl Gustav Jacob, 893
Jacobian, 893, 897
joint density function, 863, 879
jerk, 155
joule, 465
jump discontinuity, 114

k, 644
kampyle of Eudoxus, 215
Kepler, Johannes, 721
Kepler's Laws, 721, 722, 726, A21
kinetic energy, 529, 931
Kirchhoff's Laws, 501
Kondo, Shigeru, 609

Lagrange, Joseph-Louis, 272, 813
Lagrange multiplier, 813, 814, 817
lamina, 470, 858, 860
Laplace, Pierre, 764
Laplace operator, 945
Laplace's equation, 764, 945
lattice point, 254
Law of Conservation of Energy, 932
law of cosines, A26, RP2
law of gravitation, 473
law of laminar flow, 234, 477
law of natural growth or decay, 520
laws of exponents 54
laws of logarithms 65, RP4
law of sines, RP2
learning curve, 499
least squares method, 28, 811
left-hand limit, 100
Leibniz, Gottfried Wilhelm, 150, 367, 374, 508, 619
Leibniz notation, 150
lemniscate, 215
length
  of a curve, 455
  of a line segment, A5, A10
  of a polar curve, A68
  of a space curve, 707
  of a vector, 642
level curve, 740, 742
level surface, 745
  tangent plane to, 796
l'Hospital, Marquis de, 291
l'Hospital's Rule, 291, 299
  origins of, 299
libration point, 316
limaçon, A63
Limit Comparison Test, 580
Limit Laws, 104
  for sequences, 557

limit(s), 4, 95
calculating, 104
e (the number) as, 225
ε, δ, definition, A26, A27, A30, A32
existence, 751, 752
of exponential functions, 131, 132
of a function, 95, 749, 750
infinite, 124, 132
at infinity, 127, 128, A30
involving infinity, 123
of integration, 343
left-hand, 100
of natural logarithm, 126
one-sided, 100
precise definitions, A26–A34
properties of, 104
right-hand, 100
of a sequence, 7, 334, 556, A32
involving sine and cosine functions, 191, 193
of a trigonometric function, 192
of a vector-valued function, 694
linear approximation, 241, 770, 772, 776
linear density, 230, 361
linear equation, 667
linear function, 25, 675
linearization, 241, 772, 773
linear model, 25
linear regression, 27
line
equation of through two points, 665
line(s) in the plane, 90, A10
equations of, A10–A11
horizontal, A11
normal, 176, 797
parallel, A11
perpendicular, A11
secant, 90
slope of, A10
tangent, 90, 702
line(s) in space
parametric equations of, 663
symmetric equations of, 664
vector equation of, 663
line integral, 913, 916, 918, 920, 921
Fundamental Theorem for, 925
Green's Theorem, 936
with respect to arc length, 916
in space, 918, 919
of vector fields, 920, 921, 929
Stokes' Theorem, 963
liquid force, 467, 468
Lissajous figure 74, 79
lithotripsy, A14
local maximum and minimum, 159, 263, 802
logarithm(s), 34, 65
laws of, 65, RP4
natural, 66
notation for, 66
logarithmic differentiation, 223
logarithmic function(s), 34, 65
with base a, 65
derivatives of, 221
graphs of, 65, 68, 69
limits of, 126
properties of, 65, 66
logistic difference equation, 564
logistic differential equation, 495, 531
analytic solution of, 533
logistic model, 530
logistic sequence, 564
Lorenz curve, 365
Lotka-Volterra equations, 541

machine diagram of a function, 13
Maclaurin, Colin, 606
Maclaurin series, 604, 606
table of, 613
magnitude of a vector, 642
marginal cost function, 140, 236, 304, 361
marginal profit function, 304
marginal propensity to consume or save, 573
marginal revenue function, 304
mass, 858, 878, 915, 950
center of, 469, 470, 474, 859, 860, 878, 915, 951
mathematical induction, 84, 87, 561
principle of, 84, 87, A40
mathematical model, 15, 25
maximum and minimum values, 462, 802, 807
mean life of an atom, 422
mean of a probability density function, 483
Mean Value Theorem, 272
Mean Value Theorem for Integrals, 462
mean waiting time, 483
median of a probability density function, 484
method of cylindrical shells, 450
method of exhaustion, 4, 107
method of Lagrange multipliers, 814, 817
method of least squares, 28, 811
Midpoint Rule, 349, 402
for double integrals, 834
error in using, 403
for triple integrals, 881
mixing problems, 512
Möbius strip, 733, 953
modeling
with differential equations, 494
motion of a spring, 496
population growth, 56, 494, 520, 530
vibration of membrane, 594
model(s), mathematical, 15, 25
comparison of natural growth vs. logistic, 535
of electric current, 501
empirical, 26
exponential, 34, 55
Gompertz function, 537, 540
of force due to air resistance, 518
linear, 25
logarithmic 34
polynomial 30
for population growth, 494, 520, 530, 537
power function 30
predator-prey, 540
for production cost, 739, 765, 819
rational function 32
seasonal-growth, 540
trigonometric 33, 34
von Bertalanffy, 549
modulus, A72
moment
about an axis, 469, 470, 860
centroid of a solid, 879
of inertia, 861, 879, 924
of a lamina, 470, 860
of a mass, 469
about a plane, 878
polar, 862
second, 861
of a solid, 878, 879
of a system of particles, 470
momentum of an object, 529
monotonic sequence, 560
Monotonic Sequence Theorem, 561
motion in space, 716
movie theater seating, 464
multiple integrals, 832, 873
multiplication of power series, 615
multiplier effect, 573
multiplier (Lagrange) 813, 814, 817

natural exponential function, 58, 180
derivative of, 180
graph of, 180
natural growth law, 520
natural logarithm function, 66
derivative of, 221
negative angle, A18
net area, 344
Net Change Theorem, 360
net investment flow, 480
Newton, Sir Isaac, 5, 10, 107, 145, 367, 374, 618, 722, 726
newton (unit of force) 464
Newton's Law of Cooling, 499, 524
Newton's Law of Gravitation, 238, 473, 722, 909
Newton's method, 312
Newton's Second Law of Motion, 464, 718, 722
nondifferentiable function, 152
nonintegrable function, 398

normal component of acceleration, 720, 721
normal derivative, 948
normal distribution, 485
normal line, 176, 797
normal plane, 713
normal vector, 666, 712, 868
nth-degree equation, finding roots of, 213
nth-degree Taylor polynomial, 607
number, complex, A71
numerical integration, 401

O, 634
octant, 634
odd function, 20
one-sided limits, 100
one-to-one function, 61
one-to-one transformation, 891
open interval, A2
open region, 927
optics
  first-order, 625
  Gaussian, 625
  third-order, 625
optimization problems, 262, 299
orbit of a planet, 722
order of a differential equation, 496
order of integration, reversing, 849
ordered pair, A7
ordered triple, 634, 635
Oresme, Nicole, 569
orientation of a curve, 918, 934
orientation of a surface, 953, 954
oriented surface, 953, 954
origin, 634, A7
orthogonal curves, 215
orthogonal projection, 653
orthogonal surfaces, 801
orthogonal trajectory, 215, 511
orthogonal vectors, 649
osculating circle, 713
osculating plane, 713
ovals of Cassini, A65

parabola, A12
  axis, A12
  directrix, A12
  equation of, A13
  focus, A12
  reflection property, 254
  vertex, A12
parabolic cylinder, 675
paraboloid, 676
paradoxes of Zeno, 7
parallelepiped, 438
parallel lines, A11
Parallelogram Law, 640
parallel planes, 668
parallel vectors, 641
parameter, 71, 663, 695
parametric curve, 71, 695
  tangent to, 203
parametric equation(s), 71, 663, 695, 727
  for a plane, 728
  for a sphere, 728
parametric surface, 727, 777, 949
parametrization of a space curve, 708
  smooth, 709
  with respect to arc length, 709
paraxial rays, 243
partial derivative, 756–758, 762
  notation for, 758
  rules for finding, 758
  second, 762
  as slopes of tangents, 759
partial differential equations, 764
partial fractions, 391, A43
partial integration, 383–385, 838
partial sum of a series, 565, 566
parts, integration by, 383–385
pascal (unit of pressure) 468
path, 926
patterns in integrals, 400
pendulum, approximating the period of, 243, 246
percentage error, 245
perihelion, A71
perpendicular lines, A11
perpendicular vectors, 649
phase plane, 542
phase portrait, 543
phase trajectory, 542
piecewise defined function, 18
piecewise-smooth curve, 914
plane(s)
  angle between, 668
  coordinate, 634
  equation of, 663, 666, 667
  equation of through three points, 667
  horizontal, 635
  intersection of, 668
  normal, 713
  parallel, 668
  tangent to a surface, 770, 777, 796
Planck's Law, 628
planetary motion, 721
planimeter, 937
point of inflection, 160, 275
point-slope equation of a line, 19, A10
Poiseuille, Jean-Louis-Marie, 234
Poiseuille's Law, 246, 309, 478
polar axis, A55
polar coordinates, A56
  area in, A66
  changing to Cartesian coordinates, A56
  conic sections in, A70
polar curve, A57
  arc length of, A68
  graph of, A53, A62
  tangent line to, A60
polar equation, A57
  of a conic, A70
  graph of, A57
polar form of a complex number, A73
polar region, area of, A66
pole, A55
polynomial, 29
polynomial function 29
  continuity of, 116
  of two variables, 753
population growth, 55, 56, 520
  of bacteria, 519
  models, 494
  world, 56, 521
position function, 137
position vector, 642
positive angle, A18
positive orientation, 954
  of a curve, 934, 961
  of a surface, 954
potential energy, 931
potential function, 911
  conservative vector field, 943
pound (unit of force) 464
power, 142
power consumption, approximation of, 362
power function(s), 30, RP3
  derviative of, 174
Power Law of limits, 105
Power Rule, 175, 176, 200, 224
power series, 592
  coefficients of, 592
  for cosine and sine, 610
  differentiation of, 599
  division of, 615
  integration of, 600
  for exponential function, 610
  interval of convergence, 595
  multiplication of, 615
  radius of convergence, 595
  representations of functions as, 598
predator, 540
predator-prey model, 240, 540–541
pressure exerted by a fluid, 467, 468
prey, 540
prime notation, 138, 177
principal square root of a complex number, A73
principle of mathematical induction, 84, 87, A44
principal unit normal vector, 712
probability, 480, 863
probability density function, 481, 863

problem-solving principles, 83
  uses of, 169, 251, 327, 375, 428
producer surplus, 479
product
  cross, 655
  dot, 648-649
  scalar, 649
  scalar triple, 659
  triple, 659
Product Law of limits, 104
Product Rule, 183–184
profit function, 304
projection, 635, 651
  orthogonal, 653
p-series, 578

quadrant, A7
quadratic approximation, 247, 812
quadratic formula, RP1
quadratic function, 29
quadric surface, 678
Quotient Law of limits, 104
Quotient Rule, 186–187

radian measure, 190, A17
radiation from stars, 627
radioactive decay, 523
radiocarbon dating, 528
radius of convergence, 595
rainbow, formation and location of, 270
rainbow angle, 270
ramp function, 46
range of a function, 12, 673
rate of change
  average, 140, 228
  derivative as, 140
  instantaneous, 140, 228
rate of growth, 233, 361
rate of reaction, 142, 232, 360
rates, related, 256
rational function, 32, 753, A47
  continuity of, 116
  integration by partial fractions, A43
Ratio Test, 589
Rayleigh-Jeans Law, 627
reciprocal function, 32
Reciprocal Rule, 190
rectangular coordinate system, 635, A7
rectilinear motion, 320
reduction formula, 386
reflecting a function, 38
reflection property
  of conics, 254, A14
  of an ellipse, A14
  of a parabola, 254
region
  closed, 807
  connected, 927
  between two graphs, 432
  open, 927
  plane of type I or II, 845, 846
  simple, 935
  simple solid, 967
  simply-connected, 928, 929
  solid, 874, 876
  under a graph, 332, 337
regression, linear, 27
related rates, 256
relative error, 244
relative growth rate, 520
remainder estimates
  for the Alternating Series, 587
  for the Comparison Test, 580
  for the Integral Test, 581
remainder of the Taylor series, 607
removable discontinuity, 114
representations of functions, 12, 14, 15
resultant force, 645
revenue function, 304
reversing order of integration, 849
revolution, solid of, 443
Riemann, Georg Bernhard, 344
Riemann sum(s) 344
  for multiple integrals, 832, 873
right circular cylinder, 438
right-hand limit, 100
right-hand rule, 634, 655
rocket science, 820
roller coaster, design of, 183
roller derby, 889
root function, 31
Root Law of limits, 106
roots of a complex number, A76
roots of an *n*th-degree equation, 213
rubber membrane, vibration of, 594
ruled surface, 681
rumors, rate of spread, 237

saddle point, 803
sample point, 337, 343, 831
scalar, 641, 907
scalar equation, 667
scalar field, 907
scalar multiple of a vector, 641
scalar product, 649
scalar projection, 652
scalar triple product, 659
scatter plot, 15
seasonal-growth model, 540
secant function, A19
  derivative of, 194
  graph of, A24
secant line, 5, 90, 91
second derivative, 153, 704
Second Derivatives Test, 275, 803, A40
second moment of inertia, 861
second-order differential equation, 496
second partial derivative, 762
sector of a circle, A66
separable differential equation, 508
sequence, 7, 554
  bounded, 561
  convergent, 556
  decreasing, 560
  divergent, 556
  Fibonacci, 555, 563
  graph of, 559
  increasing, 560
  limit of, 7, 334, 556, A32
  logistic, 564
  monotonic, 560
  of partial sums, 565, 566
  term of, 554
series, 8, 565
  absolutely convergent, 588
  alternating, 585
  alternating harmonic, 586
  binomial, 612, 618
  coefficients of, 592
  convergent, 566
  divergent, 566
  geometric, 566
  Gregory's, 602
  harmonic, 578
  infinite, 565
  Maclaurin, 604, 606
  p- 578
  partial sum of, 566
  power, 592
  sum of, 566
  Taylor, 604, 606
  term of, 565
  trigonometric, 593
serpentine, 189
shell method for approximating
    volume, 450
shift of a function, 38
Sierpinski carpet, 574
sigma notation, 337, A37
simple curve, 928
simple harmonic motion, 206
simple region, 935
simple solid region, 967
simply-connected region, 928, 929
Simpson, Thomas, 408
Simpson's Rule, 406, 408
  error bounds for, 409
sine function, A19
  derivative of, 193, 194
  graph, 33, A23
  power series for, 610
sine integral function, 374
sink, 971
skew lines, 666

slope, A10
  of a curve, 136
slope field, 500
slope-intercept equation of a line, A11
smooth curve, 455, 709
smooth surface, 777, 868
Snell's Law, 308
snowflake curve, 632
solid angle, 977
solid region, 967
solid of revolution, 443
  rotated on a slant, 449
  volume of, 451
solid, volume of, 438, 439, 873
solution of a differential equation, 496
solution of predator-prey equations, 541
solution curve, 500
source, 971
space, three-dimensional, 634
space curve, 694–697
speed, 140, 716
sphere
  equation of, 637
  integrating over, 950
spherical coordinates, 682, 684, 885
spherical wedge, 885
spring constant, 466, 496
Squeeze Theorem, 110, 557
  for sequences, 557
standard basis vectors, 644
standard deviation, 485
standard position of an angle, A18
stellar stereography, 422
step function, 19
Stokes, Sir George, 961, 966
Stokes' Theorem, 961
strategy
  for optimization problems, 299, 300
  for problem solving, 83
  for related rates, 258
streamlines, 912
stretching of a function, 38
Substitution Rule, 375–376
  for definite integrals, 378
subtraction formulas for sine and cosine, A22
sum
  of a geometric series, 567
  of an infinite series, 566
  of partial fractions, 391, A47
  Riemann, 344
  telescoping, 569
  of vectors, 640
Sum Law of limits, 104, A35
summation notation, A38
Sum Rule, 177
supply function, 479
surface
  closed, 954
  graph of, 951
  level, 745
  oriented, 953, 954
  parametric, 727, 777, 949
  quadric, 678
  smooth, 777, 868
surface area
  of a parametric surface, 868, 869, 949
  of a sphere, 869
  of a surface $z = f(x, y)$, 870
surface integral, 949
  of vector fields, 955
  Stokes' Theorem, 963
surface of revolution, 731, 871
swallowtail catastrophe curve, 78
symmetric equations of a line, 664
symmetric functions, integrals of, 380
symmetry, 19, 380
  in polar graphs, A60
symmetry principle, 470

T^{-1} transformation, 892
table of differentiation formulas, 188, RP5
tables of integrals, 394, RP6–10
tabular function 15
tangential component of acceleration, 720
tangent function, A19
  derivative of, 194
  graph, 34, A24
tangent line
  to a curve, 5, 90, 135
  early methods for finding, 145
  to a parametric curve, 203
  to a polar curve, A60
  to a space curve, 703
  vertical, 152
tangent line approximation, 241
  to a space curve, 703
tangent plane
  to a level surface, 796
  to a parametric surface, 777
  to a surface $z = f(x, y, z) = k$, 777
  to a surface $z = f(x, y)$, 770, 779
tangent plane approximation, 770, 772
tangent problem, 4, 5, 90, 135
tangent vector, 702
tautochrone problem, 76
Taylor, Brook, 606
Taylor polynomial, 247, 607
  applications of, 619
Taylor series, 604, 606
Taylor's inequality, 607
telescoping sum, 569, A39
term-by-term differentiation and integration, 600
terminal point of a parametric curve, 72
terminal velocity, 516
terminal point of a vector, 639
term of a sequence, 554
term of a series, 565
Test for Divergence, 570
tests for convergence and divergence of series
  Alternating Series Test, 585
  Comparison Test, 579
  Integral Test, 575, 577
  Limit Comparison Test, 580
  Ratio Test, 589
tetrahedron, 662
third derivative, 154
third-order optics, 625
Thomson, William (Lord Kelvin) 935, 961, 966
three-dimensional coordinate systems, 634, 635
toroidal spiral, 697
torque, 655, 725
Torricelli's Law, 238
torsion, 715
torus, 448, 733, 872
total differential, 774
total fertility rate, 167
trace, 675
trajectory, parametric equations for, 719
transformation
  of a function, 37
  inverse, 892
  Jacobian, 893
  one-to-one, 891
  of a root function, 39
translation of a function, 37
Trapezoidal Rule, 402
  error in using, 403
tree diagram, 782
trefoil knot, 697
Triangle Inequality, A39
  for vectors, 654
Triangle Law, 640
trigonometric functions, 33, A19, RP2
  derivatives of, 190, 194
  graphs of, 33, 34, A23
  integrals of, 358
  inverse, A24
  limits involving, 191, 193
trigonometric identities, A21, RP2
trigonometric integrals, 389
trigonometric substitution in integration, 390
trigonometry review, A17, RP2
triple integrals, 873, 874
  applications of, 877
  in cylindrical coordinates, 883, 884
  over a general bounded region, 874
  Midpoint Rule for, 881
  in spherical coordinates, 883, 885
triple product, 659
triple Riemann sum, 873
trochoid 78
Tschirnhausen cubic, 215
twisted cubic, 697

type I plane region, 845, 846
type II plane region, 846
type 1 solid region, 874
type 2 solid region, 876
type 3 solid region, 876

ultraviolet catastrophe, 627
uniform circular motion, 718
unit normal vector, 712
unit tangent vector, 702
unit vector, 645

value of a function 12
van der Waals equation, 215, 769
variable(s)
  change of, 375, 894, 897
  continuous random, 480
  dependent, 12
  independent, 12
  independent random, 864
  intermediate, 782
vascular branching, 309–310
vector(s) 639
  acceleration, 716
  addition of, 640
  angle between, 650
  basis, 644
  binormal, 712
  combining speed, 647
  components of, 642, 652
  cross product of, 654, 655
  difference of, 641
  displacement, 639, 648
  dot product, 648, 649, 651
  force, 910
  gradient, 792, 794
  i, j, and k, 644, 664
  initial point, 639
  length of, 642
  magnitude of, 642
  multiplication of, 641
  normal, 666, 712, 868
  orthogonal, 649
  parallel, 641
  perpendicular, 649
  position, 642
  principal unit normal, 712
  projection, 651
  properties of, 643
  representation of, 642
  scalar mulitple of, 641
  standard basis, 644
  subtraction of, 641
  sum of, 640
  tangent, 702
  terminal point, 639
  three-dimensional, 642
  triple product, 659
  two-dimensional, 642
  unit, 645
  unit normal, 712
  unit tangent, 702
  velocity, 716
  zero, 640
vecter field
  conservative, 932
vector equation of a line, 663
vector equation of a plane, 666
vector field, 906, 907
  conservative, 911
  curl of, 941
  divergence of, 941, 944
  flux of, 957
  gradient, 910
  incompressible, 945
  irrotational, 944
  potential function, 930
  three-dimensional, 908
  two-dimensional, 907
  velocity, 909
vector product, 654
vector projection, 651
vector triple product, 660
vector-valued function, 694
  continuous, 695
  derivative of, 701
  integral of, 705
  limit of, 694
velocity, 5, 92, 137, 228, 361
  average, 6, 93, 137, 228
  instantaneous, 93, 137, 228
velocity field, 909
velocity gradient, 235
velocity problem, 92, 137
velocity vector, 716
Verhulst, Pierre-François, 495
vertex of a parabola, A12
vertical asymptote, 125
Vertical Line Test, 17
vertical tangent line, 152
vertical translation of a graph, 38
vibration of a rubber membrane, 594
viewing rectangle, 46
visual representations of a function, 12, 14, 740
Volterra, Vito, 541
volume, 439
  by cross-sections, 438, 440, 477
  by cylindrical shells, 450
  by disks, 440, 443
  by double integrals, 830
  of hyperspheres, 883
  by polar coordinates, 855
  of a solid, 438
  of a solid of revolution, 443
  of a solid on a slant, 449
  of a two-dimensional solid, 832
  by triple integrals, 877
  by washers, 442, 444
von Bertalanffy model, 549

Wallis, John, 5
Wallis product, 389
washer method, 442
wave equation, 764
weight, 465
wind-chill index, 738
witch of Maria Agnesi, 78, 189
work, 464–466, 648, 920, 926
Wren, Sir Christopher, 458

x-axis, 634, A7
x-coordinate, 634, A7
x-intercept, A11
x-mean, 865

y-axis, 634, A7
y-coordinate, 634, A7
y-intercept, A11
y-mean, 865

z-axis, 634
z-coordinate, 634
Zeno, 7
Zeno's paradoxes, 7
zero vector, 640